United States Army in Vietnam

Military Communications
A Test for Technology

by

John D. Bergen

MILITARY INSTRVCTION

Center of Military History
United States Army
Washington, D.C., 1986

Library of Congress Cataloging in Publication Data

Bergen, John D., 1942–
    United States Army in Vietnam. Military communications,
a test for technology.

    Bibliography: p.
    Includes index.
    1. Vietnamese Conflict, 1961–1975—Communications.
I. Title.
DS559.8.C6B47   1985   959.704'38   85-26647

CMH Pub 91-12

First Printing

For sale by the Superintendent of Documents, U.S. Government Printing Office
Washington, D.C. 20402

United States Army in Vietnam

David F. Trask, General Editor

Advisory Committee

(As of 15 April 1985)

U.S. Army Center of Military History

Brig. Gen. William A. Stofft, Chief of Military History

. . . to Those Who Served

Foreword

The United States Army in Vietnam series is a comprehensive collection of historical studies that record the Army's role in the Vietnam War. Included are volumes describing combat operations; the Army's role in pacification, logistics, engineer operations, medical support, and training; relations with the media; and activities at the Department of Army level.

In this volume the author develops the thesis that burgeoning technology in communications faced a severe test in Vietnam. He analyzes the advantages and drawbacks of new communications systems and the effects these systems had on decision making and on command. In so doing, he describes the difficulties that communications systems had in keeping pace with the information explosion and shows that command and control do not necessarily improve with enhanced communications. The study illustrates that the communicator's mission of "getting the message through" was not only critical to the success of combat operations but also as challenging as combat itself.

The author's clear understanding and description of these issues make this a valuable work for those responsible for the future success of command, control, communications, and intelligence. At the same time it serves as a primer for readers not fully aware of the vital part communications play in every phase of warfare.

Washington, D.C.
24 October 1985

WILLIAM A. STOFFT
Brigadier General, USA
Chief of Military History

The Author

John D. Bergen received his commission in the U.S. Army upon graduation from the United States Military Academy in 1964. He received a Master of Arts degree in Literature from Indiana University in 1971 and a Master of Military Arts and Science degree from the Command and General Staff College in 1975.

Mr. Bergen's military career included assignments as adviser to a South Vietnamese signal battalion, instructor in the Department of English at the Military Academy, and commander of the 51st Signal Battalion in Korea. During a tour as a military historian at the Center of Military History he completed the manuscript of this volume. He then served as an Army staff planner and strategist and as speechwriter to the secretary and deputy secretary of defense.

In February 1985 Mr. Bergen left public service to accept the position of staff vice president at RCA.

Preface

The Vietnam War was a conflict of great diversity and contrasts. The United States and South Vietnam, the most technologically advanced nation in the world and a tiny developing country, fought side by side against an enemy who sought to undermine American technical superiority and destroy South Vietnamese development. Events taking place in the remote villages and hamlets of South Vietnam had tremendous political significance thousands of miles away in the cities and towns of the United States. The contrasts were most profound on the battlefield. Supersonic fighter planes streaking overhead at speeds of hundreds of miles per hour gave fire support to infantrymen hacking their way through the jungle at the pace of a few miles a day. Only communications could link the strategic and tactical, fighter pilot and infantryman, American and South Vietnamese.

The diversity of America's Vietnam experience complicates the telling of the story of communications in the war. The setting of critical events and decisions changed back and forth from Southeast Asia to Washington. Issues surfaced and were resolved, only to resurface years later. Telling the signal story in a logical manner, without redundancy or constant shifts of time or setting, dictated a loose chronological structure with geographic and thematic chapters interspersed at appropriate points in the narrative.

The story begins during the closing days of World War II with the OSS agents who gathered intelligence in Indochina. It continues through the period after the Franco–Viet Minh War, when American advisers assumed responsibility for assisting the army of the new Republic of Vietnam, an era of great opportunity to forestall the Communist insurgency before it could gain momentum.

Once the Communists launched a full-scale insurgency in 1960, American communicators and advisers tried to help the South Vietnamese defend against the insurgents. But the United States had little experience in counterinsurgency warfare, and the book describes the trial and error that characterized the early counterinsurgency and pacification efforts. It also discusses the communications that the United States began installing in Thailand and South Vietnam during the early 1960s to support America's increasing strategic commitment to Southeast Asia.

Once American troops were actually committed in 1965, those strategic networks provided an austere communications base for U.S. forces. The book discusses in detail the planning for a full-scale American presence and the emergency measures taken to provide communications to the first tactical units rushed to South Vietnam. The description of the American buildup ends with a summary of organizational changes in the signal command structure that led to the consolidation of all strategic and tactical communications under one theater command.

The deployment and tactical operations of U.S. signal units throughout South Vietnam from 1965 to 1970 is treated in four chapters, each organized chronologically by geographical region to permit a better discussion of the peculiar environmental and tactical challenges faced in each corps tactical zone. The book then traces the development of strategic and fixed communications between 1965 and 1970. One chapter discusses overseas strategic links and the sophisticated fixed communications installed for military subscribers in South Vietnam; a second addresses the Integrated Wideband Communications System, the long-distance transmission network built to interconnect all those sophisticated communication facilities.

The book's chronological narrative closes with a discussion of the U.S. withdrawal between 1970 and 1973 and a brief summary of the Vietnamization program, culminating in the transfer of U.S. communications systems to the South Vietnamese. The story ends with the fall of Saigon.

Four thematic chapters and a conclusion complete the book. The first analyzes Communist communications—organization, doctrine, operations, training, and logistics. The second addresses the electronic warfare waged by communicators on both sides. The next two chapters discuss the training of American signalmen and the development and logistical support of signal equipment.

Throughout the book the emphasis is on building and installing communications rather than on signal operations. That approach is dictated by the experience of American communicators in South Vietnam. Signalmen never stopped building and expanding systems until after the American withdrawal began. They were responding to an insatiable desire for more and better communications. No operation ever failed for lack of communications, but rarely would commanders admit that they had enough communications.

In researching the varied experience of the communicator in Southeast Asia, I had the opportunity to interview over fifty signalmen who served there from 1945 to 1975 in assignments ranging from combat radioman to signal brigade commander. Those firsthand accounts, together with my own experience as a signal adviser in I Corps, helped give this narrative an authenticity and vitality that could not have been attained working only from archival records and journals.

Besides those who lived the events in this story, many others contributed to its telling. For the chance to write this book while on active duty, I am grateful to Lt. Gen. Thomas M. Rienzi and to Brig. Gen. James L. Collins, Jr., former Chief of Military History. While they provided the opportunity, it fell to several mentors to help me make best use of it—Col. James F. Ransone and Col. James W. Dunn, former chiefs of the center's Histories Division, and senior historians Charles B. MacDonald and Stanley L. Falk. I hope that they find in this history evidence that their trust was well placed.

To the historian who probably knows more than any other living American about the history of the Vietnam War, Vincent H. Demma, I also owe the gratitude of student to tireless teacher. Mr. Demma was always ready to help with background information or clues to sources that few others knew existed. Jefferson L. Powell, an accomplished archivist and patient friend, guided me through the voluminous files and documents in the government archives holding Vietnam-era records. Several other fellow Vietnam historians—George L. MacGarrigle, Jeffrey J. Clarke, Ronald H. Spector, Richard A. Hunt, and Joel D. Meyerson—offered the help and comradeship that made the project so enjoyable and rewarding.

I am particularly indebted to the two editors with whom I worked, Catherine A. Heerin and Diane Sedore Arms. Clarity and comprehension were their guiding principles, and they ensured that I adhered faithfully to those principles. In designing and drafting the maps and helping me to select the photographs that illustrate the book, Howell C. Brewer, Jr., left his creative mark on my work.

Many others, too numerous to mention, contributed in their individual ways. I am grateful to them all, but wish to single out my wife, Linda, and my sons, John and Michael, who always waited patiently while I wrote ''just one more paragraph.'' I alone am responsible for interpretations and conclusions, as well as for any errors that may appear.

Washington, D.C.   JOHN D. BERGEN
24 October 1985

Contents

Diagram

Maps

Illustrations

All illustrations are from the files of the Department of Defense and the U.S. Army Center of Military History.

Military Communications
A Test for Technology

1

The French Legacy in Indochina
1945–1960

After a protracted struggle France conquered Indochina in the 1880s. The victors spent the next fifty years establishing a colonial administration, developing prosperous rubber and mining enterprises, and constructing European-style buildings and civil works. The French rule and innovations eroded the Confucian foundations of the ancient Indochinese societies. In Vietnam, French and Vietnamese civil servants replaced village and hamlet chiefs, who traditionally had held the most important position in the Vietnamese social and governmental hierarchy. Peasant farmers lost their ancestral tenant holdings to wealthy landlords who were consolidating parcels of property into more efficient large plantations. Smoldering discontent and nationalistic sentiment finally erupted in 1930 into an uprising in the northern section of Vietnam. Reinforcements from France put down the insurgency, and thereafter a sizable French Army contingent, mainly Foreign Legionnaires and Vietnamese auxiliaries, remained garrisoned in Vietnam.[1]

To link isolated military outposts, plantations, and key governmental centers throughout the colony, a French communications company, the Postes, Telegraphes, et Telephones, built a wire telegraph network that reached the most remote areas of Indochina. Within the major cities the company also installed local communications systems that often included underground cables and central switchboards. The French communicators shunned radios, which had proved unreliable in Indochina: mountains blocked transmission paths, jungles absorbed radio waves, and the highly charged tropical atmosphere caused a crackling noise that disturbed reception.

---

[1]Ronald H. Spector, *Advice and Support: The Early Years, 1941–1960,* U.S. Army in Vietnam (Washington, D.C.: U.S. Army Center of Military History, Government Printing Office, 1983). Chapter 1, "Conquest and Revolt," chronicles French and American involvement in Indochina before World War II. Hereafter cited as *The Early Years.*

Early American Involvement

Radio first became important in the region during World War II. When the Japanese occupied Indochina in 1940 and garrisoned 50,000 troops along the coast of Vietnam, American and European businessmen fled to China, leaving behind a clandestine radio and courier network to manage their commercial interests. After the United States entered the war, the businessmen passed information they received over the network to the China-based Fourteenth U.S. Air Force. The radios gradually became a fruitful source of intelligence as they were used to provide advance notice of Japanese naval movements and to locate targets for American bombers. They also were used frequently to aid the escape of downed American pilots. By late 1944 the network had become so valuable that the Fourteenth Air Force gave the businessmen money and equipment to keep it going.[2]

When the Japanese mounted a campaign against a growing Free French and Vietnamese opposition movement late in the war, they discovered the net. One by one the clandestine radio stations that had been transmitting information to China went dead. To reestablish the intelligence net, the commander of the Fourteenth Air Force, Maj. Gen. Claire L. Chennault, requested that the Office of Strategic Services (OSS) group at Kunming, China, infiltrate agents and radio operators into Indochina.[3]

One of the first teams dispatched, an Army intelligence officer and a radioman, joined a Communist resistance group called the Viet Minh, which had been harassing Japanese logistical operations along the roads and railways northwest of Hanoi. Working closely with the guerrilla band's political leader, Ho Chi Minh, and its military commander, Vo Nguyen Giap, the two Americans were able to accumulate and radio back to China tactical intelligence concerning the Japanese as well as political information about the Vietnamese independence movement that had flourished during the Japanese domination of the French. When Japan surrendered to the United States in August, Ho Chi Minh used the Office of Strategic Services radio network to broadcast from his mountain hideout a request that the United Nations recognize Vietnamese independence from France.[4]

Since American policy concerning Indochina had not been formulated, the Office of Strategic Services cautioned its agents in Indochina—who were divided in their sentiments for the French and the Viet Minh—to remain neutral. A twelve-man team, led by Maj. Archimedes L. A. Patti and sent to Hanoi immediately after the Japanese surrender to arrange the release of American prisoners, had to mediate between the Viet Minh and the French when both sides sought

---

[2]Spector, *The Early Years*, p. 27; Interv, author with Col (ret.) Archimedes L. A. Patti, former chief of the Office of Strategic Services (OSS) in Hanoi, 14 Dec 79, Historians files, CMH.

[3]For an excellent discussion of OSS activities in Indochina during and after World War II, see R. Harris Smith, *OSS: The Secret History of America's First Intelligence Agency* (Berkeley: University of California Press, 1972), pp. 325–59. See also Memo, CG, 14th AF, for CO, OSS China Theater, 20 Mar 45, sub: Establishment of Intelligence Radio Net in French Indochina, CMH.

[4]Smith, *OSS*, pp. 332–35; Schematic, OSS, 15 Aug 45, sub: Communications Network, China Theater, CMH. The insurgents also radioed a request for the text of the American Declaration of Independence, on which Ho Chi Minh modeled his proclamation of Vietnamese independence.

4

American support. Messages transmitted from Hanoi by Major Patti's four-man communications team, which had established the first nonclandestine American station in Vietnam, provided the only firsthand information available to officials in Washington who were trying to determine the proper American position towards Indochina. Traffic was so heavy that General Chennault sent Major Patti five additional signalmen and over four thousand pounds of radio equipment. When the site of the American radio station, the Hotel Metropole, became congested with French refugees, the commander of the communications detachment, 1st Lt. Paul H. Todd, moved the station to the Americans' living quarters on the outskirts of Hanoi.[5]

A team sent to Saigon from the OSS base in Ceylon to represent American interests in the southern part of Vietnam found that there the struggle for power between the French and Vietnamese independence groups had caused more confusion and violence than in the north. Led by Maj. Peter Dewey, the team had been in Saigon only a few weeks when Vietnamese terrorists, apparently mistaking the Americans for French officers, killed Major Dewey and besieged his command post on the outskirts of Saigon. Since the attackers had cut all telephone lines entering the building, the Americans could not phone for help from British troops stationed in the city. The team's radioman had to contact the base on Ceylon, over three thousand kilometers away, and have the call for assistance relayed to the British mission in downtown Saigon. The Americans, eventually relieved by British Gurkha troops, suffered no further casualties; on 26 September 1945, Major Dewey became the first American soldier slain in Vietnam.[6]

By December 1945 the American radio stations in Hanoi and Saigon had closed down, and the last agents of the Office of Strategic Services had left Indochina. During subsequent years the French had increasing difficulty in maintaining control in Vietnam and in suppressing a vocal nationalistic movement that came increasingly under the domination of Vietnamese Communists.

After the Communists gained control of mainland China and invaded South Korea, fears of Communist domination of all Asia caused the United States to abandon its neutral policy toward Indochina and to offer military aid to the French Expeditionary Corps, which was trying to put down an insurgency by Ho Chi Minh's Viet Minh troops. The French readily accepted the offer of materiel, and the United States became inextricably involved with France's conventional approach to a very unconventional war.[7]

American Assistance Begins

To manage the military aid program in Indochina, the United States in the fall of 1950 established the U.S. Military Assistance Advisory Group, Indochina. The 65-man group, commanded by Brig. Gen. Francis G. Brink, had a

---

[5]Msg, Patti to Porter, 25 Sep 45, no. 182; Msg, Nordlinger to CO, OSS China Theater, 17 Sep 45; Msg, Patti to Porter, 24 Sep 45; Interv, author with Patti, 14 Dec 79. All in CMH.

[6]Smith, *OSS*, p. 344.

[7]Spector, *The Early Years*, pp. 99–104.

limited role; since the French wanted neither advice nor training support from the Americans, the advisers could only monitor the distribution and use of U.S. equipment. Because the Viet Minh had cut the wire lines of the Postes, Telegraphes, et Telephones outside Saigon, the French put a high priority on requests for radios. In the first year of the aid program the United States sent 3,500 radio sets to Indochina for the French Army. Life for the signal advisers was a dreary progression of inventories and inspections of the U.S. communications equipment flowing into Indochina and occasional trips to the field to monitor its use.[8]

A small group of communicators who operated a communications center and a four-channel radio-teletype link with Clark Air Base in the Philippines had a far more eventful existence. The chief signal officer of the Army had sent the team to establish a Saigon station in the Army Command and Administrative Net (ACAN), a network of radio stations that made up the thin thread of Army strategic communications binding the U.S. military missions and outposts around the world. The Saigon station, the only American communications gateway between Vietnam and the outside world, also served the U.S. embassy, which provided 80 percent of the station's traffic until 1955, when the embassy staff established direct communications with the American embassy in Manila. By that time the Saigon ACAN station was also handling all traffic between the French command in Saigon and the headquarters of the U.S. commander in chief, Pacific, in Hawaii.[9]

Despite American assistance the French Army was losing its war with the Viet Minh. Without support from the Vietnamese population the French could not venture far from their fortresses without fear of ambush by the guerrillas. Convinced that only an indigenous army, with which the Vietnamese people could identify, could halt the insurgency, American officers urged the French to organize such a force. When the reluctant French in 1951 finally did establish a Vietnamese National Army, their support was halfhearted and inadequate. The new units, led almost solely by French officers and noncommissioned officers, had to compete with French Army units which had higher priority for recruits and scarce resources. When the light infantry battalions of the fledgling Vietnamese Army deployed on their first operational mission to protect a province northwest of Hanoi, the French did not allocate them any communications. The Viet Minh swept down from nearby foothills and mauled the inexperienced and ill-equipped infantrymen before couriers could carry news of their plight to the nearest French Army reinforcements.[10]

---

[8]Ibid., pp. 115–18.

[9]History of the Phu Lam Signal Battalion (U.S. Army Strategic Communications Command) (hereafter cited as Phu Lam Sig Bn History), Nov 67, p. 1, U.S. Army Military History Institute (MHI), Carlisle Barracks, Pennsylvania; Memo, D. V. Anderson for General Williams, 21 Nov 55, sub: Reduction in the Use of MAAG Communications Facilities, no. 3, file 9, Lt Gen Samuel T. Williams Papers, CMH. For details concerning U.S. communications support to the French, see Ltr, MAAG, Indochina, to CINCPAC, 14 Oct 53, sub: French-U.S. Communications, Saigon, Vietnam, w/Incl, Translation of Ltr, General Navarre to CHMAAG, 3 Oct 53, sub: Transmitting Net, and Ltr, MAAG, Indochina, to Commander in Chief, French Forces, 26 Jan 54, sub: NATO Cipher Machine, both in CMH.

[10]Spector, *The Early Years*, p. 179.

Royal Cambodian Army Soldiers *inspect U.S. radios provided by the military aid program.*

The French rebuffed all offers from the American advisory group to train and advise the Vietnamese forces until the spring of 1954, when the Viet Minh defeated an elite 15,000-man force of the French Army at Dien Bien Phu. Before the chief of the advisory group, Lt. Gen. John W. O'Daniel, could get reinforcements for the new mission, the Viet Minh and the French, meeting in Geneva, Switzerland, agreed to a cease-fire in Indochina. The Geneva Agreements divided Vietnam at the 17th Parallel into two zones, which later came to be called the communistic Democratic Republic of Vietnam to the north and the Republic of Vietnam in the south. The agreements also stated that foreign military forces remaining in Vietnam could not be augmented beyond their strength in that country on 20 July 1954, the day the truce was signed. Thus the American advisory group had to begin training and advising the fledgling Vietnamese Army with no more than the 342-man force that had done only logistical accounting for the military aid program.[11]

American and French advisers joined in the Training Relations and Instruc-

---

[11]To handle the $1.1 billion worth of military aid given the French in Indochina since 1950, the United States had steadily increased the size of the advisory group from its original 65-man strength. Brig. Gen. James Lawton Collins, Jr., *The Development and Training of the South Vietnamese Army, 1950–1972*, Vietnam Studies (Washington, D.C.: Government Printing Office, 1975), pp. 1–3.

tion Mission to form the South Vietnamese Army into a 150,000-man force of ten divisions. They intended to organize four field divisions, each about one-half the size of a standard U.S. division, to defend against external aggression and six light divisions, each one-third the size of a U.S. division, to maintain internal security and to operate as a delaying force against an invasion from the North. Each division was to have an organic signal company; a signal battalion would support the army headquarters. American advisers considered the signal component of the army, some 4.2 percent of the entire force, far too small to support the army adequately.[12]

Remnants of the French Expeditionary Corps that remained in Indochina after the Geneva Agreements continued to operate administrative communications, consisting of telephone exchanges and teletype centers in key cities and bases throughout the land and the multichannel systems linking those facilities. American advisers intended to help the South Vietnamese build their own area communications system for administrative communications by rehabilitating the extensive civilian cable system destroyed during the Franco–Viet Minh War and by organizing signal companies for each of five regional headquarters in South Vietnam.[13]

French dissatisfaction with what they considered insufficient U.S. financial aid and increased unrest in their colonies in North Africa led them in mid-1955 to begin withdrawing units of the French Expeditionary Corps and advisers from the Training Relations and Instruction Mission. When the French withdrawal was complete in late April 1956, the South Vietnamese and their American advisers were left on their own with staggering logistical problems. The French salvaged and shipped to France or to their troops in North Africa the best of the American military assistance equipment in Indochina. That included most of the up-to-date communications equipment sent during the previous years. The remaining military supplies, many of them relics of World War II, were left uncatalogued in depots and warehouses or rotting on remote battlefields. A disordered jumble of equipment from four countries—France, the United States, Great Britain, and Canada—clogged the South Vietnamese depots. Although newly formed field units desperately needed the gear, there was no means of inventorying, assembling, and repairing it for issue. Identifying and matching electronic components to signal equipment were particularly difficult. Because the French had handled all the support for the South Vietnamese soldiers fighting alongside them in Indochina, their departure left South Vietnam without a logistical base and without native logisticians to build a new one. Since the South Vietnamese had few tech-

---

[12]DA, Assistant Chief of Staff for Intelligence (ACSI), Intelligence Translation G–6997, 31 Dec 55, sub: Balance Sheet of Vietnamese Armed Forces, 1954 and 1955, p. 136, Intelligence Document files, 70A5465/2, Washington National Records Center (WNRC).

[13]Ltr, MAAG, Vietnam, to Asst Secy of Defense, 15 Jan 56, sub: Country Statement on MDAP, Non-NATO Countries, w/Incl, Narrative Country Statement, Vietnam, as of 31 Dec 55; Ltr, Williams to Tran Trung Dung, 2 Nov 56, w/3 Incls, Army, Air Force, and Navy Force Levels. Both in CMH. For a comprehensive discussion of the rationale behind the decision for a 150,000-man force, see USARPAC, Report of the Visit of Lt Gen Bruce C. Clarke, CG, USARPAC, to Western Pacific and Southeast Asia, 6–29 Sep 55, vol. 3, sec. 4, pt. 2, 338–75–1009/55, WNRC. Although the composition and organization of the armed forces changed somewhat during subsequent years, the force levels remained stable until 1961.

French Troops *radio their position during Operation Lorraine.*

nical manuals, tools, spare parts, and technicians—the basic ingredients of a logistical system—their arsenal, however large, was virtually useless.[14]

Equipment abandoned in the field was a windfall to the Viet Minh, who could appropriate it and eventually use it against the South Vietnamese. That danger was alleviated by assignment in June 1956 of the 350-man Temporary Equipment Recovery Mission to recover and return to the United States all abandoned U.S. military assistance equipment. The men in that mission also covertly acted as advisers to the South Vietnamese Army, helping them solve staggering problems in the depots and warehouses. With the addition of the recovery mission, the advisory group in Saigon—renamed U.S. Military Assistance Advisory Group, Vietnam, after the United States created a separate military mission for Cambodia in late 1955—had 740 men (including 48 communicators and other support troops).[15]

The chief of the advisory group, Lt. Gen. Samuel T. Williams, moved all his technical service advisers into the Temporary Equipment Recovery Mission. The Signal Branch, headed by Lt. Col. Edward Andrus, had sixteen officers: nine

---

[14]Collins, *Development and Training*, pp. 2–8; Ltrs, Army Attache, Vietnam, to ACSI, DA, 10 Jun 57 and 29 Aug 57, sub: CATO (MAAG, Vietnam) Advisor Quarterly Reports, 66A3138/213, WNRC.

[15]Spector, *The Early Years*, pp. 255–62.

worked directly with the staff of the South Vietnamese Army's chief signal officer, one was assigned to each of the five military regions, one to the signal school at Thu Duc, and one to the central signal depot in Saigon. Although the signal advisers were charged with training and operational duties, most concentrated on logistics.[16]

Of all the technical service advisers, the signal advisers were faced with the most overwhelming task in the years following the French withdrawal. Untrained South Vietnamese supplymen were gathering up electronic components and spare parts. Unable to read foreign markings on the parts or to identify the type of equipment to which they belonged, they were stacking the delicate materiel in exposed storage areas where it was deteriorating quickly. The absence of an inventory control system made even equipment that was identified difficult to locate and retrieve once stored. During the first three months of 1957, signal depots processed 1,928 tons of recovered electronic materiel but issued only 381 tons to units of the newly formed divisions that desperately needed communications equipment. Even new equipment shipped from the United States to fill emergency requisitions was being lost in the warehouses. Hampered by a lack of spare parts and of Vietnamese-language technical manuals, the few experienced South Vietnamese repairmen working in maintenance facilities at the signal depots were taking an average of seventeen man-days to repair a single piece of equipment.[17]

Agreeing with General Williams' often repeated lament that logistical support for signal activities was "inadequate even for peacetime operations," Ngo Dinh Diem, the president of South Vietnam, frequently told visiting American officials that a communications capability was his most dire need. To emphasize his concern, he appointed as his chief signal officer a trusted former noncommissioned officer from the French Army, Col. Nguyen Khuong, and made clear to the South Vietnamese Army general staff and American advisers that his young protege was to receive their full backing.[18]

Although Americans and South Vietnamese generally agreed on the gravity of the signal problem, they differed on the solution. While the South Vietnamese pressed for new American signal equipment, the Americans wanted to distribute available serviceable equipment and evacuate excess and unserviceable items before considering any large-scale resupply or modernization. The South Vietnamese, recalling the removal of communications by the departing French, preferred to hoard all the equipment they could find and to seek more. A team from the General Accounting Office in Washington, while reviewing the military aid program in South Vietnam during late 1957, discovered that not only

---

[16]Interv, author with Col (ret.) Thomas P. Ross, former chief, Signal Branch, Temporary Equipment Recovery Mission, 15 May 78, Historians files, CMH.

[17]Ltr, CHMAAG, Vietnam, to General de Corps D'Armee Le Van Ty, 26 Jan 57, no. 35, file 15, Williams Papers; Ltr, HQ, MAAG, Vietnam, to OSD et al., 28 Mar 57, sub: Third Quarterly Special TERM Report—Dec 56 Through Feb 57, Incl 6. Both in CMH.

[18]Narrative Country Statement, Vietnam (hereafter cited as Country Statement for Vietnam), p. 15, Incl to Ltr, CHMAAG, Vietnam, to Asst Secy of Defense, 21 Jan 57, sub: Country Statement on MDAP, Non-NATO Countries, CMH; Memo on the Prime Needs of the Vietnamese Armed Forces, 3 Sep 58, included in the Record of Conferences with President Diem, 12 Jun 58 to 27 Dec 58; Record of Conversation Between President Diem, General Williams, and General Myers, 14 Oct 57, included in the Record of Conferences with President Diem, 16 Sep 57 to 28 Dec 57. Latter two in Williams Papers.

were South Vietnamese logisticians reluctant to evacuate excess electronic equipment, but also that they preferred to keep equipment authorized for field units under centralized control at Saigon depots. Not until 1960 did American advisers finally convince South Vietnamese signal officers to clear out the warehouses. Within the following three years the number of line items in the South Vietnamese Army's signal depot dropped from 37,000 to 18,000 with disposal of $3.5 million of excess equipment.[19]

Because of hoarding, field units had to struggle to maintain barely serviceable equipment. During an inspection of the 16th Light Infantry Division in 1958, American advisers discovered that only 40 percent of the division's radios were working and that the depots were ignoring requests for repair parts. By 1960, after signal advisers pressured Colonel Khuong to provide better support to the field, the amount of operable signal equipment rose to over 75 percent, higher-echelon maintenance facilities were overhauling obsolete electronic gear, and the Saigon signal depot was operating a production line for rebuilding tactical radios.[20]

Dramatic advances in electronics technology during the 1950s provided unexpected support to the South Vietnamese Army's desire to modernize its communications equipment. Since spare parts were no longer being produced for much of the World War II–vintage communications sets assigned to the worldwide Military Assistance Program, the Department of the Army in mid-1959 authorized advisory groups to program replacement for obsolete equipment. Having newer equipment would also make South Vietnamese and American communications more compatible should the United States ever have to intervene in the region. While planning a reorganization of the South Vietnamese Army in which the light divisions would be consolidated to create a seven-division army, General Williams told his signal advisers to include new communications equipment in tables of organization and equipment. For budgetary reasons the replacement equipment was to be programmed over three years beginning in 1960.[21]

By the early 1960s the South Vietnamese Signal Corps also had begun to reap the benefits of an ambitious training program started in 1956 by Colonel Andrus and continued by his successor as chief signal adviser, Lt. Col. Thomas P. Ross. Faced with insufficient Vietnamese technical expertise and rigid ceilings on the numbers of military advisers that could be employed in South Vietnam, during the ensuing five years the signal advisers had arranged for over 150 American and Filipino civilians to work in the depots as technical advisers and instructors. Using the training facilities of the U.S. Army, the signal advisers also enrolled

---

[19]Logistics Briefing for President Diem—29 May 58, Williams Papers; Memo, Col Nguyen Khuong for Lt Col Ross, 13 Jan 58, sub: Re-examination of the Subject Lately Discussed and Request for Assistance and Help, CMH; Ltr, HQ, MACV, 26 Apr 61, sub: Training Progress Reports of Contractor Technicians Furnished Under the Army Military Assistance Training Program, CMH; Ltr, CINCPAC to MACV, 27 Aug 63, sub: CINCPAC MAP Inspection of Military Assistance in the Republic of Vietnam, w/Incl, 339-75-1009/63, WNRC.

[20]Ltr, Col Rollin B. Durbin to Lt Gen S. T. Williams, 14 Feb 58, file 34; DF, Ch, TERM, to CHMAAG, 12 Jul 60, sub: Deadline Rate of Signal Equipment, no. 22, file 83. Both in Williams Papers. Ltr, MAAG, Vietnam, to OSD et al., 13 Jan 61, sub: Fifth Semi-Annual Special Report of TERM of Vietnam, 1 Apr 60 Through 30 Sep 60, CMH.

[21]Ltr, Adjutant General, DA, to Chief Signal Officer, 17 Aug 59, sub: Repair Parts Support of Signal and Transportation Corps Equipment Furnished MAP Recipients, MAAG records, 64A2424/1, WNRC.

South Vietnamese officers and soldiers in stateside schools and arranged for dispatch of U.S. Army mobile training teams to instruct South Vietnamese signalmen on the operation and maintenance of their equipment. By 1959, 133 South Vietnamese communicators had attended courses at the signal schools at Fort Monmouth, New Jersey, or Fort Gordon, Georgia, and fifteen mobile training teams had been to South Vietnam. Colonel Khuong sent the best graduates of those American training programs to teach at the South Vietnamese signal schools at Vung Tau and Thu Duc. Formed in 1958, by 1960 those schools had trained 6,639 communicators to fill the burgeoning ranks of the South Vietnamese Signal Corps.[22]

Besides the communications shortages in tactical units, the French departure in early 1956 had also left territorial communications in dire straits. For administrative communications, the South Vietnamese Army had only the short-range radios assigned to tactical units. To replace facilities which had been dismantled by the French, American advisers had to contract with American and Japanese civilian companies to install four dial exchanges in the headquarters complexes in and around Saigon. The South Vietnamese negotiated with the French Army and the Postes, Telegraphes, et Telephones for transfer of the cables that interlaced the capital. After completion of a Saigon-area telephone system in 1958, the South Vietnamese Army formed its first battalion-size signal unit to operate the new communications for military facilities in the capital.[23]

Outside Saigon, where pilferage and sabotage had frustrated attempts to repair the war-torn cable network, withdrawal of the French Army's multichannel systems left the South Vietnamese with only a meager Morse code radio network linking Saigon with the regional headquarters and major population centers. In 1956 American advisers obtained tactical radio-teletype sets for the South Vietnamese to use in a net from army headquarters in Saigon to each regional headquarters. But routing communications from Saigon to the divisions through the regional headquarters proved so slow that the South Vietnamese Army soon established a direct Morse code command net from Saigon to the divisions. The South Vietnamese Army used some multichannel equipment received from the United States in late 1957 to extend a long-lines system into the Mekong Delta and to provide four-channel systems from several of the regional headquarters to nearby bases.[24]

[22]Of all the South Vietnamese technical services, the Signal Corps had made the most use of U.S. Army training programs and facilities. MAAG, Vietnam, Military Aid Training Programs, sec. A1 and A2, no. 11, file 102, Williams Papers. Advisers were particularly reliant on the American signalmen who came to South Vietnam in mobile training teams to instruct their South Vietnamese contemporaries on the operation and maintenance of new items of U.S. communications equipment. Ltr, Gen Williams to Maj Gen Ralph T. Nelson, Chief Signal Officer, 19 Dec 59, no. 594, file 55, Williams Papers.

[23]Country Statement for Vietnam, pp. 16–23, Incl to Ltr, CHMAAG, Vietnam, to Asst Secy of Defense, ISA, 15 Jul 57, sub: Country Statement for MDAP, Non-NATO Countries; ibid., pp. 27–32, Incl to Ltr, CHMAAG, Vietnam, to Asst Secy of Defense, ISA, 22 Jan 58, sub: Country Statement for MDAP, Non-NATO Countries; DF, Ch, Excess and Salvage Property Officer, TERM, to Ch, TERM, 19 Jul 57, sub: Transfer of French Military Telephone Installations to ARVN. All in CMH.

[24]Memo, Signal Command, RVN, for Signal Center et al., 26 Apr 57, CMH; Country Statement for Vietnam as of 30 Jun 56, p. 15, Incl to Ltr, CHMAAG, Vietnam, to Asst Secy of Defense, ISA, 20 Jul 56, sub: Country Statement on MDAP, Non-NATO Countries, CMH; Memo, USARPAC for CINCPAC, sub: Report of Visit to Western Pacific, 18 Sep–14 Oct 56, 338–75–1009/55, WNRC.

Problems in Building a Regional Network

E ven before the French withdrew their tactical multichannel equipment from South Vietnam, American military and State Department officials in Washington had recognized the need for a more permanent communications system in Southeast Asia. They decided to build a regional network that would serve the civil, military, and commercial needs of South Vietnam, Laos, Cambodia, and Thailand and bind those developing nations closer together. *(Map 1)* Some $27 million was to come from a State Department–administered Asian Economic Development Fund and $3 million from the Department of Defense. The International Cooperation Administration, the agency that operated foreign assistance programs for the State Department, was to oversee the installation of the project. Unacquainted with communications requirements or the environment in Southeast Asia, the International Cooperation Administration negotiated a contract based on a vague proposal with two American companies, Page Communications Engineers and Hycon Eastern Company, to do an engineering survey for the regional system. Neither the Saigon field office of the International Cooperation Administration, called the U.S. Operations Mission, nor the military advisers took part in the contract negotiations.[25]

Work on the survey, called the Hycon-Page project, proceeded slowly. Unprepared for the complications of dealing with the French, South Vietnamese, and the Postes, Telegraphes, et Telephones—which was especially reluctant to cooperate with a future competitor— the American civilian contractors became entangled in endless administrative and technical difficulties. Nor had they anticipated the problem of locating secure and technically satisfactory sites in the rugged northern sections of South Vietnam or in the marshy, highly populated Mekong Delta. They had come to South Vietnam prepared only to test frequencies, take readings, and plot systems on maps.[26]

When delays in the survey interfered with completion of the military dial exchanges in Saigon, which had to be coordinated with the engineering team, General Williams protested that the stalled project was blocking the development of vital communications for the South Vietnamese armed forces. Denied any supplies to rehabilitate or install cable until completion of the integrated communications network, impatient South Vietnamese signalmen were using tactical field wire to link installations throughout the country into a makeshift administrative communications system. General Williams realized that the expedient was a poor substitute for cable and had depleted war reserves of tactical wire. Thus he asked the Pacific Command, the Hawaii-based headquarters that supervised the oper-

[25]Country Statement for Vietnam, pp. 19–21, Incl to Ltr, CHMAAG, Vietnam, to Asst Secy of Defense, ISA, 24 Aug 58, sub: Country Statement on MDAP, Non-NATO Countries, CMH; CINCPAC Staff Study, Regional Telecommunications Project, Southeast Asia, 23 Nov 59, file 566, 72A4171/1, WNRC; Ltr, Lt Gen S. T. Williams to Vice Adm H. D. Riley, 18 Mar 59, w/Incl, Memo, Summary Points on Review of Telecommunications Projects, no. 164, file 54, Williams Papers. On 3 March 1956, General Williams approved inclusion of military requirements in the regional network. Ltr, Brig Gen G. C. Carlson, Dep Ch, MAAG, to CINCPAC, 5 Nov 57, sub: Southeast Asia Communications Survey, 61A1729/1, WNRC.

[26]Interv, author with Ross, 15 May 78; Ltr, Am Ambassador to CHMAAG, 31 Jul 56, no. 380, file 8, Williams Papers.

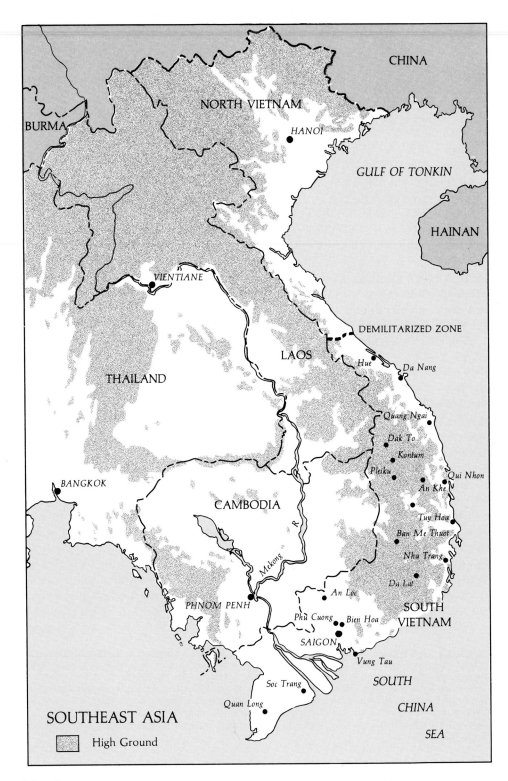

SOUTHEAST ASIA

 High Ground

MAP 1

ations of the advisory group, to find a means of administrative communications for the South Vietnamese Army to use until the completion of the regional project. In response the Pacific Command promptly contracted with a Japanese communications firm, Nippon Telephone and Telegraph Company, to perform an engineering survey for a system linking all the major military bases in South Vietnam. Within seven months the Japanese firm presented Colonel Ross with a plan that envisaged an austere microwave and very high frequency (VHF) system using available tactical equipment and materials that could be procured readily in the Orient.[27]

Although the Pacific Command encouraged General Williams to submit a request for the proposed network, the American ambassador, Elbridge Durbrow, told General Williams in February 1958 to defer plans for any military communications until completion of the Hycon-Page survey. Enforcing a country team approach in South Vietnam, Ambassador Durbrow wanted complete coordination and agreement between military and State Department officials in South Vietnam. After waiting two more months, General Williams notified the U.S. Operations Mission that if he were not given some assurance within thirty days that the Hycon-Page project would soon be completed, he would submit his request for military communications without the concurrence of the country team.[28]

The U.S. Operations Mission was relatively powerless to control the activities of the contractors in South Vietnam. While the mission was supposed to ensure that contracted work was done, the contractors submitted their reports directly to the headquarters of the International Cooperation Administration in Washington, which in turn communicated with the contractors through its regional office in Bangkok. Protesting "this means divided authority, and it will not work," the director of the U.S. Operations Mission, Leland Barrows, tried unsuccessfully to get the secretary of state to give him more control over the contractors in South Vietnam.[29] Although the management relationships did not change, General Williams' complaints did result in termination of the unsuccessful Hycon-Page contract and award of the project to Tudor Engineers, a California-based firm, for completion of the survey. The International Cooperation Administration then contracted with another communications firm, TV Associates of Indiana, to install the telecommunications project. Encouraged that the new contracts would hasten the network, General Williams acceded to Ambassador Durbrow and cut off contract talks with the Japanese communications firm.

When a member of the Pacific Command's signal (J-6) staff, Capt. John F. Moore, U.S. Navy, went to Bangkok in the summer of 1959 to ensure that the

[27]Ltr, Lt Gen S. T. Williams to Lt Gen Le Van Ty, 10 Sep 58; Ltr, MAAG, Vietnam, to CINCPAC, 26 Nov 56, sub: Military Communications Within Vietnam, no. 566, file 8; Msg, MAAG, Vietnam, 6787 to CINCPAC, 19 Nov 57, w/Incl, Memorandum for Record (MFR), no. 395, file 14. All in Williams Papers.

[28]Opposition to the Nippon project was also based on a belief that the South Vietnamese still harbored resentments against the Japanese over their wartime occupation of Indochina. MFR, MAAG, Vietnam, 26 Feb 58, sub: Country Team Meeting-25 Feb 58, no. 6, file 48; Memo, MAAG, Vietnam, for Mr. Gardiner, USOM, et al., 3 Apr 58, sub: Long Lines Communications, no. 52, file 36. Both in Williams Papers.

[29]Msg, USOM 1485 to Secy of State, 6 May 58, sub: Management of Regional Telecommunications Project, no. 7, file 30, Williams Papers.

new contractor was aware of all the military requirements and specifications that had been given to the former contractors, he found such confusion that he cautioned the commander in chief, Pacific, to avoid becoming identified with the project because "ICA [International Cooperation Administration] could properly be charged with maladministration of this project over the past four years." Expecting to find a team of communications engineers managing the $30 million telecommunications program for the government, he was surprised to discover that the chief project officer at the administration's headquarters in Washington was a chemical engineer and the regional project officer in Bangkok a retired banker. They appeared to have made little progress in planning for the regional network, and the new contractor was questioning whether there was enough money left to build it. Concluding that the International Cooperation Administration's approach to the regional telecommunications project "should be drastically changed to conform to normal engineering and construction procedures," Captain Moore recommended that the military program interim communications in Southeast Asia while awaiting completion of the regional system.[30]

On the same day that Captain Moore visited the regional project officer in Bangkok, a Senate investigating committee began hearing testimony concerning newspaper charges of gross inefficiency within the entire U.S. Operations Mission in South Vietnam. After continuing the hearings in Saigon, the subcommittee reported to Senator J. William Fulbright, the chairman of the Senate Committee on Foreign Relations, that it had indeed found serious problems with the conduct of nonmilitary aid programs in South Vietnam. It recommended that the ambassador be given more authority over planning and executing contractual work in South Vietnam and that the U.S. Operations Mission establish clearly defined goals and timetables to complete projects. The senators wanted the U.S. Operations Mission to "work itself out of a job," as they felt the military advisory group in South Vietnam was effectively doing. Although the report of the hearings dealt only peripherally with the telecommunications project, it did discuss years of delay and money wasted in an attempt to install transmitters for Radio Vietnam, the South Vietnamese broadcast network. Having uncovered so much confusion in "the tangled skein of radio projects in Vietnam," the senators recommended a "careful examination by the Inspector General of aid to radio."[31]

Shortly after the Geneva Agreements, President Diem had requested assistance to expand the primitive broadcast facilities of Radio Vietnam to reach the entire population of South Vietnam as well as parts of North Vietnam. He wanted to counter North Vietnamese propaganda broadcasts beamed to South Vietnam in an effort to undermine popular support for the new republic. Supporting the proposal, the U.S. Operations Mission contracted for installation of ten broad-

---

[30]CINCPAC, Report of Conference, 20–31 July 1959, Between Captain John F. Moore, USN, CINCPAC Staff and Director, USOM/Thailand, SEATELCOM Project Coordinator, file 050864, 72A4171/1, WNRC.

[31]U.S. Congress, Senate, Subcommittee on State Department Organization and Public Affairs to the Committee on Foreign Relations, *Hearings on the Situation in Vietnam*, 86th Cong., 1st sess., 7–8 December 1959, pp. 343–48; U.S. Congress, Senate, Subcommittee on State Department Organization and Public Affairs to the Committee on Foreign Relations, *United States Aid Program in Vietnam*, 86th Cong., 2d sess., 26 February 1966, pp. 27–28, 50–51. For a review of the aid program in South Vietnam, see John D. Montgomery, *The Politics of Foreign Aid* (New York: Frederick A. Praeger, 1962), pp. 224–32.

cast stations throughout South Vietnam. Because the U.S. Information Service was already broadcasting the Voice of America to North Vietnam from its station in the Philippines, the American ambassador deferred building a high-powered transmitter for broadcasting to North Vietnam until after the domestic network was completed. Although military advisers agreed with Diem that a South Vietnamese broadcast program aimed at North Vietnam would be more effective, both technically and psychologically, than an American program beamed from the Philippines, the advisory group was powerless to support broadcasting programs—a State Department function—with military assistance funds.[32]

While the South Vietnamese waited for the U.S. Operations Mission to arrange for the construction of the radio broadcast network, the North Vietnamese stepped up their propaganda assault on the South. By 1958 they had built high-powered transmitters that could reach all the way to the Mekong Delta, and they were jamming even the small amount of programming that the South Vietnamese were able to broadcast from their primitive facilities. In addition to the programming of Radio Hanoi, called the Voice of Vietnam, South Vietnam was harangued with Vietnamese-language broadcasts from Radio Peiping and Radio Moscow. President Diem angrily appealed to Secretary of the Army Wilber M. Brucker, during his visit to South Vietnam in September 1958, to use the influence of the Department of Defense to have a high-powered transmitter built at Hue, fifty miles south of the North Vietnamese border, to enable South Vietnam to mount a counteroffensive in the propaganda war with the Communists. Although Brucker had no authority to fill the request, he did tell General Williams to notify him periodically concerning the progress of the radio project. Williams warned him that by sending information through military channels concerning a U.S. Operations Mission project, he would be compromising his position on the country team since Ambassador Durbrow had directed that the embassy would handle all correspondence concerning the country team's activities. Secretary Brucker told General Williams to explain to the ambassador that he would be communicating his "military observations" of the progress on the project.[33]

In compiling his reports, General Williams discovered that the entire Radio Vietnam project had floundered for lack of resident expertise in the U.S. Operations Mission to monitor a technical program, the same deficiency that was delaying the regional telecommunications project. Although the mission had an assigned director of transportation, communications, and power, he was an administrator rather than an engineer and had a variety of responsibilities in addition to communications. The single knowledgeable American involved in the Radio Vietnam project, a contractor hired in 1955 to plan and engineer the network,

[32]Memo, Leland Barrows, Director of Mission, for Lt Gen S. T. Williams, 28 Nov 58, sub: National Radio Network Project, no. 83, file 37; Memo of Conversation, Arthur Z. Gardiner and Mr. Thuan, 19 Mar 59, no. 24, file 57. Both in Williams Papers. U.S. Congress, Senate, Subcommittee on State Department Organization and Public Affairs to the Committee on Foreign Relations, *Hearings on the Situation in Vietnam*, 86th Cong., 1st sess., 30–31 July 1959, pp. 103–07, 140–51.

[33]CIA, *National Intelligence Survey, South Vietnam, Section 57: Subversion* (hereafter cited as *Subversion*), Jul 58, pp. 12–13, CMH; Record of Conversation, Meeting Between Secy of Army Brucker and President Diem-3 Sep 58 at 1700, and Record of Conversation, Meeting Between President Diem and General Williams on 10 Sep 58 at 0900, both in the Record of Conferences with President Diem, 12 Jun–27 Dec 58, Williams Papers. Ltr, Williams to Brucker, 9 Oct 59, no. 475, file 55, Williams Papers.

had left South Vietnam after ordering the necessary equipment. When the equipment arrived, it had to be stored in warehouses until appropriate facilities could be built to house it; then inexperienced South Vietnamese technicians could not install it. After the Senate hearings exposed the discouraging situation, the U.S. Operations Mission rehired the same American technician who had planned the broadcasting network to complete it.[34]

Communist Communications

I mproper staffing, restrictive bureaucratic procedures, and conflicting priorities within the country team had caused confusion and delays during a time when the South Vietnamese vitally needed strong telecommunications and broadcasting to counter an increasingly aggressive political and military offensive by the Communists. While American bureaucratic delays were stalling development of a South Vietnamese communications system, the North Vietnamese were rapidly building a less ambitious but efficient communications network for their own nation. Rehabilitating the old French wire lines and using radios that the Soviet Union and China had given their new ally, veteran Viet Minh communicators had constructed a comprehensive wire and radio-telegraph system that linked every province in North Vietnam with Hanoi.[35]

Providing communications for the Viet Cong, those Communists who had secretly remained in South Vietnam after the Geneva Agreements, was far more difficult. The only legal means of communications between North and South was postcards that were supposed to contain only personal information. Exchanged on a bridge in the Demilitarized Zone at the rate of ten thousand a month from each direction, the cards afforded little opportunity to communicate covertly.[36]

Using postal addresses in third countries, especially France, the early Viet Cong communicated by letters that were carefully worded to deceive South Vietnamese counterintelligence agents whom they suspected of checking the international mail. As their resistance movement expanded in South Vietnam, the Communists established a courier network to carry strategic directions from Hanoi to the Viet Cong cells. Couriers moved up and down an old Viet Minh messenger route, later named the Ho Chi Minh Trail, that wound along the mountains on the eastern borders of Laos and Cambodia. *(Map 2)* Agents met the couriers in Cambodia, took their messages, and gave them information to take north. The agents also maintained contact with couriers who carried correspondence between Com-

[34]Memo, Arthur Z. Gardiner for Lt Gen Williams, 5 Oct 59, sub: Radio Vietnam Project, no. 78, file 57, Williams Papers.

[35]CIA, *National Intelligence Survey: North Vietnam,* Jul 64, p. 14, CMH; Rpt, Controlled American Source (CAS) 996, Am Embassy, 22 Jan 54, sub: Telecommunications in the Democratic Republic of Vietnam, Incl to Ltr, Army Attache, Saigon, to DA, ACofS, G–2, 17 Feb 54, sub: Information Received Through Local Special Assistant Liaison American Embassy, Saigon, Vietnam, file 102795, ACSI files, 66A3138/215, WNRC.

[36]704th Intelligence Det, Agent Rpt, 27 Oct 62, sub: Communications Channels Between North and South Vietnam, no. 704-5-203, file 6.249, 66A3201-R/135, WNRC.

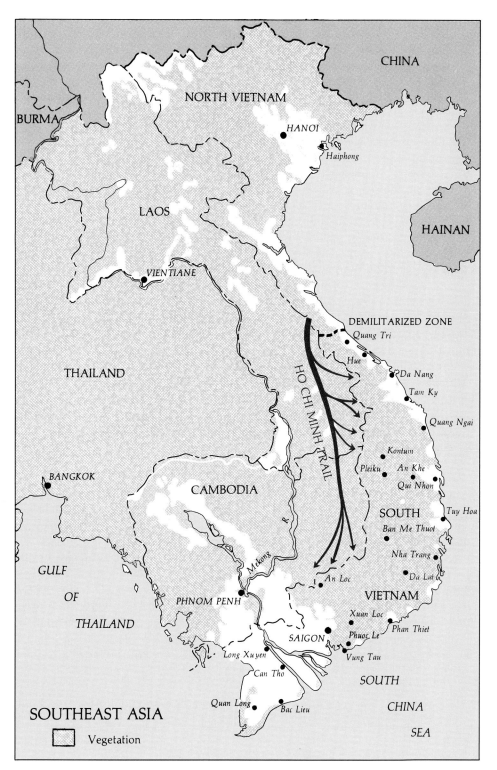

CHINA

NORTH VIETNAM

BURMA

● HANOI

● Haiphong

LAOS

HAINAN

● VIENTIANE

THAILAND

DEMILITARIZED ZONE

Quang Tri

Hue

● Da Nang

Tam Ky

Quang Ngai

HO CHI MINH TRAIL

Kontum

Pleiku ● An Khe

Qui Nhon

BANGKOK ●

CAMBODIA

SOUTH

Tuy Hoa

Ban Me Thuot

Nha Trang

GULF

Mekong

OF

THAILAND

PHNOM PENH

An Loc

Da Lat

VIETNAM

Xuan Loc

Phuoc Le ● Phan Thiet

SAIGON

Vung Tau

Long Xuyen

Can Tho

SOUTH

Quan Long

Bac Lieu

CHINA

SOUTHEAST ASIA

SEA

 Vegetation

MAP 2

munist cells within South Vietnam. The process was slow, often taking three months for a message from Hanoi to reach a cell in the South. The absence of timely communications in the early post-Geneva years probably kept the Communists from seizing several opportunities to overthrow President Diem's government during periods of political instability in Saigon.[37]

Reinstallation in 1955 of radio links between Hanoi and the South, closed down after the Geneva Agreements, made Communist communications more effective. After Hanoi established a liaison mission with the International Control Commission in Saigon in the spring of 1955, giving the Communists a legal excuse to install a radio station in South Vietnam, the North Vietnamese secretly passed high-priority messages between Hanoi and Viet Cong cells in the South. By the time the mission returned to North Vietnam in May 1958 and the station in Saigon closed down, Hanoi had smuggled radios south with radiomen who served as the communicators for groups of infiltrators from North Vietnam. Arriving in the South, the radiomen joined the cadre of newly formed cells and established contact with Hanoi on the party net, the Morse code radio net that the North Vietnamese used to control their underground movement in the South. Although most cells communicated directly with Hanoi, by 1958 the Viet Cong had established two stations to coordinate activities within South Vietnam. One, located west of Saigon near the Cambodian border, served the southern portion of the country, which the Communists called Nam Bo. The other, due west of Da Nang ten miles inside the Laotian border, served cells in the northern regions of South Vietnam, which the Communists called Intersector 5, and maintained contact with infiltration groups as they traveled along the southern half of the Ho Chi Minh Trail.[38]

Although the use of radio enabled the Communists to speed up urgent messages, it also made the underground movement more vulnerable to detection and disruption through electronic warfare. Throughout the Franco–Viet Minh War, the French Army had intercepted Viet Minh communications from several monitoring stations in Vietnam and Laos. In return for bearings and data from an American direction-finding station in Manila, the French passed signal intelligence to the American legation in Saigon. Because American advisers found the intelligence useful in following the activities of the Communists throughout Indochina, especially those with the liaison mission in Saigon, they encouraged the French to continue the intercept mission after the French Army left Vietnam in early 1956. A forty-man detachment remained to run five intercept stations until mid-1957, when the French, after disagreements with President Diem, withdrew all their communications intelligence teams from South Vietnam.[39]

When President Diem asked the United States to assume the intercept mis-

[37]Jeffrey Race, *War Comes to Long An: Revolutionary Conflict in a Vietnamese Province* (Berkeley: University of California Press, 1972), pp. 34–38.

[38]CIA, *Subversion,* pp. 2, 9.

[39]Msg, Williams to Schow, 6 Jan 55, file 96; DF, Ch, Direct Aid Div, to CHMAAG, 29 Jan 57, sub: Conversation with General Don on Intercept, and ibid., 14 Jan 59, both in no. 3, file 23. Record of Conversation Between President Diem and General Williams, 15 Mar 57, in Record of Conferences with President Diem, 31 Dec 56–12 Sep 57. All in Williams Papers. Ltr, CINC, French Forces in Indochina, to Military Attache, Am Legation, Saigon, Mar 52, 66A3138/215, WNRC.

sion, General Williams forwarded the request to the Communications Intelligence Board in Washington, the group that managed all U.S. electronic warfare activities. Despite Diem's personal plea to Allen Dulles, director of the Central Intelligence Agency and chairman of the intelligence board, American intelligence officials decided that the ceiling on the number of Americans permitted in South Vietnam and unstable internal security precluded any American electronic warfare endeavor at the time. Even when the South Vietnamese Army in 1958 discovered evidence of the communications complex in Intersector 5 and requested direction-finding equipment to pinpoint it, General Williams was unable to help. Not until 1960 did the Central Intelligence Agency give a small amount of intercept equipment to the South Vietnamese. Thus between 1957 and 1960, three critical years during which the Communists were building their organization in the South, the only radio intercept program against the Viet Cong was conducted from distant stations in neighboring countries.[40]

The South Vietnamese met similar obstacles in getting help to protect their own communications from intrusion by the Communists. Reluctant to expose American codes and cryptographic equipment to possible compromise, intelligence officials would permit General Williams only to offer the South Vietnamese the services of his signal advisers in establishing policies and standards for communications security and better procedures for using South Vietnamese codes. When President Diem irately responded that his government possessed only unsophisticated codes that had already been used by the French, General Williams naively advised him that any code would work if changed every fifteen days. Again he offered the services of the signal advisers, but only to help ensure that the old French codes were rotated frequently.[41]

Although allied electronic warfare against the Viet Cong and North Vietnamese was limited to long-range monitoring, the Viet Cong were wary of exposing the location of their agents in South Vietnam to suspected direction-finding programs. Thus they evolved a combination of couriers and broadcast radio to coordinate with the resistance movement in South Vietnam. Detailed plans and orders were sent by courier to Viet Cong committees at each military region and then disseminated through the Viet Cong chain of command to every cell.[42] At each level the Communists discussed and clarified the correspondence before forwarding it to the next echelon. After allowing several months for information to be fully disseminated, Hanoi would announce the implementation of the order or plan in a broadcast that all cells could monitor on commercial radios at the same time. The plan to revert from political subversion to armed struggle, for example, was dispatched by courier from Hanoi in November 1958, but it was not until 14 May 1959 that the Communist Party in Hanoi broadcast in Morse code over Radio Hanoi

---

[40]Msg, Washington to Saigon, 4 Jan 56, file 96; Record of Conversation Between President Diem and General Williams, 27 May 57, in Record of Conferences with President Diem, 31 Dec 56–12 Sep 57; Msg, Gaither to Williams, 2 Mar 56, file 96. All in Williams Papers.

[41]Ibid.

[42]By the late 1950s the Communists had established an underground government in the South roughly paralleling the administrative divisions of the South Vietnamese government. Although Viet Cong regions did not correspond to South Vietnamese regions, the boundaries and names of most provinces, districts, villages, and hamlets were identical for the two governments.

the signal to implement the plan, calling on its cadres in the South to rise up "struggling heroically" to "smash the U.S. imperialists and their South Vietnamese lackies."[43]

By the time Hanoi called for a widespread uprising in South Vietnam, the Viet Cong had already begun a campaign of banditry and assassination to get money and supplies for their insurgency and to break the will of government officials to resist. In a major victory in the summer of 1958, emboldened Viet Cong attacked a South Vietnamese infantry company, capturing over a hundred weapons and stealing 5 million piasters from a nearby rubber plantation. Because the South Vietnamese soldiers had shut down their radio for the night, they were unable to request reinforcements to help avert the resounding defeat. By early 1959 the Communists were assassinating over twenty governmental officials a month and controlled large areas of several South Vietnamese provinces. President Diem's suspicions that the Communists would also subvert South Vietnamese communications were confirmed in 1959 when a South Vietnamese Army captain, the chief of the communications center at the general staff headquarters, was arrested for passing cipher books to the Communists.[44]

U.S. and South Vietnamese Communications Expand

When the Viet Cong attacked a U.S. advisory detachment at Bien Hoa in July 1959 and killed two Americans, advisers and embassy officials became concerned that U.S. communications in South Vietnam could not summon assistance or coordinate an evacuation of Americans in an emergency. Since American communications within South Vietnam consisted of a nine-station Morse code net that South Vietnamese employees of the U.S. Operations Mission operated only in daylight, military advisers had come to rely almost exclusively on South Vietnamese Army communications, which in emergencies were clogged with operational traffic. Although the Army had a contingency plan to rush radios and three hundred operators to South Vietnam in an emergency, General Williams chose to request only voice radios that could be operated by advisers. In response the Department of the Army programmed for delivery within the next two years enough commercial single-sideband radios for each advisory detachment. For communications outside South Vietnam the embassy supplemented its radio-teletype link to the embassy in Manila with a single-sideband voice net linking it to the embassy in Phnom Penh, Cambodia, and to U.S. Navy ships operating in the South China Sea. To supplement the four-channel system to Clark Air Base in the Philippines, the Army station in Saigon established a reserve radio-teletype link to Bangkok. To coordinate the introduction of additional American commu-

---

[43]Ltr, Lt Gen S. T. Williams to Lt Gen Le Van Ty, 21 Jan 58, no. 58, file 34; Record of Conversation Between General Williams and President Diem, 5 May 58, in Record of Conferences with President Diem, 28 Dec 57–29 May 58. Both in Williams Papers. Foreign Broadcast Information Service, Bulletin EEE-2, North Vietnam, 15 May 69, CMH.

[44]Spector, *The Early Years*, p. 315.

nications and to avert frequency conflicts with South Vietnamese military and governmental agencies, General Williams convinced the embassy to institute regular meetings of a Communications Coordinating Committee of the country team.[45]

The number of radios and the opportunities for frequency conflicts in South Vietnam increased dramatically when the United States began responding to the intensification in hostilities with large quantities of military equipment. Recognizing that the South Vietnamese Army was ill equipped to defend against a large-scale insurgency, especially after sustaining heavy losses in equipment during Viet Cong attacks, in March 1960 General Williams asked the Commander in Chief, Pacific, Admiral Harry D. Felt, to accelerate the delivery of materiel already programmed for modernization of the South Vietnamese Army. He particularly stressed the need for an immediate airlift of tactical communications equipment to enable beleaguered South Vietnamese Army platoons and companies to coordinate their response to the widespread Communist attacks. Admiral Felt quickly approved and forwarded to Washington General Williams' request. In response the Department of the Army exhausted its depot stocks and diverted equipment under production for other military assistance programs to send the South Vietnamese Army large quantities of portable PRC–10 voice radios for company and battalion communications and enough multichannel sets to connect infantry divisions to the headquarters of the local military region. Within five months the South Vietnamese Signal Corps had undergone a modernization of its tactical communications that had been programmed to take three years.[46]

There remained, however, a desperate need to provide some means for the Self-Defense Corps, South Vietnamese militiamen guarding villages and hamlets, to summon help from the paramilitary Civil Guard at the district and province headquarters. Nor could province chiefs call for support from regular army units to repulse heavy Viet Cong attacks within their provinces. Messages could travel the hundreds of kilometers from Saigon to an army division in the northernmost part of the country faster than from a beleaguered village to a South Vietnamese Army post five kilometers down the road.[47]

Shortages of equipment and disagreement over the organization and employment of the Civil Guard and Self-Defense Corps had left the rural security forces relatively ineffective. Military advisers felt that the Civil Guard, which was assigned to the Ministry of the Interior, should be trained and equipped as a military force and transferred to the Ministry of Defense. The U.S. Operations Mis-

[45]Ltr, CINCPAC to CSA, 27 Jul 56, sub: Augmentation of MAAG and TERM, Vietnam, 091 VN, DCSOPS, 60A1053/6, WNRC; Memo, MAAG, Vietnam, for Dir, USOM, 4 Aug 60, sub: Communications Coordinating Committee, Vietnam, no. 57, file 78, Williams Papers; Rpt, Lt Col C. E. Burner, sub: Advisor Communications, Presented at the Senior Advisor's Conference, 27–29 Apr 60, and Memo, Elbridge Durbrow, Ambassador, for All Addressees on Distribution List, 8 Jul 60, sub: Master Country Emergency and Evacuation Plan for Vietnam, both in CMH.

[46]MAAG, Vietnam, Briefing for Admiral Felt, 16 Feb 59, Summary of MAAG-TERM Activities, no. 1, file 94; Msg, CHMAAG, Vietnam, 342 to CINCPAC, 11 Mar 60, no. 57, file 71; MAAG, Vietnam, Equipment Status Report Number 6, 13 Aug 60, no. 120, file 77. All in Williams Papers. Memo, Dep Secy of Defense (ISA) for Secy of Army, 29 Apr 60, and Secy of Army for Dep Secy of Defense (ISA), 27 May 60, sub: Signal Equipment for Emergency Situation in Vietnam, ISA 413.44VN, 64A2170/31, WNRC.

[47]Interv, author with Paul Katz, former communications engineer, U.S. Operations Mission, 15 May 78, Historians files, CMH.

sion, which had contracted with Michigan State University in 1956 to advise and equip the Civil Guard, believed that assigning it to the military would sever its ties with the local populace. Concerned more with the threat of invasion from North Vietnam, President Diem wanted the Civil Guard transferred to his Ministry of Defense to augment the armed forces and defend against heavily armed Communist regular units in time of war. He felt that the Michigan State advisory team had inadequately armed the guardsmen with pistols and trained them as American highway patrolmen. He especially disdained the failure of the U.S. Operations Mission to provide the Civil Guard with communications and even appealed—unsuccessfully—to other Western countries for signal equipment for that purpose.[48]

The importance of communications in combating Communist terrorism in rural communities had been acknowledged early in the conflict. In the fall of 1957 the chief of the Central Intelligence Agency's office in South Vietnam reported to the ambassador:

The lack of communications is not a point which needs much elaboration since it is a running thread through all reports submitted by American personnel close to the situation in the South. We cite merely one recent report by Mr. Hoyt of the Police Division of MSU [Michigan State University] in which he detailed his observations on an inspection trip of Civil Guard posts in the southwest. Wherever he went, the plea was the same: give us better and speedier communications. Without communications, the Central Government is not able to react speedily to counter the Communist campaign, is not able to reassure its loyal supporters in the villages that they can count on quick support when the need is great, and, in fact, is at a continual disadvantage against the well-timed covert campaign mounted by the Communists.[49]

Planning to integrate Civil Guard communications with the proposed national network, the civilian advisers working with the Civil Guard had delayed ordering equipment for rural security forces until completion of the design for the telecommunications network. While the pleas for communications were ignored amid bureaucratic haggling and technical delays, Communist domination of isolated regions that were without communications spread dramatically.[50]

By the summer of 1960, when Lt. Gen. Lionel C. McGarr arrived to replace General Williams as commander of the Military Assistance Advisory Group, little had been resolved. The Joint Chiefs of Staff had dispatched General McGarr with the mandate to draft with the South Vietnamese a plan to guide their armed forces in restoring the nation's internal security. Finding that only "immediate and extraordinary action" would avert an imminent Viet Cong victory, General McGarr quickly prepared a proposal, which came to be called the counterinsurgency plan, to redirect the primary focus of the military from defense against

[48]Record of Conversation During Protocol Visit of General I. D. White to President Diem, 16 Jan 58, in Record of Conferences with President Diem, 28 Dec 57–29 May 58, Williams Papers.

[49]Memo, Spec Asst for Liaison for Ambassador, 30 Nov 57, sub: Comments on the Increasing Seriousness of the Security Situation in South Vietnam, no. 36, file 23, Williams Papers.

[50]Memo for General Williams, 7 Mar 60, sub: Conversations With President Diem During Visit to School Installations at Nha Trang, in Record of Conferences with President Diem, 30 Nov 59–22 Aug 60, Williams Papers.

an invasion from North Vietnam to destruction of the Communist movement within the borders of South Vietnam. Believing that the armed forces and paramilitary forces should be under a single command for such a campaign, he strongly recommended that the Civil Guard be transferred to the Ministry of Defense and equipped with standard military equipment. The counterinsurgency plan also called for increasing the South Vietnamese armed forces by 20,000 men—to 170,000.[51]

In the communications annex to the counterinsurgency plan General McGarr's signal advisers reaffirmed the importance of quickly completing a national telecommunications network to enable military and governmental authorities to coordinate the pacification campaign throughout the country. Aware that completion of the network was still years away and that the purchase of commercial or military radios for the militiamen in the thousands of hamlets and villages would create staggering problems in maintenance, battery supply, training, and security, the American signal planners could only propose that the rural security forces use carrier pigeons, drums, and smoke signals.[52]

That the United States by 1960 had launched communications satellites into space but could suggest nothing more than the most primitive signaling devices for the South Vietnamese indicated the dilemma facing the advisory program. While drums and smoke signals may well have been most suitable in rural South Vietnam, American signal advisers and their Western-trained South Vietnamese Army counterparts were technically and psychologically unprepared to assist the paramilitary units with such rudimentary communications. The defeated French Army had bequeathed to the American advisers a mission circumscribed by two generations of French colonial influence and by the Geneva Conference. Impelled by fears of a Communist invasion, the country team had hastily built South Vietnamese defenses on French foundations with American blueprints, using technology and procedures appropriate in the United States. Four American engineering firms had failed to design and install an adequate communications network, the Civil Guard was organized along the lines of a state highway patrol, and the army was outfitted for conventional warfare. South Vietnam did not have the communications, either military or civilian, that it would need to overthrow the increasingly aggressive Communist insurgency.

[51]MAAG, Vietnam, U.S. Plan for Counterinsurgency in SVN, MAAG Vietnam records (1961), 64A2424/1, WNRC.
[52]Ibid., an. C, app. 7.

2

An Evolving Strategic Commitment 1960–1963

Difficulties with assistance to the South Vietnamese Army during the 1950s were aggravated by the lack of an American strategy for Southeast Asia and a consequent reluctance to allocate scarce resources to the region. Even after the United States finally developed plans for committing American troops to support treaty obligations in Southeast Asia in the late 1950s, the commander in chief, Pacific, remained hard pressed to support American contributions to the Southeast Asia Treaty Organization (SEATO). Thus in late 1960 the commanding general of the U.S. Army, Pacific, General Isaac D. White, asked the Army's Chief of Staff, General George H. Decker, to assign a signal company to the Pacific to install communications for a task force headquarters in Southeast Asia should SEATO operations plans be invoked. General Decker responded that a strictly enforced ceiling on the size of the Army and commitment of the strategic reserve to other areas of the world ruled out even such a small reinforcement in the Pacific. In the canon of worldwide American strategic priorities South Vietnam seemed destined to remain a minor front of the Cold War.[1]

Early Contingency Plans

American military assistance in Southeast Asia began at a time when the United States was preoccupied with a conventional war in Korea and was resisting the Communists by French proxy in Indochina. In the wake of the French defeat at Dien Bien Phu and a cease-fire that conceded control of North Vietnam to the Viet Minh, sobered American strategists finally developed firm plans for

---

[1]Memo, White for Decker, sub: Requirement for Activation of a Signal Operations Unit in USARPAC to Support CEOP and Contingency Operations; Msg, DA to USARPAC, DA 986117, 21 Nov 60. Both in Summary Sheet, DA, OPS PL WP, 6 Dec 60, sub: Signal Unit for USARPAC, file 1001 354, 66A2206/37, WNRC.

direct American involvement. They saw the threat as invasion by the new Democratic Republic of Vietnam or its ally the People's Republic of China.[2]

An early U.S. contingency plan for Indochina, the Limited War Plan of 1956, proposed that three American corps and eight divisions combine with ten South Vietnamese divisions and token forces from other members of the Southeast Asia Treaty Organization to halt a Communist invasion and then counterattack to seize Hanoi. The U.S. Army theater headquarters would be located in Saigon where it could use the only overseas communications in Indochina, the Saigon station in the Army Command and Administrative Net. Although only five cities in Southeast Asia—Saigon, Da Lat, Phnom Penh, Hanoi, and Haiphong—had any significant commercial telecommunications, the plan made no provisions for strategic or administrative communications within the theater. In an emergency the chief signal officer in Washington could dispatch radio teams maintained on call in the United States, but those teams were to support the Military Assistance Program in general and were available to any Military Assistance Advisory Group in the world. Until the completion of the International Cooperation Administration's regional network, projected at the time for late 1958, units deploying to Southeast Asia would rely entirely on their own organic tactical communications.[3]

Although the limited war plan did not address the threat of enemy guerrilla activities, it did propose that U.S. Special Forces teams form guerrilla units from indigenous forces to interdict the transportation of supplies and to destroy communications facilities behind enemy lines. Guerrilla battalions were to be equipped only with the PRC–6 squad radio, which had a one-mile range, and the PRC–10 man-pack radio, with an eight-mile range. Other than proposing that stations relay for one another, the plan did not say how guerrilla leaders might communicate with their far-ranging patrols or with conventional units hundreds of miles to the rear. The naive approach to communications for guerrilla units indicated that the U.S. Army did not take unconventional warfare seriously, even in a theater where it would be the most likely form of conflict.[4]

Increased terrorism in South Vietnam and attacks in Laos by North Vietnamese–supported Pathet Lao guerrillas in 1959 exposed the plans as inadequate. To counter what appeared to be a gradual escalation from political and military subversion to conventional warfare, American strategists in 1959 developed a four-phase war plan, called Operation Plan 32, for Indochina. It classified the existing level of terrorism and sporadic hostilities as phase one, a full-scale armed insurgency as phase two, an invasion by North Vietnamese regular units as phase three, and reinforcement by Communist China as phase four. Although there were slightly different versions of the plan depending on whether the Communists attacked Laos or South Vietnam, the basic concept for the conventional phases of the plan placed the theater headquarters and logistical base far to the rear in Thailand rather than in Saigon as in the limited war plan. Anticipating

[2]Spector, *The Early Years*, pp. 152, 268–71.
[3]DA, ODCSOPS, Limited War Plan-Indochina, 26 Nov 56, an. R, CMH; Ltr, DA to Deputy Chiefs of Staff et al., 25 Mar 59, sub: Signal Augmentation Plan for MAAGs and Missions, file 1101-07 (Sig Plan 1–59), 67A4843/1, WNRC.
[4]DA, ODCSOPS, Limited War Plan-Indochina, 26 Nov 56, an. N.

the shift, the chief signal officer had already established a station in Bangkok in the Army Command and Administrative Net to maintain a radio-teletype link to Clark Air Base in the Philippines. Base communications for the U.S. force were still to be handled by the proposed regional system supplemented by tactical equipment organic to U.S. combat units. Since the indigenous armed forces in Indochina were primarily responsible for the first two phases, planning for counterinsurgency communications was left to the advisers and their counterparts.[5]

Increasing tensions in Laos in late 1959 impelled the Joint Chiefs of Staff further to strengthen communications in Southeast Asia as the first step in a possible deployment of combat troops. The chief signal officer deployed a mobile radio-teletype station for a four-channel system between Vientiane, Laos, and Clark Air Base and dispatched for temporary duty the 999th Signal Company, a unit assigned to the U.S.-based strategic reserve, to be ready to install communications for any command post that might be needed in Indochina. Since the U.S. ambassadors in both Laos and Thailand felt that large increases of American military personnel there would further aggravate tensions, and because the Geneva Agreements prohibited any overt military assistance to Laos, the company had to stand by in the Philippines. Following a coup in August 1960, rightist Laotian troops fled from Vientiane to the remote panhandle area of southern Laos. To provide American communications there, men had to be drawn from the Bangkok and Vientiane stations to install and operate a new station at the border town of Savannakhet. Not until the Vientiane station was hit by mortar fire and went off the air in December 1960 did Secretary of Defense Thomas S. Gates, Jr., permit the Army to reinforce the overextended signalmen. Besides sending a team with another radio to Vientiane, the Army established a station in northern Thailand at Udorn, the site of a new Thai air base. Men from the 999th Signal Company also helped overworked communicators at the Bangkok station, where message traffic had tripled during the previous year, and took over a tactical multi-channel system that the Central Intelligence Agency had been operating between Udorn and Vientiane.[6]

Except for the eleven-man team operating the original Bangkok station, the signalmen in Laos and Thailand were from units assigned to the United States or to other areas of the Pacific. Prohibited by diplomatic agreements from assigning the men permanently to the area or from establishing signal headquarters to control the far-flung detachments, the U.S. Army, Pacific, had to delegate operational control of all Army signal units in Thailand and Laos to the signal adviser on the staff of the advisory group in Bangkok, an Air Force officer. The Signal

[5]MAAG, Vietnam, Logistics Support to OPLAN 32–59, 30 May 60, app. 5, an. A, CMH; OCSO, Signal Corps Summary of Major Events and Problems, FY–60, pp. 81–82, CMH; Transcript of Telecon, DA to USARPAC, 24 Dec 57, sub: Long Lines Support in Japan, TT-0017, ACSI files, 59A2081/560, WNRC.

[6]Memo, CINCPAC, J6112, for CINCPAC, J–6, Jul 61, sub: Staff Study Relative to Communications Electronics Support for Thailand, Laos, and Vietnam, w/Incl, Historical Review of C-E Problems in Southeast Asia, file 139447, 72A4171/2; USARPAC, G–3, Quarterly Historical Report (hereafter cited as QHR), Jan–Mar 60, 338-75-1033/19; USARPAC Signal Staff Office Report (hereafter cited as Sig Stf Ofc Rpt), Jan–Mar 62, w/Incl, Trip Rpt, Lt Col Gene D. Moore, 19 Feb 62, sub: Trip to Saigon and STARCOMPHIL, 338-75-1033/42. All in WNRC.

Corps captain commanding the Bangkok station remained responsible for administrative and logistical support of the signal detachments.[7]

The Army responded to the heightened activity in Southeast Asia in 1959 by moving the 999th Signal Company to Okinawa, where it became a pawn in an interservice dispute over strategy and service participation in Indochina. Since the commander of the U.S. Army, Pacific, was also designated commander of Joint Task Force 116, the American headquarters that would be formed to implement Operation Plan 32, the Army wanted to establish a skeleton corps headquarters on Okinawa as a staff for the task force and to assign the 999th Signal Company to support that headquarters. General James F. Collins, who replaced General White at the U.S. Army, Pacific, in early 1961, met stiff resistance from the Marine Corps and Air Force. The marines, who already had the 3d Marine Division on Okinawa, wanted to ensure that the Army did not ease the marines out of any role in Southeast Asia; the Air Force, advocating an American air campaign rather than a major ground operation to counter any Communist invasion in Indochina, emphasized reinforcement of Air Force communications and staffs in the Pacific. Not until the spring of 1962, after over a year of haggling at the Pentagon and thirty months after the arrival of the 999th Signal Company in the Pacific, did the signalmen finally learn that their stay was to be permanent and that their primary mission was to support the newly formed IX Corps headquarters and to provide initial communications for Joint Task Force 116 if it deployed to Indochina.[8]

Overseas Communications

Army signalmen also sought to make less vulnerable the overseas communications network linking Indochina with the Pacific Command headquarters 6,500 miles away in Hawaii. With only a single commercial submarine cable in bad repair linking Hawaii with Guam in the South Pacific, the United States was dangerously dependent on high-frequency radio, which the Soviet Union could jam. A new method of communications using special antennas that compressed a very high frequency radio signal into a narrow beam to obtain enough energy to bounce the signal off layers of the atmosphere offered the only promise of relief. Tropospheric scatter, or troposcatter propagation, spanned up to 400 miles by reflecting the radio beam off water vapor in the troposphere, the lowest layer of the atmosphere. *(Diagram 1)* Ionospheric scatter, or ionoscatter propagation, spanned longer distances by bouncing the beam off clouds of ionized particles in the higher ionosphere. Except for spurious signals from ionized meteor trails

[7] OCSO, Signal Corps Summary of Major Events and Problems, FY–60, p. 81.

[8] Joint Task Force (JTF) 116, 21 Feb 61, sub: JTF Operations Plan 32–61 (Phase III and IV), pp. A–5 through B–1, Incl 24 to USARPAC, G–3, QHR, Jan–Mar 61, 73A5466/1, WNRC. All of the following documents from DCSOPS 61 files deal with Army efforts to overcome opposition to the stationing of the 999th Signal Company on Okinawa: Msg, Decker to White, 13 Jan 61, 64A2207/5; Msg, Hamlett to Harkins, 30 Mar 61, 64A2207/8; MFR, 7 Apr 61, sub: Telephone Conversation Between Generals Decker and Collins, 64A2207/3. All in WNRC.

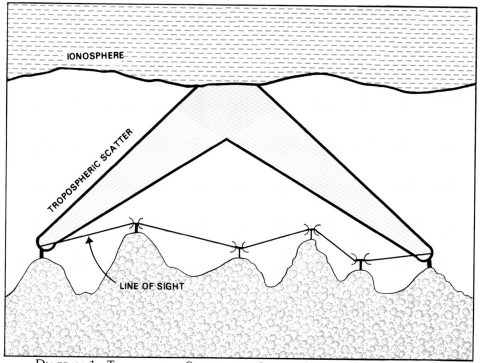

DIAGRAM 1—TROPOSPHERIC SCATTER AND LINE-OF-SIGHT COMMUNICATIONS

that caused high-pitched whistles in ionoscatter propagation, reception was far quieter than with high-frequency radio. Nor did frequencies require constant changing to adjust to the daily variations in propagational conditions that affected high-frequency radio. The propagational pattern of scatter communications also was a difficult target for enemy jammers.[9]

In May 1960 a pioneer in atmospheric scatter communications, Page Communications Engineers, used troposcatter and ionoscatter propagation to build the Army a 7,800-mile network, called the Pacific Scatter System, along the island chain from Hawaii to the Philippines. Although limited to two voice channels (one of which could be multiplexed into sixteen teletype circuits), the system provided a reassuring backup for the high-frequency network.[10] *(Map 3)*

Since the low-capacity Pacific Scatter System extended only as far as the Philippines, the United States still had to rely on the Strategic Army Communications Net, the new designation for the Army Command and Administrative Net, to reach Indochina. Besides being vulnerable to jamming, those high-

[9]William E. Lang et al., Review of U.S. Overseas Military Bases, Apr 60, pp. 29–30; Executive Office of the President, Technological Capabilities Panel of the Science Advisory Committee, Meeting the Threat of Surprise Attack, 14 Feb 55. Both in 66A3210/3, WNRC. Page Communications Engineers, Inc., Command and Staff Manual, Pacific Scatter Communications Systems, Dec 60, U.S. Army Communications Command (ACC) Historians files, Fort Huachuca, Arizona.

[10]U.S. Army Electronics Command Annual Historical Summary (hereafter cited as ECOM AHS), FY–64, pt. 1, p. 171; Maj. Frederick Eisele, "The End of an Era in Communications," *Trends*, June 1970, p. 27, first printed at the U.S. Army Signal School. Both in CMH files.

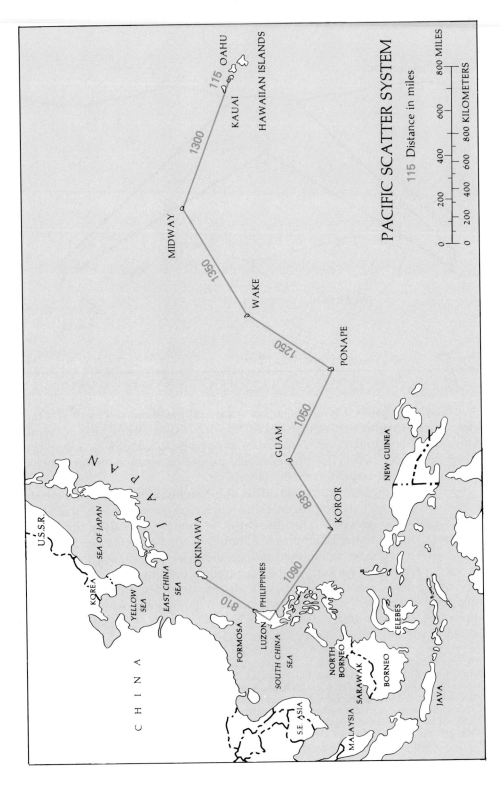

PACIFIC SCATTER SYSTEM

115 Distance in miles

| 0 | 200 | 400 | 600 | 800 MILES |

| 0 | 200 | 400 | 600 | 800 KILOMETERS |

MAP 3

frequency radio circuits were notoriously unreliable. The link between Saigon and Bangkok was the worst; during September 1961 it was usable only 69 percent of the time, compared to a 95.2 percent average for all worldwide Army systems. The undermanned stations consisted of a variety of fixed and transportable communications equipment that had been installed piecemeal during crises. Besides heat and moisture that played havoc with sensitive signal components, tropical atmospheric disturbances caused unusually severe noise in the high-frequency radio band. The location of several of the stations in confined urban areas with high levels of electrical static from motor traffic and aircraft made the noise problem even worse.[11]

Unlike their colleagues in the Atlantic, communicators in the western Pacific did not have the quiet, reliable communications offered by submarine cable. The military planned to lease circuits on a commercial undersea cable system that the American Telephone and Telegraph Company was building from Hawaii to the Philippines to replace an old cable that was no longer usable. In mid-1962 the Joint Chiefs of Staff approved plans to build a military submarine cable system, called WETWASH, from South Vietnam to the Philippines to close the link from Indochina to Hawaii.[12] Recognizing that such ventures would take several years, the Joint Chiefs of Staff in 1961 had already improved and expanded the high-frequency radio network in Southeast Asia. Since all communications from Indochina flowed eastward, leaving the entire strategic lifeline vulnerable to disruption at Clark Air Base, the Army installed a radio link westward from Bangkok to Pakistan and another link east from Saigon to Okinawa, which had become the Army's staging area and logistical base for Indochina.[13]

Regional Communications

Modernizing the old strategic communications stations with single-sideband equipment, building the Pacific Scatter System, and extending submarine cable to South Vietnam all helped to bridge the expanse of ocean that separated Indochina both physically and strategically from the United States. America was drawing increasingly closer to a strategic front that could no longer be ignored.

Improvements were also required within Southeast Asia. The channel capacity of high-frequency radio was far too small to serve as the transmission medium for a strategic network within the region. Until the U.S. Agency for International

[11]Joint Chiefs of Staff Memorandum (hereafter cited as JCSM) 37–61, 26 Jan 61, sub: Deficiencies in the U.S. Posture for Limited Military Operations, I–18079/61, ISA381, 64A2382/48, WNRC; Memo, Dir, DCA, for JCS, 6 Oct 61, sub: JOPREP-COMSUM as of 1 Oct 61, Incl to JCS 222/333, JACO (1961), DA/11, National Archives and Records Service (NARS), Washington, D.C.; Ltr, CINCPAC to JCS, 26 Aug 68, sub: PACOM Communications-Electronics Experiences, an. C, app. 1, 02K712.03/74, Office of Air Force History (OAFH).

[12]Memo, JCS for Dir, DCA, 6 Mar 62, sub: Establishment of Philippines–South Vietnam Wideband Trunk, Incl to JCS 222/385, JACO (1962), DA/12, NARS; Interv, author with Hugh Jones, former communications engineer with OCSO, 8 Feb 78, Historians files, CMH.

[13]JCS 2339/60, 10 Apr 62, sub: Bangkok-Peshawer Radio, JACO (1962), DA/605, NARS; Phu Lam Sig Bn History, pp. 1–3.

Development, which replaced the International Cooperation Administration, completed its 600-channel regional telecommunications network, there would be insufficient interconnections for headquarters, airfields, logistical bases, and commercial centers in a military emergency in South Vietnam. Since distance, terrain, and security considerations ruled out the use of cable, the U.S. Army, Pacific, planned to support Operation Plan 32 with transportable microwave radios capable of transmitting forty-five channels.[14]

Brig. Gen. Douglas E. Williams, U.S. Air Force, the Pacific Command's signal officer (J–6), found the Army's solution unrealistic. Microwave radio was limited to a straight-line, antenna-to-antenna path called line-of-sight propagation. Although setting the radios on high hills and using antenna towers might lift the radio beam over obstacles, the curvature of the earth still limited transmission range to about forty miles. Even if the Army could muster enough microwave relays and terminals to build a grid along the 700-mile length of South Vietnam, General Williams doubted there would be enough suitable secure locations for the radios. Most of the unused land in the heavily populated Mekong Delta in the south was too marshy for heavy radios and antenna towers; sites in the highlands of central and northern South Vietnam were too isolated. Simply protecting such a large number of signal sites from the Viet Cong would be a monumental undertaking. Nor could the military afford any longer to rely on the projects of a U.S. Agency for International Development that was not "fixed with the same sense of urgency felt by the military."[15]

Only troposcatter offered the capacity and long range to minimize the number of signal sites in South Vietnam. At General Williams' recommendation, in October 1961 the Commander in Chief, Pacific, Admiral Harry D. Felt, asked the Joint Chiefs of Staff to construct a high-capacity troposcatter network in South Vietnam. Similar to a backbone, the communications system would extend throughout South Vietnam and into northeastern Thailand with several nodal points from which circuits could be distributed to the field by tactical radio systems called spurs or tails. With too little equipment and money for such a complex undertaking, the Joint Chiefs of Staff approved the concept but stipulated that further action would have to await more definitive explication of the president's intentions towards South Vietnam.[16]

Admiral Felt's request for an American communications network for South Vietnam arrived at the Pentagon on the heels of news of Viet Cong successes. The Central Intelligence Agency had just reported that Viet Cong strength had increased from 4,000 to 16,000 during the previous year. Using infiltrated

---

[14]Army plans to support contingency operations before completion of the regional communications network are contained in: 9th Logistical Command, Operational Project Army–USARYIS–GEN–38–60–OP (PAC) (Revised), 15 Sep 61, 73A3183/2, WNRC; JCSM 716–61, JCS to Secy of Defense, 9 Oct 61, sub: Concept of Use of SEATO Forces in South Vietnam, *United States–Vietnam Relations, 1945–1967: A Study Prepared by the Department of Defense*, 12 vols. (Washington, D.C.: Government Printing Office, 1971) (hereafter cited as *U.S.-Vietnam Relations*), 11:297–311; DA, ODCSOPS, Limited War Capabilities Study, 4 Aug 61, DCSOPS 61, 64A2207/7, WNRC.

[15]Quote from Msg, CINCPAC to JCS, 21 Oct 61, cited in USAF, Project CHECO, Support Activities, May 64, OAFH; Interv, author with Col (ret.) Jack G. Hines, former chief signal adviser, MAAG, Vietnam, 31 Oct 77, Historians files, CMH.

[16]JCS 2339/39, 19 Dec 61, JACO (1961), DA/64, NARS.

equipment, the Communists had built an austere, but effective, strategic communications network by which military leaders in Hanoi were receiving timely intelligence and orchestrating the insurgency in the South. Conditions were worsening in Laos also.[17]

President John F. Kennedy sent General Maxwell D. Taylor to South Vietnam in the fall of 1961 to evaluate the situation and recommend an American response. General Taylor advised the president to take quick action. He felt that the United States should expand the advisory program, accelerate aid to the South Vietnamese Army, and deploy American support forces, especially aviation units, to South Vietnam. He emphasized that the United States should increase its intelligence gathering and strengthen its communications links to the region to help the Pentagon and the president formulate future strategy.[18]

To improve the flow of intelligence and strategic direction between Indochina and Washington, Deputy Secretary of Defense Roswell Gilpatric approved $2.2 million for the Army to replace all its four-channel high-frequency radios at the Saigon station with single-sideband equipment. That equipment was less vulnerable to atmospheric noise and capable of transmitting three voice and sixteen teletype channels. At a December conference in Honolulu, the chief signal adviser of the advisory group in Saigon, Col. Jack G. Hines, proposed to Secretary of Defense Robert S. McNamara an American-operated tactical radio net, which he called the Operations and Intelligence Net. The net would carry intelligence information back from the field without risking the delays and compromises of South Vietnamese Army communications channels. Secretary McNamara promptly approved $1 million for tactical radio equipment and told the Army immediately to send 282 radiomen to South Vietnam to operate the net.[19]

When at the same Honolulu meeting General Williams proposed using troposcatter radio for a base network, Secretary McNamara deferred approval. The estimated cost of $6.8 million was too high for a quick decision. At another Honolulu conference in mid-January, General Williams cited the comparative costs in men and money of installing microwave and troposcatter radios in South Vietnam. He argued that 72-channel troposcatter equipment, besides being available for contingency use, would permit replacement of many of the administrative and tactical radio nets, including the Operations and Intelligence Net, that American logistical and aviation units assigned to South Vietnam would need. A microwave network would cost only half as much as a troposcatter system, but it would take three times as many men to operate it and to guard the larger number of sites needed for the short-range radios. In those days of personnel ceilings, money often was easier to obtain than were men. Convinced, the secretary of defense approved General Williams' proposal to use troposcatter equipment to provide the backbone of a network called

[17]Rpt, CIA, 5 Oct 61, sub: Bloc Support of the Communist Effort Against the Government of Vietnam, *U.S.-Vietnam Relations*, 11:293.

[18]Military Appendix (sec. 8, par. 3), Incl to Ltr, Maxwell D. Taylor to President John F. Kennedy, 3 Nov 61, CMH.

[19]Memo, Dep Secy of Defense for Secy of Defense, 15 Dec 61, sub: Emergency Requirements for Improvements of United States Military Communications in Southeast Asia, I–18611/61, ISA 676 SEA, 64A2382/28, WNRC; Min, Secy of Defense Conference in Honolulu, Dec 61, p. 8-I-3, CMH; Interv, author with Hines, 31 Oct 77.

BACKPORCH that was to meet many current and contingency strategic and tactical communications needs in South Vietnam. The Army ordered the 39th Signal Battalion at Fort Gordon, Georgia, to deploy to South Vietnam to operate BACK-PORCH, the systems extending to the field, and the switchboards and teletype communications centers at the terminals.[20]

Since the Army had no transportable troposcatter radios, Secretary McNamara directed the Air Force to install equipment at six nodes where the Army could link into the backbone with spur systems. The Air Force then was to transfer the completed system to the Army. Since neither the Army nor the Air Force was expert in sophisticated troposcatter equipment, the secretary of the Air Force gave Page Communications Engineers a $12 million contract to install the system and to operate and maintain it for a year.[21]

The Washington-based communications firm, usually referred to as Page, built BACKPORCH using MRC–85 troposcatter sets. Each set was a complete communications station mounted on three ten-ton semitrailers, one each for a radio, a multiplexer (equipment to divide the radio signal into separate channels at the terminals), and two 150-kilowatt generators. To overcome anticipated tropical propagation problems and improve range, Page replaced the radios' normal thirty-foot transportable antenna with sixty-foot-square, billboard-type antennas set in a concrete foundation. When completely set up, eight MRC–85's provided a strategic communications backbone of 72 voice channels or 68 voice and 48 teletype channels between Saigon, Nha Trang, Qui Nhon, Da Nang, and Pleiku in South Vietnam and Ubon in Thailand.

More rugged and mobile equipment was required for the spurs to the field units. The standard Army multichannel radio, the VHF twelve-channel TRC–24 mounted on a 2 1/2-ton truck, would suffice for the short spurs. For advisory detachments farther away from BACKPORCH nodes than line-of-sight transmissions could reach, the only alternative to multiple relays was a troposcatter radio more mobile than the ponderous MRC–85. The Army had one troposcatter radio in its entire inventory, a prototype model of a single-channel radio called a TRC–80 that was being tested at Redstone Arsenal, Alabama, for possible use by widely dispersed air defense units. When Admiral Felt's original request for BACKPORCH reached the Pentagon in October 1961, enterprising staff officers in the Office of the Chief Signal Officer arranged for the manufacturer of the TRC–80, Collins Radio Company, to design a multiplexer to increase the radio's channel capacity. When Secretary McNamara approved BACKPORCH in January 1962, Collins promised to deliver to South Vietnam by July twenty sets of a 24-channel version of the TRC–80 mounted in a single 2 1/2-ton truck. The Army ordered the untested set, designated the TRC–90, for the BACKPORCH tails.[22]

[20]Min, Secy of Defense Conf in Honolulu, Dec 61, p. 8-I-1; ibid., Jan 62, pp. 43–44, CMH.

[21]Memo, Dep Secy of Defense for Secy of Air Force, 13 Jan 62, sub: Urgent Communications-Electronics Requirement in Support of U.S. Military Operations in South Vietnam, Incl to JCS 2343/68, JACO (1962), DA/1608, NARS. Final costs for each terminal approximated $600,000 for equipment, $600,000 for installation, and $350,000 for a year's operation and maintenance by the contractor. One terminal was kept as a spare.

[22]Interv, author with Brig Gen Emmett Paige, former staff officer, Signal Training Command, 28 Dec 77; Interv, author with Marie Acton, former staff officer of the Office of the Chief Signal Officer, 26 May 77. Both in Historians files, CMH.

Mustering Signalmen for Vietnam

T he Department of the Army staff had worked closely with General Williams' staff in determining communications requirements for the advisory buildup in South Vietnam. Because the Military Assistance Advisory Group, Vietnam, had no signal staff officer, the Pacific Command's signal staff did most operational planning for South Vietnam. Recognizing the need for a communications coordinator in South Vietnam, in late 1961 General Williams persuaded the advisory group chief, Lt. Gen. Lionel C. McGarr, to release Colonel Hines from his advisory duties and make him a signal staff officer. For the next three months Colonel Hines planned for signal support to the advisory buildup, arranged for the arrival of the men and equipment for the Operations and Intelligence Net, and coordinated the establishment of air request and air control nets for Air Force and Army aviation units.[23]

On 8 February 1962, the United States established the U.S. Military Assistance Command, Vietnam (MACV), as a joint subordinate command of the Pacific Command to oversee all American activities in South Vietnam. When Lt. Col. Philip S. Pomeroy was transferred from the Pacific Command staff to become MACV J–6, Colonel Hines returned to his duties as signal adviser. The first MACV commander, General Paul D. Harkins, assumed operational control over U.S. units in South Vietnam and responsibility for the advisory force. To handle administrative and logistical support of Army units in South Vietnam for the U.S. Army, Pacific, General Collins established the U.S. Army Support Group, Vietnam. Headed by Brig. Gen. Joseph W. Stilwell, the group was subordinate to the U.S. Army, Ryukyu Islands, on Okinawa. Among the first men assigned to the new support group was an advance party from the 39th Signal Battalion at Fort Gordon, Georgia.[24]

As part of the Strategic Army Corps in the U.S. strategic reserve, the battalion had been alerted for overseas duty several times since the Lebanon crisis in 1958; in the fall of 1961, in the wake of the Berlin crisis, battalion commander Lt. Col. Lotus B. Blackwell was preparing to move the battalion with two signal companies to Europe to set up a field area signal center and link into a strategic communications network. In December those orders were abruptly changed: with three signal companies the 39th Signal Battalion was to set out for the other side of the world to operate several signal centers and a combined tactical and strategic network.[25]

The 232d Signal Company (Support) from Fort Huachuca, Arizona, and the 178th Signal Company (Support) from Fort Sam Houston, Texas, were to man the signal centers; the 362d Signal Company, stationed at Fort Gordon with the 39th Signal Battalion headquarters, was to operate the troposcatter systems linking the centers. Of the three companies, only the 178th was ready to deploy over-

---

[23]Interv, author with Hines, 31 Oct 77; Msg, CINCPAC to JCS et al., 22 Nov 61, sub: Personnel Augmentation MAAG Vietnam, file 09409, John F. Kennedy Library, Boston, Massachusetts.

[24]Maj. Gen. George S. Eckhardt, *Command and Control, 1950–1969,* Vietnam Studies (Washington, D.C.: Government Printing Office, 1974), p. 31.

[25]Interv, author with Col (ret.) Lotus B. Blackwell, former commander of the 39th Signal Battalion, 4 Apr 77, Historians files, CMH.

seas. The company at Fort Gordon, redesignated the 362d Signal Company (Tropo), needed new vehicles, generators, maintenance tools, and men. As soon as the 232d Signal Company was alerted for deployment, officials at Fort Huachuca, reluctant to lose the unit, transferred its best men and equipment to units remaining at Fort Huachuca. On the other hand, the 178th Signal Company, an elite and highly trained unit with well-maintained equipment, was left intact. Although Colonel Blackwell's staff tried to handpick men from other signal units at Fort Gordon to fill out the battalion, authorities there were reluctant to impair other units and permitted no special arrangements for getting replacements. Colonel Blackwell reluctantly redistributed some men and equipment from the 178th Signal Company to improve the remainder of the battalion.[26]

Competition for signal resources was stiff throughout the Army. In response to the crisis in Berlin during the fall of 1961 the Army had deployed two signal battalions and eight signal companies to Europe from the Strategic Army Corps (STRAC) in the United States. Radio operators were pulled from signal units worldwide to operate the Operations and Intelligence Net in South Vietnam, and avionics units in the United States were depleted to form four detachments to maintain signal equipment for the aviation buildup in South Vietnam. Although the signal component of the Strategic Army Corps originally had been balanced with other support and combat units, the deployments to Europe and Southeast Asia had emphasized signal units and left the remainder of the strategic force without its necessary communications support. In every crisis since the American intervention in Lebanon, signal units had been dispatched in the first wave and remained even after tensions abated. In less-developed areas such as South Vietnam, where few communications facilities existed, early deployment of signal units was essential to build a communications base for possible commitment of combat units. And because signal units did not pose the overt military threat that combat troops did, they proved politically convenient in Cold War crises. In South Vietnam the 39th would remain for three years the only American battalion.[27]

By the spring of 1962, as the Army completed its muster of signalmen for South Vietnam, the drain on the signal force in the United States had become so great that the commanding general of the Continental Army Command, General Herbert B. Powell, started transferring signal officers and enlisted technicians from his training commands to the Strategic Army Corps to keep its signal component at the required 90 percent deployment strength. Captains were commanding training battalions usually led by lieutenant colonels. Eleven of thirty signal units in the Strategic Army Corps were classified as unfit for combat and several others were marginal. A worried General Powell wrote to Army Chief of Staff General George H. Decker, "I cannot provide complete signal support to a one corps force at the present time even though STRAC now consists of a two corps, eight division

---

[26]Interv, author with Col (ret.) Walter Levy, former S–3 of the 39th Signal Battalion, 19 Jul 78, Historians files, CMH.

[27]Ltr, General Herbert B. Powell to General George H. Decker, 30 Aug 62 and response dated 13 Sep 62. Both in Summary Sheet, DA, 10 Sep 62, sub: Signal Capability of USCONARC, file 3201241, 65A3314/29, WNRC.

force. . . . The outlook . . . appears exceedingly grim.''[28]

Although the Department of the Army noted that the immediate cause of General Powell's problem was the "large number of unprogrammed signal unit activations, reorganizations, and deployments during the last nine months" for crises in Berlin and Southeast Asia, General Powell also felt that the signal force was being depleted by the lure of high pay for experienced soldiers in a burgeoning civilian electronics industry. He wanted incentives to recruit and retain signal technicians even at the expense of other functions. As the commander of the joint U.S. Strike Command, General Paul D. Adams, argued, "I would much rather have a conventional artillery unit short in gun crews than to have a signal unit short . . . because so much in signal communications is dependent upon numerous individuals performing numerous tasks in conjunction with one another. If one is missing, then the chain is broken.''[29]

In an era of fiscal and manpower austerity, however, the Army could not strengthen its signal force. Although the chief signal officer had recognized as early as 1960 that revolutionary developments in electronics technology had put heavy demands on Signal Corps training and personnel policies, the Army had been unable to compensate for signalmen lost to civilian industry. By 1962, when the 39th Signal Battalion was mustering to go to South Vietnam, the best of the Army's scarce resources were committed to Europe. When the United States discovered later in the year that the Soviet Union was installing missiles in Cuba, the 39th even had to dispatch two mobile troposcatter teams from South Vietnam to join a task force forming in Florida. The austere manning of the Army's communications force, the weakened training base, the loss of experienced technicians, and the volatile international climate hampered not only mustering the initial signal contingent for South Vietnam but also providing replacements and logistical support during ensuing years.[30]

The 39th Signal Battalion in South Vietnam

Since the troposcatter equipment for the 362d Signal Company (Tropo) was being installed by the manufacturer and would not be ready until summer 1962, Colonel Blackwell concentrated on getting the 178th and 232d Signal Companies ready to move to South Vietnam. A 26-man advance party left for South Vietnam in early February to operate a switchboard for the new MACV headquarters and to prepare for the remainder of the battalion. By 23 March 1962,

[28]Quote from Ltr, Powell to Decker, 30 Aug 62. See also Ltr, Powell to Decker, 14 Apr 62, 250/36 (DCSOPS 62), 65A3314/9; Ltr, Powell to General Earle G. Wheeler, 6 Nov 62, 250/36 (DCSOPS 62), 65A3314/10; Fact Sheet, DA, ODCSOPS/OD GO, 18 Aug 62, sub: Status of Readiness of ARSTRIKE Signal Support Units, file 2210860, 65A3314/5. All in WNRC.

[29]Quote from Ltr, General Paul D. Adams to Lt Gen Russell L. Vittrup, 1 Aug 62, file 2210860, 65A3314/5, WNRC. See also Ltr, Powell to Decker, 30 Aug 62.

[30]Draft Ltr, DA, DCSOPS, sub: Reply to General Adams' 1 Aug Letter, file 2210860, 65A3314/5, WNRC.

the entire battalion headquarters and the 232d Signal Company were in Saigon installing communications in the buildings that housed the Military Assistance Command and the Army Support Group. The 178th Signal Company (Support) established a headquarters a month later at Qui Nhon, on the coast 260 miles north of Saigon, to install and operate communications in the northern half of the country. Headquartered at Tan Son Nhut, a large air base serving Saigon, the 232d Signal Company took responsibility for the southern half of the country. When the 362d Signal Company (Tropo) arrived, its headquarters was to be 200 miles north of Saigon in the coastal city of Nha Trang, a central location from which to manage the many troposcatter systems the company would be installing and operating.[31]

Colonel Blackwell's mission was very general: "to operate communications in support of the Military Assistance Command, Vietnam." Except for Air Force communications facilities at a few air bases and a Navy ship-to-shore station in Saigon, that mission would encompass all communications in South Vietnam. When the 39th Signal Battalion arrived, the only American military communications within the country were being provided by five mobile radio-teletype teams sent in January from Korea on a temporary assignment to connect advisory detachments in major cities until the installation of the Operations and Intelligence Net. The signalmen even discovered that the commercial single-sideband radios requested for the advisory detachments after the attack at Bien Hoa, over two years earlier, had never been installed. The Strategic Army Communications (STARCOM) station in Saigon, which had ordered them at the behest of the signal adviser, had no one to install or operate them. Within a month after the 39th Signal Battalion's arrival, the battalion's radio operators had the single-sideband net on the air to seventeen detachments. Twelve years after the arrival of the first American advisers, the advisory group finally could communicate directly with its field detachments over a full-time net operated entirely by Americans.[32]

Throughout the spring and early summer the battalion established at the principal advisory detachments, airfields, and American logistical bases small signal centers, each consisting of a switchboard, a teletype center capable of handling encrypted messages, and a single-sideband radio. The signalmen also connected neighboring centers with tactical multichannel radios; for the longer links they had to wait for the 362d Signal Company with its troposcatter equipment. In the Saigon area the 232d Signal Company removed a large switchboard from a van and installed it in MACV headquarters and took over another switchboard serving the Military Assistance Advisory Group in Cholon.[33]

At Tan Son Nhut in a small compound that the signalmen named Site Octopus, the 39th Signal Battalion built the signal center from which the tentacles of the countrywide network would extend. They consolidated in vans a variety of signal

[31]U.S. Army Support Group, Vietnam (hereafter cited as USASGV), Sig Stf Ofc Rpt, Jan–Jun 62, an. I, pt. 1, 338–75–1033/49, WNRC.

[32]Ibid.; Ltr, 39th Sig Bn to CO, USASGV, 23 Jul 62, sub: Unit Historical Report, 39th History file, 338–75–1009/103, WNRC. Included in this file are several other historical reports covering the first year of the 39th Signal Battalion's stay in South Vietnam.

[33]Interv, author with Blackwell, 4 Apr 77. The U.S. Air Force took responsibility for installing and operating a large dial switchboard for all the units on Tan Son Nhut Air Base.

equipment: a facility to relay teletype messages between the field detachments; a teletype message center for the support group; a circuit board called a toll test, where circuits traversing the Saigon area could be interconnected and monitored for quality; the multichannel radios that extended those circuits to the headquarters and support facilities in the Saigon area; and the many generators needed to power the communications complex.[34]

Although Tan Son Nhut was the heart of the battalion's communications, to avoid congestion and electrical interference around the airport Page installed the Saigon BACKPORCH terminal at a small compound just outside the city near the village of Phu Lam. From there the Army routed circuits to Site Octopus and MACV headquarters over tactical microwave systems. Phu Lam was also to be the site of the STARCOM station. When in December 1961 Deputy Secretary of Defense Gilpatric approved the expansion of overseas communications for Saigon, Colonel Hines decided to move the station from the cramped facilities in the advisory group's compound where it had been located for a decade to an area with more room to install antennas and less electrical interference from city traffic. To minimize congestion and interference at Phu Lam, he decided to install the station's receiver in a South Vietnamese Army compound at Ba Queo, near Tan Son Nhut, and to connect it by a microwave system to the transmitter at Phu Lam. By the summer of 1962 the STARCOM detachment at Phu Lam had grown from 22 to over 130 men. In summer 1962 the U.S. Army, Ryukyu Islands, to which it was initially assigned, reassigned the detachment to the U.S. Army Support Group, Vietnam, to afford better supervision. General Stilwell attached it to the 39th Signal Battalion, thus extending the battalion's responsibility to operating a portion of the worldwide STARCOM network.[35]

By September the battalion's responsibilities—operating a wide variety of communications throughout South Vietnam—had become so great, and coordination of Army communications so complicated, that General Stilwell decided to give Colonel Blackwell the new position of signal officer of the support group and to assign Lt. Col. Edwin Paulmann to command the 39th. The formation of a signal staff was long overdue. Many of the signal battalion's problems could be resolved only by complicated staffing actions that were beyond the span of control of an operational battalion, and the MACV J–6 and signal advisory staff were ill equipped to meet the support needs of a U.S. unit.

With units being spread the length and breadth of South Vietnam, logistical problems abounded. The three light aircraft assigned to the battalion were hard pressed to move heavy supplies, carry maintenance men to remote sites, or provide transportation for key staff members who supervised the battalion's communications operations. Frustrated with waiting for transportation, the battalion had begun moving its own convoys along unsecured roads. Getting money to purchase nonstandard supplies on the local economy, especially high-grade fuel for sophisticated power equipment, took extensive paperwork that was bogging down the battalion supply officer. Obtaining real estate for signal sites and clear-

---

[34]Interv, author with Lt Col Melvin J. Grones, former platoon leader and staff officer, 39th Signal Battalion, 27 Mar 78, Historians files, CMH.
[35]Interv, author with Hines, 31 Oct 77.

ance to install cables frequently caused acrimonious conflicts between signalmen and local South Vietnamese officials. The complicated and lengthy negotiations could be handled better at higher-level staffs.[36]

By arranging for logistical and construction support, the new staff was also able to help the battalion deal with a serious morale and welfare problem that threatened the effectiveness of the 39th's operation. Living in hastily erected tents since arriving in South Vietnam, the signalmen were so busy installing communications that they had little time or energy to improve their own living conditions. The large influx of Americans arriving during the spring of 1962 made the competition for construction support intense and the wait for new living accommodations long. Although most advisers were living in leased villas or permanent barracks, the signalmen stationed at Tan Son Nhut had to wait five months for South Vietnamese contractors to complete frame structures with wooden floors, screened sides, and tin roofs. For those in the field, improvements were slower. In some cases advisers or South Vietnamese soldiers made room for the signalmen in their barracks, but usually they lived in tents beside their communications vans while facilities were being constructed.[37]

Whether a signal detachment shared facilities with another unit or established its own site, the detachment commander, usually a lieutenant, still was saddled with all administrative and logistical responsibility for his own command as well as with providing communications—and often power from his generators—for all nearby American facilities. Managing dining facilities, post exchanges, and clubs, the young lieutenants had all the responsibilities of installation commanders, but not the experience, specialized training, and large staffs.[38]

Although the Viet Cong seemed to be ignoring the American signalmen, the overriding concern of most detachment commanders was to protect their units from attack or sabotage. Responsible for around-the-clock missions, detachment commanders always found it difficult to spare operators and technicians for use as security guards. Where a signal detachment shared a compound with advisers or another unit, the signalmen had help with defense. In many cases, however, they were alone and vulnerable. The shortage of engineer support hindered construction of the double fences, minefields, guard towers, and lights that the sites needed for proper perimeter security; the continuous operational mission made it difficult for detachment commanders to mount an adequate guard force. When an attempted sabotage of generators was discovered at the Phu Lam facility, General Harkins appealed to the South Vietnamese government to incorporate the critical site in the Saigon defenses. Although the South Vietnamese declined, they did dispatch a platoon of Civil Guard to help the Americans guard the strategic communications hub.[39]

---

[36]Interv, author with Blackwell, 4 Apr 77.

[37]Interv, author with Lt Col Robert C. Ed, former commander of the Pleiku Detachment, 39th Signal Battalion, 28 Dec 77, Historians files, CMH; Ltr, 178th Sig Co to 39th Sig Bn, 29 Dec 64, sub: Unit Historical Report, file U251, 72A18/14, WNRC.

[38]Ibid.

[39]Ltr, Gen Paul D. Harkins to Nguyen Dinh Thuan, Secy of State, RVN, 30 Jul 62; Ltr, Thuan to Harkins, 28 Aug 62. Both Incls to USASGV, Stf Ofc Rpt, S–2/3, Jul–Sep 62, pt. 2, doc. 33, 338–75–1033/49, WNRC.

Advisers seldom appreciated, and sometimes aggravated, the pressures on the young signal officers. When a division senior adviser ordered the site commander at Ban Me Thuot to remove an air conditioner from his teletype van and install it in the advisory detachment's command post, the exasperated officer sent General Harkins a message that he was shutting down his communications center. The air conditioner was returned—and the rash young signal officer transferred.[40]

With the battalion controlling seventeen sites by early summer, the battalion commander and company commanders had difficulty averting such crises. When problems arose at the remote sites, the young lieutenants often turned to the local signal adviser, usually the only experienced American signal officer to whom they had ready access. So dependent on the advisers did some become that one corps senior adviser tried unsuccessfully to get operational control over the detachments in his corps area.[41]

Preparing for BACKPORCH

W hile the 232d and 178th Signal Companies were adjusting to the peculiarities and challenges of South Vietnam, the signal staff at the Pentagon was planning and supervising the preparation of the 362d Signal Company (Tropo) for deployment to South Vietnam. After revising the company's manifest of men and equipment, the signal staff set about finding the resources to fill the unit. They searched depot inventories and pressured contractors for equipment. Since many men in the 362d did not have the requisite skills and training to operate sophisticated troposcatter equipment, replacements had to be found. Restrictions on transferring soldiers before two-thirds of their current tours were completed made finding men for the reinforced company difficult. When the contingent was finally assembled, it moved to the U.S. Army Signal School at Fort Monmouth, New Jersey, where a staff training officer, Capt. Emmett Paige, Jr., and a civilian educational adviser, Francis J. Herbert, had developed a training program for the company.[42]

Few of the men arriving at Fort Monmouth in the spring of 1962 had even heard of troposcatter propagation until "Tropo" was appended to the name of their unit. Most were multichannel radio operators, reared on the Army's tactical four- and twelve-channel equipment dating from the Korean War. The instructors themselves had no experience with the new radios. With too little time to prepare a new course or to acquire any troposcatter equipment, Paige and Herbert decided to instruct the men with material from the most highly technical and closely related course then taught at the school, the microwave radio repairman course. Then they would send the students to the electronic plants where the equipment they were to operate was being produced.[43]

[40]Interv, author with Ed, 28 Dec 77.

[41]Memo, III Corps Sr Adv for MACV J-6, 10 Oct 63, sub: Communications Center Operations, Col Wilbur Wilson Papers, Military History Institute, Carlisle Barracks, Pennsylvania.

[42]Intervs, author with Acton, 26 May 77, and Paige, 28 Dec 77.

[43]Interv, author with Francis J. Herbert, former education adviser, Fort Monmouth Signal School, 24 May 77, Historians files, CMH.

Although Redstone Arsenal shipped the developmental model of the single-channel TRC–80 to Fort Monmouth, the lack of another terminal for an operational link prevented any practical training. Since the TRC–90 would have a multiple-channel capability, the value of the one-channel TRC–80 even for demonstrations was limited. After classroom instruction at Fort Monmouth, the company dispersed for practical training at factories and testing grounds. The largest group, led by 1st Lt. Robert C. Ed, went to the Collins Radio Company's plant in Dallas, Texas, where the soldiers worked for six weeks with the components of the TRC–90 while the set was being assembled. Those who were to do multiplexing on BACKPORCH itself had two weeks to tinker with the MRC–85's multiplexing components on the production lines at the Radio Electronics Laboratories plant on Long Island, New York. The rest of the operators slated for BACKPORCH spent four weeks working with a modified MRC–85 transmitter being tested at Eglin Air Force Base, Florida. When the training was completed, Herbert and Paige considered that the operators were ready to operate the light TRC–90 troposcatter sets but would be dependent on the Page contractors to help with the more sophisticated MRC–85's of BACKPORCH.[44]

The scarcities in time and facilities were similar to those of World War II, when the Signal Corps had turned for technical training to civilian universities and laboratories. Now the signal educators of the 1960s went a step further in sending the men of the 362d Signal Company (Tropo) directly to the production lines. Although the instructors at Fort Monmouth felt that the soldiers would get the best possible familiarization with the very equipment they would soon be operating, they did not appreciate the extent to which modern technological components depended upon the manner in which they were linked with other pieces of equipment to form a complete operating system. Segmented training did not teach the troposcatter operators how to use the various components in harmony. No man in the company had even seen a complete MRC–85 or TRC–90 set, let alone an operational system, during his training. Despite the optimism of the instructors at Fort Monmouth, the 362d was still not ready for South Vietnam.[45]

The 362d arrived at Nha Trang in late June 1962, the TRC–90's a few weeks later. Watching the Page technicians install the sophisticated MRC–85 terminals (still painted Air Force blue), the signalmen faced this incongruity: they were about to disperse to isolated outposts in a primitive land to operate equipment so modern they had never seen it and so complex they doubted they could master it.

By 10 September 1962, the last MRC–85 had been tested, and the Air Force turned over to the 39th Signal Battalion the responsibility for BACKPORCH. Although the big troposcatter radios were on the air, Page engineers, rather than the 362d Signal Company (Tropo), were operating BACKPORCH. Awed by the complex equipment and discouraged by the civilian technicians from interfering with delicate adjustments, the soldiers contented themselves with administrative and support tasks on the backbone sites. They left the technical work to the civilians,

[44]Ibid.; Interv, author with Ed, 28 Dec 77.
[45]Interv, author with Herbert, 24 May 77; George Raynor Thompson, Dixie R. Harris, Pauline M. Oakes, Dulaney Terrett, *The Signal Corps: The Test*, United States Army in World War II (Washington, D.C.: U.S. Army Center of Military History, Government Printing Office, 1957), p. 57.

who were required by contract to stay on the sites for one year to help operate and maintain the system.[46]

The men assigned to install and operate the troposcatter tails were less fortunate, for not enough Collins representatives were available for all ten widely dispersed TRC–90 sites. Since the light troposcatter radios were initial production models, the few available technicians were inexperienced with them and were frequently stymied when design deficiencies began to develop. Air conditioners could not keep delicate components cool in the oppressive tropical heat. Rubber inflatable antennas, designed for easy transport on the compact radio van, shifted in heavy monsoon winds. Special diesel fuel had to be purchased locally for the high-speed generators which powered the radios. Only after Colonel Blackwell formed a team of manufacturer's representatives and his best military operators to modify the temperamental radios and put them on the air did the systems improve. Once all the systems were installed and turned over to military operators in early 1963, the team became a troubleshooting unit.[47]

By early fall 1962 the VHF and troposcatter tails were tied into BACKPORCH, interconnecting all the switchboards and communications centers of the 232d and 178th Signal Companies. Communications that for more than a decade had taken days through the mails or through South Vietnamese channels suddenly took minutes; but the men of the 362d Signal Company (Tropo) had little respite.

Expanding Into Thailand

With the establishment of the Military Assistance Command, Vietnam, and the completion of BACKPORCH, Admiral Felt had both an operational headquarters and a communications network ready to handle any contingency requirements in South Vietnam. In Thailand, where theater headquarters, logistical and air bases, and reserve forces would probably be located in case of a full-scale conflict in Southeast Asia, he had only an advisory headquarters and no communications network.

In March 1962 Ambassador to Thailand Kenneth Todd Young permitted the Army to send the 167th Signal Company from Fort Gordon, Georgia, to install for the Thai military an austere base system. It consisted of twenty TRC–24 radio relay sets from Udorn to Ubon along a 400-mile stretch of the Mekong River that formed Thailand's eastern border with Laos. The American signalmen were to train Thai soldiers to operate the equipment while installing the system and then return to Fort Gordon within one year. The system would help the Thais establish better communications in a region where they faced a simmering insurgency and would also be available to connect with lines in Laos should hostilities occur there.[48]

[46]Interv, author with John D. von Bergen, Page Communications Engineers, Inc., 5 Apr 77, Historians files, CMH.

[47]Interv, author with Blackwell, 4 Apr 77; Ltr, USASGV to ECOM, 1 Sep 64, sub: AN/TRC–90 Improvements, file 19, 338–75–1009/65, WNRC.

[48]USARPAC Sig Stf Ofc Rpt, Oct–Dec 61, 338–75–1033/42; Memo, CINCPAC J–6 for Adm Felt, 23 Apr 62, sub: Summary of Current C-E Projects in Thailand, file 139364, 72A4171/1. Both in WNRC.

The 167th Signal Company soon found itself involved in far more than a train-ing mission. In mid-May, Admiral Felt ordered the headquarters of Joint Task Force 116 to Thailand as a show of force to deter Communist expansion in Laos. From a base at Korat in central Thailand, the task force headquarters took control of a battle group of the 25th Infantry Division that had been participating in an exercise with the Royal Thai Army, a Marine battalion sent from Okinawa, and several Air Force units. To support the small task force, the 9th Logistical Com-mand and the 999th Signal Company also deployed from Okinawa to Korat. The 999th had to ask the 167th Signal Company for help. Only 92 of the 232 men authorized the 999th deployed to Thailand; the rest were committed to other mis-sions throughout the Pacific. Those who did deploy had been doing the com-pany's housekeeping chores and post details on Okinawa; many were technically unqualified and their equipment poorly maintained. They took several weeks to install the bare minimum communications—a switchboard for the task force head-quarters, a single teletype circuit to Bangkok that traveled over a Royal Thai Army tactical radio system, and a four-station voice single-sideband net. The 167th Signal Company, a platoon from the 125th Signal Battalion attached to the infantry battle group of the 25th Infantry Division, and a radio-teletype detachment rapidly deployed from Fort Bragg, North Carolina, saved the widely dispersed task force from being completely without communications but could not link it.[49]

Thailand was fast assuming added importance in the strategic scheme for Southeast Asia. The 9th Logistical Command was left there to control the development of a support infrastructure that included pre-positioning of main-tenance, supply, and engineer facilities. Much work was needed to build up a supporting signal network for the command. Administrative and technical problems similar to those in South Vietnam had delayed completion of the Thailand branch of the U.S. Agency for International Development's regional telecommunications network. In July 1962 Secretary McNamara suggested that the military take over the project. Unenthusiastic about becoming involved in the complex negotiations that had been dragging on for years, General Williams proposed instead that military troposcatter equipment provide the base network in Thailand until completion of the commercial system.[50]

In mid-October Secretary McNamara directed the Army to build a strategic network throughout Thailand and connect it to the BACKPORCH terminal at Ubon and authorized the purchase of sixteen additional mobile troposcatter terminals for use in Southeast Asia. Since procurement and production of the equipment would take at least a year, the 39th Signal Battalion had to perform the Thailand assignment with its already overcommitted troposcatter teams from South Viet-nam. Because the men in Thailand would be over 500 miles from the company headquarters and support facilities in Nha Trang, Colonel Paulmann had to assemble his most dependable operators to form six troposcatter teams for the

[49]After Action Report (hereafter cited as AAR), JTF 116, 8 Dec 62, an. G, 73A3330/45, WNRC; Interv, author with Col (ret.) William A. Van Sandt, former signal officer, U.S. Army, Ryukyu Islands, 14 Feb 78, Historians files, CMH.

[50]Rpt, JCS J–6 to JCS, 24 Sep 62, sub: Upgrading U.S. Military Communications-Electronics Posture in Southeast Asia, Incl to JCS 2339/90, JACO (1962), DA/605, NARS.

The Phu Lam BACKPORCH **Site**

new mission.[51]

In late 1962, after the Laotian government and the Pathet Lao formed a neutral coalition government, Joint Task Force 116 left Thailand without ever having been in combat. Admiral Felt was convinced that had there been trouble, unsatisfactory communications would have been a major drawback. To avoid a complete break-down in his command and control, he wanted a base network in Thailand con-necting Bangkok with Korat and Korat with Udorn in the north and Ubon (the terminus of BACKPORCH) in the east. Besides expediting the dispatch of the six troposcatter teams from South Vietnam for the links to Udorn and Ubon, Admiral Felt directed the Air Force to link Bangkok with Korat and several other bases in southern Thailand. The U.S. Army, Ryukyu Islands, sent the 207th Signal Com-pany to establish a permanent switchboard and communications center at Korat. The company also took control of the detachments operating the overseas radio stations at Udorn and Bangkok. In Vientiane, Laos, a six-man Army signal team remained after the Military Assistance Advisory Group closed in September 1962 to operate a tactical multichannel system to Udorn for the U.S. embassy. When the 167th Signal Company returned to the United States in the spring of 1963

---

[51]Memo, Dep Secy of Defense for Secy of Army and Secy of Air Force, 19 Oct 62, sub: Upgrading U.S. Military Communications-Electronics in Southeast Asia, Incl to JCS 2339/95, JACO (1962), DA/605, NARS; Interv, author with Blackwell, 4 Apr 77.

after installing the radio relay system along the Mekong River, half of its men were reassigned to the 207th Signal Company to assist Royal Thai Army units operating the network. On 25 August 1963, the 379th Signal Battalion was formed at Korat to consolidate all Army communications in Thailand.[52]

While improving the base communications in Thailand, the Army also sought to bolster the contingency communications that would deploy with the task force in any future emergencies. General Collins decreed that the 999th Signal Company, which had returned to Okinawa with the IX Corps, would no longer be used as a general-purpose contingency unit for the entire Pacific and assigned it to the U.S. Army Signal Group, Ryukyu Islands, where it would train expressly for service in Southeast Asia.[53] The Army earmarked the 69th Signal Battalion from the strategic reserve in the United States to be prepared to augment the 999th Signal Company if a task force sent to Southeast Asia in the future should be reinforced. The signal staff at the Pacific Command developed more realistic plans for the eventuality of committing large numbers of U.S. forces to repulse a Communist invasion of Indochina. Envisioning a buildup to 11,545 signalmen within ten months after alert, the Pacific Command planned for two signal groups, each consisting of four combat area signal battalions; the 69th Signal Battalion; and a signal supply and maintenance battalion.[54]

A stronger contingency signal force programmed for use in Southeast Asia and the deployment of troposcatter teams to Thailand compensated for a long-neglected strategic vulnerability, the lack of a regional communications network with which to coordinate allied operations within Southeast Asia. The problems with communications to support Joint Task Force 116 also precipitated a gradual shift in strategy toward reliance on military communications in place rather than on call. In such a technologically undeveloped region, where jungle, climate, and atmospheric disturbances complicated the communicator's task, mobile tactical communications provided neither the quality nor the dependability needed by a large force in an emergency. The experience of Joint Task Force 116 seemed to vindicate General Williams' earlier arguments for the semifixed BACKPORCH network in South Vietnam and spoke for a similar high-capacity military network in Thailand. On the other hand, the problem of how to structure military units and train soldiers to operate sophisticated communications equipment remained unsolved.

[52]Msg, USARMA Vientiane to DA, 26 Sep 62, CX–50, ACSI Country file, 66A3138/89, WNRC; CINCPAC Command History, 1962, p. 249, CMH; Summary Sheet, DA, OACSFOR, 9 May 63, sub: Army Signal Organization, Thailand, file 2305236, 66A3140/3, WNRC.

[53]Since the commander of the signal group was also the signal officer of the U.S. Army, Ryukyu Islands, which had responsibility for the Army Support Group in South Vietnam, the 207th Signal Company in Thailand, and all the Strategic Army Communications stations in Southeast Asia, the assignment of the 999th Signal Company consolidated responsibility for all Army communications under one man.

[54]Msg, USARPAC to USARYIS, 21 Jun 63, file 139364, 72A4171/1, WNRC; U.S. Element SEATO Field Forces, OPLAN 5/62, 14 Dec 62, SEA 43, CMH; DA, OCE, Strategic Planning Group, Logistical Support of CINCPAC Operations Plan 32–63, vol. 2, app. E-7, 66A3600/6, WNRC.

3

Mounting a Counterinsurgency, 1960–1963

Since the mid-1950s American strategy for the defense of South Vietnam had envisioned a conventional invasion by North Vietnam as the principal threat. It assumed that Saigon's military forces would slow a Communist invasion long enough for reinforcement by U.S. units. As American combat forces took the counteroffensive to regain lost territory, South Vietnamese forces would be concerned primarily with any insurgency or guerrilla harassment. In the context of this strategy American signal advisers in 1960 estimated that the South Vietnamese Army was short an entire signal group of two cable construction battalions and two radio relay battalions to meet its long-haul communications needs in withstanding an invasion. When the 39th Signal Battalion arrived in 1962, the Commander in Chief, Pacific, Admiral Harry D. Felt, directed that the South Vietnamese be given service on the BACKPORCH system. The battalion's wiremen ran a cable from each BACKPORCH terminal to the nearest South Vietnamese Army facility. From there South Vietnamese signalmen extended the borrowed circuits to major civil and military headquarters.[1]

Expanding South Vietnamese Military Communications

When American signalmen arrived, their South Vietnamese counterparts were adjusting to several years of organizational restructuring. The South Vietnamese Army had the difficult mission of conducting a defense against a conventional force and maintaining territorial security in the face of a mounting insurgency. By 1960 each of the five military region headquarters, which managed the territorial security mission, was well supported by a signal company that provided radio, wire, telephone, and teletype service. On the other hand, signal companies of the field divisions, which were intended for conventional warfare,

---

[1]MAAG, Vietnam, Logistics Support to OPLAN 32–59, 30 May 60, app. 5, an. A, CMH; Interv, author with Blackwell, 4 Apr 77.

were in disarray due to personnel shifts that resulted from a recent restructuring of the army from ten to seven divisions. Only two signal support battalions, each with fewer than 200 men, were available to provide signal logistical support to the entire army. In the Saigon area, a single unit, the 1st Signal Service Battalion, operated all garrison communications for the army general staff and other head-quarters in the capital.[2]

In 1961 the South Vietnamese established a signal group of five battalions to provide garrison communications. An expanded 600th Signal Battalion—formerly the 1st Signal Service Battalion—covered the Saigon area. Four other battalions operated switchboards and radio nets in key cities. Besides signal staff and logis-tical responsibilities for the entire army, the South Vietnamese chief signal officer supervised the commander of the signal group. He retained those duties even after the Joint General Staff created a position for a signal officer in the spring of 1962 as a counterpart to the MACV J-6.[3]

During the early 1960s President Diem reorganized the five military regions into three corps tactical zones and began a military expansion that, by mid-1962, had increased the size of the South Vietnamese Army from 140,000 to 219,000 men. The army's signal organization expanded to keep pace with the changes. Signal depot companies, which handled signal logistics in each corps area, be-came battalions. Corps signal battalions, formed from the regional signal com-panies, were assigned radio relay companies to provide multichannel communi-cations from the corps headquarters to the divisions. The small divisional signal companies, which had contained mainly Morse code radios and field telephones, were augmented with a radio-teletype and multichannel capability. Retaining a basic signal organizational structure throughout the army during the expansion, the South Vietnamese freely reconfigured individual signal units to adjust to avail-able equipment and local terrain.[4]

Concurrent with the expansion the South Vietnamese Army, with American military assistance, began building a signal structure within the Civil Guard and Self-Defense Corps. The Civil Guard received PRC–10 portable radios for the militia platoons patrolling the districts and GRC–9 radios (or the GRC–87 vehic-ular version) for the links from Civil Guard companies at the districts to battalion headquarters at each province capital and from the provinces to the corps head-quarters. Each of the 3,060 squads of the Self-Defense Corps assigned to villages and hamlets was issued a PRC–10 radio, a telephone, and 1 1/2 miles of field wire.

[2]MAAG, Vietnam, Training Visit Report 44, 1–30 Nov 59, Incl to Ltr, Am Embassy to DA, 14 Dec 59, sub: Transmittal of R-Report, 66A3138/214; MAAG, Vietnam, Training Visit Report 52, 31 Jul 60, 66A3138/213; ibid., no. 55, 31 Oct 60. All in ACSI files, WNRC. MAAG, Vietnam, Visit of General Williston B. Palmer to MAAG Vietnam, Sep 60, tabs K, L, and M, I–16273/60, ISA333, 64A2170/11, WNRC.

[3]Interv, author with My Cao-Huy, former signal battalion commander in the South Vietnamese Army, 19 Jul 77, Historians files, CMH; Interv, author with Hines, 31 Oct 77; Ltr, MAAG, Vietnam, to CINCPAC, 14 Jul 62, sub: Training Progress Reports of Contractor Technicians Furnished Under the Army Military Assistance Training Program, 1007–07 (Training Assistance), 66A3142/2, WNRC.

[4]The Presidency, RVN, Instruction 1 (translation), 5 May 61, sub: Implementation of Decree Nr 98-QP dtd 13/4/1961 Concerning Activation of Corps Areas, file 250/15, 64A2424/2, WNRC; USARPAC Intelligence Bulletin, Jul 61, pp. 24–26, 49–52, CMH; Fact Sheet, MAAG, Vietnam, Jul 62, sub: Status of Communications Equipment in ARVN, VN Debriefing file, 338–74–555/8, WNRC; Ltr, MAAG, Viet-nam, to CINCPAC, 6 Jun 61, sub: Additional FY 61 MAP Requirements—MAAG-Vietnam, CMH.

The local signal depot battalion coordinated the distribution of the new equipment and the establishment of a maintenance and repair parts supply program. Besides providing logistical support, South Vietnamese Army signal units established training programs for recruits from the local territorial units, many of whom had never before seen a radio or telephone, and provided instructors to the Civil Guard training centers.[5]

By the early 1960s the South Vietnamese Signal Corps had a well-established schooling program. The only branch to operate a school at the army's major school center at Thu Duc as well as a separate training center at Vung Tau, the Signal Corps taught thirty-one different courses, far more than any other branch. The most competent graduates of the schools had been sent to the U.S. Army schools at Fort Monmouth or Fort Gordon for more advanced signal training. To make best use of those graduates of the American schools, the South Vietnamese chief signal officer had assigned them directly to instructor duty at the signal school or training center.[6]

Although South Vietnamese equipment and training steadily improved, their communications remained far more austere than those in the U.S. Army. Lacking special nets dedicated solely to intelligence, air and fire support, and logistics, they transmitted all communications on their busy command nets. After a trip to South Vietnam in the fall of 1961, General Maxwell D. Taylor reported to President Kennedy that insufficient means of transmitting intelligence information from field units to higher headquarters precluded a timely reaction to tactical intelligence. This was one of the most serious deficiencies in the South Vietnamese Army.[7]

Special-Purpose Communications Support

T he U.S. Army's Special Military Intelligence Activity worked with the South Vietnamese to improve transmission of tactical intelligence. Responsible for clandestine intelligence operations throughout South Vietnam, the unit operated a high-frequency communications net between its bases at Saigon, Hue, and Ban Me Thuot. At each base, intelligence officers using several agent handlers controlled a net of South Vietnamese agents who reported on Viet Cong activities. The weakest link in the intelligence-reporting system was between agent and agent handler. Agents were often unable to keep their transmitters hidden from the Viet Cong and in good operating order. Many were poorly trained in operating techniques. Faced with a high failure rate in maintaining contact between agents

[5]JCSM 228–61, JCS to Secy of Defense, 11 Apr 61, sub: Recommendations on South Vietnam, *U.S.-Vietnam Relations*, 11:19–21; Fact Sheet, MAAG, Vietnam, Jul 62, sub: Status of Communications Equipment in the Civil Guard and Self Defense Corps, VN Debriefing file, 338-74-555/8, WNRC.

[6]Incl 17 to Ltr, Army Attache, Saigon, to DA, ACSI, 28 Feb 57, sub: CATO (MAAG Vietnam) Advisor Quarterly Reports, ACSI files, 66A3138/214; MAAG, Vietnam, Training Visit Report 53, 31 Aug 60, pp. 20–25, ACSI files, 66A3138/213; DF, USARPAC G-3 to Staff Chiefs, 9 Feb 60, sub: USARPAC Air Ground MAP Advisory Team Report (1959), 338-75-1009/55. All in WNRC.

[7]Military Appendix (sec. 8, par. 3), Incl to Ltr, Taylor to Kennedy, 3 Nov 61, CMH.

and handlers, the Special Military Intelligence Activity arranged for agents to use letter drops to communicate with the handlers. Agent handlers were equipped with the RS–1 radio, a reliable high-frequency radio tested and used extensively by the Central Intelligence Agency in Southeast Asia. The handlers continued to communicate with the Special Military Intelligence Activity and with agents who used small commercial receivers to monitor broadcasts from agent handlers at a prearranged time and frequency.[8]

The RS–1 radio proved itself ideal for other programs in South Vietnam. In late 1961 the Central Intelligence Agency, using twelve-man U.S. Special Forces teams, began mobilizing Montagnard tribesmen into paramilitary units known as Civilian Irregular Defense Groups. Reliable communications were needed to link isolated villages with one another for defense and to transmit intelligence on Viet Cong infiltration and activity in remote, sparsely populated border and highland regions. Settled in fortified villages and camps from which they conducted patrols and border surveillance and largely responsible for their own defense, the Montagnards placed a special trust in their American sponsors for assistance and protection. That trust resided in a very real sense in dependable communications that enabled Americans to respond to threats to the Montagnards.[9]

Because the Green Berets had a unique mission and worked under the control of the Central Intelligence Agency, they could obtain equipment normally unavailable to more conventional U.S. units. Since the Army lacked a lightweight patrol radio that could transmit over long distances, the chief signal officer arranged for the agency's RS–1 to be adopted for military use and renamed the GRC–109. Well suited to the difficult terrain and atmospheric conditions of South Vietnam, the compact radio had such reliable propagation that it transmitted a good signal even through the severe atmospheric noise encountered during nighttime hours in the tropics. Equally important, the radio operated from a variety of power sources: AC electrical outlets, DC batteries, or a hand-operated generator. Because batteries deteriorated rapidly in the humid heat and AC power was hard to find in the field, American communicators had discovered that power was the critical variable in the communications equation in South Vietnam. Perhaps because the radio could transmit only Morse code (it could receive both Morse code and voice), it was never adopted for regular American or South Vietnamese units, which were becoming increasingly dependent on teletype and voice communications.[10]

[8]Ltr, 500th Intelligence Gp to USARPAC, 29 Jan 63, sub: Report of Clandestine Activities, Jul–Dec 62, 70A2825/4; Ltr, MACV to U.S. Army Intelligence School, sub: Operational Data on Current Status of FOI Operations in SVN, file 6.249, 66A3201R/28; DF, Ch, SMIAT, to CO, 500th Intelligence Gp, 16 Jul 62, sub: Communications Survey, file 22.1 (Electronics), 66A3201R/28; MFR, Special Activities Section, Operations Branch, 8 May 62, sub: Thailand Operations, file 6–2412, 66A3201/155. All in ACSI files, WNRC.

[9]Col. Francis J. Kelly, *U.S. Army Special Forces, 1961–1971*, Vietnam Studies (Washington, D.C.: Government Printing Office, 1973), pp. 19–64.

[10]USASF-V (Prov), Col George C. Morton, Debriefing Rpt (hereafter cited as Morton Debriefing Rpt), 1 May 62–6 Nov 63, p. 75; Research Analysis Corporation, Draft Technical Memorandum, U.S. Army Special Forces Operations Under the Civilian Irregular Defense Group Program in Vietnam (1961–1964), p. 213. Both in CMH. Records of staff actions leading to adoption of the GRC–109 are in DCSOPS files 61, no. 2111781, 64A2207/1, WNRC.

Installed in the communications bunker of each Special Forces camp, the reliable high-frequency set provided the sole communications link from the isolated camps to the CIA's Saigon headquarters. In late 1962, as the number of detachments increased, the radio net grew to an unwieldy twenty-four stations. At the same time, the CIA and the Defense Department decided that control of the paramilitary program should be transferred to American military authorities in South Vietnam. The Special Forces then assumed complete responsibility for their communications and established separate nets in each corps area for each field team, or A detachment, to report back to its controlling unit, a B detachment, which in turn would communicate with headquarters of the Special Forces in Nha Trang.[11]

The isolated detachments took great care to keep open their single radio lifeline. Although normally only one man of the A team was a communicator, all learned to operate the radios and most became adept at Morse code. They protected their radios and generators in sandbagged bunkers and installed several antennas so that if communications were lost with the B detachment's net control station, contact still might be made with the headquarters at Nha Trang or with Saigon. When it became apparent that the Viet Cong zeroed in on the antennas during attacks on the camps, the teams provided an alternate means of transmitting by burying long wire antennas eighteen inches underground in bamboo pipes. Despite the skepticism of some technical experts, the antennas worked well in several emergency situations.[12]

The far-flung Special Forces units made little use of wire communications. Generally, wire was employed only for alert lines connecting guard posts in base camps, although primitive wire switching arrangements were employed to detonate claymore mines and booby traps on the perimeter of the camps. After BACKPORCH was built, the 39th Signal Battalion installed cable to link the Special Forces headquarters in Nha Trang to the nearby troposcatter terminal for communications to MACV headquarters in Saigon.[13]

The communicators at the B detachments and the Special Forces headquarters had problems not shared by their contemporaries in the field. The radioman at each A detachment, usually an experienced noncommissioned officer, had to check into the radio net only once a day and to make contact with the B detachment in emergencies. A five-man communications section at the B detachments, on the other hand, had to operate a communications center and continually to monitor radio nets for calls from Special Forces headquarters or the A detachments. In addition to myriad administrative and logistical responsibilities, at the headquarters in Nha Trang the 26-man communications section had to operate separate nets to each B detachment and a teletype communications center. Because

[11]Morton Debriefing Rpt, p. 70; Research Analysis Corporation, Draft Technical Memorandum, U.S. Army Special Forces Operations Under the Civilian Irregular Defense Group Program in Vietnam (1961–1964), p. 210.

[12]Interv, author with Capt Richard D. Pete, USA Special Warfare Training Center, 17 Jan 77; Interv, author with Col Anthony J. Scibilia, former signal officer, 5th Special Forces Group, 14 Sep 78. Both in Historians files, CMH.

[13] USASF-V (Prov), Col Theodore Leonard, Debriefing Rpt (hereafter cited as Leonard Debriefing Rpt), 7 Nov 63–7 Aug 64, pt. 2, pp. 11–12, CMH; Morton Debriefing Rpt, pp. 70–74.

Communicator Checks *into the Operations and Intelligence Net at My Tho.*

men from either the headquarters or B team communications sections had to replace casualties from the field camps, their ranks were often depleted.[14]

Advisory Communications

While the Special Forces carefully husbanded their communications to ensure help would be available when needed, better-protected advisory teams with regular South Vietnamese Army units were far less dependent on communications. In fact, some advisers in the field felt that newly installed communications would eliminate the independence that separation from higher headquarters had previously conferred. Just as the single-sideband radios ordered in 1959 for a military advisory net had remained in storage until the arrival of the 39th Signal Battalion, it appeared that advisers would neglect the Operations and Intelligence Net that Secretary McNamara ordered installed. Since the equipment for the net—

[14]Morton Debriefing Rpt, pp. 72–74; Research Analysis Corporation, Draft Technical Memorandum, U.S. Army Special Forces Operations Under the Civilian Irregular Defense Group Program in Vietnam (1961–1964), p. 214; 5th Special Forces Group, Col John H. Spears, Debriefing Rpt, 31 Jul 64–1 Jul 65, p. 4, CMH.

almost 200 Morse/voice radios and fifteen radio-teletype sets—arrived in South Vietnam before the operators, the signal advisers stored it in warehouses.

By the time all 232 radio operators arrived, the 39th Signal Battalion had installed the single-sideband net to most advisory detachments. Since many advisers felt that a second parallel net was superfluous, operators destined for the net often found themselves working as clerks and guards, and the advisers loaned some of the radios to the South Vietnamese Army.[15]

In December 1962 the net was operating only between Saigon and the corps headquarters; Colonel Blackwell arranged for the transfer of the operators and equipment to the 39th Signal Battalion. When the Operations and Intelligence Net was finally complete, it comprised several different AM radio nets. A radio-teletype net linked MACV headquarters to advisers at the I, II, and IV Corps (a new headquarters formed in 1963) located at Da Nang, Pleiku, and Can Tho. A multichannel system linked MACV headquarters with III Corps advisers at Bien Hoa. Within each corps a radio-teletype net linked the corps and division advisers. Since troposcatter systems extended the backbone to the divisions, those radio-teletype nets were eventually relegated to backup duty. Below division level, advisory teams at regiments, battalions, provinces, and training centers operated their own radios as required.[16]

Air-Ground Coordination

O f greatest concern to advisers were communications coordinating tactical air support provided by Army and Marine Corps helicopters and Air Force fighters. Good air support depends on centralized control of air requests, which requires efficient long-distance communications, and forward air control in the target area, which requires coordinated air-to-ground communications. Encountering environmental, linguistic, and technical problems in establishing a tactical air control system in South Vietnam, the Air Force found communications to be "the foremost problem affecting air operations in Vietnam."[17]

Although as early as 1958 the Military Assistance Advisory Group had planned to provide the South Vietnamese with communications for air-ground operations, not until January 1962 when the U.S. Air Force established a standard Tactical Air Control System in South Vietnam was there any effective means of directing air support. Under the Air Force's system, Air Support Operations Centers at the corps headquarters processed requests for air strikes and forwarded them by single-sideband voice radio to an Air Operations Center jointly operated at Tan Son Nhut Air Base. There, missions were planned and transmitted to fight-

---

[15]Intervs, author with Ed, 8 Dec 77, with Hines, 31 Oct 77, and with Blackwell, 4 **Apr 77.**

[16]MACV, Intelligence Guide and Operating Procedures, 15 May 62 (w/revision 4 Jan 63), pp. 9–11, ACS 63–1273, ACSI files, 66A3138/165, WNRC; Ltr, MACV to USASGV, 13 May 62, sub: Letter of Instructions, Incl to 39th Sig Bn Stf Ofc Rpt, Feb–Jun 62, 338–75–1033/50, WNRC; CINCPAC History, 1962, p. 56.

[17]MS, USAF, Project Corona Harvest, USAF Activities in Southeast Asia, 1954–1964, Jan 73, p. 17, K239.032, OAFH.

ers standing by at airfields throughout South Vietnam. Since the Air Force radios initially available for communicating such rapidly changing information over long distances were mounted in small vans without air conditioning, the equipment was plagued by overheating and communications were never dependable. The completion of BACKPORCH in September 1962 brought the first reliable communications between the airfields, the operations centers in the field, and the control center at Tan Son Nhut.[18]

Since the BACKPORCH tails extended only to division headquarters, the backbone network only partially improved communications from the actual users of air support—the South Vietnamese infantry companies in the field—to the Air Support Operations Centers at the corps headquarters. With the South Vietnamese using their busy voice and Morse command nets to send the requests back to corps and to obtain clearance for the proposed air strikes from provincial authorities, the requests were often lost among the operational traffic or arrived at the Air Support Operations Centers too late to obtain an effective response. Adding to the problem was reluctance of South Vietnamese staff officers to forward requests for air strikes without the personal approval of the commander at each level lest they later be held accountable in the event of a mistake. South Vietnamese ground commanders and their American advisers understandably had little confidence in the system.[19]

In search of a solution, signal and aviation advisers arranged for U.S. Air Force liaison officers to accompany South Vietnamese battalions on combat operations and to use portable single-sideband radios to communicate directly with the Air Support Operations Centers. But the advisers were unable to convince the South Vietnamese Joint General Staff to remove a requirement that air support requests be passed over the command net for approval by each member of the chain of command. The liaison officers still could only use their single-sideband radios to notify the operations centers that the requests were on the way so that staff officers could begin preparing for the mission.[20]

For a time U.S. Special Forces teams in South Vietnam, because of their close working relationship with the CIA, circumvented the laborious procedures for requesting air support by radioing the agency's field office in Saigon. The duty officer there would simply telephone Tan Son Nhut Air Base, and the aircraft would be dispatched. A request would also be passed through the district, province, and corps, but that step was a mere formality. The Special Forces' freewheeling use of CIA channels to obtain air support ran into difficulty in late 1962.

---

[18]Robert F. Futrell, *The Advisory Years to 1965,* The United States Air Force in Southeast Asia (Washington, D.C.: Government Printing Office, 1981), pp. 142–43.

[19]MS, Riley Sunderland, Evolution of Command and Control Doctrine for Close Air Support, Mar 73, pp. 36–42, CMH; MS, Maj Robert A. Rowley, FAC Operations in Southeast Asia, 1961–1965 (hereafter cited as FAC Operations), Jan 72, pp. 56–71, K168.01–68, OAFH.

[20]MS, Lt Col Robert A. Rowley, The Air Force in Southeast Asia; Tactics and Techniques of Close Air Support Operations, 1961–1973 (hereafter cited as Tactics and Techniques), Feb 76, K168.01–08, OAFH; Memo, III Corps Sr Adv for Div and Special Zone Sr Advs, 4 Oct 63, sub: Compliance with Air Request Procedures; Ltr, MACV to Corps Sr Advs, 11 Oct 62, sub: Separate Air Request Net for RVNAF, both in Wilson Papers.

When a province chief was denied permission by his corps commander to mount an operation, he decided to proceed anyway and asked the local Special Forces detachment to get him air support. Although the air strikes contributed to a highly successful operation, when the Joint General Staff learned how the province chief had obtained his air support, it insisted that all requests, including those from Special Forces, be processed through the Tactical Air Control System.[21]

Even when air support was summoned properly, linguistic and equipment incompatibilities complicated communications over the battlefield. Beginning in late 1961, the small South Vietnamese Air Force was reinforced by U.S. Air Force combat aircraft and U.S. Army armed helicopters. With that much support involved in an operation, communications often degenerated into a bilingual babel with South Vietnamese fighter pilots talking to their wingmen, who might be either South Vietnamese or American; U.S. Army helicopter pilots talking to advisers of South Vietnamese ground units; South Vietnamese ground commanders talking to South Vietnamese airborne observers; and forward air controllers trying to keep them all shooting at the enemy instead of at each other.[22]

Most forward air controllers flew light observation planes which during the Korean War had been labeled the L–19 but which had been redesignated the O–1 and in South Vietnam were nicknamed "bird dogs." Since the planes, as all Air Force aircraft, had radios in the upper spectrum of the very high frequency band while Army helicopters and ground troops had lower band radios, the forward air controller strapped an infantryman's portable PRC–10 radio to the back of the seat to provide a means of communicating with Army helicopters and the troops he was supporting. That expedient had obvious drawbacks. Clumsy for the pilot to operate and cumbersome in the confined cockpit, the low-powered radios also had a limited range over jungle areas. To talk to the fighter aircraft he was controlling, he still had to switch to his very high frequency radio.[23]

When the U.S. Air Force began equipping its tactical aircraft in South Vietnam with the ARC–44 FM radio, which was compatible with the Army's radios, U.S. and South Vietnamese Air Force fighter pilots and forward air controllers, U.S. Army helicopter pilots, and South Vietnamese ground commanders and their advisers finally had a common radio net. By late 1962, 18 U.S. Air Force and 30 South Vietnamese Air Force aircraft had the radios, while 142 planes were still to be outfitted. By the fall of 1963 all A–1H fighters and O–1 observation planes in South Vietnam were equipped with the ARC–44's. Although removal of the technical barriers to air-ground and air-air communications improved air control over the battlefield, the air request system remained slow and ineffective due to South Vietnamese reluctance to change the request procedures. American signal

[21]MS, Rowley, FAC Operations, p. 67.

[22]A personal account of the first American forward air controller in South Vietnam is in Maj. (ret.) Douglas K. Evans, "Reinventing the FAC: Vietnam, 1962," *Air Force Magazine* 63 (February 1980): 71–75. Memo, II Corps Sr Adv for CO, MACV, 15 Aug 62, sub: Development of More Effective Close Air Support Operations in II Corps Tactical Zone, Wilson Papers; 2d Air Division History, Jul–Dec 64, Counterinsurgency Lessons Learned, vol. 3, K526.01, OAFH.

[23]MS, Rowley, FAC Operations, p. 54; Memo, DA, OPS OD FE, for Dir Opns, ODCSOPS, 26 Feb 62, sub: Joint Staff Visit to CINCPAC, . . . Thailand, app. E, ACSI files, 66A3138/82, WNRC.

advisers were unable to moderate the restrictive South Vietnamese regulation of air request communications.[24]

Signal Advisers

T he number of Army signal advisers, which increased from thirty-nine to fifty during the advisory buildup in 1962, was never sufficient to permit them to influence communications throughout all the levels of the South Vietnamese Army. Nor were the best American Signal Corps officers always to be found in South Vietnam. Although Secretary of Defense Robert S. McNamara had launched the advisory buildup with the injunction, "We have got to have our first team there in South Vietnam," personnel officers in Washington gave the highest priority and status to assignments with regular signal units, especially those in Europe. Once regular U.S. units were sent to South Vietnam, it became even more difficult to keep the advisory ranks filled with top-quality officers.[25]

The many good signal officers who did volunteer to go to South Vietnam had to struggle to avoid becoming involved in their South Vietnamese counterparts' responsibilities. As during the 1950s, logistical chores, especially coordination with other advisers at the depots and higher staffs to resolve supply problems, still proved troublesome. Signal advisers continually were tempted to fill South Vietnamese needs for signal parts and equipment through American supply channels rather than using the slower and cumbersome South Vietnamese logistical system. Because South Vietnamese commanders were reluctant to put their superiors in a position where they might have to lose face by denying a request, some ignored their own channels and automatically turned to their advisers. Although signal advisers were usually two grades junior to their counterparts, in a few cases where commanders became excessively reliant on advisers, American signal officers became de facto commanders of South Vietnamese units. While dependence on the American advisers diminished as the South Vietnamese gained more confidence in their own logistical system, it never disappeared entirely.[26]

In spite of the temptation to circumvent the South Vietnamese logistical system, the majority of American and South Vietnamese communicators worked well together. By 1963 many South Vietnamese Signal Corps officers had attended

[24]Validity of Current U.S. Army Airmobile Doctrine, 10 May 62, pp. 37–38, Incl 7 to 45th Transportation Bn, Stf Ofc Rpt, Feb–Jun 62, 338–75–1033/50, WNRC; AF Logistics Command History, 1 Jul 62–30 Jun 63, an. F, p. 6, K201–42, OAFH; MACV, Summary of Highlights, 8 Feb 62–7 Feb 63, p. 153, and Msg, COMUSMACV MACJ3 1178 to AIG 924, 1 Mar 63, both in CMH.

[25]Memo, McNamara for Secy of Army and CSA, 21 Dec 61, sub: Requirement for Advisory Personnel in Vietnam, Incl to Memo, CSA for Dep Chiefs of Staff et al., 22 Dec 61, DCSOPS 61 file, 64A2207/5, WNRC; Interv, author with Van Sandt, 14 Feb 78.

[26]Except for a few Signal Corps warrant officers assigned as logistical advisers, most maintenance assistance was performed on a contract basis by U.S. and Filipino civilian technicians. For copies of their reports, see File 1007-07 (Training Assistance), 66A3142/2, WNRC. Ltr, CINCPAC to MACV, 27 Aug 63, sub: CINCPAC MAP Inspection of Military Assistance in the Republic of Vietnam, p. 16, 338–75–1009/63, WNRC.

one of the Army's signal schools in the United States. Returning to South Vietnam, these officers shared with their American signal advisers a common doctrinal foundation in signal operations and the ability to converse in English. Since the South Vietnamese Army was organized along the same lines as the U.S. Army and was provisioned with the same equipment that most advisers had used earlier in their careers, the American signal adviser usually found that his previous troop experience adequately prepared him to assist his counterpart in planning conventional tactical operations. Only the austerity of South Vietnamese communications was strange to American signalmen.[27]

While the common doctrinal foundation made the signal adviser's job easier, it also left him and the South Vietnamese signal officers ill prepared to establish communications for the counterinsurgency being conducted in South Vietnam. During the early 1960s the signal schools in the United States made little attempt to focus on operations in Southeast Asia. The signal officers basic course at Fort Gordon for newly commissioned officers contained only one hour of instruction dealing with counterinsurgency communications; the advanced course at Fort Monmouth, which prepared officers for assignments as company commanders and battalion staff officers, offered only three hours of counterinsurgency-related instruction. Nor were quotas available for American signal officers in Vietnamese-language courses or at a special school established at Fort Bragg, North Carolina, to train advisers destined for South Vietnam. Such special training was reserved for officers in the combat arms.[28]

The role of signal adviser was a difficult one. It required the ability to communicate technical concepts in simple terms as well as the delicate balance of tact and persuasiveness demanded of all advisers. Responsibilities were seldom clearly defined, and signal advisers had to walk a fine line to avoid becoming overbearing in accomplishing their mission. For example, although signal advisers were supposed to encourage their counterparts to assist local security forces in the countryside, few became involved with paramilitary units or provincial authorities in their unit's tactical zone. Finding their counterparts unwilling to divert attention from routine training and maintenance in their own units and lacking schooling or experience in counterinsurgency tactics, advisers could not forcefully urge and competently advise their reluctant counterparts to pay sufficient attention to their territorial responsibilities. Most signal advisers contented themselves with helping their counterparts confront the formidable array of more conventional challenges facing the South Vietnamese Signal Corps as it attempted to absorb new equipment, train thousands of recruits, and develop communications procedures for working with supporting aircraft.[29]

For those who did become involved in counterinsurgency communications, there were only two basic guides to follow: the signal annex of General McGarr's counterinsurgency plan and a booklet, *Tactics and Techniques of Counter-Insurgent*

---

[27]Interv, author with Lt Cols Edward MacDonald and Kenneth Whitten, former signal advisers, 8 Jul 77, Historians files, CMH.

[28]Memo, ODCSOPS, DA, for Dir, Joint Staff, 28 Jul 61, sub: Status of Development of Counterguerrilla Forces, DCSOPS 61 file, 64A2207/8, WNRC.

[29]Interv, author with MacDonald and Whitten, 8 Jul 77.

Operations, based on experiences in South Vietnam and on several historical studies of other counterinsurgencies, which had been prepared by the Command and General Staff College at Fort Leavenworth, Kansas. Similar to the counterinsurgency plan, the booklet contained a tentative doctrine that emphasized communications for long-range patrols and guerrilla forces. It did not address the requirements of coordinating territorial security beyond discussing various means for paramilitary units and villages to alert regular units to the presence of the enemy and to call for help when attacked. For those purposes the booklet listed many of the primitive, but imaginative, techniques mentioned in the counterinsurgency plan: drums, flares, balloons, pigeons, and smoke.[30]

Those ambitious signal advisers who experimented with the seemingly simple communications techniques found them difficult to implement. Establishing a common understanding of visual and audio signals required laborious coordination and education. Such unusual items as helium for balloons and pigeon feed required special handling and storage facilities. Before carrier pigeons sent from Fort Monmouth could prove their worth, they succumbed to disease or landed in the cooking pots of hungry South Vietnamese militiamen. Militiamen did successfully use drums, flares, and smoke to summon help during attacks in cases where the jungle was not so dense as to block the signal. Villagers were reluctant, however, to use such overt signals simply to announce the presence of Viet Cong lest they provoke an attack. The Viet Cong, on the other hand, sometimes used the signals to lure South Vietnamese relief forces into a trap.[31]

The chief of a British advisory mission to South Vietnam, Robert G. K. Thompson, who had played a prominent role in putting down a Communist insurgency in Malaya during the 1950s, believed that such primitive one-way communications were inadequate. Arguing that the village, an important entity in the South Vietnamese political hierarchy, required two-way communications, he emphasized the importance of communications in projecting governmental authority to the rural population as well as in triggering response to enemy attacks. Thompson convinced President Diem and General McGarr that radio communications were necessary between villages, districts, and provinces and that South Vietnamese Army units had to monitor the nets for emergency calls. General McGarr directed the senior adviser in the II Corps Tactical Zone to test ways in which the South Vietnamese Army might contribute to a more sophisticated political-military network.[32]

The signal adviser to the II Corps tested a radio signaling system in Darlac Province in the Central Highlands and a telephone warning net in a district of the coastal province of Phu Yen. The Darlac project used PRC–10 FM radios in villages to communicate to district headquarters, which could use the local Civil Guard's GRC–9 AM radio to communicate with province headquarters and nearby

---

[30]MAAG, Vietnam, U.S. Plan for Counterinsurgency, an. C, app. 7; MAAG, Vietnam, *Tactics and Techniques of Counter-Insurgent Operations,* 15 Nov 60 (revised 10 Feb 62), pp. E–1 through E–8. Both in CMH.

[31]Interv, author with MacDonald and Whitten, 8 Jul 77.

[32]Ltr, Thompson to Diem, 11 Nov 61, Dispatch 205, CMH; Ltr, McGarr to Diem, 2 Dec 61, Incl to Ltr, McGarr to Gen George H. Decker, 6 Dec 61, DCSOPS 61 file, 64A2207/1, WNRC.

South Vietnamese units. The telephone net in Phu Yen Province was a simple point-to-point field wire system connecting tactical phones in villages, district headquarters, and local South Vietnamese units.[33]

To set up the radio net in Darlac, soldiers from the signal company of the 23d Infantry Division, based in the mountains near Ban Me Thuot, trained village militiamen to operate FM radios, loaned them equipment, and helped them fabricate antenna extensions from bamboo poles and welding rods. After months of such assistance and painstaking coordination between South Vietnamese signal officers, provincial authorities, and advisers, the practice nets were put into use. Although the Viet Cong cut some telephone wires, the communications proved generally satisfactory. Most failures were attributable to human, rather than technical, problems. Village chiefs, direly warned by the soldiers against losing the equipment, often hid it at night, just when it was most needed.[34]

The village chiefs' fears of retribution were not unfounded. South Vietnamese signal officers jealously guarded their communications equipment and had only reluctantly loaned it to the villages. Unenthusiastic about devoting time and effort to the project, the army quickly recalled its gear when the Self-Defense Corps received its own communications equipment. Since the paramilitary soldiers required their signal equipment for outposts, roadblocks, and roving patrols, the rural communities were again without communications. Feeling that the tests, although they worked, took more resources and coordination than could be expected on a countrywide basis, the signal advisers did not try to reinstitute the experiment.

The Village and Hamlet Radio System

W ith the strong support of Secretary McNamara, the research and development arm of the Department of Defense, the Advanced Research Projects Agency, had begun sponsoring more thorough scientific studies of counterinsurgency techniques and equipment. Given the responsibility to administer the primary research program in Southeast Asia, which was called Project Agile, the Army established a field agency, the Army Concept Team in Vietnam, to coordinate requirements and field testing with the advisers and development of equipment with depots and manufacturers in the United States. The team's work produced modifications to equipment and special antennas for improving communications in the peculiar terrain and propagational environment of Southeast Asia. By 1963 the Army was considering forty-nine different new electronic devices for transmitting warnings, signaling aircraft, and conducting two-way commu-

---

[33]Memo, II Corps Sr Adv for CG, II Corps, 12 Dec 61, sub:Village Alert and Warning System; Memo, II Corps Sr Adv for CG, II Corps, 26 Feb 62, sub: Darlac Province Early Warning System; Memo, II Corps Sr Adv for CG, II Corps, 29 Oct 62, sub: Early Warning System-Phu Yen Province. All in Wilson Papers.

[34]Memo, II Corps Sr Adv for CO, MACV, 2 Oct 62, sub: Village Early Warning System, w/2 Incls, Wilson Papers.

nications in a counterinsurgency environment. Although many items of equipment tested by the team, especially in the fields of avionics and heliborne command and control communications, were eventually adopted for general use, only a single-sideband portable radio that the Special Forces tested for the research agency was adopted specifically for counterinsurgency warfare.[35]

Despite the elaborate testing program of the Advanced Research Projects Agency and the Army Concept Team in Vietnam, it was civilian engineers working for the Department of State who developed the radio best suited for counterinsurgency operations. Only after its military potential became apparent did the Department of Defense begin assisting the project. In 1960 the U.S. Operations Mission formed a Public Safety Division to assume from the Michigan State University advisory team the responsibility for assisting the South Vietnamese government's paramilitary and police forces. Recalling previous problems with management of communications projects by bureaucrats instead of engineers, the U.S. Agency for International Development hired experienced American communications engineers to establish and operate a Telecommunications Directorate for the new Public Safety Division in South Vietnam. When one of those engineers, Paul Katz, designed a portable radio for the national police in April 1961, a communications program called the village and hamlet radio system was born.[36]

After rejecting various military radios as too heavy, complex, or expensive and failing to find any available commercial police radios built for the long-range communications that the police in South Vietnam required, Katz designed a twenty-watt AM radio that he called a TR–20. By October 1961 he had obtained from an American electronics company, Radio Industries, a satisfactory bid and a promise to begin delivery of 2,000 TR–20's in three months. While waiting for the radios to arrive, Katz set up a program to train operators and technicians. His cadre consisted of forty-five South Vietnamese soldiers, all graduates of the U.S. Army's signal schools, and four former Special Forces soldiers. Once trained, the small cadre split into teams to install the new radios in villages throughout South Vietnam. Perceiving that the radios had military as well as civil utility, enabling villages to alert the South Vietnamese Army to the presence of Viet Cong, in February 1962 Secretary of Defense McNamara directed the U.S. Army to assist the U.S. Operations Mission with the project.[37]

In early March, twenty-one men from the advance party of the 39th Signal Battalion joined the U.S. Operations Mission's installation teams working in the

---

[35]Seymour J. Deitchman, *The Best Laid Schemes: A Tale of Social Research and Bureaucracy* (Cambridge: MIT Press, 1976), pp. 67–68; Min, Secy of Defense Conf in Honolulu, Dec 61, p. 8–M–1, CMH; OCSO, Army Long Range Capabilities Plan, 1964–1983, Mar 63, an. G, file 230416, 66A3140/1, WNRC; Joint Research and Testing Activity, Second Semi-Annual Progress Report, 1 Jul–31 Dec 64, Project 2F–251.0, 15 Jan 65, pp. 44–46, 68A3305/2, WNRC.

[36]Interv, author with Paul Katz, former communications engineer, U.S. Operations Mission, 4 May 78, Historians files, CMH. The complete story of the village and hamlet radio program is contained in CORDS, Public Safety Div, Telecommunications Annual Report, 1966, 1 Jul 67, and CORDS, Public Safety Div, Telecommunications Projects Report, 1956–1968, 1 Jan 69, both in CMH.

[37]Interv, author with Katz, 4 May 78; Min, Secy of Defense Conference in Honolulu, Feb 62, pp. 16, 58, CMH.

provinces of Gia Dinh, surrounding
Saigon, and An Xuyen, a Viet Cong
stronghold in southernmost South Vietnam. Attempting to halt the installation
of a radio in a village of An Xuyen on
20 March 1962, the Viet Cong provided
the first test of the radios as a warning
device. While a small security force held
off the attacking Viet Cong, the technicians installed the radio and called
the district headquarters. Hastily dispatched reinforcements ambushed the
withdrawing insurgents. When the Viet
Cong attacked another installation team
as it moved by boat along a canal in An
Xuyen, one man was drowned, the first
member of the 39th Signal Battalion to
die in South Vietnam. Despite the interference of the Viet Cong, the installation teams' work, which usually enjoyed the enthusiastic support of the

Paul Katz *trains a Montagnard radio operator.*

villagers, proceeded rapidly. Inaugurating use of the radio in a village was often
attended by much ceremony and seemed to confer considerable honor on both
the village and village chief, who for additional prestige and for security often
kept the radio in his home.[38]

By May 1962, 215 village radios had been installed, and it appeared that a goal
of installing all 2,000 sets by December would be met. Secretary McNamara's concern, however, had passed from the village to the smallest government unit, the
hamlet. The South Vietnamese government had begun an ambitious project, the
Strategic Hamlet Program, to deny the Viet Cong access to the rural populace
by moving the people into fortified hamlets. Worried lest the program fail if the
isolated hamlets were unable to call for assistance when besieged, McNamara
wanted radios installed in the hamlets.[39]

Since hamlets were normally clustered around a village, the TR–20, which had
a range of twenty kilometers, was unnecessarily powerful—and expensive—to
serve as a hamlet radio. Meeting with military signal advisers, Katz drew up
specifications for smaller versions of the village radios and sent them to Radio
Industries. Rapidly fabricating a five-watt radio, the TR–5, and a hand-held one-
watt version, the HT–1, the company sent prototypes to South Vietnam. Given
to the Special Forces for testing, the HT–1 proved its worth when a patrol used
it to call for fire support during a surprise attack on a Montagnard training camp
at Buon Enao in the Central Highlands. The Special Forces discovered that one
seemingly good feature of the radio could cause problems: a button that, when

---

[38]Interv, author with Blackwell, 4 Apr 77; Rpt, Hilsman to Governor Harriman, 18 Jun 62, *U.S.-Vietnam Relations*, 12:472.
[39]Min, Secy of Defense Conference in Honolulu, May 62, p. 5, CMH.

Antenna for the TR–20 *is installed at Lac Hoa village in the delta.*

activated, destroyed the entire circuit board to keep it from falling into the hands of the enemy. South Vietnamese irregulars on patrol occasionally pushed that button either by mistake or as an excuse to return to camp in keeping with a dictum to be followed when communications were lost. To avoid future problems, Paul Katz eliminated the self-destruct feature when the hamlet radio went to full production.[40]

Having seen the capability of the village and hamlet radios, the Special Forces ordered sets for all their camps in South Vietnam. The voice capability of the TR–5 and TR–20 was an advantage over the Morse code transmission of the GRC–109 for communications between nearby camps. They were even more enthusiastic about the HT–1. Powered by flashlight batteries, which were easy to obtain, it had a range in the jungle of fifteen kilometers, far more than they could expect from their portable military voice radios.

Considering the larger radio suitable for more dispersed hamlets and the hand-held models ideal for hamlets clustered near their parent villages and for militiamen on patrol, the military was also convinced of the worth of the radios in the counterinsurgency being conducted in the countryside. Secretary McNamara approved the expenditure of $1 million to help the U.S. Operations Mission to purchase 3,000 portable radios and 700 TR–5's for the village and hamlet radio

[40]Interv, author with Katz, 4 May 78; Leonard Debriefing Rpt, p. 11.

program. To relieve the members of the 39th Signal Battalion, who were needed to man newly constructed signal centers, the chief signal officer in early October dispatched the 72d Signal Detachment, a 75-man team from Fort Benning, Georgia. Before returning to the United States six months later, the signalmen installed 2,613 radios in villages and hamlets throughout the country. Continuing the program with civilian contract technicians, the U.S. Operations Mission installed additional radios in villages and hamlets, at border police posts and customs points, and on naval craft. After developing special flexible antennas that would bend in tunnels, the mission even established a railway security net with TR–20 radios installed in every railroad train and forty-five radios located in stations along the railroad line between Saigon and Quang Tri.[41]

Because the radios were a prime target during Viet Cong attacks, the South Vietnamese kept a large stock of spare radios. After the first radio was captured in May 1962, only a month after it was installed, the number of radios destroyed or captured steadily increased. By January 1963 seventeen South Vietnamese radio operators had been killed and twenty-seven radios lost or damaged. The enemy's focus on the radios seemed to indicate that he saw them as a threat because they improved the South Vietnamese government's commitment both to the security of the countryside and to the success of the Strategic Hamlet Program.[42]

By early 1963 over two thousand hamlets and villages were connected by radio to district and province capitals. Communications support to counterinsurgency operations was now in being and had proven its value in several instances. Although the new nets would help the South Vietnamese Army pursue its counterinsurgency mission, it was still too early to determine whether the army would wholeheartedly reorient its operations.

The Viet Cong

W hile new equipment helped local hamlet and village residents contend with the Viet Cong, South Vietnamese and American signalmen were finding that Communist communicators were becoming more formidable adversaries. When in 1962 the Viet Cong began to suspect the extent to which the Americans and the South Vietnamese were intercepting their communications, the signal officer at the clandestine Communist headquarters in the South, the Central Office for South Vietnam, established stringent procedures for protecting radio communications. Thenceforth most traffic was encrypted, frequencies and call signs were changed daily, and the length of radio transmissions was cut drastically.[43]

Recognizing that such measures would only partially foil sophisticated

---

[41]Min, Secy of Defense Conference in Honolulu, 23 Jul 62, pp. 4–1 through 4–3; CORDS, Telecommunications Projects Report, 1956–1968; Ltr, Dir, USOM, to CG, MACV, 14 Mar 63, CMH.

[42]Memo, II Corps Sr Adv for Div and Special Zone Sr Advs, 13 Jan 64, sub: USOM Village/Hamlet Radio, Wilson Papers; Msg, COMUSMACV MACJ3 0759 to AIG 924, 8 Feb 63, CMH.

[43]Cap Doc, 24 Aug 67, TIR RVN 114–67, file 516–02(77) TIR VN 2, A69–21/2, Army Security Agency (ASA), Arlington Hall Station, Virginia; CICV Rpt, VC C–E Capability in RVN–Part 2 (ST 67–006), 3 Dec 65, pp. 6–8, 319–74–053/3, WNRC.

American electronic warfare experts, the Viet Cong increasingly turned to courier communications. By late 1962 the Viet Cong had interlaced South Vietnam with a simple, but effective, messenger system, called the communications-liaison network. Managed by the Military Post Office Division of the Central Office for South Vietnam and operated by communications-liaison units in each province, the network filled most of the communications needs of the political and military apparatus of the Viet Cong and of the North Vietnamese military units operating in South Vietnam. At several points along the western borders of South Vietnam the network linked up with a communications-liaison corridor running along the Ho Chi Minh Trail to North Vietnam.[44]

The nucleus of the communications-liaison system within South Vietnam was the way station, a small base of operations and relay point usually established in a Viet Cong–controlled village near a messenger route. Besides being a place where couriers from nearby districts and military units could pick up and deliver messages, the stations, built approximately a day's journey apart, also served as rest stops where infiltrating personnel could sleep and eat. Porters and couriers set out along the route at a scheduled time each day to meet their counterparts coming in the opposite direction from adjacent stations. Rendezvousing after about a five-hour walk, the couriers transferred their charges and messages and returned to their base stations. On the following day the messages, infiltrators, and supplies were relayed farther along the route in the same manner.

Although the system was slow, it was secure. Because couriers and porters knew only the locations of their own stations, the capture of one agent did not compromise a complete link of the network. Guards patrolled the route and protected the communications-liaison agents at road crossings and bridges where they might be detected.

Procedures were different for courier operations in urban areas. Traffic on the important link connecting the headquarters of the Central Office for South Vietnam in the jungle west of Tay Ninh with clandestine Viet Cong cells in Saigon moved openly, but undetected. Each day a courier from Saigon met a messenger from Viet Cong headquarters for lunch at a restaurant in Tay Ninh and surreptitiously exchanged paper bags containing messages. Taking the afternoon bus back to Saigon, the courier kept the messages in his home until late in the evening, when he would leave them in a garbage can behind a school in downtown Saigon. During the night a taxi driver would pick them up and deliver them.[45]

The success of the Viet Cong insurgency was due in part to combining military and political committees at each echelon of their organizations, from the Central Office for South Vietnam to Communist-controlled hamlets. The communications doctrine reflected this system. Couriers carried civil and military traffic in the same pouch; the same radioman operated stations in the party radio net,

---

[44]Discussion of the communications-liaison network within South Vietnam is based on MACV History, 1968, vol. 1, pp. 122–23, CMH; Rand Corporation, *Insurgent Organization and Operations: A Case Study of the Viet Cong in the Delta, 1964–1966,* Rand Memorandum, RM–5239–ISA/ARPA, Aug 67, pp. 151–54; CIA Rpt, Guide to a Viet Cong Province, May 71, pp. 15, 42–44, CMH.

[45]Intel Rpt, MIC, 27 Jan 65, sub: Commo-Liaison Agent, reel 40, Advanced Research Projects Agency, Research and Development Field Unit (ARPA RDFU).

which linked all political cadres, and the military net used for controlling tactical operations.

The Merging of Civil-Military Communications

A lthough the South Vietnamese had similarly sought to integrate their counterinsurgency by giving military unit commanders primary responsibility for the pacification of the countryside in their tactical zones, in practice two distinct chains of command remained and separate communications networks supported the army and the governmental hierarchy. Tactical equipment and borrowed BACKPORCH circuits linked the military chain of command from company level to the Joint General Staff. On the civilian side, the installation of village and hamlet radios extended communications from hamlet to village to district; Civil Guard communications linked district, province, and corps; single-sideband radios provided by the Telecommunications Directorate of the Public Safety Division linked province chiefs directly with President Diem and his staff in Saigon. While those means of vertical communications for both military and governmental officials flourished, the development of lateral communications, so important in coordinating a defense against the combined political-military offensive of the Viet Cong, depended on informal agreements between local military and provincial officials and the ability of South Vietnamese signal staffs to coordinate frequencies, procedures, and support arrangements.[46]

South Vietnamese signal officers tended to neglect basic elements of staff coordination and thorough planning of communications. Because signal officers often failed to ascertain the call signs and frequencies of supporting units, it was not unusual to see fighters, waiting to provide air support, circling over a battlefield while an observation plane swooped low to drop written messages containing the correct radio information to the ground troops. Coordination of communications for pacification operations was weakest. Capitalizing on the absence of lateral communications between adjacent provinces, the Viet Cong habitually operated near provincial boundaries where they could slip across a border and escape before neighboring security forces could be notified. When army and Civil Guard units joined for combined search and clear operations, lack of signal planning and rehearsals caused communications breakdowns that permitted Viet Cong being pursued by the army force to slip through Civil Guard blocking positions. Even during static security missions, failure to make routine communications checks and to update frequency changes occasionally left a besieged militia unit unable to contact the appointed military reaction force. Since signal advisers were assigned only down to division level, they had little opportunity to assist the regimental and battalion communications officers in the field.[47]

[46]AAR, Long An Sector, TF Opn, 1–2 Jan 63, frame 44, reel 39, ARPA RDFU.
[47]DF, Sr Adv, 5th Inf Div, to Sr Adv, Bien Hoa Sector, 26 Jun 63, sub: AAR, frame 6; DF, Sr Adv, 5th Inf Div, to CHMAAG, 8 Jul 63, sub: AAR, frame 20; Ltr, Long An Sector Advisory Team to Sr Adv, 7th Div, 16 Jul 63, sub: After Action Report. All on reel 39, ARPA RDFU.

By late summer of 1963 signs that the South Vietnamese signal officers and their advisers had learned from their mistakes began to appear. When the Joint General Staff ordained that each corps and province headquarters establish an intelligence center where information gathered by governmental, military, and police forces could be collected, analyzed, and disseminated, communicators drew up plans to consolidate military and civil communications resources to support the intelligence centers.

The intelligence centers helped centralize communications at key headquarters. The centers also enabled closer coordination between military and civilian authorities in preparing pacification plans. In turn, those plans provided for the integration of communications among army regiments and battalions, paramilitary forces, and rural communities. One of the first of those plans was a new pacification plan for Long An, a strategic province just south of Saigon, written in late 1963. It incorporated techniques from General McGarr's original counterinsurgency plan, lessons from the tests conducted by the II Corps advisers, and the experiences of those managing the village and hamlet radio program. The plan proposed an entire array of signaling devices—telephones, radios, flares, and smoke—to link the Civil Guard, Self-Defense Corps, local authorities, and South Vietnamese units.[48]

As the South Vietnamese Army refined its counterinsurgency tactics, the government began winning the countryside back from the Viet Cong. In April 1963 the Central Intelligence Agency, which in 1960 had felt the Viet Cong were on the verge of victory, declared that the insurgents' progress was blunted. As new territory was recaptured from the Viet Cong, technicians rushed to install radios in the local hamlets and villages. By September 1963 nearly every one of the almost 1,700 villages controlled by the government had at least one village radio, and the U.S. Operations Mission stood ready to install radios in the remaining 700 villages still in Viet Cong hands.[49]

Whether or not the appearance of success in 1963 was the result of more aggressive, better-executed operations or of a slackening of the Viet Cong effort, communications played an important role. Better communications enabled South Vietnamese forces to benefit from unprecedented air support through improved mobility and fire support. Better communications enabled intelligence information to be reported with greater speed and delivered in the time needed to respond to it. Improved intelligence with hamlets and villages paid dividends in both military and political terms, as did the expansion of communications among and between remote tribal settlements in the highlands. In many ways, communications were the unifying factor in improved plans and operations. Lessons learned by trial and error, by borrowing from civilian agencies, and by tapping

---

[48]Memo, Secy of Defense for President, 2 Oct 63, sub: Report of McNamara-Taylor Mission to South Vietnam, *U.S.-Vietnam Relations,* 12:554–58; Ltr, Sector Advisory Team, Pleiku Province, to Sr Adv, II Corps, 15 Oct 63, sub: Intelligence Funds, Incl to Ltr, MACV to Sr Adv, I Corps, et al., 28 Dec 63, sub: Coordinated Intelligence Center Concept, file 204–58(201–45), 69A702/1, WNRC; Long An Province, OPLAN Long An, 1 Nov 63, an. G, reel 39, ARPA RDFU.

[49]CIA, Prospects in South Vietnam, 17 Apr 63, NIE 53–63, *U.S.-Vietnam Relations,* 12:523; Msg, COMUSMACV MACJ3 5637 to AIG 924, 28 Jun 63, in Headway Rpt file, CMH.

the fruits of American technology helped establish a variety of communication networks suitable for counterinsurgency operations.

4

Technical and Tactical Vulnerabilities, 1963

By late 1962 optimistic intelligence estimates and the anticipation of improvements in the counterinsurgency campaign sparked proposals to reduce American military participation in South Vietnam. Anticipating that by 1967 a small U.S. advisory mission would be sufficient, Secretary McNamara directed the Army to plan for the gradual withdrawal of American communications. Signal representatives of the Pacific Command proposed a phased withdrawal of the 39th Signal Battalion, leaving only a signal detachment to operate the mission's communications after 1967.[1]

In midsummer 1963 General Harkins directed that the first 79 signalmen would leave by the end of the year as part of a general 1,000-man withdrawal of military personnel. In anticipation of turning over the 39th Signal Battalion's tactical multichannel TRC–24 sets to the South Vietnamese Army, he also directed the new commander of the 39th Signal Battalion, Lt. Col. Earl R. Velie, to train South Vietnamese soldiers to operate the twelve-channel equipment. The South Vietnamese were to use the American radios to replace their four-channel sets and to install spurs off the BACKPORCH system to enable the U.S. Army to return its light troposcatter TRC–90's to the United States for use in the strategic reserve. The larger MRC–85's on BACKPORCH were to be left in place and operated by Americans until the AID commercial system was completed. Except for the possibility of retaining a strategic link from Saigon to Ubon in northeastern Thailand, Colonel Velie was told to anticipate that all troposcatter equipment would be withdrawn by 1967.[2]

During the summer of 1963 hints that American optimism was premature began to appear. Political and religious dissension undermined military success. Although pacification plans indicated that both South Vietnamese Army officers and their American advisers had learned from their experiences with counterin-

---

[1]Ltr, CINCPAC to JCS, 25 Jan 63, sub: Comprehensive Plan for South Vietnam, 338–74–555/8, WNRC.
[2]JCS 2343/257, 3 Jul 63, sub: Report of MG Krulak, USMC, Visit to Vietnam, 23 Jun–1 Jul 63, JACO (1963), DA/69, NARS; Msg, COMUSMACV to CINCPAC, 18 Jan 64, sub: Transfer of TRC–24 VHF Equipment to RVNAF, CMH.

surgery warfare, the South Vietnamese had yet to exhibit the determination and ability to implement those plans or a requisite understanding of the political and social subtleties of the conflict with the Viet Cong. For communicators, more technical danger signs indicated that the comprehensive withdrawal plan should be implemented only with caution. Deficiencies in the original design and installation of BACKPORCH and deterioration of equipment prematurely aging in the harsh tropical environment had begun to cause noise interference and to expose previously undetected weaknesses in the communications system. Saddling inexperienced South Vietnamese communicators with technical problems and vulnerabilities that American engineers had yet to resolve promised further to impair communications and to impede development of the South Vietnamese Army.[3]

Technical Challenges

A lack of spare equipment and alternate routing on BACKPORCH, on which both Americans and South Vietnamese had come to rely for most tactical and administrative communications, was the source of the vulnerability of the communications system. Without some built-in redundancy, that is, some means of backup communications, the entire network was exposed to interruption from technical malfunctions or enemy action at any one of its nodal (connecting) points. A single grenade, detonated near exposed wire distribution boxes at Nha Trang, for example, could put out of service the entire $12 million BACKPORCH system and render useless all the multichannel radios, switchboards, and teletype communications centers connected to the backbone system.[4]

Although BACKPORCH and its tributaries comprised a multitude of expensive equipment, a tangled maze of field wire and cable held together the network. Without that wire and cable, circuits would terminate uselessly in the radio vans. Wire interconnects between radio vans permitted long-distance circuits passing through a node, called tandem circuits, to transit from one system to another; wire extensions from radio vans to local switchboards and teletype communications centers gave subscribers their only access to the network. Colonel Blackwell's men had installed mobile patch panels at each node to coordinate the distribution of wire and cable; but the tactical panels lacked adequate patching and testing equipment to handle high-quality, precisely tuned BACKPORCH circuits.[5] Feeling that patching cords introduced a signal loss in circuits and fearing

---

[3]For similar reasons, signal officers also questioned the wisdom of transferring American troposcatter equipment to the Thais. Msg, CINCPAC to COMUSMACTHAI, 7 Sep 63, sub: CE Base Thailand Problems, file 139364, 72A4171/1, WNRC; Interv, author with Lt Col (ret.) Earl R. Velie, former commander of the 39th Signal Battalion, 12 May 77, Historians files, CMH.

[4]Interv, author with Lt Col (ret.) Carlos E. Vogel, Jr., former executive officer of the 39th Signal Battalion, 16 Jan 78, Historians files, CMH.

[5]The two models of patch panels sent to South Vietnam, SB–611 and SB–675, were shelters with large signal plug boards covering the walls; every circuit terminated at the patch panel was connected behind one of the plugs. Cross-connections between circuits were made by inserting a patching cord from plug to plug.

Colonel Velie *briefs the MACV staff on the 39th Signal Battalion.*

that circuits could be disrupted if someone inadvertently pulled out a patch cord, some troposcatter operators had "hard-wired" circuits, a procedure that involved bypassing the patch panel and soldering interconnecting wires directly to the distribution boxes outside each radio van. Other operators bypassed patch panels in the haste of installing high-priority circuits. Distribution boxes became so cluttered that it was impossible to trace circuits and make changes without installing a new line.[6]

Besides having inadequate facilities to distribute circuits over intersecting systems, communicators in the 39th Signal Battalion lacked equipment to filter out noise and to balance signal and power levels as circuits shifted from lower-quality tactical radios to the sophisticated strategic network. Although the Air Force had given its engineering agency responsibility to design patching and technical control facilities during the installation of BACKPORCH, Air Force technicians working under tight deadlines with new equipment and without knowledge of the ultimate circuit requirements apparently slighted the problems at the nodes in order to concentrate on engineering the radio links. Not until the fall of 1962, when the Defense Communications Agency (DCA) prescribed standards and

---

[6]Interv, author with Vogel, 16 Jan 78; MS (draft), USASCC, U.S. Army Signal Communications Support in Southeast Asia, 1951–1967, 1 Dec 69, p. 24, CMH.

procedures to the Army for integrating BACKPORCH with tactical systems, were those systems-engineering requirements finally considered. By then it was too late; communications were installed and operating.[7]

To meet the technical standards of the Defense Communications Agency, inherent incompatibilities between strategic and tactical equipment had to be eliminated or adjusted. The backbone equipment had soldered connections and was precisely calibrated for commercial-quality circuits; when the Army's mobile tactical radios and switchboards hooked into those circuits, they introduced interference which threw the whole network out of kilter. Audio levels and signaling frequencies varied between different equipment, and the 39th Signal Battalion lacked ancillary equipment to amplify or moderate different audio levels and to convert or filter out conflicting signal frequencies between the disparate equipment on tandem (connecting) links. Often the inexperienced signalmen unknowingly aggravated the problem. For example, the MRC–85 troposcatter sites had sophisticated grounding systems with almost direct paths to electrical ground measuring less than five ohms; those systems were carefully engineered and calibrated. But the TRC–24 operators had no such capability. When they pulled their tactical vans up to connect into the backbone system, they would hammer a six-foot ground rod into the earth, giving at best a high-resistance, fifty-ohm path to ground, which created an electrical ground imbalance and a source of circuit noise that made the Page engineers shudder.[8]

If BACKPORCH had had a technical control facility, normally the nerve center of a communications network where the systems are checked, problems located, and circuit adjustments planned, the source of many of the problems could have been identified.[9] Since no transportable technical control facilities had been developed for military use, the 39th Signal Battalion had brought only patch panels to South Vietnam to test and control circuits. Not only did the 39th Signal Battalion have inadequate test and control facilities, when it arrived in South Vietnam it also had no qualified controllers. The battalion commander quickly requested augmentation and recalled his most experienced radio operators from the field to establish a makeshift battalion control center. Because there was a worldwide shortage of circuit controllers, only a few were sent in response to his request, and they were initially less qualified than the radio operators to work on the unfamiliar network in South Vietnam.[10]

---

[7]Msg, USAF to GEEIA, 19 Jan 62, sub: Implementing Directive for Backbone Tropo System in SVN, 02K168.06/138, OAFH; Memo, Dep Secy of Defense for Dir, DCA, 19 Oct 62, sub: Upgrading US Military Communications-Electronics Posture in Southeast Asia, Incl to JCS 2339/95, JACO (1962), DA/605, NARS; Ltr, CINCPAC to JCS, 26 Aug 68, sub: PACOM Communications-Electronics Experiences, an. C, app. 1, 02K712.03/74, OAFH. For a discussion of the early history of the Defense Communications Agency, which was founded in 1960, see Chapter 8.

[8]Joint Logistics Review Board, *Monograph 5: Communications*, Dec 69, app. A, p. 12, 71A2351/6, WNRC; Interv, author with Blackwell, 4 Apr 77; MS, USAF, Project Corona Harvest, Command Control and Communications, 8 Oct 70, pp. 123–24, K143.50103-3, OAFH.

[9]Technical control facilities were also called facilities controls, systems controls (SYSCONS), and toll tests. The men who worked in such facilities were called tech controllers, circuit controllers, or, simply, controllers. Occasionally the terms acquired slightly different meanings, but most communicators and laymen were oblivious to the different connotations.

[10]Interv, author with Blackwell, 4 Apr 77.

Since the duties of the facilities controller varied throughout the Army, depending on the types of equipment and configurations of systems in each theater, the Army did not even try to teach the specialty at the signal schools. Although a few graduates of each course for fixed-station radio operators at Fort Monmouth were sent to the National Military Command Center at Fort Ritchie, Maryland, for special on-the-job training as facilities controllers, most men received the specialty designation after working in the field in a facilities control and receiving on-the-job training for one year. Few could qualify, especially as junior enlisted men, for the great demands of the job. Besides requiring a comprehensive technical knowledge of every type of communications equipment installed on a system—switchboards, teletypes, multiplexing, and radio—the position also demanded a talent for getting operators who were assigned to different units and often separated by thousands of miles to work together. Equipment varied from unit to unit: in South Vietnam controllers working in the Phu Lam station were troubleshooting a few crucial channels on fixed high-frequency equipment, while those working at the BACKPORCH nodes handled hundreds of circuits on both simple tactical equipment and sophisticated troposcatter systems. Yet when a man was assigned to South Vietnam, he came with the uniform identification of facilities controller, no matter what his experience. Despairing of ever receiving enough good facilities controllers, signal officers in South Vietnam usually selected the best operators from multichannel and troposcatter teams to work in the facilities controls, an expedient that weakened already understrength radio teams.[11]

Because the division of responsibilities between the military and the contractor had never been precisely defined in the BACKPORCH contract for circuit control and patching, circuit controllers could expect little assistance from the Page technicians. While most problems ocurred at the nodes where the circuits connected to tactical equipment, Page was responsible for the circuits only between the MRC–85 terminals connecting the long-range links of the system.[12]

To correct the complex array of technical faults in BACKPORCH would take years of hard and expensive work: gaining experience with new techniques and equipment, refining relations between military and civilians, and building permanent facilities. In April 1963 the Army Support Group had submitted requests for fixed-plant cabling and test facilities and large electrical power plants, but by that time plans were being made to reduce American involvement in South Vietnam and ambitious fixed-plant communications projects were discouraged. The 39th Signal Battalion would have to use its own tactical resources to strengthen the communications network until the Americans left South Vietnam.[13]

---

[11]Interv, author with James L. McIntosh, chief instructor, Technical Controller Course, Fort Gordon, 9 Jan 78, Historians files, CMH; Info Brief, DA, ODCSPER, 6 May 64, sub: Signal Problems-39th Signal Bn, CMH; 362d Sig Co History, 1964, p. 4, 338–75–1009/146, WNRC; Interv, author with Blackwell, 4 Apr 77.

[12]Interv, author with Blackwell, 4 Apr 77; USARPAC, Final Report, Communications Evaluation in Southeast Asia (COMSEA), 30 Jun 69, see an. C, Communications Resources Management, p. 137, 72A2315/14, WNRC; Ltr, CINCPAC to JCS, 26 Aug 68, sub: PACOM Communications-Electronics Experiences, an. C, app. 1.

[13]Interv, author with Velie, 12 May 77; USASGV, Sig Stf Ofc Rpt, 1 Apr–30 Jun 63, pt. 1, and ibid., 1 Jul–31 Aug 63, pt. 1, both in 338–75–1009/88, WNRC.

Confronting the wire distribution and circuit control problem, Colonel Velie had all BACKPORCH sites rewired and fabricated large distribution frames in buildings at the three most critical nodes—Nha Trang, Pleiku, and Tan Son Nhut. Using equipment borrowed from the Air Force, he also installed a makeshift technical control facility, called a toll test, at each of the three distribution frames. Since the rewiring was done with the only available materials—field wire and cable strung above ground—and the critical distribution facilities were installed in primitive, unprotected buildings, Colonel Velie's modifications, while improving technical standards, did little to eliminate the vulnerability of communications to enemy action.[14]

Seeking that security through redundancy of communications, Colonel Velie tried to rejuvenate the Operations and Intelligence Net, which had fallen into disuse; but he was unable to muster the men and equipment to exercise the net even on a weekly basis. Because the teletype machines that were components of the radio vans had been installed in communications centers on operational circuits wired into the backbone system, the radio operators could test the nets only in the voice and Morse code modes. Nor could the radio operators, who were augmenting the teletype operators in the communications centers, be spared for long from their posts at the teletype machines to maintain and test their radio and generator equipment. The exercises served only to demonstrate how dependent on BACKPORCH the advisers had become and how inadequate tactical equipment was in providing even a fraction of the service that everyone was accustomed to receiving from the semifixed troposcatter radios.[15]

Strengthening the Backbone Network

L ight troposcatter radios provided an apparent solution to the quest for a backup to the BACKPORCH net. If a system could be installed from Tan Son Nhut Air Base to Pleiku, headquarters and operations centers located in the Saigon area would have an alternate gateway into BACKPORCH. Loss of the sites at Phu Lam or Nha Trang would no longer cripple General Harkins' command and control over activities in the two northern corps areas. To provide that vital redundancy, General Harkins gave the 39th Signal Battalion the mission of installing a 24-channel system, called CROSSBOW, from Tan Son Nhut through a relay at Da Lat to Pleiku. *(Map 4)*

With troposcatter equipment in short supply, the commander of the 362d Signal Company, Capt. Arthur P. Chesley, had first to consolidate every piece of spare TRC–90 equipment at his headquarters in Nha Trang and then arrange for airlift to Saigon, Pleiku, and Da Lat. Although the TRC–90's for Pleiku and Saigon were dispatched without delay, the equipment bound for Da Lat awaited transport

---

[14]362d Sig Co History, 1963, p. 2, 338–75–1000/146, WNRC; Intervs, author with Velie, 12 May 77, and Vogel, 16 Jan 78.
[15]232d Sig Co History, 1963, p. 7, 338–75–1000/145; 178th Sig Co History, 1963, p. 11, 338–75–1000/144. Both in WNRC. Interv, author with Velie, 12 May 77.

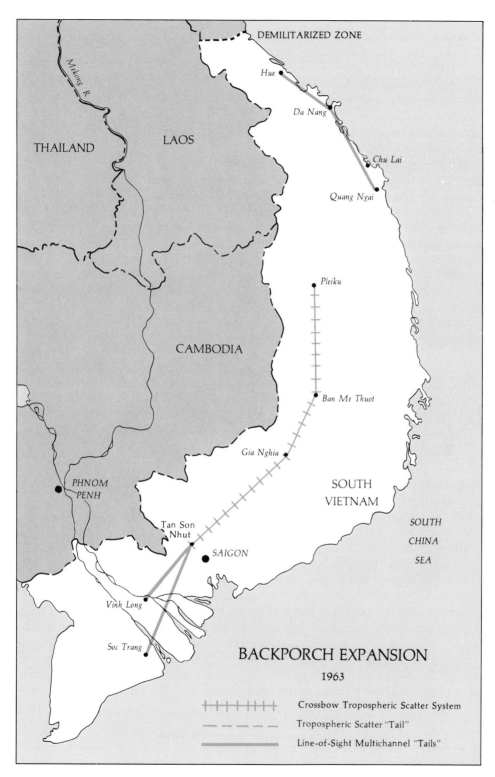

DEMILITARIZED ZONE

Mekong R.

THAILAND

LAOS

Hue

Da Nang

Chu Lai

Quang Ngai

Pleiku

CAMBODIA

Ban Me Thuot

Gia Nghia

SOUTH
VIETNAM

PHNOM
PENH

SOUTH

CHINA

SEA

Tan Son
Nhut

SAIGON

Vinh Long

Soc Trang

BACKPORCH EXPANSION

1963

+++++++++ Crossbow Tropospheric Scatter System

– – – – – Tropospheric Scatter "Tail"

━━━━━ Line-of-Sight Multichannel "Tails"

MAP 4

almost a month and then was temporarily lost when the cargo aircraft carrying it was unable to land at the fog-shrouded airport high in the mountains near Da Lat. Unloaded at another remote airstrip and then moved to still another airstrip by cargo handlers who were unaware of the original destination of the radio vans, the equipment was missing for several weeks. By the time the 39th Signal Battalion finally located the troposcatter sets and had them moved to Da Lat, it was late summer and two precious months had passed since Captain Chesley had received his mission to install CROSSBOW.[16]

Even as the equipment was being unloaded at Da Lat, opposition to the entire project was mounting from an unexpected source. Because President Diem's sister-in-law, Madame Nhu, wanted to erect a religious statue on the hill where the terminal was to be installed, Captain Chesley was told he would have to find another site. When he reported that technical or security limitations precluded use of any other locations in the area, the MACV J–6, Col. Philip S. Pomeroy, had to resurvey the entire system. Deciding to add another relay, he directed the 39th Signal Battalion to move the relay at Da Lat fifty miles west to Gia Nghia to link with Saigon and Ban Me Thuot. The already established link between Ban Me Thuot and Pleiku would complete the CROSSBOW net.

When Captain Chesley's reconnaissance of the Gia Nghia area revealed that only a primitive dirt airstrip high in the mountains served the region, he decided to hazard an overland move of the two big radio rigs from Da Lat to Gia Nghia. Although he was gambling possible loss of the expensive equipment in a Viet Cong ambush or an accident on the treacherous road to avoid the expected frustrations and delays involved in making an air movement, he accepted the risk and gave the men the order to move out.

The trip proved more difficult than he had imagined. A team of signalmen from the Ban Me Thuot site who had driven down to Da Lat to guide the teams to Gia Nghia found the road far too narrow and steep for a return trip with the large troposcatter vans; the teams would have to head for the flat coastal plain to make the trek north to Ban Me Thuot where they could join the only other road to Gia Nghia. To span the fifty miles between Da Lat and Gia Nghia, the men would have to travel over three hundred miles through Viet Cong–controlled country.

Shepherding the valuable cargo, the only uncommitted tactical troposcatter sets in the U.S. Army, a small signal convoy set out from Da Lat under the protection of a single .50-caliber machine gun mounted on one of the trucks. After stopping overnight at Phan Rang, the men traveled up the coast to Nha Trang. Halting only long enough to pick up supplies at company headquarters in Nha Trang, the teams then joined a well-protected supply convoy bound for Ban Me Thuot. Learning upon arrival in Ban Me Thuot that the scheduled weekly convoy to Gia Nghia would not be leaving until the following day, the signalmen set out alone on the final leg of their long journey to Gia Nghia. That risky deci-

---

[16]The account of the efforts of the troposcatter operators to install CROSSBOW is based on Interv, author with Lt Col Arthur P. Chesley, former commander of the 362d Signal Company, 28 Dec 77, Historians files, CMH.

sion proved fortuitous: the Viet Cong ambushed the regular convoy on the following day. Captain Chesley's gamble had worked.

The teams were less successful in putting the system on the air. Although they quickly made contact with Ban Me Thuot, they were unable to close the link with Saigon, over one hundred miles to the south. Apparently overextended, the signal kept fading in and out.[17]

While Colonel Velie's men struggled to establish some redundancy for communications in South Vietnam, communicators in Thailand were having problems even in establishing a communications base. In attempting to install a troposcatter system with TRC–90 radios between key bases at Korat, Ubon, and Udorn, the men whom the 362d Signal Company had sent to Thailand in late December 1962 had encountered problems similar to those experienced on CROSSBOW. Using a consolidated relay at Roi Et, they had established radio contact between the three locations by late winter; however, the channels were plagued by intermittent noise and fading that drowned out voice conversations and disrupted transmission of teletype pulses. The situation had caused little consternation until May 1963 when members of the Southeast Asia Treaty Organization held an exercise of their contingency forces in Thailand. Due to the failure of the troposcatter system to provide reliable area communications for the exercise, which was the mission of the American contingent to the international force, the tactical multichannel systems of the Royal Thai Army and Air Force had to carry most of the area and strategic communications during the exercise. An embarrassed Admiral Felt directed General Collins to ensure that the Army had twenty-four good voice channels connecting Korat, Udorn, and Ubon by the end of the year.[18]

Believing that the span between Roi Et and Ubon, which exceeded the 150-mile maximum range of the TRC–90's, was the basic cause of the problem, Brig. Gen. Douglas E. Williams, the Pacific Command signal officer, advised the Army to find better relay locations. When the teams disbanded the consolidated relay at Roi Et to establish separate relays directly on the paths of the two systems, management and logistical problems supplanted technical and propagational difficulties. With the relays separated, the small nucleus of troposcatter expertise in Thailand—two technical representatives from the Collins Radio Company and a few experienced enlisted men—was fragmented. Because there were few helicopters in Thailand, travel between sites was difficult; visits by the technical assistants to the far-flung sites involved several days of driving over rugged country and, in the case of the isolated relay for the Korat-Ubon system at Surin, a journey by railroad flatcar into the mountains.[19]

Although the men at the sites in Thailand were not exposed to the dangers that threatened their counterparts in South Vietnam, they were more isolated and had a lower priority for support. With only the bare minimum of resources

---

[17]362d Sig Co History, 1963, p. 6.

[18]Interv, author with Chesley, 28 Dec 77; Msg, CINCPAC to CINCUSARPAC et al., 23 Oct 63, sub: CE Base Thailand, file 139364, 72A4171/1, WNRC.

[19]Memo for File, CINCPAC J612, 16 Aug 63, sub: Report of Informal Meeting at CINCUSARPAC Signal Office 14 Aug 63 to Discuss Army Communications Assets and Problems in Thailand, file 139364, 72A4171/1, WNRC.

for operational needs, troposcatter operators lacked spare equipment to use for switching components within sets to isolate malfunctioning parts. Under those conditions, troubleshooting was an inexact and laborious procedure. Once the year's supply of repair parts that had been issued with the sets was exhausted, acquiring a replacement for a defective part became even more difficult than finding the source of the problem. Since demand statistics for determining stockage criteria had yet to be developed for the new equipment, requisitions for repair parts usually had to be sent all the way back to the manufacturer through a convoluted route that wound its way from a remote mountaintop site in Thailand through depots in Okinawa and Japan to the Collins factory in Dallas, Texas. For example, a critical tube that had been ordered in August 1963, shipped from the factory in December, and received in Thailand in February 1964 curtailed the operation of the relay at Surin for over five months.[20]

Moving the relays did little to improve the quality of the systems. Troposcatter operators tried every conceivable expedient to eliminate noise and fading on their channels. Finding that raising antennas produced some improvement, but limited by the fact that each set was issued with only enough antenna-connecting material (called wave guides) to reach from the antenna to the radio when the antenna was at standard height, one enterprising site chief even built a platform on which he raised both the antenna and the troposcatter van. Still, the quality of the systems was below standard. When General Williams told Admiral Felt that only decreasing the range between radios by adding more relays would improve the systems, Felt extended his deadline for installation of the network to give the Army time to procure more TRC–90's. He warned General Williams to ensure that the Thai military continued to provide communications to key bases with its tactical equipment.[21]

Acting on recommendations of technical representatives in Southeast Asia and taking advantage of lessons learned by the men of the 39th Signal Battalion, the Collins Radio Company modified its troposcatter set. The new set, the TRC–90A, was used to fill orders for additional sets for Southeast Asia. Because the inflatable antennas issued with the original TRC–90's were easily perforated by shell fragments and tended to shift in even moderate winds, Collins engineers developed a rigid parabolic dish antenna with a ten-foot diameter to replace the fifteen-foot parabolic inflatable antennas. They also increased the output of the sets' air-conditioning units, which had proved inadequate in the tropical climate, and installed equipment in racks that could be swung out for easier cleaning and maintenance. In listing the capabilities of the new equipment, Collins also ac-

[20]Msg, COMUSMACTHAI to CINCPAC, 7 Nov 63, sub: CE Base Thailand; Msg, DEPCOMUS-MACTHAI to CINCPAC, 7 Jan 64, sub: CE Base Thailand. Both in file 139364, 72A4171/1, WNRC. ECOM AHS, FY-64, pt. 2, p. 461, CMH. Because the TRC–90 was classified as a "limited procurement item," spare parts were unavailable in regular supply channels, and requisitions had to be specially processed when they reached the National Inventory Control Point in Philadelphia. When the TRC–90 was finally classified a standard item of equipment on 28 October 1963, the U.S. Army Electronics Command received authority to list parts in military supply catalogs and store them in depots. Interv, author with Maj Jay R. Hern, former contracting officer for the TRC–90, 22 Feb 78, Historians files, CMH.

[21]Interv, author with Chesley, 28 Dec 77; Msg, CINCPAC to PACAF and COMUSMACTHAI, 19 Nov 63, sub: CE Base Thailand, file 139364, 72A4171/1, WNRC.

knowledged what every troposcatter operator in the 39th Signal Battalion already knew: the TRC–90A should be rated not at a 150-mile range, but at 100 miles.[22]

Although additional troposcatter equipment was also required in South Vietnam to improve Crossbow and replace low-capacity tactical multichannel sets on spur systems, General Harkins agreed that Thailand should receive priority over his command in South Vietnam for the new troposcatter radios. While Admiral Felt was most concerned with the importance of the base system in Thailand to support contingency operations, General Harkins saw it as his vital link to supporting air bases in Thailand and to the overseas communications facilities operated by the STARCOM stations at Bangkok and Udorn. Until the Thailand base system was installed, there would be a 200-mile gap in communications between the terminus of Harkins' Backporch at Ubon in northeastern Thailand and those air bases and overseas stations.[23]

Connecting to Thailand

S ince the Phu Lam station was General Harkins' only link to the outside world, he needed access to the two overseas stations in Thailand—at Bangkok and Udorn— as backup. Comprising a teletype relay and switchboard in Bangkok connected by microwave to a transmitter and receiver in Bang Ping, some fifty miles away, the Bangkok overseas station provided standard single-sideband service— sixteen teletype and three voice circuits—to Phu Lam, Okinawa, and the Philippines. The Udorn station, which served the American military mission in Laos until 28 April 1965, gave similar service over a link to Okinawa.[24] Once a troposcatter link between Bangkok and Udorn was working reliably, the Bangkok overseas station, connected to faraway Vientiane by a combined troposcatter and multichannel link, could serve American subscribers in Laos and the Udorn station could be left in a standby condition.[25]

Besides the roundabout routing from Saigon to Bangkok through the Backporch and Thailand troposcatter systems and the direct single-sideband link between the Phu Lam and Bangkok STARCOM stations, communications planners envisioned a 48-channel troposcatter system, the longest in the world, between the capitals of the two countries. Although the Department of the Army had con-

[22]Msg, CINCUSARPAC to COMUSMACV, 28 Aug 63, sub: Troposcatter Communications Equipment for COMUSMACTHAI, file 139364, 72A4171/1, WNRC; Ltr, Communications-Electronics Subcommittee to the Army Technical Committee, sub: Reclassification of Radio Terminal Set AN/TRC–90B from Limited Production (LP) to Standard B, CMH. Even as the TRC–90A was being deployed to Southeast Asia, the Army was testing a completely transistorized troposcatter radio, called the TRC–90B, equipped with a 29-foot parabolic antenna that promised to work at ranges up to 150 miles.

[23]Msg, MACV to USARPAC, 10 Sep 63, sub: TRC–90 Tropo Equipment for Thailand and Vietnam, file 139364, 72A4171/1, WNRC.

[24]Since American presence in Laos was to be kept to a minimum for diplomatic reasons, the STARCOM station serving Laos was located in Udorn, Thailand, and connected to the mission in Vientiane by a tactical multichannel link.

[25]USARPAC, Base Development Plan 1–64, Southeast Asia, vol. 6, ch. 9, p. 1, 69A606/1, WNRC; Memo, USARPAC Sig Ofcr for G–3, 6 Dec 63, sub: Current Status of Signal Actions, CMH.

tracted with the Philco Radio Company in mid-1962 to install the link, Philco had encountered problems in putting the system on the air. Difficulties in building a firm foundation in marshy ground for the heavy billboard antennas required by the radios caused delays at first. After the equipment was finally installed and operating, Philco engineers discovered that the radio signal faded in and out. When the Army's chief civilian engineer for the Pacific, Hugh Jones, went to Southeast Asia in November 1963 to investigate the problems, he took with him a representative of the National Bureau of Standards, Edward Florman, to take measurements at different locations and times of the strength of the signals received from the two terminals. Although the two men were unable to determine conclusively the direct cause of the fading, they did find that the location of the terminal in Thailand seemed to be at the root of the problem. While the receiver at Bangkok experienced the mysterious fading, test equipment at other locations in south-central Thailand measured a strong steady signal coming from Saigon. Based on the findings of the two engineers, Admiral Felt told his staff to prepare a plan to move the Thailand terminal to one of the sites with good reception and to link it with the headquarters complexes in Bangkok and Korat.[26]

Expanding the STARCOM Station

R ecognizing that a reliable alternate route through Thailand for overseas communications was still far in the future, Admiral Felt pressed for immediate improvements to the overseas facility in South Vietnam. The STARCOM station's transmitters had been moved from Saigon to a compound near the village of Phu Lam on the outskirts of the city, which also was the location of the Backporch terminal serving Saigon. The Saigon STARCOM detachment still operated the principal message relay center for U.S. communications centers throughout South Vietnam as well as the Saigon overseas switchboard in facilities built over a decade earlier to serve a small advisory mission. Hampered by primitive equipment and cramped quarters, the communications center regularly had a message backlog. The switchboard rarely completed over twenty overseas telephone calls a day, no surprise considering that the overseas switchboard was an SB–22, a tactical board normally used with field wire by infantry companies and capable of handling only twelve subscribers. Those deficiencies at the Saigon communications center and overseas switchboard aggravated problems with circuits that had already been attenuated by routing them throughout the Saigon area over low-quality tactical radio systems. From the STARCOM communications center and long-distance switchboard in Saigon, several twelve-channel TRC–24 radios extended the overseas circuits to Phu Lam for transmission to the worldwide STARCOM network. A 45-channel tactical microwave link connected the

---

[26]Interv, author with Jones, 8 Feb 78, and Edward Florman, former engineer with the National Bureau of Standards, 22 Feb 78, Historians files, CMH; Msg, DCA to DA, 21 Jan 64, sub: Bangkok-Saigon Troposcatter System, and Msg, OIC, Comm Ctr, Saigon, to OIC, Comm Ctr, CINCPAC, 10 Jan 64, Staff Service Nr. 0009, both in file 139364, 72A4171/1, WNRC.

STARCOM receiver station, located near Tan Son Nhut Air Base at Ba Queo, to the Phu Lam transmitter. Other tactical multichannel systems connected the BACKPORCH terminal at Phu Lam to Site Octopus at Tan Son Nhut, from which all in-country circuits were extended to the various subscriber headquarters in the Saigon area.[27]

Although primitive facilities and the back-and-forth rerouting of circuits over tactical radios seriously disrupted communications in the Saigon area, signalmen were unable to speed the completion of construction of a consolidated STARCOM station at Phu Lam that had been approved in December 1961. First, work was delayed by prolonged negotiations with South Vietnamese authorities for acquisition of land around the site for security fences and minefields; then construction was hampered by swampy ground that caused foundations to sink when heavy equipment was installed in the buildings. Spurred by Admiral Felt's emphasis in the fall of 1963, the project was finally expedited. On 1 January 1964, the Phu Lam STARCOM station, complete with a new fifty-line tape relay and sixty-line switchboard, opened for service and the Saigon STARCOM station in the advisory group compound closed. Because Phu Lam lacked space for both transmitting and receiving antennas, the receiver remained at Ba Queo. In a subsequent inspection, the facility met the tough standards of the Defense Communications Agency except for a lack of spare radios, a problem quickly rectified by transferring radios from Bangkok.[28]

A Winter of Turbulence

T he final months of 1963 were difficult times for signal officers. While Admiral Felt was becoming increasingly impatient with delays of new communications projects, signalmen were still being told to plan for withdrawal. In December the 39th Signal Battalion lost 79 men as its contribution to the 1,000-man withdrawal announced the previous summer.[29] Already overworked radio operators were conducting courses to train South Vietnamese soldiers on the battalion's tactical radio relay equipment in anticipation of turning the equipment over to the South Vietnamese. Yet the demands for improvements to communications operated by the 39th Signal Battalion had not diminished. Signalmen were buffeted by uncertainty: forge ahead or wind down?[30]

While troubled by doubts over the course of future events, Colonels Pomeroy and Velie also were discouraged over the failure to accomplish improvements

[27]Phu Lam Sig Bn History, pp. 4–6; USASCV Quarterly Historical Summary (QHS), 1 Apr–30 Jun 64, pt. 2, tab K, 339–75–1009/63, WNRC.

[28]Ltr, Ch, DCA, SEA, to Dir, DCA, 20 Mar 64, sub: Report of Operational Evaluation of DCS Station Saigon, VN, and 4th Ind, USARPAC to Dir, DCA, same sub, file 19, 338–75–1009/65, WNRC; Phu Lam Sig Bn History, pp. 4–6; USASGV, Sig Stf Ofc Rpt, 1 Jul–31 Aug 63, pt. 1, 338–75–1033/49, WNRC.

[29]The loss was tempered by transfer of fifty-four of those spaces to the recently formed 379th Signal Battalion in Thailand and termination of the 39th Signal Battalion's responsibility for operations in Thailand.

[30]362d Sig Co History, 1963, p. 2.

begun the previous summer. Even after rewiring the troposcatter sites and testing tactical backup communications, they knew the BACKPORCH system was still vulnerable to both enemy action and technical malfunctions. To provide an alternative to BACKPORCH, they had endured transportation delays and eviction from a hilltop, only to discover when they finally found a site on which to install a relay for the CROSSBOW system that their equipment was insufficient for the task. On 17 December 1963, Colonel Velie handed over command of the 39th Signal Battalion to Maj. Leo T. White to devote his full attention to the position of signal officer of the Army Support Group, Vietnam. Velie then resolved to clarify the fate of American communications in South Vietnam and to find the logistical and personnel support his former command so desperately required.[31]

Political and tactical developments were to add a note of urgency to Colonel Velie's resolution. The uncertainties concerning future U.S. policy towards Southeast Asia following President Kennedy's assassination in late November, just three weeks after the overthrow and assassination of President Diem, aggravated an already nebulous situation. When President Lyndon B. Johnson reaffirmed American commitment to South Vietnam while also declaring that the United States would continue with plans to withdraw, signal officers were left in their limbo of uncertainty. As the winter wore on, Americans became increasingly skeptical that the South Vietnamese were ready to accept any additional responsibilities. The assassination of President Diem was followed by another coup in January.[32]

In that period of turbulence South Vietnamese signal officers became more concerned with remaining in favor with South Vietnam's new leaders than with managing their communications responsibilities. Ignoring valuable signal experience and technical competence, the new regime transferred President Diem's proteges to unimportant posts. Although new South Vietnamese signal commanders changed little of substance in the Signal Corps, they dismantled Diem's private communications network, which he had installed to connect his palace with loyal officials and military headquarters should normal communications channels be usurped by coup forces.

Diem's private communications had failed to help him during his final days. When dissident officers took control of all telecommunications facilities outside the palace grounds during the early hours of the coup, Diem tried to summon assistance from the field using a radio-teletype station that had been operating since the mid-1950s for just such a situation. When his supporters failed to respond, Diem escaped through a sewer system to a friend's house in Saigon from which he used secret telephone lines, previously installed underground, to direct his palace guard and to maintain contact with the radio van at the palace. On 2 November he called the palace with news of his capitulation.[33]

The political turbulence and military inertia that followed provided fertile soil for the growth of the Viet Cong movement. Using signal gear captured from

---

[31]Until Major White's arrival, Colonel Velie had held the positions of battalion commander and signal officer simultaneously. Intervs, author with Chesley, 28 Dec 77, and Velie, 12 May 77.
[32]*U.S.-Vietnam Relations*, vol. 3, pt. IV.B.3, p. 37.
[33]Ibid., vol. 3, pt. IV.B.5, pp. 56–58.

demoralized South Vietnamese units to supplement stocks of homemade and infiltrated communications equipment, the Viet Cong were outfitting all their guerrilla units with tactical radios as well as improving the area communications network for the Communist governmental apparatus in South Vietnam. They had also become more bold in their use of electronic warfare. Viet Cong communicators were using captured equipment to monitor and intrude in South Vietnamese radio nets. Using captured smoke grenades, they were also signaling unsuspecting American pilots to land and ambushing the helicopters on the ground.[34]

Viet Cong strength and tactical audacity increased throughout the winter; by early spring about twenty-five thousand full-time soldiers and seventy thousand part-time guerrillas were fighting in their ranks. As the South Vietnamese government began to lose gains it had made the previous summer in expanding control over the countryside, the number of secure strategic hamlets dropped steadily and the village and hamlet radio program began to suffer. With many roads cut by the enemy, radio operators were unable to take radio batteries to district capitals for recharging. Casualties depleted the ranks of operators, repairmen, and supply clerks needed to keep the program staffed. When attacking villages and hamlets, the Viet Cong seemed especially interested in capturing or destroying radios.[35]

Even when radios were kept operational, they often failed to perform their intended function: to coordinate protection of the countryside by South Vietnamese paramilitary and regular forces. Because South Vietnamese Army units were constantly shifting to different areas to counter a Viet Cong threat or disrupt suspected military coups, radio operators in the villages and hamlets found it difficult to maintain contact with their counterparts in the military units designated to answer calls for assistance from local hamlets and villages. When calls did get through, repeated failures of the army units to provide help quickly made the villagers wonder whether it was worth the risk of keeping communications operating.[36]

By February it was apparent that the village and hamlet radio program was rapidly disintegrating at the very time it was most needed. The U.S. Operations Mission, which was still helping the South Vietnamese government's Directorate of Posts and Telecommunications with the radios, issued a plea to the military advisers in each province to help rejuvenate the program. In responding to the request, advisers had difficulty even locating the radios. Some had been captured or destroyed by the Viet Cong; most had been hidden or appropriated by the Civil Guard for use in outposts and on patrols. Even in the province of Long An,

---

[34]CINCPAC, OPLAN 32–64 (Phase II), 15 May 64, an. D, pp. 2–5, CMH; *U.S.-Vietnam Relations*, vol. 3, pt. IV.C.1, p. 21; Ltr, Sr Adv, Abn Bde Adv Det, to MACV, 15 Jan 64, sub: Combat Opns AAR, roll 39, ARPA RDFU.

[35]Memo, II Corps Sr Adv for Div and Special Zone Sr Advs, 13 Jan 64, sub: USOM Village/Hamlet Radios, Wilson Papers; CINCPAC, OPLAN 32–64 (Phase II), 15 May 64, an. D, p. 3; Memo, Sr Adv, III Corps, for CG, III Corps, 10 Apr 64, sub: Estimate of the Situation in III CTZ (1st Qtr 64), Wilson Papers.

[36]Memo, Sr Adv, III Corps, for CG, III Corps, 10 Apr 64, sub: Estimate of the Situation in III CTZ, pp. 7–8; *U.S.-Vietnam Relations*, vol. 3, pt. IV.C.1, p. 16.

which supposedly had a model communications network, the province chief had withdrawn radios from the most threatened hamlets and ordered the rest hidden in the homes of village chiefs to keep them from falling into the hands of the Viet Cong. Throughout the countryside South Vietnamese hamlet and village chiefs were reluctant to expend the precious manpower needed to keep radios continuously on the air so that they would be ready to call for help. The village chiefs believed that help would probably never be rendered, and their skepticism undermined the advisers' efforts to reestablish the nets.[37]

Recognizing that American military and civilian communications advisers had to coordinate their efforts if the deterioration of communications in the countryside was to be reversed, Colonel Pomeroy urged establishment of a joint Communications-Electronics Committee to report directly to the U.S. ambassador. On 30 April 1964, a group composed of American communicators from the embassy, the U.S. Operations Mission, the U.S. Information Service, and the military services met for the first time under Colonel Pomeroy's chairmanship. A short time later the South Vietnamese established a similar committee, and the two groups set about the difficult task of coordinating the rebuilding of civil-military communications in rural South Vietnam.[38]

The distressing developments of the winter sparked a complete reexamination in Washington of the scope and dimensions of American efforts in South Vietnam. In mid-March President Johnson strongly reasserted American commitment to the preservation of South Vietnam's independence and authorized the secretary of defense to prepare plans for an increase in air and advisory support to the South Vietnamese. To strengthen American influence in the countryside, McNamara decided to expand the advisory program to the district level and to increase the size of battalion advisory detachments. Determined to avoid a repetition of the previous winter, when the buildup of the Viet Cong and the political maneuvers of many South Vietnamese officers took American officials by surprise, McNamara also wanted advisers to put increased emphasis on passing intelligence concerning both the enemy and the South Vietnamese back from the field. Many advisers with field units below the division level were still relying on the South Vietnamese for all their communications. Since that situation obviously was not conducive to communicating information about the South Vietnamese, low-level advisory communications would have to be improved.[39]

Because not enough American radio operators were assigned to small field advisory detachments to operate radios on a 24-hour basis, the original Operations and Intelligence Net had fallen into disuse at province, battalion, and regimental level. As radio communications were deemphasized in favor of BACK-PORCH circuits, the few available radio operators, usually the only junior enlisted men assigned to advisory detachments, were frequently drafted to serve as drivers, clerks, and sentries and gradually lost their proficiency with Morse code and com-

---

[37]Memo, Dir, USOM, for USOM Divs and Field Units, 24 Feb 64, sub: USOM/PSD Village/Hamlet Radio Project, file 19, 338–75–1009/65, WNRC; Memo, Sr Adv, III Corps, for CG, III Corps, 10 Apr 64, sub: Estimate of the Situation in III CTZ, an. R.
[38]MACV History, 1964, p. 174, CMH.
[39]*U.S.-Vietnam Relations*, vol. 3, pt. IV.B.3, pp. 38–51 and vol. 3, pt. IV.C.1, p. 35.

munications techniques. By early 1964 almost $1 million of equipment that had been issued for the Operations and Intelligence Net could not even be found: earlier advisers, unable to use the radios, had loaned them to South Vietnamese units and failed to reclaim them before leaving the country.[40]

To correct the dearth of low-level advisory communications, Colonel Pomeroy requested FM voice portable radios that would be simple enough for the advisers to use without benefit of a trained radio operator. Shortly after his request was handed to Secretary McNamara during a trip to South Vietnam in March 1964, the Department of the Army shipped 500 PRC–10 voice radios to South Vietnam for advisers.[41]

Shortages of Skilled Personnel

Problems in transmitting intelligence information during the winter crises had also highlighted deficiencies in the new Phu Lam STARCOM station. Investigating a complaint from General Harkins that his daily intelligence summaries to the Pacific Command and the Joint Chiefs of Staff were being delayed in communications channels, Colonel Pomeroy found that a lack of experienced facilities controllers in the Phu Lam station was hindering resolution of routine technical problems and restoral of outages on overseas circuits. As a temporary solution the STARCOM station in Hawaii sent its most experienced controller to Saigon to act as an interim chief and instructor within the facilities control at Phu Lam. Continually occupied with handling crises, however, he rarely had an opportunity to train his charges and had to remain at Phu Lam permanently. Unlike commanders of the 39th Signal Battalion, the STARCOM station's commander, Maj. Jimmy C. Sutton, had only one noncommissioned officer and three inexperienced enlisted men to run an entire facilities control on a 24-hour basis. He had no pool of troposcatter operators from which he could draw substitute controllers.[42]

Commanders of the 39th Signal Battalion always had been able to balance shortages and accomplish new missions by juggling troposcatter operators and using civilian contractors on BACKPORCH as if they were organic members of the battalion. To meet additional missions for light troposcatter and multichannel teams on the BACKPORCH tails, for example, they often transferred soldiers from the MRC–85 sites, which they knew the Page civilians could operate alone. By early 1964, however, personnel reductions and reassignments that cut the battalion's

---

[40]Memo, Sr Adv, II Corps Regtl Tng Ctr, for MAAG Sig Ofcr, 26 Sep 62, sub: MAAG Communications Facilities, Wilson Papers; Interv, author with Col Charles W. Brown, former signal adviser, 21st ARVN Division, 23 Mar 77, Historians files, CMH; Memo, III Corps Sr Adv for Dep CO, MACV, 6 May 64, sub: Review of Intelligence Efforts, Communications, Forces, and Mobility of Sectors; Memo, Sr Adv, III Corps, for Sr Adv, Divs and Sectors, 8 Jul 63, sub: Estimate of the Situation in III CTZ (2d Qtr 63); Ltr, Brig Gen Delk M. Oden, Chief, Army Section, MAAG, to Col Wilbur Wilson, Sr Adv, III Corps, 26 Dec 63. Latter three in Wilson Papers.

[41]MACV History, 1964, p. 179; Interv, author with Brown, 23 Mar 77.

[42]Memo, USARPAC Sig Ofcr for G–3, 7 Feb 64, sub: Current Status of Signal Actions, CMH; Ltr, STARCOM Station (6600), Vietnam, to U.S. Army Support Command, Vietnam (hereafter cited as USASCV), 4 Jun 64, sub: Facilities Control Personnel, file 19, 338–75–1009/65, WNRC.

strength by almost four hundred men had depleted the reservoir of manpower.[43] *(Map 5)*

Of those soldiers remaining in the 39th Signal Battalion in the spring of 1964, most were young and inexperienced. The 362d Signal Company, for example, had only 35 percent of its authorized noncommissioned officers; young enlisted men, just graduated from the signal school at Fort Monmouth, filled the rest of the company's enlisted leadership positions. Since the battalion had only eight of an authorized twenty-one captains, it placed first and second lieutenants, of whom 80 percent were on their first assignment, in command of most of the thirty-two communications sites in South Vietnam. To muster sufficient personnel to keep all operational systems on the air, the battalion commander had to abandon temporarily the unreliable CROSSBOW system.[44]

Alarmed by the deterioration in the capabilities of the 39th Signal Battalion, especially concerning troposcatter operations, and by the worsening military and political situation in South Vietnam, the commander of the U.S. Army Support Group, Vietnam, Brig. Gen. Joseph W. Stilwell, requested immediate reinforcement of the battalion's troposcatter teams. He stressed that unless the battalion received experienced and completely qualified replacements, rather than the kind of novices it had been getting, the Page civilians would have to take complete control of BACKPORCH.[45]

Causing reverberations all the way to the Pentagon, General Stilwell's message prompted the Department of the Army's Inspector General, Maj. Gen. H. Dudley Ives, to send a team to the Pacific to investigate the problem with signal assignments. The inspector general's team found fourteen messages, dating from as early as December 1962, that the staff of the U.S. Army, Pacific, had sent to the Pentagon to alert the Department of the Army to shortages of experienced signal personnel in South Vietnam. The team concluded that the 39th Signal Battalion's problems resulted from a low priority given to assignments to Southeast Asia by the Signal Branch of the Office of Personnel Operations in Washington and a general naivete concerning the demands made on communicators in South Vietnam. Conditions had worsened progressively over the two years the 39th Signal Battalion had been in South Vietnam. Although inexperienced, the first year's contingent of signalmen had received special training and deployed as a full-strength unit; individual replacements sent the following year had neither the opportunity to train at the factory nor the intensive unit orientation given their predecessors.[46]

Although the chief signal officer had planned to repeat the expedient used

---

[43]In December 1963, when there were more than 1,400 men in the 39th Signal Battalion, the battalion was overstrength. By 30 April 1964, only 1,090 men remained in the 39th Signal Battalion, 259 men were assigned to the STARCOM station, and 192 officers and noncommissioned officers were working as signal advisers. Fact Sheet, OCC-E to Secy of Army, 6 Jun 64, sub: Communications Activities in VN, CMH; 39th Sig Bn History, 1963, pp. 1–3, file U249, 72A18/4, WNRC.

[44]Ltr, 39th Sig Bn to USASCV, 24 Jun 64, sub: Technical Assistance for AN/TRC–90, file 19, 338–75–1009/65; USASGV QHS, 1 Jan–31 Mar 64, pt. 1 (Signal), pp. 3–11, 338–75–1009/63; 178th Sig Co History, 1963, p. 14, 338–75–1000/144. All in WNRC.

[45]Msg, USASGV to CINCUSARPAC, 18 Jan 64, CMH.

[46]Memo, USARPAC Sig Ofcr for G–3, 21 May 64, sub: Current Status of Signal Actions, CMH.

SIGNAL CORPS SITES

December 1962

● Original 32 Sites

NORTH VIETNAM

DEMILITARIZED ZONE

Quang Tri

Hue ● Phu Bai

LAOS

Da Nang

THAILAND

SOUTH VIETNAM

Quang Ngai

Kontum

Pleiku

Qui Nhon

CAMBODIA

Saigon Special Area
Site Octopus
DISTRA
MAAG
MACV
III Corps
Sig Supply & Maint

Tuy Hoa

Ban Me Thuot

Duc My

Nha Trang

Gia Nghia

Da Lat

Phuoc Vinh

Bien Hoa AFB

Tan Son Nhut AFB ■ SAIGON

My Tho

Phu Lam

Sa Dec

Vinh Long

Vung Tau

Can Tho

Soc Trang

Bac Lieu

SOUTH

CHINA

SEA

MAP 5

with the first contingent, sending troposcatter operators to manufacturers' factories for instruction, a major reorganization of the Army had intervened. Responsibility for training on equipment at contractors' facilities had become a matter of dispute between the Continental Army Command, which had assumed the Army's training mission, and the new Army Materiel Command, which provided logistical support for all Army equipment. Until the dispute was resolved, the Army was unable to fund and implement a training program for the troposcatter operators. By the time the Army gave the mission to the Continental Army Command, signalmen had already been dispatched to the 362d Signal Company (Tropo) without any troposcatter training to replace the original operators who were completing their one-year tours.[47]

The organizational turbulence also interfered with the flow of the replacements, who in some cases were diverted to other areas of the Pacific before reaching South Vietnam. The Department of the Army, separated from the 39th Signal Battalion by ten thousand miles and three layers of the command structure (U.S. Army, Pacific; U.S. Army, Ryukyu Islands; and U.S. Army Support Group, Vietnam), found it difficult to keep up with happenings in the battalion. Communication of personnel information was so bad that it was not until Lt. Col. Frank K. Gardner arrived in South Vietnam in April 1964 to replace Colonel Velie, who was due to complete his one-year tour, that the Office of Personnel Operations learned that Colonel Velie already had turned over command of the 39th Signal Battalion to Major White in December.[48]

Until President Johnson declared in March 1964 that the United States was determined to give the South Vietnamese as much help as they required to defeat the Communist insurgency, American units in South Vietnam had to compete with other units worldwide for limited Army resources as well as to languish at the distant end of the long organizational pipeline. Plans to withdraw from South Vietnam by 1965 had made any new investments of men and money there seem wasteful. The Army was emphasizing signal support for combat divisions in Europe and for contingency forces in the United States.[49]

Preoccupied with a major reorganization of the Department of Defense that lessened the influence of the Army signal staff at the Pentagon, the last Chief Signal Officer, Maj. Gen. David P. Gibbs, had little opportunity to resolve problems in South Vietnam. Since 1962 Army signal staff officers had been busy overseeing the proper disposition of those responsibilities that the chief signal officer had been instructed to transfer to other agencies. While divesting himself of all operational functions except the Army Photographic Agency, he was also

---

[47]DF, CSO to DCSOPS, 4 May 63, sub: Training of Personnel in Operations and Maintenance of Tropo Scatter Communications Equipment; Msg, DA to USCONARC, DA 926828, 10 Apr 63. Both in file 2303001, 66A3140/17, WNRC.

[48]Interv, author with Col Frank K. Gardner, former signal officer of the Army Support Command, Vietnam, 9 Jan 78, Historians files, CMH. Colonel Gardner became the signal officer of the Army Support Command, Vietnam (the title of the headquarters had been changed from Army Support Group, Vietnam, in April), and Major White remained as commander of the 39th Signal Battalion.

[49]During 1963, for example, the U.S. Army Electronics Command at Fort Monmouth, the Signal Corps' logistical agency, was heavily involved with construction of a European troposcatter system and the outfitting of the 11th Signal Group, activated in May 1963, as the Army's strategic reaction signal force. ECOM AHS, 1 Aug 62–30 Jun 63, p. 97, CMH; Interv, author with Van Sandt, 14 Feb 78.

reorganizing his own staff which, on 1 March 1964, became the Office of the Chief of Communications-Electronics, subordinate to the Office of the Deputy Chief of Staff for Operations.[50]

By the spring of 1964 the new signal staff had finished reorganizing and could begin concentrating on signal activities that had been given a higher priority by virtue of President Johnson's new commitments to South Vietnam. But little could be done quickly to improve the communications situation in South Vietnam. When in the spring of 1964 Secretary McNamara approved a 179-man augmentation to the 39th Signal Battalion—consisting primarily of troposcatter operators—as part of the buildup authorized in March by the president, few qualified tropo-scatter operators were left to send. A requirement to station a soldier in the United States for two years between overseas tours precluded sending back the experienced operators who had already served with the 39th Signal Battalion. Lacking troposcatter equipment for practical training, the schools had failed to produce fully qualified replacements.[51]

In July 1962 instruction in troposcatter theory was first added to the microwave repairman's course at the signal school at Fort Monmouth and in December 1962 to the microwave radio officer's course. Surveys of the graduates of the microwave courses who were assigned to troposcatter teams in South Vietnam—approximately 15 percent of the total number of graduates—demonstrated that the school's instruction in theory had failed to prepare them to install and maintain an operational troposcatter system in the field. Even those few who had an opportunity to spend five additional weeks of schooling at the Air Force's troposcatter course at Keesler Air Force Base, Mississippi, where training sets were available, felt inadequate to the challenge of tying together the disparate electronic equipment on the network in South Vietnam.[52]

Pleas for troposcatter equipment for practical instruction at the signal school had been fruitless. Every available set had been sent to South Vietnam, and special production of nonstandard equipment used in only one area of the world simply to meet the needs of the school was deemed prohibitively expensive. The lesson was not lost on Army leaders, however. The commanding generals of the Army Materiel Command, the Continental Army Command, and the Combat Developments Command, the Army's newly created agency for developing doctrine, signed a memorandum of understanding agreeing to coordinate thoroughly future equipment development and personnel training for every new major item of equipment. The commanding general of the Continental Army Command, General Herbert B. Powell, also wanted to amend the Army Master Priority List, the primary authorization document for the entire Army, to ensure that schools and training centers would receive a portion of the first production run of new equipment. Although the unfortunate experience of the signal school

---

[50]DA, DCSOPS, AHS, FY–65, ch. 2, pp. 2–3, CMH. For a discussion of the reorganization of the Army signal staff, see Chapter 8.

[51]U.S. Army Signal Center and School (hereafter cited as USASCS) AHS, 1964, pt. 1, pp. 50–51, CMH.

[52]Interv, author with Col (ret.) Charles E. Burner, former director of the Department of Specialist Training, U.S. Army Signal School, Fort Monmouth, 16 Sep 77, Historians files, CMH; USASCS AHS, 1964, pt. 2, an. K, and ibid., 1 Jul 62–31 Dec 63, pt. 1, pp. 65–66, both in CMH.

influenced those important innovations, they did little to remedy the immediate needs of the school. Troposcatter equipment remained unavailable until production in the spring of 1964 of the TRC–90A's that had been ordered the previous summer to meet increased operational requirements in Southeast Asia. In April 1964 the first two troposcatter sets arrived at Fort Monmouth; it was another three months before instruction began and twenty-eight weeks before the first students to train on that equipment graduated.[53]

In lieu of a full-fledged troposcatter training program at the signal schools, the Army had decided to have manufacturers' representatives train soldiers on new equipment in the field while also helping them to install, operate, and maintain the equipment. Expressing personal confidence in the field training concept, called on-the-job training, the Chief Signal Officer, Maj. Gen. Earle F. Cook, had optimistically declared in October 1962 that the 39th Signal Battalion would be prepared to take over the BACKPORCH system completely from Page Communications Engineers when the first contract expired on 31 August 1963.[54]

Although few men in the field shared General Cook's belief that adequate training could be conducted in the hectic atmosphere of an operational site, both military operators and civilian technicians made a valiant attempt to make on-the-job troposcatter training work. Because candidates for the microwave course had to be intelligent simply to qualify for the highly technical schooling, the graduates learned quickly. Having had the benefit of practical schooling at manufacturers' factories, the first wave of troposcatter operators sent to South Vietnam performed well. Although the best members of that original contingent were extended a few months in South Vietnam to train the new group of operators arriving in the summer of 1963, their successors, who had no practical training at the factory, were left to continue their field training under the tutelage of the Collins and Page contractor representatives in South Vietnam.[55]

With only two technicians in South Vietnam, Collins Radio Company could provide little instruction to operators on the fourteen widely dispersed TRC–90 teams. Page, with contractors at each MRC–85 site, was better staffed to conduct on-the-job training. Although there had been no provision in the original contract for training responsibilities, Page assigned one of its senior engineers, Bernard Banks, to direct a training program in South Vietnam. Banks traveled to the different sites to conduct short courses on various aspects of the radio and multiplexing equipment; but the focus of his program was to be a tutor-apprentice relationship established between the soldiers and the Page civilians.[56]

---

[53]Interv, author with Harold Silverstein, former member of the OCSO, 26 May 77, Historians files, CMH; Memorandum of Understanding, USCONARC, sub: New Equipment Training and Support, and Ltr, USCONARC to DA, DCSOPS, 11 Jan 63, sub: Initial Supply of Equipment to U.S. Army Schools and Training Centers, both in Tab L of USCONARC Agenda, School Commandants' Conference, 1965, CMH.

[54]Interv, author with Marie Acton, former member of OCSO, 2 May 77, Historians files, CMH; USARPAC, History of the U.S. Army Buildup and Operations in RVN, 1 Feb–31 Dec 63, pp. 213–15, CMH; Interv, author with Blackwell, 4 Apr 77.

[55]Ltr, 39th Sig Bn to USASCV, 24 Jun 64, sub: Technical Assistance for AN/TRC–90, with 1st Ind, USASCV to USARYIS, 6 Jul 64, file 19, 338–75–1009/65, WNRC.

[56]Interv, author with Bernard Banks, Page Communications Engineers, 5 Apr 77, Historians files, CMH.

Although the Page technicians made every effort to train their military counterparts while working shifts together, often the civilian technicians were too busy keeping the terminals on the air and installing new circuits to help the soldiers. Since the contractors were understandably reluctant to let the military operators work unsupervised on the equipment lest they put the delicate components out of tune, the military operators gradually gravitated to the administrative work at the station and learned little about operating or maintaining the equipment.[57]

Despite General Cook's optimism and Banks' efforts, most of the Page contractors felt that the military never would be able to operate the big BACKPORCH terminals alone. A one-year tour, they believed, provided insufficient time for acquiring adequate experience, and the complete turnover of personnel every spring on the anniversary of the 39th Signal Battalion's arrival eliminated even a modicum of continuity. A policy of shifting soldiers who demonstrated some affinity for operating the complex troposcatter gear to the lighter troposcatter radio sites, where contractor support was austere, contributed to the turbulence. Some of the contractors believed that the prospect of full military manning was a ploy to encourage their firm to hold down the price of future contracts.[58]

The young lieutenants and noncommissioned officers commanding the sites were even more pessimistic. They had no experience with troposcatter communications, let alone the ability to prepare and supervise training programs with the equipment. Despite a persistent shortage of experienced supervisors, site commanders were responsible for managing operations, security, administration, maintenance, and messing on the remote sites, a challenge for the most mature and experienced of leaders under the best of conditions. Although most commanders were performing their housekeeping chores surprisingly well, none had demonstrated any capability for conducting training programs. By early 1964 it had become apparent to the men in the field that the contractors were going to have to remain if the system was to stay on the air.[59]

The prospect of depending on civilians to operate a vital military program in a hostile environment was unsettling to many military men. They felt that civilians were not bound by the same allegiances that kept soldiers at their posts when bullets started flying. During negotiations for a new BACKPORCH contract in summer 1963, General Collins had expressed his displeasure with overreliance on Page. Although General Harkins wanted to retain the full complement of ninety-nine Page representatives, General Collins' opposition had forced him to compromise on sixty-two contractor representatives. The one-year, $1.99 million contract signed with Page on 29 August 1963, just two days before the first year's contract was to expire, eliminated civilian supervisors at the sites and emphasized the contractor's training and maintenance, rather than operational, responsibilities.[60]

---

[57]Intervs, author with von Bergen, 5 Apr 77, and Blackwell, 4 Apr 77.

[58]Intervs, author with von Bergen, 5 Apr 77, and with William Cleverly, former officer in the 39th Signal Battalion and engineer with Page Communications Engineers, 19 Apr 77, both in Historians files, CMH.

[59]USASGV QHS, 1 Jan–31 Mar 64, pt. 1, pp. 10–11; Interv, author with Velie, 12 May 77.

[60]USARPAC, History of the U.S. Army Buildup and Operations in RVN, 1 Feb–31 Dec 63, pp. 213–15; ibid., 1 Jan–31 Dec 64, p. 150; Memo, USARPAC Sig Ofcr for G–3, 8 Nov 63, sub: Current Status of Signal Actions. All in CMH.

The MRC–85 Site at Qui Nhon

By 1963 the precedent for using civilians as instructors and repairmen, as opposed to operators, for military equipment had been well established. For eight years the Military Assistance Advisory Group had been employing contract civilians to provide maintenance assistance and training for the South Vietnamese Army. Indeed, civilians had been largely responsible for building the South Vietnamese Army's signal supply system. The Page contractors, furthermore, had proved to be experts at keeping the big MRC–85 troposcatter radios in good repair. Technicians had helped design the big terminals, had installed them in South Vietnam, and had applied numerous major modifications to the field assemblies. No soldier on a one-year tour could be expected to know the workings of the equipment the way they did.[61]

Despite the rewording of the contract to deemphasize Page's operational responsibilities, the military still relied on Page to perform the most important technical functions in the day-to-day operation of the sites. The continued dependence went unnoticed until January 1964 when General Stilwell announced that the shortage of qualified troposcatter operators might soon force him to leave

[61]Ltr, MAAG, Vietnam, to CINCPAC, 26 Apr 61, sub: Training Progress Reports of Contractor Technicians Furnished Under Army Military Assistance Training Program; Memo for Record, H. D. Ludeman, IWCS Project Engineer, 3 Nov 66, sub: IWCS Integration of AN/MRC–85. Both in CMH. Interv, author with von Bergen, 5 Apr 77.

BACKPORCH completely in the hands of the contractor to gain sufficient manpower to keep the TRC–90's on the air. That prospect perturbed General Collins, who reiterated his opposition to civilian operation of BACKPORCH and suggested that additional military operators would be available when the 39th Signal Battalion turned over its tactical TRC–24 radios to the South Vietnamese.[62]

By early summer the tactical radios were yet to be transferred and the requirement for qualified military operators for the light troposcatter radios had drawn practically every soldier from the MRC–85 sites. In July 1964 a new MACV commander, General William C. Westmoreland, notified Admiral U. S. G. Sharp, who had replaced Admiral Felt as commander in chief, Pacific, in February, that he needed additional military spaces for the TRC–90 teams and requested permission to give Page Communications Engineers full responsibility for operating the MRC–85's.[63]

Admiral Sharp endorsed the request for more military men to the Joint Chiefs of Staff but opposed full civilian operation of BACKPORCH on the theory that the system was too vital to military operations to rely on contract operation in a combat environment. He told General Westmoreland to retain a minimum military capability in case the civilians should abandon the system in an emergency. Reminding Admiral Sharp that the military operators then in South Vietnam were qualified only as apprentices to work under close skilled supervision, Westmoreland warned that they would be capable of operating the system alone for only a brief time and that he needed ninety-six more military spaces to achieve even that limited capability.[64]

Sharp's suggestion to use tactical multichannel operators to augment troposcatter crews indicated a continued underestimation of the dimensions of the unique demands—technical, logistical, and training—placed on communications personnel in Southeast Asia by the requirement to operate sophisticated, modern equipment. While becoming increasingly enamored of the potentials for greater efficiency and manpower savings in military applications of technology, the Army still assumed that technology was easily mastered by familiarization courses and on-the-job training.

On the other hand, Admiral Sharp's support of General Westmoreland's requests for personnel augmentations demonstrated a growing awareness that more attention needed to be directed to Southeast Asia. Forgotten were the optimistic plans for American withdrawal; in their stead was a guarded hope that increased

---

[62]Msg, USASCV to CINCUSARPAC, 22 Jan 64, sub: Staffing of AN/MRC–85 System; Msg, CINC-USARPAC to CGUSARYIS, 21 Apr 64, same sub. Both in CMH.

[63]Although the 39th Signal Battalion had trained over one hundred South Vietnamese soldiers to operate the TRC–24 radios, General Westmoreland, feeling that the equipment might be needed to support the buildup of advisers, did not authorize release of the radios to the South Vietnamese. The Army later shipped TRC–24's to the South Vietnamese through the Military Assistance Program. Msg, COMUSMACV to CINCPAC, 18 Jan 64, sub: Transfer of TRC–24 VHF Equipment to RVNAF; Info Brief, DA, OCC-E, 20 Nov 64, sub: Communications in RVN; Msg, CINCUSARPAC to USASCV, 22 Apr 64, sub: Staffing of MRC–85 System; Msg, MACV to CINCPAC, 1 Jul 64, sub: Additional Communications Support for RVN. All in CMH. USASGV QHS, 1 Jan–31 Mar 64, pt. 1, p. 14.

[64]Msg, CINCPAC to JCS, 21 Aug 64, sub: Staffing of MRC–85 System; Msg, MACV to CINCPAC, 1 Oct 64, sub: Additional Communications Support for RVN; Msg, CINCPAC to JCS, 12 Oct 64, sub: Additional Communications Support for RVN. All in CMH.

American support, especially in the expansion of the advisory program, would enable the South Vietnamese to regain the ground they had lost the previous year.

Setbacks and difficulties with communications had demonstrated to American communicators in South Vietnam that they, like the South Vietnamese, had ground to gain and technical weaknesses to correct. Many of the problems they had encountered were of their own making. At the same time, the successes of the Viet Cong had alerted communicators that they should be aware of the vulnerability of their communications and should be prepared to support a stepped-up level of military operations against an increasingly aggressive adversary. No longer could they underestimate the Viet Cong or overestimate the capability of technology to solve the complex problems facing Americans and their South Vietnamese allies.

5

New Approaches, 1964

President Johnson's stated commitment to carry on the work begun by his predecessor dispelled the uncertainty over continued American signal support in South Vietnam. By early 1964 the 39th Signal Battalion had prepared to expand its ranks with reinforcements. The arrival of new advisers and Special Forces, and an expansion of Vietnamese and American air operations during the following months, provided new missions for U.S. signalmen. The unabated insurgency in South Vietnam, renewed aggression by Communist forces in Laos, and the heightened bellicosity of Hanoi's actions all gave a sense of urgency to the efforts of American signal units in Southeast Asia to complete projects yet unfinished and to improve existing operations.

A Tactical Unit Adapts to Fixed Communications

O ne of the most far-reaching innovations was undertaken to strengthen existing communications and conserve manpower. With the arrival in late 1963 of a new executive officer, Maj. Carlos E. Vogel, Jr., whose military and civilian background was in fixed, commercial-type communications, the 39th began dismounting mobile equipment and consolidating operations into fixed facilities. Vogel improvised distribution frames to improve the wiring at the BACKPORCH nodes at Tan Son Nhut, Pleiku, and Nha Trang. To obtain additional circuits between Saigon and Da Nang, he even devised a way to install multiplexing equipment from tactical TRC–24 multichannel sets in the MRC–85's. The unorthodox mixture of two generations of electronic gear increased the capacity of the BACKPORCH systems from seventy-two to eighty-four channels. Wherever possible Vogel had equipment dismounted from vans, consolidated into communications bunkers, and modified for fixed-plant use. Operations from central facilities required fewer operators and supervisors and permitted the consolidation of power and ancillary equipment for greater efficiency.[1] Vogel's actions started a trend toward using commercial-type facilities for tactical communications in Southeast Asia.

The battalion's tactically oriented signal officers opposed Major Vogel's innovations and unauthorized expedients. They felt he was running a dangerous risk by compromising the battalion's mobility. They also pointed out that supply regulations forbade separating components from end items. Since company commanders had difficulty keeping track of the numerous teletypewriters, ringers, power supplies, and other components removed from their mobile vans, they wanted to be relieved of accountability for the sets and to be rid of the useless shelters and the vehicles that carried them. But officials at the inventory control point on Okinawa refused to accept the empty shelters unless they contained every component originally issued with them.[2]

Major Vogel ran into additional logistical difficulties in trying to add another relay to the CROSSBOW system to improve its propagation. The battalion's supply officer convinced him that the battalion had insufficient nonsignal resources—water and fuel tankers, building materiel, and dining gear—to support another site. Listed on the Army rolls as a tactical unit, the 39th Signal Battalion was not authorized the myriad of items needed to live and work in the fixed base camps of South Vietnam. Only by "scrounging," an old Army expedient that involved begging, borrowing, and trading for equipment that was unavailable through normal supply channels, could the officers and enlisted men of the battalion acquire the resources to build and improve their operational sites and living quarters.[3]

To help the 39th solve some of its supply problems and obtain the unauthorized, nonstandard equipment it needed, the signal staff of the U.S. Army Support Command, Vietnam, was enlarged. Six officers and a noncommissioned officer joined the signal officer, Lt. Col. Frank K. Gardner, a master sergeant, and a few officers detailed from the 39th Signal Battalion. Their job was to ensure that requisitions from the 39th Signal Battalion had proper justification and to coordinate the battalion's requests with appropriate logistical and engineer staff sections. With increased staff assistance the 39th Signal Battalion was able to obtain materials to build concrete pads for its troposcatter vans to keep them from sinking into the mud and tipping during the rainy season. It also constructed roofs over vans and generators which, after sitting for over two years in the extremes of the tropical climate, were being damaged by dust and leaking water. To eliminate moisture that was contaminating the fuel used to power the generators, the battalion replaced old rusted fuel drums with permanent storage tanks.[4]

Besides deterioration of equipment exposed to the forces of nature, the bat-

[1]Interv, author with Vogel, 16 Jan 78; Msg, MACV to CINCPAC, 15 Sep 64, sub: BACKPORCH Expansion, CMH.

[2]Interv, author with Lt Col Sebastian Lasher, former CO, 178th Signal Company, 16 Jan 78, Historians files, CMH.

[3]Interv, author with Vogel, 16 Jan 78; Interv, author with Lt Col (ret.) Leo T. White, former CO, 39th Signal Battalion, 3 Nov 77, Historians files, CMH.

[4]USASCV QHS, 1 Jul–30 Sep 64, pp. 5–6, 338–75–1009/92; Memo, Lt Col Frank K. Gardner for General Giers, 1 Sep 64, sub: Problem Areas in Vietnam, file 19, 338–75–1009/65. Both in WNRC.

talion also had to compensate for man-made changes in the environment around its sites. It built towers to raise antennas over newly erected buildings that blocked radio transmission paths. To avoid noise and signal disruptions caused by new airfields, where flight paths sometimes crossed directly in front of antennas and navigational beacons and radars emanated interfering radiation, the battalion had to reposition many radios and antennas.[5]

Priority of effort during renovations went to sites in the Mekong Delta area, which had been neglected because signal advisers planned to use the Southern Toll commercial network, the only section of the AID regional network being constructed in South Vietnam, to carry military communications from the delta to Saigon. When Southern Toll was finally completed during the summer of 1964, military communicators discovered that they would have to correct equipment incompatibilities and to install extensive cabling through populated areas to connect tactical communications lines with the commercial network. Col. Robert E. Kimball, who replaced Colonel Pomeroy as MACV J–6 in June 1964, decided to forsake using the Southern Toll network and to build instead an area system using tactical multichannel equipment to support American advisers and units in the delta. *(Map 6)* To lift the line-of-sight transmission paths of the tactical radio relays over the horizon of the delta lowlands, Colonel Gardner obtained 125-foot antenna towers from the Phu Lam STARCOM station. The battalion commander, Lt. Col. Leo T. White, reorganized the battalion to form a provisional unit, called Delta Company, to relieve the 232d Signal Company of all communications responsibility except radio relays for the IV Corps area.[6]

Supporting the Special Forces

A ugmentation and improvements were also needed for the Green Beret communications detachments, which had become overextended in trying to link the forty-nine camps in the ever-expanding Special Forces organization in South Vietnam. Still relying primarily on slow Morse code nets, the Special Forces lacked the means to enter into the long-lines network provided by the 39th Signal Battalion. In the summer of 1964 the Special Forces signal officer, Lt. Col. James V. Bailey, requested that a Special Forces signal company be assigned to South Vietnam to operate base radio stations, switchboards, and teletype communications centers at the headquarters in Nha Trang, at a Special Forces operations center in Saigon, and at the B detachments in each corps area.[7] When the Special Forces formed the 5th Special Forces Group in October 1964 to control all Special Forces activities in South Vietnam, the Department of the Army responded to Colonel

[5]Memo, Sig Ofcr, USASCV, for Chief of Staff, USASCV, 30 Jun 64, sub: Communications Paper for General Stilwell, file 19, 338–75–1009/65, WNRC.

[6]USASCV QHS, 1 Jul–30 Sep 64, p. 9, 338–75–1009/92; Delta Co, 39th Sig Bn, History, 1964, file U252, and 39th Sig Bn History, 1964, p. 3, file U250, both in 67A533/18, WNRC. Msg, COMUSMACV to CINCPAC, DAIN 428735, 1 Oct 64, sub: Additional Communications Support, CMH.

[7]Later in the year, responsibility for the corps areas was transferred to C detachments, and B detachments were assigned regions within each corps area.

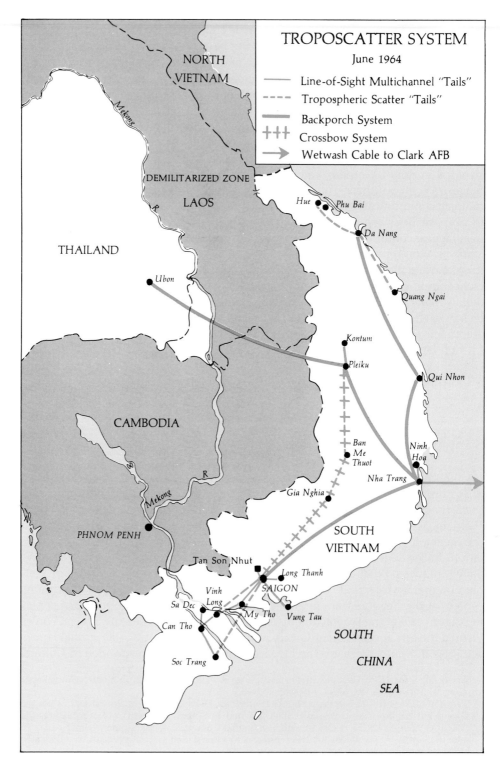

TROPOSCATTER SYSTEM

June 1964

——— Line-of-Sight Multichannel "Tails"
- - - - Tropospheric Scatter "Tails"
━━━ Backporch System
+++ Crossbow System
──▶ Wetwash Cable to Clark AFB

NORTH VIETNAM

DEMILITARIZED ZONE

LAOS

THAILAND

Mekong

Ubon

CAMBODIA

Mekong
R

PHNOM PENH

R

Hue
Phu Bai
Da Nang

Quang Ngai

Kontum
Pleiku

Qui Nhon

Ban
Me
Thuot

Ninh
Hoa

Gia Nghia
Nha Trang

SOUTH
VIETNAM

Tan Son Nhut
Long Thanh
SAIGON

Vinh
Long
Sa Dec
Can Tho
My Tho
Vung Tau

SOUTH

CHINA

SEA

Soc Trang

MAP 6

Bailey's request by dispatching a 140-man signal company, commanded by Capt. Benjamin Rapaport, to South Vietnam.[8]

The importance of efficient communications for the Special Forces was amply demonstrated in September 1964 when paramilitary soldiers revolted against their South Vietnamese Special Forces officers. Rapid communications from an isolated camp to Saigon were critical in determining the facts of the situation and influencing Vietnamese actions. After killing seventy-three South Vietnamese soldiers and government officials and imprisoning U.S. Special Forces soldiers in the Bon Sar Pa Special Forces camp, the Montagnard rebels threatened to march on the provincial capital of Ban Me Thuot. Although South Vietnamese Army officers wanted to quell the revolt by attacking the camp, American advisers feared for the lives of the imprisoned American soldiers and worried that South Vietnamese military intervention might provoke a general Montagnard uprising throughout the Central Highlands. They persuaded the South Vietnamese to give them time to try to negotiate and end the rebellion. To enable American negotiators to maintain close coordination with MACV headquarters in Saigon and to ensure that the South Vietnamese president, General Nguyen Khanh, had the means to restrain his army commanders from attacking the dissidents, General Westmoreland instructed Colonel Kimball to establish direct lines of communications between Ban Me Thuot and Saigon.[9]

Attention quickly turned to Detachment 6 of the 178th Signal Company, serving the U.S. advisory team with the 23d South Vietnamese Division at Ban Me Thuot. The MACV Assistant Chief of Staff for Operations (J–3), Brig. Gen. William E. DePuy, established a command post at the division and appropriated the advisory team's signal center consisting of an SB–86 switchboard, a message center with secure teletype, a radio-teletype station of the Operations and Intelligence Net, a single-sideband station, a rebroadcast station, and a four-channel radio relay link to Pleiku. The 362d Signal Company also patched several circuits from its troposcatter CROSSBOW link between Ban Me Thuot and Pleiku over the BACK-PORCH system to Saigon.[10]

From Ban Me Thuot to the Bon Sar Pa Special Forces camp, where the II Corps senior adviser, Col. John F. Freund, negotiated with the rebel leaders, there were only FM voice communications. During the tension-filled talks, Colonel Freund carried a PRC–10 radio on his back and held the microphone in such a way that his conversations were transmitted to aircraft circling overhead, which passed reports back to the command post in Ban Me Thuot. After hours of negotiating, Colonel Freund used his radio to call in helicopters to evacuate the hostages. Alerted by advisers in Ban Me Thuot that the South Vietnamese were then preparing to attack the Montagnard rebels still holding the camp, General Westmoreland asked General Khanh to give Colonel Freund more time to persuade the Montagnards to lay down their arms. Just before the attack was to begin, General

[8]Interv, author with Col (ret.) James V. Bailey, former signal officer, 5th Special Forces Group, 16 Jan 78; Interv, author with Lt Col Douglas Yardis, former Special Forces signal officer, 14 Feb 78. Both in Historians files, CMH.

[9]For a complete narrative of the events surrounding the Montagnard uprising, see General William C. Westmoreland, *A Soldier Reports* (Garden City: Doubleday & Co, 1976), pp. 78–81.

[10]178th Sig Co History, 1964, p. 23, 338–75–1000/144, WNRC.

178th Signal Company Member *operates an SB–86 switchboard at the Hue communications site.*

Khanh used the BACKPORCH system to telephone the 23d Division command post and countermand the attack order. A few hours later, Colonel Freund convinced the rebels to surrender, and the crisis ended without further bloodshed.[11]

The Montagnard incident, like the several other political crises that occurred in 1964, exhibited the importance of communications to low-level detachments and isolated camps. Although the 39th Signal Battalion tried to maintain communications with as many locations as it could, many were beyond its reach. With scores of new advisory teams being established at subsectors and battalions throughout the countryside, Colonel Kimball, the MACV J–6, began a program of replacing short-range FM radios with single-sideband voice radios.

To reach isolated advisers, the Military Assistance Command, Vietnam, also used the Saigon-based American Armed Forces Vietnam network (AFVN). The 39th Signal Battalion transmitted AFVN programming over BACKPORCH channels to its field detachments, which used either surplus commercial broadcasting equipment or modified military radios to rebroadcast throughout their local area. During an attempted coup in September 1964, when dissident South Vietnamese soldiers took control of the Saigon telephone system, AFVN was for a short time

[11]Interv, author with Bailey, 16 Jan 78.

the only means to keep Americans throughout South Vietnam apprised of developments in Saigon.[12]

Strengthening South Vietnamese Army Communications

A merican advisers believed that the South Vietnamese Army required more efficient nationwide communications to link its fractionalized ranks as well as to control military operations in remote areas. Saddled with outdated military equipment, the South Vietnamese could no longer afford to wait for the Americans to expand their network or for the Agency for International Development to complete its telecommunications project. The Signal Branch of the Military Assistance Advisory Group had been planning a new permanent multichannel long-distance network, to be called Military Telecommunications Network, Vietnam. A fortuitous sequence of events gave the project much-needed momentum. A new signal doctrine for the South Vietnamese Army, which advisers in the training sections of the Signal Branch and their Vietnamese counterparts had been writing for over a year, was completed and published just as the project was starting. Thus the signal engineers had a written guide that was current and acceptable to both the Americans and the South Vietnamese Army. Since the chief of the project, Maj. Rolland M. Favre, Jr., had taught many of the South Vietnamese signal officers involved in the project at the signal school at Fort Monmouth, he had already built the rapport so necessary to winning the cooperation of the South Vietnamese. Then in May, when the Military Assistance Advisory Group was discontinued as a separate agency and the Signal Branch became a subagency of the MACV Logistics Directorate (J–4), the signal engineers found themselves working alongside the logisticians who would coordinate the materiel supply and construction requirements for the project.[13]

Just as Major Favre completed his preliminary engineering studies and finished compiling a list of requirements for the military network, worsening relations between the United States and a leftist government in Indonesia caused a sharp cutback in military aid to that country and freed Military Assistance Program funds for distribution to other areas in the Pacific Command. Major Favre rushed to Hawaii with the communications plan for the network to make the first bid for the money; concurring with the ambitious project, the Pacific Command readily transferred $17 million of the Indonesian aid funds to the Military Assistance Program for South Vietnam.

The Pacific Command's financial commitment to the Military Telecommunications Network, Vietnam, invigorated logistical support to South Vietnam's signal program. Depots throughout the Pacific released long-awaited communica-

[12]MFR, MAC J–6, 12 Oct 64, sub: Operation of AFRC Satellite Stations, Incl to USASCV QHS, 1 Oct–31 Dec 64, Sig Stf Ofc Rpt, pt. 2, 338–75–1009/92, WNRC.

[13]Discussion of the development of the Military Communications Network, Vietnam, is based on Intervs, author with Col (ret.) Howard E. Porter, former chief, Signal Branch, MACV, 3 Apr 78; with Lt Col (ret.) Rolland M. Favre, former staff officer, Signal Branch, MACV, 4 Apr 78; with Col (ret.) Wilbur A. Scudder, Jr., former staff officer, MACV J–6, 15 Feb 78. All in Historians files, CMH.

tions equipment for upgrading the remaining World War II–vintage stocks in the South Vietnamese signal inventory. Recognizing that the chief of the Signal Branch, Col. Howard E. Porter, needed officers with special talents—an easy temperament and technical expertise—to help the South Vietnamese with their major technological rehabilitation, Colonel Kimball permitted him to have first choice of all advisers assigned to South Vietnam. Because so much of the Military Telecommunications Network, Vietnam, involved fixed-plant facilities, Colonel Porter chose officers with electrical engineering degrees or recent experience with civilian communications companies. Corresponding with former instructors and employers, those officers informally obtained much-needed assistance for the South Vietnamese project. From the Bell Telephone Company came manuals on pole line construction; the Department of Agriculture, which through its Rural Electrification Administration regulated small exchanges installed in rural areas of the United States, provided manuals on subjects ranging from numbering schemes for dial telephone exchanges to specifications for manhole covers. Using newly obtained equipment and textbooks borrowed from the signal school at Fort Monmouth, advisers quickly established courses in the operation and maintenance of the new gear at the South Vietnamese signal school at Vung Tau.[14]

During the next several years all those fortuitous events bore fruit. By the late 1960s the South Vietnamese had a communications network connecting all major bases and key towns. Although austere by American standards, it provided the South Vietnamese military with its first countrywide telephone and teletype system. The network reduced the dependence on borrowed channels from the American systems or single-channel radio for long-distance communications.

Expanding the Base in Thailand

In Thailand, American signal advisers were also working to establish long-distance military communications for their counterparts. Although the Thai portion of the AID regional network, consisting of cable and microwave systems linking most major cities, was completed in early 1964, the cost of leasing service had proven too expensive for Thai military units. Despite an investment of $3 million and continuing interest in the project by Secretary McNamara, the Department of Defense was unable to convince the Thai government, which had formed a commercial company to run the system, to allocate channels to its armed forces.[15]

In April 1964 several new light troposcatter TRC–90A sets were installed to establish a reliable U.S. communications system linking major bases at Ubon, Udorn, and Korat to Bangkok. A month later, the member nations of the Southeast Asia Treaty Organization conducted an exercise in Thailand. Again the Ameri-

---

[14]Intervs, author with Cols Porter, 3 Apr 78, and Favre, 4 Apr 78.
[15]Msg, DEPCOMUSMACTHAI to CINCPAC, 8 Jan 64, sub: Thai Commercial Circuits; Msg, CINCPAC to JCS, 28 Aug 64, sub: Lease of Circuits in Thailand TOT System; Info Brief, DA, OCC-E, 23 Nov 64, sub: Lease of Communications Circuits . . . Thailand (TOT). All in CMH.

cans found that contingency communications were not ready. To replace a large number of inoperative radios awaiting spare parts in the 999th Signal Company, which deployed to Thailand for the exercise, the U.S. Army had to arrange for an airlift of equipment from depots in the United States. Only the existence of the light troposcatter system prevented a repetition of the breakdown of communications that had hampered Joint Task Force 116 two years earlier. Even so, with insufficient channels on the new system and few reliable tactical extensions to field command posts, the communications base for the theater was still too weak to support major combat operations.[16]

Concern for the adequacy of communications in Thailand heightened after the Communists took the offensive in Laos in May. Admiral Sharp alerted the U.S. Army, Pacific, to be prepared to deploy signalmen to help the Thais operate the tactical equipment used on their military network. He also wanted the U.S. staff in Thailand to begin planning to integrate all U.S. and Thai military systems and the commercial network into a single base system that would be available in case of complete mobilization. Called the Joint Circuit Allocation and Requirements Group, the committee was composed of representatives of all U.S. Army and Air Force headquarters in Thailand and headed by Col. Frederick D. Ritter, U.S. Air Force, the J–6 of the Joint U.S. Military Advisory Group, Thailand. During June the new signal staff surveyed the meager communications available to bind together the air and logistical bases that formed the strategic backbone for the American defense of the Southeast Asian mainland.[17]

Seeking central technical controls from which they could monitor and adjust the communications systems, the survey team found that the entire countrywide network was interconnected at Ubon, Udorn, and Korat only by tactical patch panels, which were designed to handle short-distance circuits temporarily installed between brigade headquarters. Even worse was the haphazard way in which the circuits were extended from the network. Ill equipped to install high-quality, permanent interconnects between American troposcatter terminals, Thai military and commercial facilities, and local subscribers, the 379th Signal Battalion—a tactical unit—had to use field wire and tactical radio relay to traverse miles of rugged country and congested areas. Lacking telephone poles or underground cables, wiremen were continually repairing lines cut in accidents or stolen for the valuable copper they contained. Conditions were so bad that the critical cable connecting the Backporch terminal and the TRC–90A at Ubon, the link between the base networks of South Vietnam and Thailand, was strung across a river on the rail of a bridge that was frequently under water during the rainy season. At the first meeting of the Joint Circuit Allocation and Requirements Group on 22 July 1964, Colonel Ritter assigned several short-term projects to Army and Air Force signalmen in Thailand to rectify the most serious problems. He sought to com-

---

[16]USARPAC, Base Development Plan 1–64, Southeast Asia, vol. 6, 69A606/1, WNRC; Memo, USARPAC Sig Ofcr for G–3, 14 May 64, sub: Current Status of Signal Actions, and CINCPAC History, 1964, pp. 416–17, both in CMH.

[17]Msg, CINCPAC to DEPCOMUSMACTHAI et al., 13 Jun 64, sub: CE Base Thailand, file S–65, 72A4171/1; Msg, CINCPAC to JCS, 4 Jul 64, sub: Review of Communications Support for CINCPAC OPLAN 32–64, file S–130, 72A25/1. Both in WNRC.

plete those projects by 28 August, a deadline for planning purposes that Admiral Sharp had imposed on him.[18]

Responding to the Tonkin Crisis

C risis intervened before the deadline. After North Vietnamese patrol boats attacked U.S. Navy ships in the Gulf of Tonkin in early August 1964, President Johnson authorized reprisal air raids against the boats and their bases in North Vietnam; the execution of a contingency plan for Southeast Asia became more than a mere probability. On 6 August the Joint Chiefs of Staff alerted strategic reaction forces to be prepared to move to Thailand in support of Operation Plan 37, a contingency plan for operations against North Vietnam. Two reinforced brigades from the 25th Infantry Division on Hawaii and the 173d Airborne Brigade from Okinawa, together with a large augmentation of support units, readied for deployment to Southeast Asia.[19]

The Gulf of Tonkin crisis provided a stark reminder to communicators in Southeast Asia of the deficiencies in their systems. Realizing that U.S. Air Force units in Thailand might have to launch strikes against North Vietnam, General Westmoreland directed the installation of additional direct channels from the Air Operations Center at Tan Son Nhut to air bases at Udorn and Warin, near Ubon. Meeting that requirement should have involved making simple connections, called strapovers, within patch panels and distribution frames at each intermediate terminal; however, a lack of common procedures among the various Army and Air Force units that operated transmitting and receiving stations and inadequate technical controls along the circuit paths delayed installation of the new service and even disrupted circuits that had already been in operation. So badly had communications deteriorated in the hectic days following the crisis that General Westmoreland warned Admiral Sharp that ''air operations currently stagnated through inability to pass frag orders.''[20]

An easing of the crisis and cancellation of the contingency alert for American forces relieved the pressure on communications. A sobered Admiral Sharp, however, realized that communications problems in Southeast Asia were too complex to resolve without outside assistance. He told his staff to prepare a proposal for the Department of Defense to provide the resources to integrate fully all communications in Southeast Asia. Meanwhile, communicators in Thailand and South

[18]Interv, author with Chesley, 28 Dec 77; Ltr, JUSMAG THAI (JTJ6) to CINCPAC J-6 et al., 5 Aug 64, sub: Letter of Transmittal (Minutes of First Meeting JOCARG), 72A4171/1, WNRC.

[19]The 1,641-man signal contingent alerted with the support augmentation comprised the following units: 2d Signal Group (HHD) and 228th Signal Company (Radio Relay VHF) from Fort Bragg, North Carolina; 54th Signal Battalion (Corps) from Fort Hood, Texas; 972d Signal Battalion (Supply and Maintenance) and 128th Signal Company (Depot) from Tobyanna Army Depot, Pennsylvania; 56th Signal Company (Forward Supply and Maintenance) from Fort Lewis, Washington; two signal detachments supporting Hawk missile battalions from Fort Bliss, Texas; and the 999th Signal Company (Support) from Okinawa. NMCC OPSUM Supplement 113–64, 18 Aug 64; Msg, DA to CGUSCONARC et al., DAIN 363674, 5 Aug 64. Both in Historians files, CMH.

[20]Quote from Msg, COMUSMACV to CINCPAC, 10 Aug 64, sub: Circuit Activation: Udorn-TSN; Msg, DEPCOMUSMACTHAI to CINCPAC, 16 Aug 64. Both in CMH.

Vietnam were to do everything possible to shore up communications against a possible resurgence of hostilities.[21]

Colonel Ritter decided that commercial circuits had to be reserved for immediate use in case trouble again erupted and failure of the tenuous military communications in Thailand caused another disruption of service to air bases. Obtaining approval for the vital backup service plunged the Pacific Command's signal officers into a staffing quagmire. Recently criticized by the General Accounting Office for wasteful leasing of commercial telephone service in Japan, defense officials were wary of entering into new leasing arrangements. Before the Joint Chiefs of Staff would consider the request, they wanted the Pacific Command to explain in detail why the existing military base communications plus those communications that would be organic to deploying contingency units were insufficient. The signal staff also had to estimate the costs of the lease and declare whether they would represent gold outflow, a concern related to U.S. balance of payments problems. Since only the State Department was authorized to negotiate with Thailand for any commercial service, the Joint Chiefs cautioned Admiral Sharp to determine the anticipated costs without making "indiscrete inquiries" of Thai officials.[22]

After ten days of frantic staff work, the Pacific Command signal staff compiled a detailed justification for the leasing request. Admiral Sharp explained to the Joint Chiefs of Staff that communications needed for the various contingencies that he might be required to meet in Thailand exceeded by about 50 percent the capacity of communications then installed. Because microwave equipment had limited range and tropical interference hampered high-frequency radio, Admiral Sharp felt his primary contingency communications, transportable microwave and single-sideband terminals, would do little to alleviate the deficiencies in Thailand's communications. Since the Joint Chiefs had refused his request for deployment of a contingency communications center and radio station as a backup to the Phu Lam station during the Tonkin crisis, Admiral Sharp was reluctant to depend on support from outside the theater during a future emergency. Until long-term improvements to the base system were completed, the Thai commercial system offered the only reliable augmentation to his inadequate long-distance communications in Thailand.[23]

The Pacific Command staff estimated that it would cost $145,000 to install cable and equipment to connect American facilities and the Thai network and an additional $95,000 each year to reserve fifty-four circuits on the commercial system, based on an expected use of thirty days per year. Anticipating approval of the vital request to lease the circuits, Admiral Sharp asked the Army to send him radio relay teams to establish temporary links between the U.S. troposcatter terminals at Korat, Udorn, and Ubon and local offices of the Thai commercial

---

[21]Ltr, JUSMAG THAI to CINCPAC et al., 10 Sep 64, sub: Minutes of the Second Meeting of the Joint Circuit Allocation and Requirements Group-Thailand, file C-384, 72A25/24, WNRC.

[22]Comptroller General, Rpt to the Congress, Excessive Charges for Leased Telephone Service Incurred by United States Forces in Japan, Feb 64, file 201-45 (GAO01964), 67A4846/1, WNRC; Msg, JCS to CINCPAC, 18 Aug 64, sub: Agreement to Lease Circuits in Thailand Toll System (TOT), CMH.

[23]Msg, CINCPAC to JCS, 28 Aug 64, sub: Lease of Circuits in Thailand TOT System; Msg, DA, CC-E, to USARPAC et al., 25 Aug 64, sub: TSC-16 Contingency Package. Both in CMH.

network. The Department of the Army tasked the 4th Infantry Division at Fort Lewis, Washington, to deploy six five-man tactical radio relay teams for temporary duty in Thailand, but not until February 1965 did Secretary of Defense McNamara approve that leasing arrangement.[24]

With added urgency conferred by the Tonkin crisis, other previously deferred communications projects in Southeast Asia received quick approval. On 26 August the Joint Chiefs of Staff finally approved the proposal made during the spring to relocate the equipment on the Bangkok-Saigon troposcatter system. Based on the recommendations of the engineers who had investigated propagational problems on the long system, the Joint Chiefs gave the Army permission to move the Thailand terminal to Green Hill northeast of Bangkok and to extend the system to Bangkok with microwave radio. To strengthen communications in South Vietnam, the signal officer of the Army Support Command, Col. Frank K. Gardner, traveled to Okinawa to enlist the support of the U.S. Army, Ryukyu Islands, in obtaining high-quality fixed equipment for the 39th Signal Battalion in order to release mobile equipment for the tactical uses for which it was intended. Although there had been a great reluctance at the U.S. Army, Pacific, to approve requests for fixed installations in Southeast Asia since talk of withdrawal the previous year, the signal officer in Okinawa, Col. William A. Van Sandt, promised to approve dial telephone exchanges for MACV headquarters and General Westmoreland's alternate command post at Vung Tau. Colonel Van Sandt also approved Colonel Gardner's request for buildings at Tan Son Nhut to house the net control stations for the Operations and Intelligence Net, the in-country single-sideband net, and a message relay for all in-country teletype communications.[25]

Colonel Gardner recognized that hybridizing tactical equipment offered an inferior substitute for standard, fixed-plant communications. He shared the concern of some officers of the 39th Signal Battalion that the unit would be unable to perform a mobile tactical mission if it was called upon to deploy rapidly from its fixed sites. After investigating the causes of communications difficulties in Thailand during the Tonkin crisis, the Joint Circuit Allocation and Requirements Group expressed similar doubts about the utility of tactical communications equipment to fulfill requirements for highly reliable, rapid communications between major American and allied headquarters. Being on the brink of war in Southeast Asia had convinced the Pacific Command signal staff that significant changes in quality as well as quantity had to be made to communications in that vital region.[26]

[24]Info Brief, DA, OCC-E, 27 Nov 64, sub: 4th Infantry Division Radio Relay Teams on TDY in Thailand; Msg, DA, CC-E, to CGUSCONARC and CINCUSARPAC, 26 Aug 64, sub: TDY of C-E Teams to Thailand. Both in CMH. Memo, Secy of Defense for CJCS, 23 Feb 65, sub: Lease of Communications Circuits from Telephone Organization of Thailand in Support of Contingency Operations, Incl to JCS 222/813-1, 26 Feb 65, JACO (1965), DA/2, NARS.

[25]Msg, OCC-E to CINCUSARPAC and DCA, 26 Aug 64, sub: Plan for Bangkok-Saigon Communications Improvement, CMH; Msg, DCA to DA, 21 Jan 64, sub: Bangkok-Saigon Troposcatter System, file 139364, 72A4171/1, and Ltr, USASCV Sig Ofcr to CofS, 29 Aug 64, sub: Visit to Okinawa, 16–22 Aug 64, file 19, 338–75–1009/65, both in WNRC. Interv, author with Col Frank K. Gardner, former signal officer, USASCV, 20 Sep 77, Historians files, CMH.

[26]Interv, author with Gardner, 20 Sep 77; Ltr, JUSMAG THAI to 379th Sig Bn et al., 10 Sep 64, sub: Minutes of Second Meeting of the Joint Circuit Allocation and Requirements Group-Thailand, CMH; Msg, CINCPAC to JCS, 6 Sep 64, sub: Communications Support for CINCPAC OPLAN 32–64, file 139441, 72A25/1, WNRC.

Developing plans, especially for as complex and expensive an undertaking as a regional communications system, in the crisis atmosphere that pervaded the headquarters in the Pacific during the late summer of 1964 was difficult. With the entire staff of the Pacific Command preoccupied with daily developments in Indochina, coordination of staff proposals went slowly. Continually adjusting plans to address problems newly illuminated by post-Tonkin assessments also complicated and delayed formulation of a comprehensive signal plan. Before signal officers at the Pacific Command could complete even a draft proposal for the integrated network, changes made to meet immediate needs and approval of previously requested projects further complicated their planning. In the request finally dispatched to the Joint Chiefs of Staff on 3 October, Admiral Sharp presented communications requirements of such great capacity and high standards that they demanded equipment similar to that found in the United States.[27]

In presenting a rationale for the expensive proposal—about $20 million for construction and $4 million annually for contractor assistance—Admiral Sharp emphasized that the lessons learned by communicators in Southeast Asia during the previous two years dictated a complete shift in strategic communications planning. Only an established integrated network, rather than an accumulation of diverse transportable communications sets of limited capacity, could provide a sufficient base to support a strategy that depended on rapid airlift of large numbers of tactical forces who would need operational communications as soon as they landed. He reminded the Joint Chiefs of Staff that experiences with exercises in support of contingency plans of the Southeast Asia Treaty Organization and the Pacific Command had demonstrated the shortcomings of light tactical equipment in rapidly establishing a long-distance network. They confirmed the soundness of having semifixed heavy troposcatter equipment, as in South Vietnam, already providing a communications base. Admiral Sharp also pointed out the inherent dangers in depending on established commercial systems for military requirements. Delays in obtaining circuits in Thailand had demonstrated the political and economic obstacles to rapid conversion of those networks, while experiences with the Southern Toll in South Vietnam suggested serious technical and logistical barriers to easy interconnection of civilian and military systems.[28]

To provide redundancy within the proposed network, Admiral Sharp wanted alternate systems between every major base in South Vietnam and Thailand. For transmission of sensitive data and secure-voice (ciphony) signals the network had to have quiet channels with a wide bandwidth. He requested that the integrated network be engineered to the high-quality standards of commercial transmission systems and be equipped with effective technical controls to monitor circuit performance to ensure maintenance of those standards. At the major nodal points Admiral Sharp also wanted the capability to interconnect entire sections of two

[27]Msg, CINCPAC to JCS, 3 Oct 64, sub: CE Base SE Asia, CMH.

[28]Ibid.; Joint Logistics Review Board, *Monograph 5: Communications*, Dec 69, an. C, p. 3, 71A2351/6, WNRC; MACV History, 1964, p. 178, CMH.

systems, a feature called wideband or through-group patching.[29]

While concerned by the high cost of Admiral Sharp's proposal, the Joint Chiefs of Staff recognized that the permanent integrated system would release for contingency use the light troposcatter sets then providing base communications in Southeast Asia and that it could be transferred to the Thais and South Vietnamese when the United States withdrew support forces from Southeast Asia. Approving the concept, they sent Admiral Sharp's proposal to the Defense Communications Agency for drafting of a technical proposal, called a systems plan. Anticipating that the Army would be given the mission to operate the network, General Gibbs alerted the U.S. Army Strategic Communications Command, the unit that operated nontactical communications for the Army.[30]

At a meeting in Hawaii in mid-December, Defense Communications Agency, Army, and Air Force representatives from Southeast Asia endorsed the draft systems plan. Formulated to "provide on an expedited basis an integrated wideband communications system in Southeast Asia by expanding or using, where possible, existing facilities to meet CINCPAC's OPLAN 32," the systems plan seemed to cover every aspect of Admiral Sharp's proposal.[31]

The DCA planners agreed with Admiral Sharp that the communications-electronics effort in Southeast Asia had failed to keep pace in capacity, reliability, quality, and redundancy with the expansion of American interests and also felt that national commercial systems provided insufficient reliability for military operations. Their plan emphasized that the susceptibility of communications in Southeast Asia to interruption from natural causes, electronic warfare, or physical attack dictated a need for redundancy based on diversity in routing as well as diversity in modes of propagation.[32]

The systems plan envisioned the installation of fixed microwave and troposcatter terminals at major bases in Thailand; replacement of the tactical multi-channel equipment in the Saigon area with fixed microwave facilities; and

---

[29]When routing circuits from one system to another, wideband patching eliminates the need to convert each individual channel from the carrier frequency to voice frequency, a process called demodulation, and then to modulate it again for transmission on a new system. Since modulation processes introduce more equipment into the communications path, possibilities for attenuation and malfunctions are increased, and the problems of installing and restoring individual circuits are magnified.

[30]Msg, CC-E to CGUSASCC, 16 Oct 64, sub: Southeast Asia Communications, CMH; Rpt, JCS 2339/160, 13 Nov 64, sub: Integrated U.S. SEA Wideband Communications, JACO (1964), DA/605, NARS. This report contains the complete file of Admiral Sharp's original requests and the response of the Joint Chiefs of Staff to requirements for a fixed integrated network for Southeast Asia. Msg, CINCPAC to JCS, 28 Nov 64, sub: CE Base SE Asia; Msg, CINCPAC to JCS, 12 Dec 64, sub: CE Base SE Asia; Msg, CINCPAC to JCS, 12 Dec 64, sub: Integrated U.S. SE Asia Wideband Communications System. All in CMH.

[31]DCA, Systems Plan for an Integrated U.S. Wideband Communications System in Southeast Asia, 28 Dec 64, 72A4171/2, WNRC. The term Integrated Wideband Communications System (IWCS) became the name of the base network in Southeast Asia.

[32]Diversity in routing means that alternate paths are installed between important points, as the 39th Signal Battalion attempted with CROSSBOW. Propagational diversity, which includes such variations as space diversity, frequency diversity, and polarization diversity, compensates for interruption of a radio signal by transmitting more than one signal and selecting the best signal at the receiver. In space diversity, a pair of antennas separated a frequency wavelength apart are used at both transmitter and receiver; in frequency diversity, two frequencies are transmitted; in polarization diversity, antennas are both vertically and horizontally polarized. Dual diversity is the application of a single type of propagational diversity; quad diversity is the concurrent employment of two types.

extensive modification and upgrading of the Backporch terminals in South Vietnam. Favoring the continuation of overall responsibility for communications in Southeast Asia by the Army, the plan recommended that the Strategic Communications Command operate the integrated system. In the only significant addition to the proposal submitted by Admiral Sharp, the plan also emphasized that the Defense Communications Agency, and not the Army, should be responsible for managing the network. To handle that responsibility, it provided for the agency to open a support center in Saigon to perform engineering, systems control, and coordination of circuit requirements.[33]

Satellite Communications

E ven as engineers were planning a sophisticated telecommunications system for Southeast Asia, signalmen in Saigon had already entered the space age of communications. Fearing disruption of the high-frequency radio links between the United States and Southeast Asia during the Tonkin crisis, the Joint Chiefs of Staff rushed to South Vietnam a radio terminal capable of transmitting thousands of miles around the globe by using as a relay a man-made satellite orbiting in space. In August 1964 signalmen from the Army's Satellite Communications Command established two clear channels from Tan Son Nhut to Hawaii, the first operational satellite communications system in history.[34]

The sudden activation of the satellite link to Saigon culminated almost two decades of research and experimentation with extraterrestrial relays that had begun on 10 January 1946, when technicians at the Signal Corps laboratories at Fort Monmouth used a military radar set to bounce radio echoes off the moon, the earth's natural satellite. Soon after the orbiting of the first artificial satellites in the late 1950s, the Army installed a radio repeater in a satellite and successfully tested the concept of communications relays in space. By 1963 the military had joined with the newly created National Aeronautics and Space Administration in a venture called Project SYNCOM to orbit a series of satellites over the equator. Placed in an eastward orbit at 6,800 miles an hour and at an altitude of 22,300 miles, called a synchronous orbit, each satellite remained at a fixed point in relation to the earth. This eliminated the need for tracking antennas which would require powerful motors and precise servomechanisms.

To convince dubious military commanders and cost-conscious congressmen of the potentials of satellite communications, the Army sent a five-man crew, led by WO Jack H. Inman, on a tour of the United States with an experimental mobile terminal, the Mark IV (X). From parade grounds, parking lots, and field exercise sites, the satellite terminal communicated through the SYNCOM satellites with

[33]DCA, Systems Plan for an Integrated U.S. Wideband Communications System in Southeast Asia, 28 Dec 64.

[34]Interv, author with CW2 (ret.) Jack H. Inman, former satellite terminal team chief, 15 Oct 79, Historians files, CMH; U.S. Army Satellite Communications Agency, SATCOM 1966, pp. E–1 through E–4, file 139571, 72A25/6, WNRC.

Satellite Communications Equipment Is Unloaded

fixed stations in California and New Jersey. The Tonkin crisis disrupted the demonstration tour. With only one day's notice, Inman's team flew to Saigon and had its terminal on the air within a few hours of landing.[35]

In October the Army dispatched to Saigon a more advanced terminal, called the Mark IV (I) and later redesignated the TSC–55, that had been built to specifications developed from data gathered during the demonstrations and tests of the Mark IV (X). The prototype terminal remained in Saigon as a backup. The Joint Chiefs of Staff also dispatched a terminal mounted on the USNS *Kingsport* to the South Pacific to be available should the land-based terminals be put out of action. Discovering that the SYNCOM satellite was occasionally masked from Hawaii because the rocket that had launched it into space had had insufficient power to propel it into a perfect equatorial orbit, the Joint Chiefs of Staff moved the *Kingsport* to Guam, where during periods of interruption it could relay the signal from

---

[35]The best discussions of the development of military satellite communications are contained in MS, U.S. Army Strategic Communications Command (USASCC), NASA's Role in the Development of Communications Satellite Technology, 1965; USASCC AHS, FY–66, app. F. Both in CMH. Memo, Secy of Defense for JCS, 5 Jul 62, sub: Defense Communications Satellite Plan, Incl to JCS 222/481, 11 Jul 62, p. 2173, JACO (1962), DA/13, NARS. The concept of orbiting satellites in a synchronous orbit was developed in 1957 by Signal Corps technicians working with the Army Ballistic Missile Agency at Redstone Arsenal, Alabama. Letter to the Editor, William C. Pittman, in *Military Review* 59, no. 4 (April 1979):76.

Antennas at the Tan Son Nhut Satellite Communications Site

the Saigon terminal to Hawaii over the newly completed transpacific cable.[36]

The opening of the transpacific cable in early 1964 provided an extension of commercial-quality communications from the United States to the South Pacific. By late December that vital capability was extended to South Vietnam with the completion of the $21 million WETWASH project: a 55-mile microwave link between Clark Air Base and San Miguel on the coast of Luzon Island in the Philippines, which was also the location of the cablehead for the transpacific cable; a 600-mile submarine cable from San Miguel to Nha Trang; a 200-mile troposcatter link from Nha Trang to Phu Lam; and a technical control facility in Nha Trang. The new sixty-channel system offered far better quality communications than single-sideband radio and doubled the number of overseas circuits entering Southeast Asia. Because WETWASH included a modern, fixed technical control at the transfer point between the submarine cable and the troposcatter system at Nha Trang, communicators could also route channels from the Philippines for distribution north to Da Nang and west through the BACKPORCH terminal at Ubon to Bangkok. With the rerouting of those single overseas circuits to other points in Southeast Asia, the vulnerability of having a single overseas gateway to South

[36]Interv, author with Inman, 15 Oct 79; USASCC AHS, FY–65, app. B, pp. 5, 19, 21; Msg, DCS to USASATCOM, 31 Aug 64, sub: Deployment of USNS *Kingsport*; Msg, JCS to CINCPAC, 3 Sep 64, sub: DOD Use of SYNCOM. All in CMH.

113

Vietnam at Phu Lam was finally reduced.[37]

In the waning days of 1964, as technicians at the Phu Lam station switched overseas communications from noisy radio systems to the clear channels of WETWASH, American signal officers finally began to feel optimistic that long-disregarded vulnerabilities in communications might soon be resolved. Although communications had been found wanting during the Tonkin crisis, the problem had infused the concerns and needs of communicators with a beneficial urgency. In addition, advisers obtained new financial support for a major rehabilitation of South Vietnamese communications. The Special Forces network was reinforced by a signal company, and with the assistance of a larger signal staff at the Army Support Command, the 39th Signal Battalion obtained engineer and logistical support to improve its facilities. The Joint Chiefs of Staff approved long-awaited improvements to base communications in Thailand, and advances were made in connecting bases in Thailand with BACKPORCH in South Vietnam.

Besides instilling a note of urgency, the Tonkin crisis in August provided strategic insights for staff planners who were trying to alleviate communications weaknesses in Southeast Asia. When Admiral Sharp had evaluated his communications capabilities for Southeast Asia in June, he had done so with the assumption that transportable communications packages from his own Pacific Command contingency stocks and from the U.S.-based strategic reaction force would be available for emergency needs. The reluctance of the Joint Chiefs of Staff to commit any reinforcements during the Tonkin crisis had left Admiral Sharp with only those communications already installed in Southeast Asia and the experimental satellite terminal. Had the enemy escalated the crisis, alerted signal units would have had insufficient time to move to South Vietnam and install adequate communications for the three-division reaction force alerted for rapid deployment to Southeast Asia. To support a cautious and flexible American strategy adequately, Admiral Sharp had become convinced that an improved communications base had to be established.

Communicators had also gained important technical insights during the busy summer of 1964. Because they had lacked sufficient resources to build separate communications for operational and administrative traffic, or for tactical and strategic needs, they had consolidated many varieties of disparate, and often incompatible, equipment into a signal network to blanket the vast land area of Southeast Asia. They had used trial and error, employing fabricated equipment and making special modifications for each individual circuit. When the Tonkin crisis struck, they were unable to alter in hours what had taken months to install. In attempting to reroute circuits from Saigon to air bases in Thailand, signalmen at the nodes in the field had neither the ancillary equipment to handle interconnections between incompatible equipment nor the technical control facilities to manage the changes and installation of new circuits.

By December 1964 the lessons of Tonkin had been examined and applied.

---

[37]MS, USAF, Project Corona Harvest, Command Control and Communications, 8 Oct 70, vol. 3, p. 1, K143.50103-3, OAFH; Rpt, JCS 222/248, 3 Aug 62, sub: Establishment of Philippines–South Vietnam Wideband Trunk, JACO (1962), DA/13, NARS.

Responding to communications requirements developed by theater signal staffs to support American strategy for Southeast Asia, the Defense Communications Agency developed a plan to integrate the region's communications systems into a single modern network, the Integrated Wideband Communications System, that would extend the commercial-quality communications provided by satellites and submarine cables all the way to the battlefield.

6

Planning for War, January–July 1965

Although the new year began with the promise of improvements in communications within Southeast Asia, worsening political and military conditions in South Vietnam dampened American optimism. The critical military situation created a need to accelerate the installation of communications that overwhelmed hopes of making improvements in an orderly manner. Exploiting political dissension in the South Vietnamese government, the Communists conducted an aggressive political and military offensive in the South Vietnamese countryside. Emboldened Viet Cong attacked the large air base at Bien Hoa in November 1964, killing two Americans and four South Vietnamese soldiers; on Christmas Eve, terrorists planted a bomb in the Brink Hotel, an American facility in Saigon, killing two more Americans and destroying the AFVN broadcasting station.[1]

The South Vietnamese Army, weakened by the political bickering of its officers, seemed unable to halt the new wave of Viet Cong terrorism and growing military prowess. Even its communications were affected. Worried that dissidents might seize the communications network, the South Vietnamese high command kept badly needed tactical radios in American compounds to provide an alternate communications system in the event of a coup attempt.[2]

Air Support Communications Tested in Combat

R esupplied during the fall with new weapons and radios infiltrated from North Vietnam, Viet Cong main force units kept pressure on the harassed South Vietnamese Army. The first major encounter of the new year occurred when the Viet Cong attacked Binh Gia, a small "new life" hamlet, located east of Saigon

[1]Rapidly installing powerful tactical high-frequency radios in another building, American communicators had the station back on the air within twenty-four hours. Interv, author with Col (ret.) Wilbur A. Scudder, Jr., former staff officer, MACV J–6, 15 Feb 78, Historians files, CMH.
[2]Ltr, SMIAT (Special Military Intelligence Advisory Team) to 500th Intelligence Gp, 10 Apr 65, sub: Monthly Activities and Status Report, file 2–12 (ORLL), 1965, 70A593/1, WNRC.

in Phuoc Tuy Province where the Viet Cong had been conducting their resupply operations.[3] Throughout the first week of 1965, two Viet Cong regiments methodically destroyed a battalion of South Vietnamese marines and two South Vietnamese ranger battalions that had been committed piecemeal to relieve the hamlet. As General Westmoreland later noted, the battle marked "the beginning of an intensive military challenge which the Vietnamese government could not meet within its own resources."[4]

For signalmen the battle reawakened earlier fears about the vulnerability of American communications and the small amount of extra equipment available to cover likely combat losses. The battle also highlighted the persistence of poor planning for supporting artillery and air support and a need to perfect air-ground communications. A lack of coordination of air requests and poor air-ground communications between U.S. and South Vietnamese Air Force fighter planes and ground forces had left the ground troops at Binh Gia with only the support of U.S. Army helicopters, which proved to have insufficient firepower to rout the large force.[5]

Only four months earlier, after similar problems contributed to the defeat of another South Vietnamese battalion, General Westmoreland had sent a five-man team of U.S. Army and Air Force officers—including a representative of the MACV signal staff, Capt. William V. Paul, Jr.—to the field to investigate the functioning of the air support system. After visiting every South Vietnamese division and talking with commanders and their advisers, the team concluded that a history of unfulfilled requests for Air Force support had destroyed all confidence in the air request system. Ground commanders preferred to rely on lightly armed, but dependable, helicopter support that their Army advisers could readily summon from the Air Support Operations Center at each corps headquarters. The South Vietnamese government, for both safety and bureaucratic reasons, still refused permission for Air Force planes to provide air support unless the request for the strike was approved at every echelon of the military and governmental hierarchy. Thus, a request had to travel a circuitous route from an infantry company through district, regimental, and provincial headquarters, usually competing with operational and administrative traffic on general-purpose radio nets. It often became lost or was deliberately delayed by overly cautious South Vietnamese officials, who, fearing recriminations for approving an air strike that might cause casualties among South Vietnamese Army units or civilians, held requests for support until the appropriate commander could personally approve them. Even if a request reached the Air Operations Center in Saigon, which assigned all Air Force missions, aircraft dispatched to provide fire support had to be guided over the target by a South Vietnamese forward air controller. Rather than endure the delays and uncertainties inherent in such laborious procedures, South Vietnamese Army

---

[3]The strategic hamlets were renamed new life hamlets in 1964.

[4]Admiral U. S. G. Sharp and General William C. Westmoreland, *Report on the War in Vietnam (as of 30 June 1968)* (Washington, D.C.: Government Printing Office, 1969), p. 95.

[5]DIA, Intelligence Bulletin, Binh Gia Action Report, 4 Jan 65, CMH. For an analysis of air support problems during the battle of Binh Gia, see HQ AF, The Battle of Binh Gia (Project Checo), 27 Dec 65; MS, Rowley, Tactics and Techniques. Both in OAFH.

commanders simply replaced Air Force support with Army helicopter gunships.[6]

Captain Paul's survey group recommended that the South Vietnamese eliminate the requirement for approval of air strikes by each level of the chain of command and establish an air request net for direct communications from field units to Air Support Operations Centers at each corps headquarters. Although the investigators supported the requirement to have air strikes guided by a forward air controller, they recommended that American air controllers be permitted to coordinate strikes of U.S. aircraft. To implement the recommendations, the MACV signal staff established a standard frequency, which it called a flight-following net, on which any ground unit equipped with an FM radio could make a call to any aircraft in the area. The signal staff also established bilingual distress calls and emergency procedures for the flight-following net and devised visual signaling procedures for air-ground communications when radios were unavailable.[7]

Despite earlier recognition of the need for a new air request system, the improved procedures were put into effect only after the losses at Binh Gia once again demonstrated their necessity. The South Vietnamese high command remained reluctant to ease restrictions on air support. In late January 1965, when the South Vietnamese first permitted the U.S. Air Force to use jet fighters in direct support of ground units, they also relaxed the requirement to have South Vietnamese forward air controllers present during air support operations by fixed-wing aircraft. Then in March, the head of the South Vietnamese high command, Maj. Gen. Tran Van Minh, issued a directive establishing a South Vietnamese air request net as the primary means for requesting immediate air support. In the following months, as ground commanders discovered the ease with which air support could be had, their use of the more heavily armed fixed-wing aircraft increased dramatically.[8]

Troubles with BACKPORCH

While American advisers were resolving procedural problems with air support, the Army Support Command was encountering technical difficulties with the backbone system. During early January 1965 the BACKPORCH network was suddenly afflicted with a mysterious fading effect so severe that transmission of teletype pulses was no longer possible. Although Page engineers shut down each terminal for six hours for maintenance—the first time the terminals had been off the air since the network was installed in 1962—they were unable to overcome the interference. In response to an urgent request for technical assistance, the Defense Communications Agency quickly dispatched an eleven-man team, headed by Capt. Henry Gorman, U.S. Navy, the chief of the agency's Pacific field office, and Joseph Rose, a chief engineer from the agency's head-

---

[6]Interv, author with Lt Col William V. Paul, former staff officer, MACV J-6, 16 Nov 77, Historians files; MACV History, 1964, pp. 82–84, 180. Both in CMH.

[7]MFRs, USASCV, 17 Dec 64 and 11 Jan 65, sub: Improved Monitoring of Radio Frequencies, CMH.

[8]CINCPAC History, 1965, p. 44, CMH.

quarters in Washington, to inspect the entire BACKPORCH net.[9] The team split into three groups: two groups traveled to different sites to evaluate system performance, training, and logistics; the other remained in Saigon to study the overall design of the network and to analyze propagational factors.[10]

One of the members of the latter group, Edward Florman of the National Bureau of Standards, had investigated during the fall of 1963 the difficulties with the Philco troposcatter system between Bangkok and Saigon. In studying the propagation conditions affecting BACKPORCH, the group had the benefit of data he had gathered in the previous tests and a significant amount of scientific research that his findings had generated. To overcome attenuation and refraction of troposcatter beams in the atmosphere, engineers had been using a formula, called the refraction index, that considered the variables of temperature, humidity, and air pressure in determining how high to adjust the power of a troposcatter radio signal. Florman's measurements of the Philco system had demonstrated that application of the standard formula was counterproductive in Southeast Asia during winter months, when thermal layers caused the upper atmosphere to be uncharacteristically warmer than the lower air, a condition called temperature inversion.[11]

After conferring with representatives of the U.S. Air Force Weather Squadron at Tan Son Nhut and the chief of the local South Vietnamese meteorological station, the inspection team discovered that the temperature inversions in South Vietnam during January 1965 had been the most severe in recent history. Attempting to overcome a mysterious fading of signals caused by the atmospheric anomalies, operators had been adjusting their transmitting power to the highest possible levels. Since that practice pushed systems beyond proper thresholds, a situation akin to driving a car continually at maximum revolutions per minute, they were unwittingly putting signal levels out of synchronization and causing equipment to wear out at an excessive rate. To minimize the effects of the fading, the team advised the Page engineers to discontinue using the refraction index during thermal inversions and to use frequency diversity on BACKPORCH.[12]

Besides diagnosing the causes of propagational problems, the inspection team also documented many of the technical and personnel problems that had been plaguing BACKPORCH since its installation. The team members found that most local fabrications and equipment modifications made by the 39th Signal Battalion to improve the system were only partially successful; indeed, a few were actually detrimental. In modifying the MRC–85's to add twelve additional chan-

[9]Besides representatives of the Defense Communications Agency, the team consisted of men from the Advanced Research Projects Agency, the U.S. Army Strategic Communications Command, the U.S. Army, Ryukyu Islands, the 39th Signal Battalion, Page Communications Engineers, and the National Bureau of Standards.

[10]Msg, COMUSMACV to CINCPAC, 13 Jan 65, sub: MRC–85 Tropo Equipment, CMH; DF, USARPAC G–3 to CofS, 29 Mar 65, tab R, in Folder, Items of CINCUSARPAC Interest, 338–75–1009/63, WNRC. A thorough discussion of the activities and findings of the inspection team is contained in an undated DCA-PAC Rpt, BACKPORCH Evaluation Survey: January–February 1965, in CMH.

[11]Ltr, E. F. Florman to Maj John Bergen, 23 Jan 78; USASCC, Tropospheric Scatter Transmission Loss Anomalies Observed on a Long Tropical Path, Jul 65. Both in CMH.

[12]Interv, author with Joseph Rose, engineer, Defense Communications Agency, 30 Jan 78, Historians files, CMH; DCA-PAC Rpt, BACKPORCH Evaluation Survey: January–February 1965, pp. 13–14, 22.

nels, for instance, signalmen had widened the bandwidth of the radio signal, providing an opportunity for noise to enter the entire system.[13]

In March 1965 Admiral Sharp passed the team's recommendations, which contained a number of technical modifications not included in plans for the proposed Integrated Wideband Communications System, to the Army for correction. The signal officer of the U.S. Army, Pacific, Col. John C. Liggett, reminded the Pacific Command that many of the improvements required additional work from Page not covered in the existing contract for operation and maintenance of the system and that technical details and engineering of proposed modifications had to be explored completely before negotiating a new contract and ordering expensive new equipment. At the insistence of the Defense Communications Agency, however, Admiral Sharp told the Army to prepare contracts without delay to meet the recommendations of the report.[14]

While Colonel Liggett searched for materials and negotiated new contracts to make the recommended technical modifications, signalmen in South Vietnam began correcting those problems for which they had the resources. Removing tactical multiplexing equipment from the MRC–85's, they withdrew the improvised channels from the system. At Nha Trang, technical controllers moved all circuits passing through a makeshift toll test facility to the permanent technical control that had been built as part of the WETWASH project. Colonel Gardner prepared formal written agreements to delineate carefully the specific responsibilities of the contractor and the military for technical and training functions. The contractors consented to intensify the on-the-job training program, and signal officers agreed to stabilize the assignments of soldiers to allow their training to be conducted at a single site.[15]

Interim Solutions

I mproving the technical condition of BACKPORCH was complicated by the indefinite status of the Integrated Wideband Communications System, which was being considered by the Department of Defense, and by concurrent programs to build alternate systems within Southeast Asia as backup to BACKPORCH and to the Phu Lam station. After the attack on Bien Hoa in November 1964, General Westmoreland became concerned that the Viet Cong might target communications facilities. On 16 December he requested that the Joint Chiefs of Staff deploy to South Vietnam two MRC–85's and a contingency radio communications center package that since the Tonkin crisis had been held on alert in the United States. Lacking any redundancy in either the overseas radio facilities or the in-country backbone network, General Westmoreland felt that he could ill afford to wait for

[13]DCA–PAC Rpt, BACKPORCH Evaluation Survey: January–February 1965, pp. 26–27.
[14]Msg, CINCUSARPAC to CINCPAC, 20 Mar 65, sub: BACKPORCH Upgrading; Msg, CINCPAC to CINCUSARPAC, 27 Mar 65, same sub; Msg, DCA to DCA PAC, 5 May 65, same sub. All in CMH.
[15]Msg, USARYIS to CINCUSARPAC, 9 Apr 65, sub: BACKPORCH Upgrading; Interv, author with Gardner, 20 Sep 77. Both in CMH.

contingency equipment to be sent from the United States. Disapproving the request for positioning all of the backup overseas stations in South Vietnam, Admiral Sharp gave the Pacific Air Force the mission, should anything happen at Phu Lam, of operating the small radio and communications center at Tan Son Nhut as an interim overseas station. Because MRC–85's could not be moved and installed as readily as contingency radio stations, Admiral Sharp approved the request for pre-positioning of the MRC–85's in South Vietnam and asked the chief of staff of the Air Force to send two MRC–85's to Westmoreland.[16]

In January 1965, before the backup equipment arrived, the BACKPORCH system was struck with the interference and technical problems that brought the DCA team to South Vietnam. Fearing that all communications might be lost, General Westmoreland decided that he had to have some alternative to the single-axis backbone until completion of the integrated wideband network. He proposed using the two new MRC–85's to link Saigon and Pleiku and moving the light troposcatter equipment from the unsatisfactory CROSSBOW to build a second system along the northern coastal axis, Nha Trang–Qui Nhon–Quang Ngai. To install a southern coastal system between Vung Tau and Nha Trang, he wanted the 11th Signal Group, the Army's strategic reserve signal force in the United States, to send him six teams with new light troposcatter sets, called TRC–90B's. Since the MRC–85's to replace CROSSBOW would not be ready for shipment until mid-March and since the Army was reluctant to release the six troposcatter teams with the only long-range multichannel equipment left in the Army's contingency stocks, Admiral Sharp deferred a response to General Westmoreland's proposal to install an alternate network.[17]

On 7 February 1965, the Viet Cong attacked an American advisory compound and airfield near Pleiku, killing 8 Americans, wounding 104, and destroying eleven aircraft. General Westmoreland's concern for backup communications assumed a new urgency. Reacting swiftly, President Johnson sent American planes on air strikes against a large communications and logistical complex near Dong Hoi in North Vietnam; the United States began evacuating American dependents from South Vietnam; and U.S. Marine Corps units arrived from Okinawa to protect installations in the northern corps of South Vietnam. America's stake in South Vietnam suddenly became much greater.

Troubled by the Viet Cong attack on American bases and by the report of the DCA inspection team, which had left Tan Son Nhut on 8 February on one of the evacuation aircraft, Admiral Sharp increased his efforts to find a means for emergency restoral of the BACKPORCH system. He told General Westmoreland to prepare, with the assistance of the Defense Communications Agency, a detailed plan for restoring all communications in Southeast Asia. The Air Force was to expedite delivery of the previously ordered MRC–85's and to hold all its uncommitted troposcatter equipment in the Pacific ready for deployment within seventy-two hours to either South Vietnam or Thailand; the U.S. Army, Pacific, was to

[16]Msg, CINCUSARPAC to CINCPAC, 16 Dec 64, sub: Transportable Mobile Contingency Communications, CMH.

[17]Msg, COMUSMACV to CINCPAC, 19 Jan 65, sub: Expansion RVN Long Lines System; Msg, CC-E DA to CINCUSARPAC, 10 Feb 64, same sub. Both in CMH.

The TRC–90 Terminal at Quang Ngai

be ready to operate any restoral equipment sent by the Air Force. In approving the actions, the Joint Chiefs of Staff reminded Admiral Sharp to include some provision for establishing an alternate overseas communications facility at Nha Trang in case Phu Lam and Tan Son Nhut were lost.[18]

The MACV Assistant Chief of Staff for Communications-Electronics (J–6), Col. Robert E. Kimball, assigned his radio officer, Capt. James F. Slingo, the mission of preparing the restoral plan; he was joined by Maj. Emmett Paige, Jr., who had established the troposcatter training course at Fort Monmouth and who had since been reassigned to the DCA field office in the Philippines. After assigning a restoral priority to every circuit traversing BACKPORCH, the two signal officers tried to engineer an alternate system using contingency equipment to reroute the highest-priority circuits. They discovered that with available contingency equipment only 10 percent of the service then being provided could be restored and that service would be of inferior quality and time-consuming to install. Since the thirty-foot transportable antennas issued with heavy troposcatter sets were inadequate to span the distances between all but two of the existing BACKPORCH sites, special sixty-foot antennas with concrete foundations would have to be constructed before those contingency sets could be put into operation. The two

---

[18]Msg, CINCPAC to JCS, 22 Feb 65, sub: BACKPORCH Restoral; Msg, JCS to CINCPAC, 3 Mar 65, same sub. Both in CMH.

123

officers concluded that the only realistic means of restoring any service immediately in Southeast Asia would be by an existing system similar to that requested by General Westmoreland in January.[19]

Admiral Sharp finally agreed with the concept of an in-being alternate network, but changed General Westmoreland's plan, which envisioned an alternate MRC–85 link between Saigon and Pleiku. Instead, Sharp told the U.S. Army, Pacific, to use the new MRC–85's being sent by the Air Force to install a system between Pleiku and Da Nang. He requested that the U.S. Army Electronics Command attempt to upgrade CROSSBOW between Pleiku and Saigon, using equipment developed for the new TRC–90B. To build temporary bypasses around BACKPORCH, he convinced the Joint Chiefs of Staff to send him the six troposcatter teams from the Army's strategic reserve. He later requested and received augmentation of additional heavy troposcatter sets that the Air Force had been using in the Mediterranean area. With those sets the 39th Signal Battalion built systems from Da Nang to Ubon, Thailand, and from Vung Tau to Cam Ranh Bay, a planned site for a new American air and logistical base thirty kilometers south of Nha Trang.[20]

Difficulties encountered in installing the restoral systems during late spring and early summer 1965 confirmed the conclusions of Captain Slingo and Major Paige that troposcatter equipment—although nominally mobile—was inflexible and difficult to install. Arranging for shipment and installation of the original two MRC–85's that General Westmoreland had requested in December involved considerable coordination between the Army and Air Force chiefs of staff, the Pacific Command, the Military Assistance Command, Page, and the Air Force Logistics Command. Since the sets had to be made compatible with other equipment on BACKPORCH and frequencies had to be set in the factory, the MRC–85's had to be overhauled before shipment from the United States. Special air and ground transport arrangements had to be made for the heavy vans. In South Vietnam, Colonel Gardner had to negotiate a contract with Page to engineer the new systems and build fixed antennas and concrete pads for the vans. Discovering that even some of the restoral systems' sixty-foot antennas were insufficient to meet DCA's technical standards, which were the criteria for any system that might eventually become part of the proposed integrated network, Page had to build several huge 120-foot billboard antennas. Over six months elapsed between General Westmoreland's request for the supposedly transportable contingency equipment and the time it was on the air.[21]

The Department of the Army had difficulty finding enough troposcatter personnel to man the restoral systems and the WETWASH troposcatter link, which the

---

[19]Interv, author with Col James E. Slingo, former staff officer, MACV J–6, 1 Feb 78, Historians files, CMH; Msg, COMUSMACV to CINCPAC, 17 Mar 65, sub: BACKPORCH Restoral; Msg, CINCUSAR-PAC to COMUSMACV, 30 Mar 65, same sub. Both in CMH.

[20]Msg, CINCPAC to JCS, 22 Feb 65, sub: BACKPORCH Restoral; Msg, CINCPAC to JCS and CINC-USARPAC, 6 Mar 65, same sub. Both in CMH.

[21]Msg, USASCC to DA and CINCUSARPAC, 6 Apr 65, sub: BACKPORCH Expansion; Msg, CINC-USARPAC to USASCC, 17 Jun 65, sub: Da Nang MRC–85 Terminal; Msg, USARYIS to USASCV, 22 Apr 65, sub: Contingency MRC–85s; Msg, USARYIS to CINCUSARPAC, 22 Apr 65, sub: Installation of MRC–85 BACKPORCH Restoral Sets. All in CMH.

Army took over from the Air Force in June 1965. Although the signal school was finally graduating troposcatter operators trained on the TRC–90, and some of those men were being sent to an Air Force school for three additional weeks of training on the MRC–85, the number of graduates was sufficient to meet requirements only as they existed before the expansion of the BACKPORCH system. Since no records had been kept listing those signalmen who had received on-the-job training during the early years in South Vietnam, personnel officers in the Pentagon were unable to locate experienced troposcatter operators still in the Army. Even when those veterans of the 39th Signal Battalion were found, they could not be involuntarily reassigned to South Vietnam until they had been back in the United States at least two years. It was not until the fall of 1965, after the Army lessened the two-year overseas reassignment restriction to nine months for certain critical skills in South Vietnam and expanded its training courses, that shortages of troposcatter operators were alleviated.[22]

The specter of increased hostilities after the Pleiku attacks in February raised the prospect of the loss of the ninety-seven civilian contractors from Page and Collins in South Vietnam. Although the technicians had faithfully remained on the job during attacks and had even joined in the defense of the site at Qui Nhon when the Viet Cong attacked on 10 February, General Westmoreland worried that he had little control over the contractors and requested enough military operators to man the systems permanently in case the civilians withdrew. Advised of the difficulties in obtaining military operators, he accepted assurances from the contractors that they intended to remain at their posts in the face of stepped-up hostilities. They never let him down.[23]

While the perils of war failed to intimidate the civilian contractors, inflexible procurement regulations almost succeeded in disrupting contractor support. In response to new directives that all contracts issued by the U.S. Army, Ryukyu Islands, would be negotiated in strictly open bidding, the command's signal officer, Col. William A. Van Sandt, informed Page that the original contract for operation and maintenance of BACKPORCH, which had previously been automatically extended, would be opened for competitive bidding. That development alarmed the commander of the U.S. Army Strategic Communications Command, Maj. Gen. Richard J. Meyer, who expected to be given responsibility for BACKPORCH when the integrated network was completed. Concerned that a new contractor would be unable efficiently to assume control of the network while Page was still installing the restoral systems, Meyer urged the U.S. Army, Ryukyu Islands, to extend the contract with Page. In corresponding directly with the U.S. Army, Ryukyu Islands, a subordinate command of the U.S. Army, Pacific, General Meyer had ignored the chain of command. His actions irked General John K. Waters, the U.S. Army, Pacific, commander, who notified General Meyer that

---

[22]Msg, CINCUSARPAC to DA, 13 Mar 65, sub: BACKPORCH Upgrading Restoral; Msg, DA to USCONARC et al., 26 Mar 65, sub: BACKPORCH Restoral; Msg, DA to CINCPAC et al., 30 Mar 65, sub: BACKPORCH Restoral and Expansion. All in CMH.

[23]Msg, COMUSMACV to CINCPAC, 11 Feb 65, sub: BACKPORCH Restoral, CMH; Interv, author with Thomas M. Shimabukuro, former engineer, Page Communications Engineers, Inc., 21 Feb 78, Historians files, CMH.

Colonel Van Sandt was proceeding properly in opening the contract to competitive bidding. Waters assured General Meyer that the U.S. Army, Pacific, would be most careful in ensuring contractor competence as it reviewed the bids, and he pointedly reminded Meyer that he was very interested in BACKPORCH since the Department of the Army had not told the U.S. Army, Pacific, that it would lose operational responsibility for BACKPORCH. The contract worries ended in May when Page won the competitive bidding. At a cost of almost $1.8 million, the Washington, D.C.–based company would continue operating and maintaining BACKPORCH and the troposcatter portion of WETWASH for at least another year.[24]

Tactical Operations

While signal staff officers were formulating restoral plans, coordinating contractor support, and procuring contingency equipment, the 39th Signal Battalion was becoming increasingly busy in tactical operations in the two northern corps areas of South Vietnam. In the I Corps area, the newly arrived 9th U.S. Marine Expeditionary Brigade required base communications at Da Nang; in the II Corps area, the South Vietnamese, for the first time in the war, were moving division-size forces into Viet Cong strongholds. When the headquarters of the 22d South Vietnamese Division moved from its mountain base west of Pleiku to a coastal area near Phu Cat that was heavily populated with Viet Cong, the American signal detachment supporting the division's advisers became the first unit of the 39th Signal Battalion to fulfill the strictly tactical mission for which the battalion was originally formed. The signalmen quickly pulled their equipment from buildings and bunkers and remounted it in vans. Within hours after completing an uneventful 100-mile road march, they had installed a field signal center near Phu Cat and had established radio-teletype and single-sideband links with their sister detachment supporting the II Corps advisory team, seventy miles to the west at Pleiku. Within a few days they connected their switchboard and communications center to Pleiku with a system using a recently fielded, experimental troposcatter set, the MRC-80.[25]

The battalion also interlaced the Central Highlands and the coastal areas of II Corps with tactical radio relay systems. Although the signalmen were rarely able to obtain a direct line-of-sight path between many sites in the mountainous area, they discovered that diffraction of very high frequency radio waves off a mountain sometimes even improved the quality of a link, an unpredictable phenomenon called obstacle gain. Benefiting from this phenomenon, a radio system spanning the rugged country between Da Lat and Ban Me Thuot covered

[24]Interv, author with Van Sandt, 14 Feb 78; Msg, USASCC to USARYIS, 20 Mar 65, sub: BACKPORCH FY–66 M&O Contract; Msg, CINCUSARPAC to USASCC, 24 Mar 65, sub: BACKPORCH FY–66 Contract; Msg, USARJ to CINCUSARPAC, 26 May 65, sub: Contract Award Approval. All in CMH.

[25]In January the 39th Signal Battalion had received three prototype models of the MRC–80, a medium-range, four-channel troposcatter radio that the Army was testing. Ltr, 39th Sig Bn to USARPAC, 12 Apr 65, sub: Command Report, 1 Jan 65–31 Mar 65, file 139616, 72A25/7, WNRC.

fifty-five miles, a distance almost twice the radio's normal maximum range. Even though many of the systems installed during the spring of 1965 remained in operation only a short time, the endeavors of the 39th Signal Battalion's radio relay teams produced empirical data—frequencies, antenna adjustments, and azimuths—that their successors later used to plan systems for support of American units deployed to the II Corps area. Much of the information they supplied could never have been determined without actually attempting to make the links.[26]

When the 22d South Vietnamese Division returned to the Central Highlands in May, the troposcatter teams that had provided the link from Phu Cat to Pleiku moved north to connect the III Marine Amphibious Force, the new Marine headquarters in Da Nang, to the Marine aviation units located sixty miles to the south at Chu Lai. By that time, the 11th Signal Group at Fort Lewis, Washington, had also deployed the six TRC–90B's and six additional microwave teams to South Vietnam for the BACKPORCH restoral mission.[27]

Based on a technical survey of CROSSBOW, the Military Assistance Command decided to dismantle the ill-fated system and build a new system from Saigon to Pleiku with the TRC–90B's. The new commander of the 39th Signal Battalion, Lt. Col. James J. Dorney, personally searched for a relay location for the new system. After flying over the highlands in a helicopter for several days, he finally decided on an isolated height about five miles east of Da Lat called Lang Bian Mountain. Although the site could be reached only by helicopter, it commanded a panoramic view of the highlands and was near enough to Da Lat so that it could serve as both a relay station and a terminal serving the town. In attempting to move the equipment by helicopter to the mountain top, however, the signalmen were stymied by strong wind currents that threatened to dash the heavy radio sets, swaying precariously in slings under the helicopters, against the face of the mountain. A South Vietnamese engineer company, assisted by the troposcatter operators, painstakingly had to build a primitive road and tow the valuable vans up the mountain with a bulldozer. Not until the summer of 1965 was the system on the air.[28]

Much of the equipment used during the spring of 1965 to expand tactical communications throughout the two northern corps areas had been airlifted to South Vietnam at the personal direction of Army Chief of Staff General Harold K. Johnson. During Johnson's visit to Saigon in mid-March, the commanding general of the U.S. Army Electronics Command, Maj. Gen. Frank W. Moorman, had accompanied him. Moorman returned to Fort Monmouth determined to

---

[26]Msg, MACV to USASCV, 19 Mar 65, sub: VHF Radio Systems, CMH.

[27]To bypass manpower ceilings and constraints on the reassignment of personnel to South Vietnam, the radio teams, which contained veterans of duty in South Vietnam, were sent in a temporary duty status and remained assigned to their parent units at Fort Lewis. Msg, USASCC to 11th Sig Gp, 23 Mar 65, sub: TCS of C-E Equipment and Teams to RVN; Msg, DA to USASCC and CINC-USARPAC, 26 Mar 65, sub: Warning Order, Troposcatter Terminal Teams; Msg, COMUSMACV to CINCPAC, 19 Apr 65, sub: Microwave Equipment; Msg, CINCPAC to CINCUSARPAC, 30 Apr 65, sub: Microwave Teams. All in CMH.

[28]Interv, author with Col (ret.) James J. Dorney, former CO, 39th Signal Battalion, 16 Feb 79, Historians files, CMH; 23d MHD (Military History Detachment), 362d Signal Company (Tropo): The Employment of Tactical Tropospheric Scatter Equipment and Units in Support of Operations in Vietnam, 25 Apr 66, pp. 43–45, 68A75/11, WNRC.

modernize the deteriorating communications equipment in South Vietnam. He expedited the delivery of $3.8 million of tactical multichannel and radio-teletype equipment to the 39th Signal Battalion during the following month. He also dispatched electronics engineers to South Vietnam to investigate problems with CROSSBOW. They returned with specifications for an improved version of the TRC–90, which would be called a TRC–132. With the help of the Avionics Division of the Electronics Command's laboratories, signal depots were also fabricating navigational equipment to handle an expected surge of Army air operations in South Vietnam.[29]

To handle the equipment rushed from the United States, the 39th Signal Battalion's logistics officer, Capt. Parlan L. McGivern, and his twelve-man shipping and receiving section used every available means of transportation—air, coastal barge, military convoy, and commercial truck. During April alone, they moved over 430,000 pounds of signal materiel from ports to signal detachments throughout South Vietnam. Although the old equipment was to have been evacuated for overhaul and replenishment of depot stocks, General Westmoreland, foreseeing a buildup of new signal units in South Vietnam, obtained permission to repair and retain the replaced equipment for redistribution to newly arriving units.[30]

Preparing for the Buildup

C onsideration of signal augmentations by units, rather than simply reinforcement of the 39th Signal Battalion by contingency teams, had begun in early February 1965 when Colonel Gardner, anticipating deployment of a logistical command to South Vietnam, requested contingency forces from the Operation Plan 32 troop list (signal group headquarters, combat area signal battalion, and signal support company) and additional troposcatter operators and avionics maintenance men. Noting that the 39th Signal Battalion was so undermanned that it was unable to meet its then current missions, let alone to support any future assignments, the U.S. Army, Ryukyu Islands, forwarded Colonel Gardner's request to the U.S. Army, Pacific, with the recommendation that it be "implemented without delay." At U.S. Army, Pacific, headquarters Colonel Liggett only partially supported the proposal. He acknowledged a need for augmentations totaling 420 communicators to man recently completed sites in the I Corps area, to operate contingency equipment provided by the Air Force, and to staff another battalion headquarters to improve control over a burgeoning signal operation that

[29]Status reports on the progress of ECOM support to the buildup in South Vietnam are contained in Ltrs, ECOM to AMC, dated 29 Apr 65, 7 Jul 65, and 17 Sep 65. All in ECOM Historians files, Fort Monmouth, New Jersey.

[30]Interv, author with Col (ret.) Kenneth G. Ring, former signal officer, U.S. Army Support Command, Vietnam, 21 Feb 78, Historians files, CMH; Ltr, 39th Sig Bn to CINCUSARPAC et al., 14 Jul 65, sub: Command Report, 1 Apr 65–30 Jun 65, file 139616, 72A25/7, WNRC; Msg, USARYIS to CINCUSARPAC, 6 May 65, sub: Signal Equipment in Southeast Asia, CMH.

had become too unwieldy for the 39th Signal Battalion to handle alone. Interpreting recent guidance from the Pentagon as mandating a "conservative approach" to personnel increases, Colonel Liggett refused approval for all reinforcements intended for projected requirements such as the proposed logistical command. In sending the entire request back for reconsideration, he also pointed out that the combat area signal battalion included in Colonel Gardner's request would need substantial modification for the unique communications requirements in South Vietnam.[31]

Although Colonel Gardner agreed that conventional signal units were inappropriately designed for conditions in South Vietnam, he had requested standard units from the Operation Plan 32 troop list in order to obtain reinforcements more quickly. Colonel Gardner was undaunted by the discouraging response from the U.S. Army, Pacific, or by a lack of support from the MACV J–6, Colonel Kimball, who also believed signal reinforcements unnecessary. Gardner convinced the MACV Chief of Staff, Maj. Gen. Richard G. Stilwell, that the United States could ill afford to wait until a buildup had already commenced to dispatch signal units. Deploying communications support involved not only the mustering of men and equipment but also comprehensive engineering studies, time-consuming site surveys, and extensive construction. To support an increase of 5,000 support troops—a figure that President Johnson was expected to approve for a logistical command—Colonel Gardner felt he needed at least 700 additional signalmen. After Colonel Gardner had justified his requirement on a man-by-man basis, General Stilwell told him to ready his successor, Lt. Col. Kenneth G. Ring, to present the proposal to General Johnson during his upcoming visit.[32]

When the MACV staff met with General Johnson on 12 March, Colonel Ring's briefing was first on the agenda. Halfway into Ring's presentation, General Johnson asked why he was requesting "bits and pieces" of signal reinforcements rather than entire signal units. General Stilwell responded that in an effort to minimize requirements, his signal staff had developed support for the anticipated 5,000-man buildup on an individual rather than unit basis. When General Johnson responded that he wanted requirements for a 20,000-man logistical buildup, General Westmoreland halted the briefing and sent all his staff members back to reevaluate their needs. On the following morning, Colonel Ring outlined a proposal for a 1,400-man signal force that included the units that Colonel Gardner had previously requested plus a signal maintenance company. After he explained how each unit would be tailored for operations in South Vietnam, General Johnson approved the proposal and told General Westmoreland to include it in his buildup plans.[33]

---

[31]Msg, USASCV to USARYIS, 4 Feb 65, sub: Additional Signal Personnel, Equipment; Msg, CINCUSARPAC to USARYIS, 11 Mar 65, sub: Request for Additional Signal Capability, RVN. Both in CMH.

[32]When Colonel Gardner completed his tour in March, Colonel Ring, who had commanded the 39th Signal Battalion since the departure of Colonel White in the fall of 1964, replaced him as Army Support Command signal officer and turned over his command to Colonel Dorney. Intervs, author with Ring, 21 Feb 78, and Gardner, 20 Sep 77.

[33]After the briefing, Colonel Ring changed the designation of the signal support company, which was intended for headquarters-type communications in Saigon, to a communications center operations company. Interv, author with Ring, 21 Feb 78.

Within a few weeks of General Johnson's return to the United States, the Department of the Army alerted for deployment by June to South Vietnam the 2d Signal Group from Fort Bragg, North Carolina; the 41st Signal Battalion (Combat Area) from Fort Lewis, Washington; and the 593d Signal Company (Communications Center Operations) and the 56th Signal Company (Forward Supply and Maintenance) from Fort Gordon, Georgia. Colonel Ring submitted a detailed proposal for structuring the units through the U.S. Army, Pacific, to the Department of the Army. Brig. Gen. John Norton, who assumed command of the Army Support Command, Vietnam, on 1 April, tried unsuccessfully on two occasions to obtain advance parties from the incoming signal units to coordinate restructuring and plan for their reception, but he was stymied by a prohibition on early deployments. In late April, less than a month before the scheduled departure of the first signal units, he discovered that the reinforcement units were scheduled to go to South Vietnam without being modified because the U.S. Army, Pacific, had not forwarded the request for restructuring to the Pentagon.[34]

The proposal for restructuring, called a troop unit change request, was stalled at the headquarters of the U.S. Army, Pacific, while personnel, logistical, and signal staffs analyzed and debated the proposed changes. Although Colonel Ring had sent an advance copy of the changes to the signal staff at the Pentagon, officers in Washington, reluctant to tamper with established units that had trained together for years and had built up an esprit that would be lost in a reorganization, were content to see the request overtaken by events.[35]

Deciding that the Army Support Command, Vietnam, would have to circumvent command channels, General Norton dispatched Colonel Ring and an officer from the 39th Signal Battalion, 1st Lt. Billie N. Thomas, to Washington with the proposal. Informing General Gibbs, chief of communications-electronics at the Department of the Army, of the impending arrival of his representatives, General Norton irately implied that the "almost inconceivable situation" had been caused by a lack of concern and understanding in Hawaii and Washington for the unique needs of the conflict in Southeast Asia. He was so determined to obtain modified units that he facetiously offered to change his request for a signal battalion to a counterinsurgency battalion to appease any tradition-bound signal officers who might be reluctant to alter standard signal battalions.[36]

On 3 May 1965, Colonel Ring presented his proposal for the restructuring of the signal units bound for South Vietnam to a large assembly at the Pentagon consisting of representatives of each Army staff section and the commanders and staffs of the designated signal units. When irreconcilable disagreements arose,

[34]Fact Sheet, DA, OCC-E, 11 May 65, sub: Tactical Communications in Vietnam, tab B, file 139387, 72A4171/1, WNRC; Msg, Brig Gen Norton MAC 1725 to Lt Gen Harrell, 29 Mar 65; Msg, Lt Gen Harrell WDC 2739 to Brig Gen Norton, 1 Apr 65; Msg, Brig Gen Norton MAC 2132 to General Waters, 17 Apr 65; Msg, JCS to CSA/CINCSTRIKE, 24 Apr 65, sub: Deployment of US Army Signal Units. All in CMH.

[35]Ltr, Col (ret.) John C. Liggett to Maj John D. Bergen, 15 May 78; Interv, author with Col (ret.) Rodney P. Harrington, former plans officer, USARPAC Signal Office, 27 Jul 78, Historians files. Both in CMH.

[36]Msg, Brig Gen Norton MACV 2325 to Maj Gen Gibbs, 29 Apr 65, CMH; Msg, CINCUSARPAC to DA, 28 Apr 65, sub: Signal Augmentation to RVN, CMH. In the latter message USARPAC finally "defers to the recommendations from . . . agencies in RVN," concerning the requested changes.

the group sent the proposal directly to General Johnson for resolution. He returned it within an hour with the direction: "Give him [Ring] what he wants." For the next three days the Army staff met with representatives of the designated units and arranged for the transfer of unnecessary personnel and equipment and the requisition of augmentations. To ensure that the deployment—less than three weeks away—began on schedule, the Army staff arranged to ship any personnel or equipment not immediately available directly to South Vietnam within forty-five days. To avert morale problems, General Norton sent a message squelching rumors that he intended to make command changes when the units reached South Vietnam. Although several of the officers in the units had recently served in South Vietnam and were not required to return, they volunteered to deploy with their commands.[37]

While the Army Support Command was coordinating plans with the Department of the Army for receiving signal reinforcements, the signal staffs at the Military Assistance Command and the U.S. Army, Ryukyu Islands, were planning base communications for a rapidly expanding American force. The U.S. Marine Corps was spreading its forces along the coast of the northernmost corps area; on 6 May the first Army combat unit, the 173d Airborne Brigade from Okinawa, arrived in South Vietnam to protect American installations at Bien Hoa and Vung Tau in the III Corps area. At Cam Ranh Bay, an isolated coastal harbor thirty miles south of Nha Trang, American engineers were building a major air and sea port that would require extensive communications. While Colonel Kimball's staff in Saigon shifted available contingency equipment to serve the new units and bases, Colonel Van Sandt's men on Okinawa searched depots throughout the Pacific for signal materials, transferred equipment from other projects, and negotiated modifications to civilian contracts to install the new communications facilities.[38]

In coping with constant changes and new missions, signal officers in Southeast Asia increasingly came into conflict with the signal staffs in Hawaii. Colonel Van Sandt felt that peacetime supply and procurement procedures, which took six to eight months to gain approval of projects, were insufficient for the rapidly changing situation in Indochina. Thus, he had been submitting emergency requisitions for fixed facilities to the U.S. Army, Pacific, and purchasing cable equipment in Japan rather than ordering it through American supply channels. Maintaining that those expedients, while sometimes resolving an immediate need, caused additional work and delays over the long run, Colonel Liggett warned that future requests for support to Southeast Asia would have to conform more closely to applicable directives or be denied.[39]

The Pacific Command applied similar pressures to the joint signal staff in Saigon. When General Westmoreland requested in May that supporting head-

[37]Msg, Maj Gen Oden WDC 3826 to Brig Gen Norton, 5 May 65; DA, DCSOPS, AHS, FY-65, pt. 3, an. K, pp. 14–17. Both in CMH. Interv, author with Ring, 21 Feb 78.

[38]Intervs, author with Van Sandt, 14 Feb 78, and Scudder, 15 Feb 78.

[39]Interv, author with Van Sandt, 14 Feb 78; Interv, Raymond Thompson with Col Clarence Driscoll, former staff officer, U.S. Army, Ryukyu Islands, 19 Mar 67, Historians files; Msg, CINCUSARPAC to USARYIS, 29 Mar 65, sub: Emergency Communications Requirements. All in CMH.

quarters treat requirements for communications support in South Vietnam with greater urgency, Admiral Sharp replied that the Military Assistance Command, Vietnam, in its haste to obtain additional communications, was wasting valuable signal resources. Rather than seeking additional communications equipment for piecemeal commitment, Admiral Sharp wanted signalmen in South Vietnam to reevaluate existing sole-user service and to engineer switching systems to consolidate dedicated circuits into a more efficient common-user telephone and teletype system.[40]

Engineering for the communications expansion in South Vietnam during the spring of 1965 was indeed a problem. The small staff at the Ryukyu Islands headquarters, which was supposed to provide all communications engineering support for Southeast Asia, was inadequately manned to handle planning for an endeavor that had taken on a wartime intensity. Signal engineers had to design communications for partially defined requirements submitted by headquarters with little knowledge of proposed locations or missions and to develop the comprehensive data required by peacetime regulations to justify funds. At the same time, they were providing specifications for contract modifications to shift resources from previously approved projects to new, high-priority programs. For example, the dial switchboard that Colonel Gardner had sought for an alternate MACV command post after the Tonkin crisis had been thoroughly engineered and was about to be installed at Vung Tau when it had to be diverted to serve the new base at Cam Ranh Bay. When General Johnson finally announced in May that the Strategic Communications Command would eventually assume responsibility for BACKPORCH from the U.S. Army, Pacific, the task of the signal engineers became more complicated. Since the Strategic Communications Command would be paying for the operation and maintenance of systems that Colonel Van Sandt was planning, technical specifications and designs had to be approved by the staff of the Strategic Communications Command, Pacific, in Hawaii before implementation. To avoid endless coordination and delays, staff officers in Okinawa and Saigon had been meeting requirements for additional service by requesting more contingency multichannel equipment for sole-user circuits rather than performing complex engineering of consolidated common-user systems.[41]

The overburdening of the engineering staff on Okinawa shifted much of the responsibility for detailed technical planning to the MACV signal staff. The Operations Division, J–6, headed by Lt. Col. Gerald Dean, planned and supervised the development of the restoral communications network in the early spring; when the buildup began, it ensured that communications requirements of new units were met. The Plans Division, headed by Lt. Col. Charles C. Burrus, tried to anticipate those requirements and to program beforehand the means to fulfill

[40]A sole-user or dedicated circuit, sometimes called a hot line, is routed directly from subscriber to subscriber, while a common-user circuit terminates in a switchboard that serves many subscribers. Msg, COMUSMACV to CINCPAC, 9 May 65, sub: Communications Expansion; Msg, USASCV to USARYIS and CINCUSARPAC, 17 May 65, same sub; Msg, CINCPAC to COMUSMACV, 25 May 65, sub: Provision of Additional Circuits RVN; ibid., 28 May 65, sub: Communications Resources. All in CMH.

[41]Interv, author with Van Sandt, 14 Feb 78; Msg, USARYIS to CINCUSARPAC, 8 Apr 65, sub: USASCC Representation at BACKPORCH Negotiations, CMH.

them. To perform the technical engineering to transform adviser-oriented communications into a U.S. theater communications network, Colonel Burrus convinced Colonel Porter to transfer to him some of the advisers and engineers who had been planning the military communications system for the South Vietnamese Army. In moving from the advisory staff to the J–6 staff, Maj. Wilbur A. Scudder, Jr., and Capt. John W. Pugh, two experienced electrical engineers commissioned to design telephone and teletype networks for the American expansion, brought with them the plans and expertise they had acquired in planning South Vietnamese communications.[42]

Designing American communications proved to be a more difficult undertaking. Because of day-to-day uncertainty concerning the magnitude of the buildup and prohibitions against requesting resources for future unprogrammed needs, plans had to be both flexible and limited. Since the Integrated Wideband Communications System was expected to be installed within a year, Scudder and Pugh had to plan either interim facilities or communications that would be compatible with commercial equipment.

A disagreement between General Westmoreland and the U.S. ambassador, retired General Maxwell D. Taylor, over the proper strategy to follow in committing American troops also complicated signal planning. Emphasizing a continuation of an advisory and support role, Ambassador Taylor wanted a slower introduction of American combat troops with their role restricted to the defense and security of coastal enclaves around key installations and cities to free the South Vietnamese to confront the Viet Cong in the field. While still leaving the primary conduct of the war to the South Vietnamese Army, General Westmoreland wanted to use American troops in a more traditional mobile offensive role to search out and defeat the Viet Cong. Adoption of Taylor's enclave strategy would dictate more fixed communications centers and switchboards with permanently installed cable lines extending service throughout heavily populated areas in the enclaves and high-capacity multichannel systems to link widely dispersed enclaves; the more traditional approach espoused by General Westmoreland would involve standard communications operations using organic tactical equipment.[43]

Ultimately a compromise between the two approaches evolved. The Americans were to build logistical bases in coastal enclaves and defend them with mobile tactical units capable of conducting wide-ranging offensive operations. The BACK-PORCH system would have to be extended to those enclaves not already served by the area network, and fixed communications would have to be installed within enclaves for logistical units as well as for tactical units when they were garrisoned there. When tactical units moved to the field during operations, communicators would have to continue supporting rear headquarters remaining in the enclaves while also extending the fixed system to the field with tactical communications equipment. Incompatible tactical and fixed equipment would have to be connected during every field operation. Because of prohibitions against building a commu-

---

[42]Interv, author with Scudder, 15 Feb 78.

[43]For a discussion of the development of strategy and plans during the spring of 1965, see MS, Walter G. Hermes, Department of the Army: The Buildup, 1965–1967 (cited hereafter as The Buildup), chs. 2–5, CMH.

nications base for projected requirements, those tactical units that moved into base areas not already served by BACKPORCH would at first need to use their tactical equipment to establish their garrison communications and still save sufficient equipment to move out on operations.[44]

Besides a lack of strategic direction from Washington, the signal staff in Saigon had inadequate historical or doctrinal information to engineer a common-user system to meet the needs of the buildup anticipated and taking place in South Vietnam. In withdrawing dedicated circuits from subscribers reluctant to give up service they had come to depend on, Major Scudder and Captain Pugh had few standards or guides to apply in convincingly comparing needs and priorities. For conventional units, they used Army and Air Force field manuals, many of which were written with World War II conditions as a basis, to determine the number of telephones authorized to each element on a typical staff. For the advisory detachments and many of the nonstandard units, they first had to calculate usage rates and patterns empirically. They made hourly profiles to determine how much traffic each channel carried and conducted exhaustive message analyses to tabulate the precedence, classification, and length of messages being handled by each communications center. Because the network had few technical control facilities where circuits could be monitored or large switching centers at which all lines interconnected, the gathering of that data was fragmented and time-consuming.[45]

When Admiral Sharp began pressuring the Military Assistance Command, Vietnam, to improve its communications engineering, Colonel Burrus, to augment his two overworked communications engineers, requested three additional engineers by name: Thomas M. Shimabukuro, an employee of Page; Gilbert Sylva, an Air Force civilian telephone engineer; and Maj. Lewis F. Magruder, a staff officer with the Defense Communications Agency. In approving the loan of the three, Admiral Sharp recognized that they not only would add valuable technical expertise to the MACV engineering staff, but would also infuse MACV's planning with the perspectives of all the major communications agencies involved in South Vietnam.[46]

Beginning in early 1962 when BACKPORCH was being built, Shimabukuro had served in South Vietnam as Page's chief of maintenance operations for over two years until reassigned to the company's headquarters in Washington. When BACKPORCH began encountering technical and propagational difficulties in January 1965, Page sent him back to South Vietnam to correct the situation. After working to remedy the deficiencies discovered by the DCA inspection team, he returned to Washington to design technical controls to interconnect tactical communications with the proposed Integrated Wideband Communications System. When he moved to the MACV J–6 planning group, he performed transmission engineering studies to determine the net loss that telephone and teletype circuits would encounter as they traveled over the different routes of the network. Since the

---

[44]*U.S.-Vietnam Relations*, vol. 5, pt. IV.C.6, pp. 7–8.

[45]Interv, author with Scudder, 15 Feb 78.

[46]Msg, COMUSMACV to CINCPAC, 8 Jun 65, sub: Temporary Communications Engineer Personnel Augmentation; Msg, CINCPAC to CINCPACAF, 9 Jun 65, sub: Comm Engineering Personnel Augmentation. Both in CMH.

Defense Communications Agency graded its circuits for data transmission, the most sensitive mode of communications, Shimabukuro had to design circuits to have the same audio strength over a 7,000-mile transmission path as the Bell system in the United States required for a 3,000-mile transcontinental telephone call. Gilbert Sylva, an expert in the field of fixed-plant switching and cable equipment, designed terminal and repeater assemblies required for different transmission paths, while Scudder and Pugh mapped out where units were projected to locate and determined the service required in each area. Major Magruder ensured that all equipment was compatible and that each circuit met the technical standards of the Defense Communications Agency.[47]

Uncertainties and Obstacles

W hen the MACV engineering team began its project in June to develop a comprehensive telephone and teletype plan to support the buildup in South Vietnam, it was considering support for a 40,000-man force consisting of advisers, combat support and logistical units, a U.S. Marine Corps brigade, and an Army airborne brigade. By the time it submitted the plan to the Pacific Command in September, the size and composition of the force had changed considerably. Almost 100,000 men, including two more brigades and an airmobile division, were already in South Vietnam, and plans were being made to add another 100,000 men by the end of the year. Command arrangements had also changed. To command U.S. Army combat and support units in South Vietnam, in the summer of 1965 the U.S. Army, Vietnam (USARV), replaced the U.S. Army Support Command, Vietnam; and responsibility for U.S. tactical operations was divided between the III Marine Amphibious Force in the northern corps; an Army corps headquarters, Field Force, Vietnam, in the two central corps zones; and the corps senior adviser in the delta. The signal engineers constantly had to adjust their plans to conform to the evolving chain of command. Since the American combat effort shifted by the summer from the III Corps zone to the Central Highlands, different types of signal equipment also had to be programmed.

As planning for the buildup progressed throughout the spring of 1965, signal officers in Washington suffered through the same uncertainties that plagued the engineers in South Vietnam. After dispatching marines to protect American bases and ordering air raids on North Vietnamese bases in retaliation for the Viet Cong attacks on Pleiku and Qui Nhon, President Johnson, anxious to avoid unnecessary escalation of hostilities, took a cautious approach toward further commitment of troops or mobilization of American military might. When the president authorized the 20,000-man buildup in April, which included the 1,400 communicators in the 2d Signal Group, General Westmoreland warned that a signal group was sufficient only to support the augmentation then planned. If the decision was made to expand the force further, additional signal reinforcements had to be

[47]Intervs, author with Scudder, 15 Feb 78, and Shimabukuro, 21 Feb 78.

programmed. Yet the signal staff at the Pentagon lacked definitive guidance on which to base future programs because the president, trying to balance political and military concerns, was temporizing his approval of any long-range plans. To demonstrate American determination, he intended to counter every aggressive move of the Viet Cong until the Communist leaders realized that the cost of continuing the war was prohibitive. The Communists held the key to whatever future actions would be taken.

Recognizing that such an approach made it difficult to project future needs or to build a base in South Vietnam to be ready should more troops be sent, Secretary McNamara encouraged the military to continue planning for a wide range of alternatives. In a letter to the secretaries of the military services, he even said that they were to consider that they had an unlimited appropriation available for financing of aid to South Vietnam and that money was not to stand in the way of consideration of any option. Yet the blank check would prove difficult to cash. To ensure that expenditures of funds were based on sound requirements, peacetime budgetary and administrative procedures continued in force. Fiscal considerations still had to include gold flow concerns and had to project the cost of continuing use of equipment over future years. Justifications had to detail the reasons why existing resources were insufficient and to show why alternative proposals had been rejected. Since McNamara's appointment as secretary of defense, military planning had conformed to that kind of analytical approach, but the services found it especially difficult to apply to South Vietnam, where future needs were contingent on the enemy's moves and on political considerations.[48]

Responding to urgent requests from the U.S. Army, Pacific, for money to build the fixed antennas for the expansion of BACKPORCH and for equipment to upgrade CROSSBOW, the Department of the Army had to require that hard-pressed signal officers in the Pacific provide within one week "cost data developed by object class for period FY–66 thru 71 . . . to include engineering assistance, installation costs and any additional contract technicians."[49]

Faced with long lead times required to produce sophisticated electronic equipment and to construct complex communications facilities, the Pentagon had to assemble data quickly. Hampered by uncertain requirements, multiple alternatives, and laborious staffing procedures, signal planners in the field were unable to respond quickly with needed data. They found it particularly difficult to define detailed circuit requirements and perform comprehensive technical studies to determine the best means of providing required service for each of several alternative force packages being considered at the Pentagon. Besides being bound by technical concerns that other staffs did not have to consider, signal staff officers, planning for the commitment of particularly expensive equipment, also faced unique fiscal constraints. Since requirements for documentation and justification became progressively more stringent as the costs of requests increased, signal officers often found themselves preparing proposals for approval at the highest

---

[48]*U.S.-Vietnam Relations*, vol. 5, pt. IV.C.6, p. 107.
[49]Msg, DA to CINCUSARPAC, 30 Mar 65, sub: BACKPORCH Restoral and Expansion, CMH.

levels of the Department of Defense.[50]

Seeking to cut through some of the red tape imposed by the Department of Defense and to get permission to build a cushion against unexpected—and hence not readily justified—demands, the Joint Chiefs of Staff in April 1965 asked the secretary of defense to remove "administrative and procedural impediments that hamper us in the prosecution of this war."[51] Although refusing to relax fiscal and administrative procedures deemed intrinsic to management of the Department of Defense, Secretary McNamara responded with firmer planning guidance. In presenting that information to members of the Army staff in late April, Under Secretary of the Army Stanley R. Resor said that they should plan for a force of three U.S. divisions in South Vietnam. He also told them to assume modification of peacetime policies restricting the frequency of overseas assignments, reconstitution of the strategic reserve forces in the United States, and, most importantly, mobilization of the reserves.[52]

For signalmen, the strategic reserve already needed reconstituting. When the 82d Airborne Division was committed in May 1965 to help quell an insurrection in the Dominican Republic, the debilitating effects of support to South Vietnam on the signal reserve became apparent. Had the area of operations been larger, the Strategic Communications Command would have been unable to deploy any long-distance multichannel equipment; all its troposcatter sets were in Indochina. Even some U.S.-based divisions had lost signal and aviation units to Southeast Asia. The crisis in the Dominican Republic demonstrated the urgency of making definite decisions on the magnitude of the commitment to South Vietnam before the strategic reserve forces in the United States more seriously eroded.[53]

Before deciding on the extent of mobilization required to keep the Army strong enough to fulfill America's worldwide commitments while fighting in South Vietnam, Secretary McNamara went to General Westmoreland in early June for an updated projection of his needs for South Vietnam. Although he initially responded with an immediate requirement for 17 combat battalions and an increase by October 1965 to 33 battalions, heavy losses within the South Vietnamese Army during June prompted him to increase the projection to 44 battalions—a 175,000-man force—by fall and a possible need for 100,000 more troops in 1966. To provide the required additional manpower and to enlarge the training and logistical base for such a commitment, Secretary McNamara recommended to President Johnson that he ask Congress to authorize a call-up of 234,000 reserves and national guardsmen, including 125,000 for the Army, and to increase draft calls to add another 145,000 men to the Army. On 28 July the president announced his support of General Westmoreland's request for a 44-battalion force for South Vietnam and approved an increase of 235,000 men in Army strength, but stunned Army planners by declining to authorize mobilization of the reserves.[54]

---

[50]Joint Logistics Review Board, *Monograph 5: Communications*, Dec 69, pp. 34–35, 71A2351/6, WNRC.

[51]*U.S.-Vietnam Relations*, vol. 5, pt. IV.C.6, p. 108.

[52]Memo, Resor for CSA, 27 Apr 65, sub: Action Necessary to Meet Possible Developments in VN, CMH.

[53]DA, DCSOPS, AHS, FY–65, pt. 3, an. K, pp. 18–21, CMH.

[54]Ibid., an. F, CMH. This source contains an excellent discussion of the problems facing the Army staff after the president decided not to call up the reserves.

The shock was deepest at the Army training centers and schools. Because the reserves, already trained and outfitted for their mission, were not to be called, new draftees would have to be quickly prepared to meet the ambitious timetable set by General Westmoreland's request. After the televised broadcast of the president's decision, the surprised staff at the U.S. Army Southeastern Signal School at Fort Gordon, where most of the Army's enlisted communicators were trained, worked through the night to begin preparations to turn the school and training center to a wartime footing. Of all the branch schools, those of the Signal Corps were left in the worst predicament by the decision on reserves. In past wars the Signal Corps had relied on the large pool of experienced reservists working in the commercial communications industry to man sophisticated equipment that it would take months to teach recruits to operate. For the Vietnam War those experienced men would not even be available as instructors.[55]

Recognizing that scarce personnel resources would have to be carefully husbanded until Army schools began producing sufficient numbers of graduates, the Department of Defense liberalized its pay and promotion policies to halt a flow of experienced soldier technicians to better-paying civilian jobs. Congress approved pay raises averaging from 12 to 33 percent and provided funds to pay a reenlistment bonus to soldiers in highly critical skills, many in the fields of electronics and communications, to induce them to remain in the service after completion of their first enlistment. The Department of Defense also lifted stringent ceilings on promotions, which by the summer of 1965 had left over 150,000 positions in the Army filled by men in lower grades than their jobs demanded; under the new rules outstanding soldiers could be promoted to private first class with only four months' service and to sergeant with two years' service. Retirees with critical skills were offered a one-grade promotion to return for a two-year enlistment; others who were about to retire were involuntarily extended for six months.[56]

Personnel assignment and administration policies were also changed to ensure that military men were placed in the position for which they were best suited. To free more military men for service in South Vietnam, the signal school at Fort Gordon converted 41 percent of its military slots to civilian positions. The Army also modified its system of designating military occupational specialties: job classifications were modernized to reflect technological changes during the ten years since the system had last been changed and a new alphanumerical code was established to identify both occupational and skill relationships.[57]

While Army schools and personnel systems were undergoing drastic changes, logisticians were improving support programs for vital electronic equipment. General Moorman established a special office at Fort Monmouth that managed critical items of communications equipment and repair parts required in South Vietnam and coordinated with a similar group at the Pentagon. Called the Viet-

---

[55]Interv, author with John Holleran, deputy chief of resident training, U.S. Army Southeastern Signal School, Fort Gordon, 11 Jan 77, Historians files, CMH.

[56]MS, Hermes, The Buildup, ch. 9, pp. 13–14.

[57]In the new system, for example, a wireman (36C) progressed from an apprentice (36C10) to a senior supervisor (36C50). USCONARC Agenda, School Commandants' Conference, 1965, tab R, CMH.

nam Support Expediting Task Force, it had the authority to coordinate directly with any level of the Department of Defense to resolve problems delaying support of designated critical materiel, called FLAGPOLE items.[58]

By the summer of 1965 it seemed that everything demanded special attention— personnel, equipment, transportation, and communications. Ever since the year had begun so inauspiciously with the Viet Cong victory at Binh Gia, the pace of events had been fast but the goals only dimly defined. While the Department of Defense deliberated over long-range plans such as the Integrated Wideband Communications System, Army signal officers in the Pacific and at the Pentagon took action to satisfy immediate signal needs that would make those plans obsolete before they could be implemented.

Problems that had been festering for years were given emergency treatment to keep them from aggravating a worsening tactical situation. American advisers convinced the South Vietnamese to alter archaic air support procedures. Higher headquarters began trying to eliminate technical problems and vulnerabilities that had bothered communicators in South Vietnam since the construction of BACK-PORCH. Reinforcements for the overcommitted 39th Signal Battalion were finally on their way to South Vietnam.

By summer, as signal officers in the United States built a logistical and training base to sustain those improvements and reinforcements, their contemporaries in South Vietnam struggled to keep communications operating until the arrival of help from the United States. The efforts of both those in the United States and in Southeast Asia were complicated by bureaucratic procedures unsuited to wartime situations and by ill-defined organizational relationships. Before those problems could be resolved, they were overtaken by events.

[58]MS, Hermes, The Buildup, ch. 11, pp. 14–15.

7

Securing the Base of Operations
July 1965–March 1966

Since the marines and the Army airborne troops sent to South Vietnam in the spring of 1965 were operating from well-established enclaves, their communicators traveled light. Besides a radio detachment of the 999th Signal Company for a link back to Okinawa, the contingency forces had only tactical radios and enough telephone wire for small field command posts. To take advantage of the backbone network already installed, the new American units had only to run wire to the communications centers and switchboards operated for nearby advisory teams by the 39th Signal Battalion.[1]

While conducting patrols and airmobile assaults to flush out Viet Cong hiding in the jungles around the enclaves, the units did encounter difficulties with radio communications. Because heavy vegetation absorbed the signal of the old PRC–10 infantry FM voice radio carried by the Americans, communications between patrols and base camps was sporadic. Only when the communications officer of the 173d Airborne Brigade sent radio operators with portable radios aloft with airborne forward air controllers to relay traffic between ground stations did communications begin to improve. However, the limited numbers of aircraft restricted use of the expedient to operations large enough to merit a forward air controller. When an inability to call for fire support and reinforcements during routine daily patrols began to cause heavy casualties, the brigade commander, Brig. Gen. Ellis W. Williamson, told General Westmoreland that he vitally needed better portable radios for his men. That request led to the dispatch of an emergency shipment of a new transistorized FM voice radio, the PRC–25, that was destined to make the greatest impact on communications of any item of equipment in the war.[2]

---

[1]Ltr, 173d Abn Bde to DCSOPS, 1 Sep 65, sub: Command Report, 1 May 65–31 July 65, 72A7128/129, WNRC.

[2]Ibid., p. 36 and Incl 1; Msg, USASCV to COMUSARYIS, 12 Jun 65, sub: Urgent Requirement for AN/PRC–25 Series Radio Sets for Vietnam, CMH.

A New Combat Radio

I n 1964 MACV signal advisers had discovered the advantages of the PRC–25 when a few models had been sent to South Vietnam for testing. More power-ful than the PRC–10, the PRC–25 could transmit over a greater range in the jungle. Advisers also had discovered that it was easier to find a clear frequency with the newer set. Although the two radios were compatible, the PRC–25 could operate over a far greater frequency span than its predecessor. With South Vietnamese, Americans, and even Viet Cong using captured radios, all in the same frequency spectrum, interference was fast becoming a greater liability of the PRC–10 than its short transmitting range. Despite the technical advantages of the PRC–25, MACV signal officers had been unable to obtain approval for its adoption as the standard adviser radio; logisticians felt the new radio was too expensive and would overtax maintenance facilities geared to support the older radio.[3]

By the time General Williamson requested improvement of the tactical radios in the 173d Airborne Brigade, General Westmoreland agreed that it was an "urgent battlefield requirement" and asked the Army to send 2,000 radios for advisers and U.S. combat troops as expeditiously as possible. Response was swift: the U.S. Army Electronics Command released its entire stock of new radios—1,000 sets—and began an emergency procurement of the remainder of the order. The commander of the Electronics Command, Maj. Gen. Frank W. Moorman, made plans to issue the radios to units deploying to South Vietnam in the future. Anticipating that the radios would be exposed to hard use, the Army Materiel Command permitted the Electronics Command to compute resupply and repair needs of the radios at combat rates. Although the Electronics Command had the first PRC–25's in the hands of radio operators in South Vietnam within a few weeks of General Westmoreland's request, General Moorman warned that units should keep the old radios until he could establish a reliable support package for the new set. He anticipated that launching a complete changeover to a new item of equipment while deploying units to a combat theater might cause problems.[4]

Recognizing that the new radios, although more powerful, would still be restricted to the line-of-sight limitations of FM radio, the avionics laboratories of the Electronics Command were developing a standard airborne radio relay con-figuration, called the ARC–121, that when mounted in a Caribou aircraft could automatically retransmit six different FM nets. After final testing by the 11th Air Assault Division, an experimental division which was itself being tested at Fort Benning, Georgia, the radio was to be produced for Army-wide use. In the mean-time, laboratory technicians at Fort Monmouth developed a retransmission kit

[3]MACV History, 1965, pp. 388–90, CMH.

[4]Msg, USASCV to COMUSARYIS, 12 Jun 65, sub: Urgent Requirement for AN/PRC–25 Series Radio Sets for Vietnam; Msg, COMUSMACV to CINCUSARPAC, 16 Jun 65, sub: AN/PRC–25 Radios for Vietnam; Msg, CINCUSARPAC to CGUSASCV, 19 Jun 65, sub: Urgent Requirement for AN/PRC–25 Series Radio Sets for Vietnam; Msg, USAMC to USAECOM, 12 Jul 65, sub: Radio Set AN/PRC–25/GRC–125 for Vietnam. All in CMH. Ltr, ECOM to ACofS, Force Development, 18 Aug 65, sub: Retention of Radio Sets AN/PRC–8, –9, and –10 by Units Being Deployed to Southeast Asia, VN file, Electronics Command (ECOM) Historians files, Fort Monmouth, New Jersey.

that units in the field could build and install in a helicopter.[5]

Since airborne retransmission was impractical for the around-the-clock serv-ice required by advisers assigned to sectors and subsectors throughout South Viet-nam, they needed portable high-frequency radios with a voice capability. Although they had been issued old, but reliable, high-frequency radios for their nets, a short-age of operators qualified in Morse code, the primary mode of transmission of those radios, left them dependent on the South Vietnamese for most of their com-munications. The MACV Assistant Chief of Staff for Operations (J–3), Brig. Gen. William E. DePuy, was concerned that when American units began moving into the countryside, the advisers would need a means of coordinating directly with those units to arrange mutual support between Americans and South Vietnamese and to obtain area clearance for American fire missions. DePuy wanted the ad-visers to have a means of long-distance voice communications from even the most remote subsector. The Electronics Command ordered enough sets of a new port-able single-sideband radio, the FRC–93, which the Special Forces had been test-ing in the Central Highlands for the Army Concept Team in Vietnam, to equip each sector and subsector. [6]

Assigning Responsibilities

While the Military Assistance Command, Vietnam, and the Electronics Com-mand were attending to the tactical needs of American combat units and advisers, the 2d Signal Group, commanded by Col. James J. Moran, was build-ing an area communications system that would provide telephone communica-tions to each sector headquarters as well as to the bases of American combat and logistical units. The first elements of the group arrived in late May. By July 1965 the 2,900-man group consisted of the 39th Signal Battalion, the 41st Signal Bat-talion, and the 593d Signal Company. Dividing the responsibility for communi-cations between the two battalions, Colonel Moran assigned the two northern corps to the 41st Signal Battalion, commanded by Lt. Col. James G. Pelland, and reduced the area of operations for Colonel Dorney's 39th Signal Battalion to the III and IV Corps. The 362d Signal Company, operating the troposcatter termi-nals on the BACKPORCH system and the tails, he placed directly under his head-quarters. To reduce turbulence during the shift in responsibility, he transferred to Colonel Pelland's battalion the 178th Signal Company, which had been oper-ating communications in the northern corps for the 39th Signal Battalion, and assigned Company D, 41st Signal Battalion, to Colonel Dorney. Colonel Pelland assigned the 178th Signal Company to the I Corps area, his Company A to the II Corps headquarters in Pleiku, and his Companies B and C to the coastal en-claves of Qui Nhon, Nha Trang, Cam Ranh Bay, and Phan Rang. Colonel Dorney

---

[5]In July 1965 the 11th Air Assault Division became the 1st Cavalry Division (Airmobile).

[6]Msg, COMUSMACV to CSA and CG, AMC, 29 Jul 65, sub: Issue of New Narrow Band FM and HF SSB Radios for US Use in the RVN; MACV History, 1965, p. 310; USARV Sig Ofcr, Command Rpt, Oct–Dec 65, par. 4e. All in CMH.

used the recently assigned Company D, 41st Signal Battalion, to provide III Corps communications and the 232d Signal Company and his own Company D to continue operating in the southernmost IV Corps. To the 593d Signal Company, which had been attached to the 39th Signal Battalion upon arrival in mid-July, he gave the mission of providing all communications in the Saigon area.[7] *(Map 7)*

While Colonel Moran was busy defining area responsibilities for his new command, General Westmoreland was also making some organizational changes. On 20 July 1965, he disbanded the U.S. Army Support Command, Vietnam, and created the U.S. Army, Vietnam, to command all Army troops except advisers in South Vietnam. Although command of the new headquarters, which functioned as an Army component command, rested with General Westmoreland as the senior Army officer in the theater, the day-to-day direction of the U.S. Army, Vietnam, was exercised by the deputy commanding general, Brig. Gen. John Norton, who had formerly commanded the U.S. Army Support Command, Vietnam. As the signal officer for the new headquarters General Norton chose Col. Thomas W. Riley, Jr., who had been handling many of the actions concerning the Vietnam buildup on the Department of the Army staff; the former Army Support Command signal officer, Lt. Col. Kenneth G. Ring, continued as Colonel Riley's deputy. Since the 2d Signal Group was assigned to the U.S. Army, Vietnam, Colonel Riley exercised staff supervision over the 2d Signal Group just as the Support Command signal officer previously had provided staff supervision to the 39th Signal Battalion. Colonel Moran assumed responsibility for all Army signal operations in South Vietnam except for the satellite terminal and the Phu Lam STARCOM station, which were assigned to the U.S. Army Strategic Communications Command.[8]

Since General Johnson gave to the Strategic Communications Command the mission to operate the proposed Integrated Wideband Communications System, which included the existing BACKPORCH system, in the summer of 1965 the commander of the Strategic Communications Command, Maj. Gen. Richard J. Meyer, dispatched to Saigon a 54-man cadre from the 11th Signal Group at Fort Lewis, Washington, to establish the U.S. Army Strategic Communications Command, Southeast Asia. To lead the troops operating the Strategic Communications Command's facilities in South Vietnam, General Meyer appointed Lt. Col. Jerry J. Enders as the first commander of the U.S. Army Strategic Communications Command, Vietnam.[9]

Besides the satellite and STARCOM facilities, Colonel Enders also took responsibility for the Philco system between South Vietnam and Thailand, a nemesis to the Strategic Communications Command since it was begun in 1962. The Bangkok terminal was being moved to Green Hill, the site recommended by the

---

[7]178th Sig Co History, 1965, p. 9, 338–75–1000/144; 2d Sig Gp, Command Rpt, 1 Jul–30 Sep 65, pp. 15–31, 72A7128/7. Both in WNRC.

[8]Eckhardt, *Command and Control,* pp. 49–52, 90; Ltr, USARV to CINCUSARPAC, 15 Nov 65, sub: Quarterly Command Report for 1st Quarter FY 66, 68A1507/1, WNRC.

[9]MACV History, 1965, pp. 380–90; Maj. Gen. Thomas Matthew Rienzi, *Communications-Electronics, 1962–1970,* Vietnam Studies (Washington, D.C.: Government Printing Office, 1972), pp. 26–27; Memo, CG, USASCC, for CSA and VCSA, 10 Jan 66, sub: Improved Communications in SE Asia, CMH.

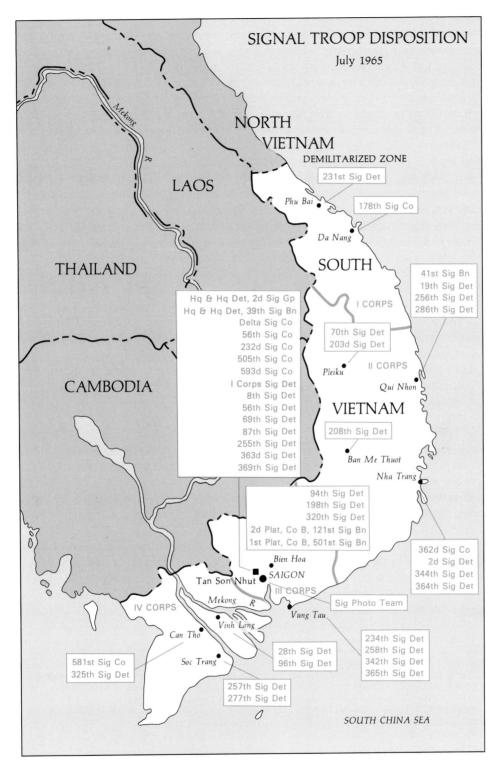

SIGNAL TROOP DISPOSITION

July 1965

NORTH VIETNAM

DEMILITARIZED ZONE

231st Sig Det

178th Sig Co

Phu Bai

Da Nang

SOUTH

LAOS

THAILAND

I CORPS

41st Sig Bn
19th Sig Det
256th Sig Det
286th Sig Det

Hq & Hq Det, 2d Sig Gp
Hq & Hq Det, 39th Sig Bn
Delta Sig Co
56th Sig Co
232d Sig Co
505th Sig Co
593d Sig Co
I Corps Sig Det
8th Sig Det
56th Sig Det
69th Sig Det
87th Sig Det
255th Sig Det
363d Sig Det
369th Sig Det

70th Sig Det
203d Sig Det

CAMBODIA

Pleiku

II CORPS

Qui Nhon

VIETNAM

208th Sig Det

Ban Me Thuot

Nha Trang

94th Sig Det
198th Sig Det
320th Sig Det
2d Plat, Co B, 121st Sig Bn
1st Plat, Co B, 501st Sig Bn

362d Sig Co
2d Sig Det
344th Sig Det
364th Sig Det

Bien Hoa

Tan Son Nhut SAIGON

III CORPS

Mekong R

IV CORPS

Vung Tau

Sig Photo Team

Vinh Long

234th Sig Det
258th Sig Det
342th Sig Det
365th Sig Det

Can Tho

28th Sig Det
96th Sig Det

581st Sig Co
325th Sig Det

Soc Trang

257th Sig Det
277th Sig Det

SOUTH CHINA SEA

Mekong

R

MAP 7

National Bureau of Standards. Since General Westmoreland decided that he wanted his alternate headquarters to be at Vung Tau, Colonel Kimball recommended moving the Saigon terminal of the intercountry system to Vung Tau to support it. Communications engineers protested that the move made all their testing and precise engineering worthless and that the new system might encounter the same problems as its predecessor. Although tactical considerations swung the argument, it was apparent by the summer of 1965 that the skeptics were correct and that technical obstacles might prevent the 471-mile system from ever coming on the air.[10]

In Thailand, the Army and Air Force had taken a variety of interim measures while awaiting the Integrated Wideband Communications System. Negotiations between the Department of Defense, the State Department, and the Thai government to reserve circuits on the Thai commercial network had gone slowly. The Army had been unable to sign funding agreements with the Agency for International Development until March 1965 and was negotiating with local Thai authorities for clearances to install cable interconnects from the offices of the commercial network to American facilities even as cable crews were doing the work. By summer 1965 the interconnects were still only half completed.[11]

The situation in Thailand brightened upon cancellation of a military assistance project in Indonesia. When relations between the United States and President Achmed Sukarno's leftist regime had seriously deteriorated in 1964 and the United States had suspended all military assistance to Indonesia, enough troposcatter equipment to connect eight sites became available. Although release of the equipment to Admiral Sharp was delayed by the reluctance of the U.S. ambassador to give up the only leverage he had with the Indonesian government, in September 1965 the State Department finally authorized the Pacific Command to use the equipment in Thailand. Because the Pacific Command's engineering office had been planning for the release of the equipment and had already earmarked the precise site of each terminal in Thailand, the sets were quickly installed. By late fall most of the systems using that equipment were on the air. Replaced TRC–90's were brought to a central point at Korat; but because they needed extensive overhaul, they were unavailable for immediate use.[12]

Those TRC–90 transportable troposcatter sets had suddenly become a critical commodity. Foreseeing the delay in installing the wideband network and facing the task of supporting a troop buildup far exceeding that for which the system had been planned, Admiral Sharp had already asked the Joint Chiefs of Staff for permission to use contingency equipment as an interim base network until the

[10]Interv, author with Brig Gen Emmett Paige, commanding general, U.S. Army Communications Systems Agency, 2 Sep 77, Historians files, CMH; Msg, CINCPAC to USASCC, 18 Nov 65, sub: Green Hill-Vung Tau Tropo System, CMH.

[11]Msg, JCS to CINCPAC, 1 Mar 65, sub: Approval of JCS 222/813 dtd 17 Oct 64; Msg, DEPCOM-USMACTHAI to CINCPAC, 15 May 65, sub: Lease of Circuits in TOT System; Msg, 9th Log Cmd to DA, 24 May 65, sub: Thailand Interconnect C-E Base Project. All in CMH.

[12]CINCPAC History, 1965, pp. 175–78; Interv, author with Jones, 8 Feb 78; Msg, DA to USAMC, 15 Mar 65, sub: Fixed Communications System-Indonesia, CMH; 207th Sig Co History, 1965, 338-75-1000/145, WNRC; Memo, Asst Secy of Def (I&L) for Asst Secy of Army (I&L) et al., 22 Jul 65, sub: Systems Plan for an Integrated U.S. Wideband Communications System in SEA, in JCS 222/874 (12 Aug 65), JACO (1965), DA/4, NARS.

wideband system could be expanded and installed. Recognizing that some of the interim facilities would be absorbed into the projected system, the Joint Chiefs approved Admiral Sharp's request with the understanding that the U.S. Army Strategic Communications Command would be responsible for operation of the interim Integrated Wideband Communications System. Because the Strategic Communications Command already had all twelve of its contingency troposcatter and microwave teams attached to the 2d Signal Group, General Meyer told Admiral Sharp that the Pacific Command would have to assist in tying together the base network in Southeast Asia until the Integrated Wideband Communications System was operational. The Pacific Air Force dispatched large MRC–98 troposcatter sets, which were similar to the MRC–85's, to expand the network in Thailand and to build alternate routes in South Vietnam to be available in case of enemy disruption of BACKPORCH. Those alternate routes consisted primarily of a system connecting Vung Tau with Cam Ranh Bay and another connecting Da Nang with Ubon, Thailand. For maximum redundancy the terminal serving Da Nang was located on Monkey Mountain, about five miles from the BACKPORCH terminal. To integrate those systems built with the Air Force's heavy troposcatter equipment into an alternate network, the 2d Signal Group drew the mission of installing systems from Vung Tau to Saigon, from Nha Trang to Cam Ranh Bay, and from Monkey Mountain to the BACKPORCH terminal in Da Nang.[13]

General Norton only reluctantly agreed to divert his hard-pressed microwave and troposcatter assets to a mission of the Strategic Communications Command. He considered the lack of adequate long-distance communications a major deficiency in his capability to command and control American combat units and was determined to retain as much multichannel capability for tactical use as possible. He had already encountered considerable difficulty in convincing the Military Assistance Command to release circuits on BACKPORCH to link his far-flung tactical and logistical Army units because the advisory detachments and Air Force units that had been using the circuits for the past three years felt they needed every circuit assigned to them.[14]

Supporting Tactical Operations

E ven before Colonel Moran had learned that he would have to support the strategic communicators, he had begun to consolidate his mobile tropo-

---

[13]Msg, CINCPAC to JCS, 10 Jul 65, sub: MRC–98 Deployments; Msg, JCS to CSA et al., 13 Aug 65, sub: Communications Resources Required to Support Southeast Asia Contingency Operations; Msg, DA to CGUSASCC, 14 Aug 65, sub: Cam Ranh Bay Communications; Msg, DA to CINCUSAR-PAC, 31 Aug 65, sub: Cam Ranh Bay–Nha Trang M/W Link; Msg, CGUSASCC to CINCUSARPAC, 24 Aug 65, sub: Cam Ranh Bay Communications; Msg, CINCPACAF to CINCUSARPAC, 21 Sep 65, sub: RVN Communications Support; USARV Sig Ofcr, Command Rpt, Oct–Dec 65, par. 4. All in CMH.

[14]Msg, USARV to CINCUSARPAC, 17 Sep 65, sub: Cam Ranh Bay Communications, CMH; Incl 15 to Ltr, FFV to USARV, 15 Oct 65, sub: Command Report, 30 Sep 65, file 228–07, 72A7128/2, WNRC; Ltr, USARV to CINCUSARPAC, 15 Nov 65, sub: Command Report, 1st Qtr FY 66, p. 16, 68A1507/1, WNRC.

The View From Lang Bian Mountain

scatter assets, using Lang Bian Mountain as a relay center, for more efficient long-haul communications between the Central Highlands and new bases in the coastal areas of II Corps. To increase capacity from twenty-four to forty-eight channels on the new troposcatter system operating from Saigon to Lang Bian Mountain to Pleiku, he used the terminals from the dismantled CROSSBOW system. The sets at Pleiku and Saigon were merged with the nearby terminals on the newer system and the sets from Ban Me Thuot were moved to Lang Bian. The two sets from the relay at Gia Nghia were used to replace the low-capacity MRC–80's on the heavily used link between Da Nang and the Marine aviation units at Chu Lai. The vans at Gia Nghia, having made the dangerous journey from Da Lat to the mountain site two years earlier, had to make another precarious journey through enemy territory to the nearest airfield twelve miles away.[15]

Besides installing part of the long-haul communications for the base network, Colonel Moran also had to set up base communications for the large port complex under construction at Cam Ranh Bay. His signal group, like the Army at large, was ill equipped for such a mission. On the theory that radio relay had rendered cable obsolete for tactical use, the Army during the early 1960s had come to rely on commercial firms to fill all its cabling needs; equipment was no longer

---

[15] 2d Sig Gp, Command Rpt, 1 Jul–30 Sep 65, pp. 8–10; USARV Sig Ofcr, Command Rpt, Oct–Dec 65, par. 4, CMH.

148

Aerial View of the Lang Bian Site

stocked, and instruction in cable splicing had been removed from the curriculum of the signal schools. In response to Colonel Moran's request for assistance on the Cam Ranh Bay project, during the summer of 1965 the Department of the Army hastily assembled veteran cablemen into a cable construction unit, the 578th Signal Company, and dispatched them to the 2d Signal Group. Meanwhile, procurement officers began scouring the United States and the Pacific for the 26 million feet of heavy cable that Colonel Moran felt he needed. While awaiting equipment for the local cable plant, the 578th Signal Company began setting up a dial switchboard in the port complex at Cam Ranh Bay and connecting it with a similar switchboard that the Air Force was installing at a nearby air base.[16]

Many of the new multichannel systems being installed in the II Corps zone were to connect bases established by the 1st Brigade, 101st Airborne Division, which had arrived in late July 1965 from Fort Campbell, Kentucky. Leaving a battalion to protect Cam Ranh Bay, the brigade commander, Col. James S. Timothy, took the rest of his unit north to Qui Nhon. After securing a base near Qui Nhon for logistical units moving into the area, the soldiers pushed inland along Highway 19 to An Khe to secure a site for the forthcoming arrival of the 1st Cavalry Division (Airmobile). When the division arrived from the United States in early

[16]Ibid., pp. 5–6, 23, and app. 14; Msg, CINCUSARPAC to CC-E, 12 Aug 65, sub: Communications Requirements for Cam Ranh Bay, CMH.

September and became sufficiently established to assume the task of defending the base, the men of the 101st Airborne Division moved back to an area south of Qui Nhon to cover arrival of the Capital (Tiger) Division of the Army of the Republic of Korea. After transferring security responsibilities to the South Koreans, the airborne troopers, less the battalion at Cam Ranh Bay, moved down the coast to the vicinity of Phan Rang to build their own base camp.[17]

A signal platoon from the 501st Signal Battalion, the 101st Airborne Division's organic signal unit, had accompanied the brigade to South Vietnam. Although it was to provide multichannel links from the brigade headquarters to each battalion, the brigade signal officer, Capt. Richard J. Meyer, Jr., discovered that his units were too scattered for the tactical multichannel sets to be of much help. When he requested assistance from the 2d Signal Group, Colonel Moran gave the 41st Signal Battalion the mission of supporting the brigade with multichannel links to each battalion.

Keeping up with the air, road, and water movement of the airborne brigade along the coast of the II Corps area was a difficult challenge for Colonel Pelland's men. Organized for area communications coverage, the signal battalion was adept at installing communications in the base areas that the brigade secured for incoming units and connecting those bases to the backbone system; but the signalmen were ill equipped to maintain direct command communications between the brigade and its subordinate battalions, a mission normally given not to an area support battalion but to a division or corps signal battalion.[18]

In the III Corps area, the 39th Signal Battalion was also called upon to provide tactical command communications. In mid-September 1965 the 173d Airborne Brigade deployed from Bien Hoa to nearby Binh Duong Province to secure a base for the incoming 1st Infantry Division. The 232d Signal Company, which previously had provided only base communications for static advisory detachments, sent teams to the field to link the brigade's forward command post to its base at Bien Hoa with multichannel, telephone, and teletype communications. When in October the 1st Brigade, 1st Infantry Division, joined the 173d Airborne Brigade and South Vietnamese infantrymen in a drive into the heart of a Viet Cong base area, called the Iron Triangle, the 39th Signal Battalion, together with a signal platoon from the 1st Division's organic 121st Signal Battalion, installed communications for a combined field command post and provided multichannel links back to the base at Bien Hoa. For tactical communications to subordinate units, the communications platoons organic to each brigade operated FM and single-sideband voice nets.[19]

In August 1965 General Westmoreland established Task Force Alpha (later renamed Field Force, Vietnam) at Nha Trang to control all American and South Korean combat units in the II and III Corps. A company of the 41st Signal Battalion provided communications for the corps-size headquarters until the arrival in mid-

[17]Ltr, 1st Bde, 101st Abn Div, to DCSOPS, 12 Jan 66, sub: Command Report for Quarterly Period Ending 31 Dec 65, 72A7128/27, WNRC.

[18]Ltr, 1st Bde, 101st Abn Div, to 101st Abn Div, 16 Sep 65, sub: After Action Report: Movement of 1/101st Airborne Division to Vietnam, 67A5216/11, WNRC.

[19]173d Abn Bde, Command Rpt, 1 Aug–31 Dec 65, Incls 10, 13, 16, 72A7128/29, WNRC.

October of the 54th Signal Battalion (Corps) from Fort Hood, Texas. The battalion, commanded by Lt. Col. John L. Whisler, quickly dispatched detachments to the headquarters of each major unit subordinate to the field force. From each location Colonel Whisler's men operated a multichannel system, two radio-teletype sets, and a communications center for traffic back to the field force headquarters in Nha Trang. To ensure that those channels of communication remained unburdened by routine traffic, the field force's signal officer, Col. Richard C. Horne, instituted a twice-daily helicopter courier run. Because a South Korean Marine brigade that arrived in October had inadequate organic communications, Colonel Horne also directed Colonel Whisler to provide the Korean Marine units with communications down to the battalion level instead of simply to the brigade headquarters.[20]

In early November the 54th Signal Battalion participated in its first combat operation: a detachment supported the Korean marines during a sweep of the coast north of Nha Trang. Thereafter, whenever a maneuver unit moved, its supporting signal detachment moved with it; a detachment from the 2d Signal Group supported any rear element left to operate the base.[21]

Although the 2d Signal Group and the 54th Signal Battalion had little difficulty supporting bases and combat operations in the coastal lowlands of II Corps, they were unable to extend their systems to the U.S. Special Forces camps and units of the 1st Cavalry Division (Airmobile) based far inland in the Central Highlands. For Special Forces communicators at camps strung out along South Vietnam's mountainous western border, keeping communications facilities operating in the face of enemy attacks on the camps posed special problems. In most cases, the Viet Cong focused their initial assault on the communications bunkers. That was the situation, for example, at a camp at Bu Dop on the southwestern fringe of the Central Highlands.

When two Viet Cong battalions attacked the camp just after midnight on 20 July 1965, the radioman barely escaped a rocket explosion that destroyed his single-sideband radio. Making his way to a storage bunker where the radios used on patrols were kept, he found an HT-1, the small, hand-held radio obtained from the Agency for International Development, and was able to call a relay station operated by a Special Forces B detachment to request a flareship to illuminate the area outside the camp's perimeter. He returned to the command post to find all other Americans either killed or wounded and a badly decimated force of soldiers of the Civilian Irregular Defense Group barely holding out. By the time the flareship arrived, the Viet Cong and the South Vietnamese were fighting at such close quarters that the radioman was unable to call in fire support, but the illumination enabled the defending riflemen and machine gunners to hold off the attack until daybreak. At that point, hearing the Viet Cong playing bugles as a signal to withdraw, the radioman used his small radio to direct air strikes

---

[20]Ltr, FFV to USARV, 15 Oct 65, sub: Command Report for the Quarter Ending 30 Sep 65, pp. 8–9, file 228–07; ibid., 14 Jan 66, sub: Command Report, 1 Oct 65–31 Dec 65, pp. 21–22, w/Incl 1, Ltr, FFV to 1st Air Cav Div et al., 31 Dec 65. Both in 72A7128/2, WNRC.
[21]Ltr, 54th Sig Bn to FFV, 24 Jan 66, sub: Command Report for Period, 27 Jun 65–31 Dec 65, pp. 4–11, 72A7128/47, WNRC.

as the enemy fell back. To make it more difficult in the future for the enemy to cut vital radio communications links, the commander of the 5th Special Forces, Col. William A. McKean, directed Green Beret signalmen to install all radios in underground bunkers and to bury long wire antennas underground.[22]

Although the isolated Special Forces detachments had little hope of obtaining additional support from conventional signal units, the 1st Cavalry Division, which was patrolling the strategic corridor from Qui Nhon on the coast to Pleiku, the principal town in the Central Highlands, had the benefit of far more signal resources. The division's organic signal unit, the 13th Signal Battalion, provided all internal divisional communications; a detachment of the 54th Signal Battalion, commanded by 1st Lt. William W. Toney, handled communications to the field force headquarters at Nha Trang.

Upon learning in the summer of 1965 of General Westmoreland's plan to commit the cavalry division along Highway 19, Colonel Moran had recognized that the communications grid covering the distance from Pleiku to Qui Nhon would be insufficient and requested an additional signal company for the area. When the 586th Signal Company, commanded by Capt. Frank Cosentino, arrived at Qui Nhon in early September in response to the request, Colonel Moran attached the company to the 41st Signal Battalion. Colonel Pelland assigned the company the mission of installing base camp communications at An Khe and supporting the American and South Korean units located in the vicinity of Qui Nhon and Phu Cat.[23]

While the company's wire crews installed telephones to logistical units in the coastal enclave around Phu Cat and Qui Nhon, the radio relay platoon installed a multichannel system along the route from Qui Nhon to Phu Cat to An Khe to Pleiku. Because of intervening hills, the radiomen established a relay point on Vung Chua Mountain, a hill outside Qui Nhon that was destined to become a major node in the long-lines network.[24]

While the signalmen were installing communications in the coastal enclaves, Captain Cosentino sent a fifty-man detachment to An Khe to establish a headquarters for his company and to begin work on the 1st Cavalry Division's base communications. Some of the men moved to the top of a nearby hill, Hon Cong Mountain, to join teams from the 13th Signal Battalion in constructing a radio relay site. Within a few weeks they were joined by a multichannel team from the 54th Signal Battalion and an air control communications team from the 17th Aviation Battalion. Because the Viet Cong controlled the slopes of the mountain, the forty signalmen on the hill had to be resupplied entirely by helicopter.[25]

While the communicators set up their equipment, the commander of the cavalry

---

[22]Incl 14 to Ltr, 5th Special Forces Gp (hereafter cited as 5th SFG) to CINCUSARPAC, 10 Oct 65, sub: Command Report for Quarterly Period Ending 30 Sep 65, and Incl 23, Msg, CO, 5th SFG, to Det COs, 3 Aug 65, both in 68A1507/1, WNRC. Interv, author with Vernon W. Gillespie, former Special Forces officer, 18 Jan 77, Historians files, CMH.

[23]Ltr, 1st Cav Div to DCSOPS, DA, 10 Jan 66, sub: Quarterly Command Report, 2d Qtr FY 66, pp. 1–2, 72A7128/2, WNRC.

[24]23d MHD, The 586th Signal Company (Support) in Support of Operations, An Khe, Vietnam, p. 2, 338–75–1000/148, WNRC.

[25]Ibid., pp. 28–30.

division, Maj. Gen. Harry W. O. Kinnard, sent an engineer company to the hilltop to build a security fence around the site and to construct bunkers for the radio vans. When the engineers completed their work, an infantry squad that had been providing security for the site also withdrew. Because the signalmen were operating communications around the clock, it was difficult to free enough men for an adequate guard force.

As might have been predicted, the Viet Cong soon tested the defenses. On an overcast night in February 1966, they tried to overrun the hilltop, in the process killing three guards and wounding several others, but the guard force delayed the attackers long enough for the rest of the men on the site to organize a defense. Because an enemy rocket blew up fuel tanks and satchel charges set most of the generators afire, there was sufficient illumination to enable the signalmen to bring the attackers under accurate small arms fire. When they finally beat back the attack after three hours of fierce fighting, they discovered that the bunkers that the engineers had built had done their job. Although Viet Cong dead lay all about the operations area, the signal equipment remained unscathed. After helicopters arrived at daybreak with new generators to replace those that had been destroyed, the radios on the site came back on the air.[26]

General Kinnard meanwhile was employing his maneuver forces to the west of An Khe to search for the enemy's main forces. To keep in contact with the airmobile brigades roaming the mountainous region, the division signal officer, Lt. Col. Tom M. Nicholson, depended primarily on single-sideband radio. The brigades themselves used FM voice radios and the helicopters' VHF radios for communicating with battalions and companies. When the brigades stopped to establish a field command post, Colonel Nicholson airlifted a four-channel terminal to their locations, and the 13th Signal Battalion, through a radio relay on Hon Cong Mountain, established the austere communications systems with which General Kinnard and his staff controlled the division.[27]

The Ia Drang Battle

W hen the *630th North Vietnamese Division's 33d Regiment* in late October attacked an isolated U.S. Special Forces camp at Plei Me, southwest of Pleiku, the 1st Cavalry Division's search for its adversary came to an abrupt end. The Special Forces and South Vietnamese relief forces beat back the attack, and the air cavalrymen pursued the enemy in the jungle-covered hills west of the camp and in the valley of the Ia (River) Drang in the shadow of the Chu Pong Massif along the Cambodian border. For the entire month of November bitter fighting

[26]Ibid., pp. 31–32; 13th Sig Bn History, 1966, p. 8, 67A5337/18, WNRC.

[27]While conventional units usually had twenty-four telephone and teletype circuits from division headquarters to each brigade, the airmobile brigades had only four channels to division headquarters: a direct telephone link from the S–3 to the division G–3, a secure teletype circuit, and two common-user lines from the brigade switchboard to the division switchboard. Ltr, Brig Gen Tom M. Nicholson to Maj Gen Thomas M. Rienzi, 11 May 71, CMH; 1st Cav Div, 1st Air Cavalry Division Operations in Vietnam, August 1965–March 1968, p. 4, file 228–03, 72A4722/14, WNRC.

raged as American and North Vietnamese units met for the first time in the war. Losses were high on both sides, but the superior mobility and firepower of the air cavalrymen finally won the day. As the remnants of three North Vietnamese regiments straggled back into Cambodia, the Communists saw their plans to drive a wedge into the heart of South Vietnam blunted. Communications had played an important role in the American success.[28]

Through Morse code nets relayed by a station at Dong Hoi in southern North Vietnam, Communist leaders in Hanoi stayed in constant contact throughout the battle with the staff of the *630th North Vietnamese Division*. While keeping that long-distance strategic link operational, signal officers of the *630th Division* were less successful in maintaining tactical communications with regiments committed to the fighting. Because of heavy losses from bombings by American B–52 air-craft and surprise airmobile raids on communications sites, the 120-man signal company of the *33d North Vietnamese Regiment* was rendered ineffective early in the battle. As the regiment tried to flee westward, the regimental commander lacked the communications to notify his superiors of his plight. While the *33d Regiment* was being roundly defeated, the commander of the *32d North Vietnamese Regiment* stood by unknowingly with his uncommitted troops within striking distance.[29]

Like the commander of the *630th North Vietnamese Division*, General Kinnard also had uninterrupted strategic communications during the battle. Soon after the first encounter at Plei Me, he moved his command post forward from An Khe to Pleiku, where he could coordinate directly with the South Vietnamese II Corps commander and with the staff of the Special Forces C detachment that controlled the camps in the Central Highlands. Being a major nodal point on BACKPORCH, Pleiku presented the division with direct entry into the countrywide area communications networks through which Kinnard could contact MACV headquarters in Saigon, which in turn used the Phu Lam overseas station to sum-mon from bases in Guam, over a thousand miles away, the B–52's that bombed the *33d North Vietnamese Regiment* with such accuracy. Using the multichannel terminal operated at Pleiku by the 586th Signal Company, the division also en-tered the local area network serving the Highway 19 corridor to coordinate with coastal support bases. Since Lieutenant Toney moved one of the 54th Signal Bat-talion's multichannel terminals to Pleiku with the forward command post, General Kinnard also had a direct twelve-channel command link to the field force head-quarters in Nha Trang.[30]

The division's forward command post was mounted in a detachable cargo com-partment of a CH–54 Sky Crane helicopter containing a twelve-line switchboard, a four-channel multichannel terminal, six FM voice radios, and a shelf of pre-wired telephones and teletypewriters, all installed and ready to operate. The 13th Signal Battalion thus had communications for the division staff on the air within a matter of minutes after a helicopter set the pod on the ground in Pleiku. The command post remained there throughout the battle; as the brigades moved

---

[28]Ibid.
[29]Rpt, 1st Cav Div, The Lure and the Ambush, CMH.
[30]1st Cav Div, Quarterly Command Rpt, 2d Qtr, FY 66, pp. 19, 32.

Field Switchboard Supports Airmobile Operations

farther west in pursuit of the North Vietnamese, Colonel Nicholson sent FM retransmission stations and multichannel radio relays to Dragon Mountain, a hill near Pleiku, to extend the range of the command post's communications.[31]

While generally satisfied with communications from the forward command post of the division to the brigades, General Kinnard was less pleased with communications on the battlefield. An inability of brigade and battalion commanders to maintain constant contact with their subordinate units, he felt, restrained the field commanders from maneuvering their airmobile forces to take advantage of a rapidly changing tactical situation. As the battalions pursuing the North Vietnamese ventured farther west toward the border, the signals from their PRC–25 radios were often masked by mountains or attenuated by heavy foliage. Unable to move the vans containing single-sideband radios into the rough country, the cavalrymen were deprived of the long-range capability of those radios. To stay in control of wide-ranging maneuver units, brigade and battalion commanders had to go aloft to use helicopter-mounted radio consoles that the division had tested in Georgia and fortunately had retained when moving to South Vietnam. Although the heliborne command posts enabled the commanders to control their forces, requirements for fuel and maintenance limited the availability of the

[31]Interv, author with Lt Col John M. Smith, former brigade signal officer and division radio officer of the 1st Cavalry Division, 8 Mar 78, Historians files, CMH.

155

Signalman *using a PRC–25 guides in air assault choppers.*

helicopters. Rarely using the heliborne command posts more than six hours a day, commanders tried to save them for critical actions.[32]

By rotating two aircraft that had been specially equipped for FM radio retransmission, Colonel Nicholson was able to keep an airborne retransmission station continuously circling ten thousand feet above the division's area of operations for twenty-eight days. Although airborne retransmission increased the range of the PRC–25 radios on the ground from five to sixty miles, it had its limitations. Each aircraft could handle only six nets, a fraction of those in the division, at any one time. Greater range afforded by airborne retransmission also meant frequency interference problems. Since frequencies were assigned by area, propagating a signal far beyond its planned range with the omnidirectional FM antennas interfered with nets in other areas.[33]

Frequency interference was a major cause of the lack of tactical communications about which General Kinnard complained. When pursuing the North Vietnamese into the western reaches of Pleiku Province, the division employed frequencies assigned for use far to the east in the An Khe area of Binh Dinh Province. In the II Corps area those same frequencies had already been assigned

[32]1st Cav Div, Quarterly Command Rpt, 2d Qtr, FY 66, pp. 19, 32; Interv, author with Lt Col Karl P. Killingstad, former signal officer, 2d Brigade, 1st Cavalry Division, 28 Mar 78, Historians files, CMH.
[33]1st Cav Div, Quarterly Command Rpt, 2d Qtr, FY 66, pp. 19, 32.

to the South Vietnamese Army or to American advisers. To overcome the resulting interference, commanders and radio operators experimented with other frequencies until finding one that was clear and then appropriated it for their own use. Interference and changes in net frequencies—often announced over the air without encryption—made operation of the nets chaotic. Aware that the uncoordinated frequency changes, called bootlegging, were forbidden by joint U.S.-South Vietnamese directives and worried that the enemy would exploit information concerning frequencies and call signs transmitted in the clear, Colonel Nicholson told his radio officer, Capt. John M. Smith, to publish new Signal Operating Instructions for the entire division.[34]

By that time, however, most units had found a workable frequency, and when Captain Smith tried to put his revised Signal Operating Instructions into effect, commanders objected that the new change would throw their nets into confusion again. General Kinnard canceled the change. Even after the division returned to An Khe in December, when Colonel Nicholson tried to make the routine periodic changes to frequencies and call signs that security regulations mandated, he was stymied by wary commanders who remembered the radio confusion in the Ia Drang.[35]

As the 1st Cavalry Division was pursuing the North Vietnamese into the Ia Drang in November 1965, farther to the south in III Corps the 1st Infantry Division completed its deployment to South Vietnam. Meeting the division's units as they disembarked at the Saigon port, detachments from the 39th Signal Battalion provided communications during the march to the division's staging area at Bien Hoa and then to its new home at Di An, on the northern approaches to Saigon. Remaining in its base only a short time, the division, accompanied by communications teams of the 39th Signal Battalion, embarked on a combined American–South Vietnamese operation against Viet Cong forces in the vicinity of the Michelin Rubber Plantation. The battalion's signalmen operated a combined field command post and installed communications from field headquarters back to Di An and Bien Hoa.[36]

Although the arrival of the 41st Signal Battalion in July 1965 had reduced the 39th Signal Battalion's geographical responsibilities, the field operations and an expansion of headquarters in the Saigon area during the summer and fall had stretched the battalion's span of control to the breaking point. The MACV staff had grown so large that it was spilling over into buildings throughout Saigon. While serving all those locations, the battalion also had to bring communications to the headquarters and facilities of a fast-growing logistics command; to the new headquarters of the U.S. Army, Vietnam, in Long Binh, twenty-five kilometers northeast of Saigon; and to the headquarters of allied nations that were assisting the South Vietnamese. For each additional mission Colonel Dorney usually

---

[34]Signal Operating Instructions are documents listing the frequency and call sign assignments for radio nets.

[35]Interv, author with Smith, 8 Mar 78; National Security Agency (NSA), Deadly Transmissions, Dec 70, pp. 66–70, K370.04–6, OAFH, contains a discussion of an Army Security Agency study of communications security problems during the Ia Drang battle.

[36]Ltr, 39th Sig Bn to USARPAC, 8 Jan 66, sub: Ltr of Transmittal, w/Incl, Quarterly Command Rpt, 1 Oct–31 Dec 65, pp. 1–4, file C–171, 72A25/7, WNRC.

received some augmentation from the 2d Signal Group, and at one point he was responsible for over two thousand men in eight companies and six detachments. By November his battalion was sorely understaffed to handle the area responsibility for the two southern corps as well as communications for all the headquarters in and around Saigon.[37]

Recognizing that the buildup would cause just such an overburdening of the 39th Signal Battalion, General Westmoreland had requested a battalion especially for the Saigon–Long Binh area. In November the 1,300-man 69th Signal Battalion, commanded by Lt. Col. Charles R. Myer, arrived in Saigon to relieve the 39th Signal Battalion of its responsibilities for communications in the South Vietnamese capital. To augment Colonel Myer for that formidable mission, Colonel Moran transferred to him the 593d Signal Company, which had been operating communications for the 39th Signal Battalion at the MACV headquarters since its arrival in June, and assigned to him the 580th Signal Company, a recently arrived cable construction company. After turning over the communications facilities that the 39th Signal Battalion had been operating in the Saigon area for the past three and a half years, Colonel Dorney moved his headquarters to Vung Tau. There he installed communications for a port and airfield while continuing with his mission of area communications support for the III and IV Corps.[38]

The 69th Signal Battalion was the first significant reinforcement of communicators in South Vietnam since the arrival of the 2d Signal Group early the previous summer. When plans were being made for the group during the spring, the Army signal staff had anticipated that Colonel Moran's men would be assisting the 39th Signal Battalion in supporting a modest buildup of some 20,000 logistical troops. In fact, since April 1965 close to 100,000 men in over 700 combat and support units had deployed to South Vietnam. *(Map 8)*

To obtain sufficient fighting strength to blunt Viet Cong advances, General Westmoreland had heavily weighted the buildup in favor of combat units. By November, with two Army divisions, two Army airborne brigades, and a large number of American marines and South Korean infantrymen and marines in South Vietnam, General Westmoreland's holding strategy seemed to have worked; the enemy appeared to be on the defensive. Priority for precious cargo space on the transports and the docks of Saigon and Cam Ranh could finally be given to units waiting to deploy to build the logistical and communications base for Southeast Asia.[39]

Although the successes of the 1st Cavalry Division in the Ia Drang and of the 1st Infantry Division in the Michelin Rubber Plantation operations had validated General Westmoreland's decision to neglect building a base before conducting tactical operations, the constant stream of units entering South Vietnam brought a flood of new subscribers that overburdened the communications system at the very time that communicators were trying to move to the field to support tactical

[37]Ibid.; Interv, author with Col (ret.) James J. Dorney, former commander of the 39th Signal Battalion, 9 Feb 78, Historians files, CMH.
[38]Ltr, 69th Sig Bn to USARV, 11 Jan 66, sub: Command Report for Period Ending 31 Dec 65, pp. 1–7, 72A7128/24, WNRC.
[39]MS, Hermes, The Buildup, ch. 7.

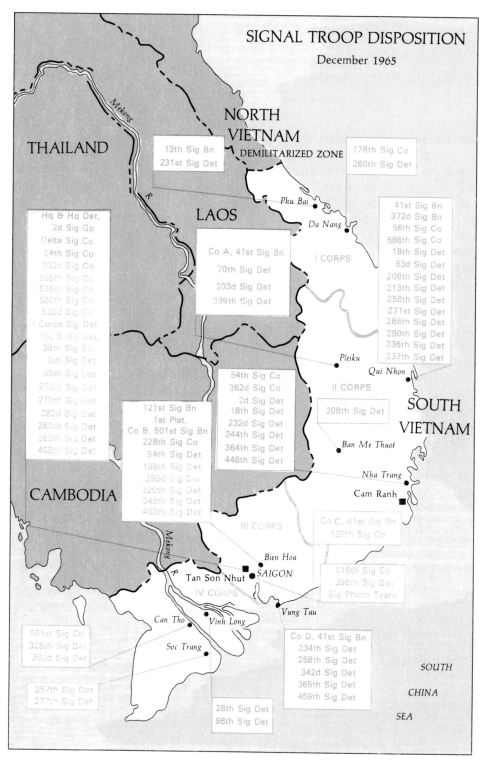

SIGNAL TROOP DISPOSITION
December 1965

THAILAND

NORTH VIETNAM
DEMILITARIZED ZONE

13th Sig Bn
231st Sig Det

178th Sig Co
260th Sig Det

Phu Bai

LAOS

Da Nang

I CORPS

41st Sig Bn
972d Sig Bn
56th Sig Co
586th Sig Co
19th Sig Det
63d Sig Det
209th Sig Det
213th Sig Det
256th Sig Det
271st Sig Det
286th Sig Det
290th Sig Det
336th Sig Det
337th Sig Det

Hq & Hq Det,
2d Sig Gp
Delta Sig Co
54th Sig Co
232d Sig Co
505th Sig Co
518th Sig Co
580th Sig Co
583d Sig Co
I Corps Sig Det
Hq & Hq Det,
39th Sig Bn
8th Sig Det
69th Sig Det
255th Sig Det
279th Sig Det
282d Sig Det
285th Sig Det
369th Sig Det
455th Sig Det

Co A, 41st Sig Bn

70th Sig Det

203d Sig Det

339th Sig Det

Pleiku

Qui Nhon

54th Sig Co
362d Sig Co
2d Sig Det
18th Sig Det
232d Sig Det
344th Sig Det
364th Sig Det
446th Sig Det

II CORPS

208th Sig Det

SOUTH VIETNAM

121st Sig Bn
1st Plat,
Co B, 501st Sig Bn
228th Sig Co
94th Sig Det
198th Sig Det
293d Sig Det
320th Sig Det
349th Sig Det
453th Sig Det

Ban Me Thuot

Nha Trang

Cam Ranh

CAMBODIA

III CORPS

Co C, 41st Sig Bn
128th Sig Co

Bien Hoa

Tan Son Nhut SAIGON

518th Sig Co
J96th Sig Det
Sig Photo Team

IV CORPS

Vung Tau

Can Tho Vinh Long

Soc Trang

Co D, 41st Sig Bn
234th Sig Det
258th Sig Det
342d Sig Det
365th Sig Det
459th Sig Det

SOUTH

CHINA

SEA

581st Sig Co
325th Sig Det
363d Sig Det

257th Sig Det
277th Sig Det

28th Sig Det
96th Sig Det

Map 8

operations. Quoting a complaint of the Air Force Chief of Staff, General Joseph McConnell, that "communications were shot to hell in South Vietnam," *Washington Post* columnist Drew Pearson had even devoted part of his widely read column to the problems with communications in the war zone.[40]

An Overtaxed System

Because communicators had tended to consolidate their meager resources to support fighting units, many staff officers and Air Force subscribers, who had become accustomed to direct hot lines, suddenly found themselves with only a telephone extension from a switchboard or a teletype entry to a local message relay center. Their communications were then considerably slower. Because of inadequate long-lines systems, the trunk circuits that comprised the communications pipeline became so clogged that switchboards and teletype communications centers pumping traffic into the network became backed up. Frustrated by long waits for open long-distance lines, some impatient subscribers would further tie up the system by convincing harried switchboard operators to reroute their calls through other switchboards. Discouraged by telephone problems, others would write high-precedence messages to be handled by the communications centers. The near breakdown of the telephone system began to cause a breakdown of the teletype system. In one month—November 1965—the daily message volume at teletype relay points in South Vietnam increased from 26,000 to 36,000 messages and backlogs rose to over 4,000 messages. As the system became so saturated that beset operators were literally wading in teletype tape, the rate of mistakes and misrouting of traffic increased dramatically. Retransmissions of lost or garbled messages and coordination traffic between communicators rose to 60 percent of the total traffic in the system.[41]

Overseas circuits were also overtaxed. Besides a heavy demand for service to bases throughout the United States to coordinate the arrival of new units, the encounter with North Vietnamese regular units in the Central Highlands had generated a steady stream of urgent messages and telephone calls between Saigon and Washington. Concerned with the strategic and political implications of the battle, the president and his advisers wanted to know even the most minute details of the 1st Cavalry Division's fight in the Ia Drang. That flood of high-precedence traffic drastically slowed the normal flow of administrative and logistic communications.[42]

Logistical support in South Vietnam was already restricted by a lack of direct high-quality channels to Okinawa, the major offshore logistical base for Army and Marine units operating in Southeast Asia. Although the U.S. supply system

---

[40]*Washington Post,* 14 Nov 65.

[41]MACV History, 1965, pp. 392–94, CMH; Joint Logistics Review Board, *Monograph 5: Communications,* Dec 69, app. D, p. 3, 71A2351/6, WNRC.

[42]Joint Logistics Review Board, *Monograph 5,* app. D, pp. 3–4; Interv, author with Lt Gen (ret.) Walter E. Lotz, Jr., former MACV J–6, 20 Sep 78, Historians files, CMH.

depended on high-speed data processing for requesting materiel and providing inventory status, the STARCOM net from Phu Lam to Okinawa could handle data communications at only the slow speed of ten cards per minute. Since the Philippines and Okinawa were also connected only by a high-frequency radio link, data sent from Phu Lam to the Philippines over the high-quality WETWASH cable at a rate of 100 cards per minute still was delayed in retransmission to Okinawa. In frustration, communicators had begun airlifting boxes of data processing cards from South Vietnam and the Philippines to Okinawa.[43]

With the exception of Okinawa, a good submarine cable network interconnected the Pacific. Realizing, however, that the WETWASH and transpacific cables were vulnerable to sabotage or accidental breaks, Admiral Sharp was alarmed that communicators were becoming too dependent on submarine cable. Although the atmospheric anomalies endemic to that area of the world caused the Phu Lam and Bangkok stations to be the worst performers in the entire Defense Communications System (DCS), Admiral Sharp warned communicators to continue to maintain some high-priority operational circuits over the radio links to ensure uninterrupted service should the cables be severed. To provide a backup to the Phu Lam station, he also wanted a fixed overseas radio and tape relay facility for the Nha Trang area. While the Defense Communications Agency drew up plans for a permanent strategic station to meet Admiral Sharp's request, General Meyer dispatched a transportable station from the contingency stocks of the Strategic Communications Command for temporary use.[44]

By December the Strategic Communications Command, having shipped since spring over two hundred tons of communications equipment worth $5 million to South Vietnam, had significantly augmented overseas communications to that country with transportable equipment. Besides eliminating the vulnerability of having only one gateway station, the contingency package sent to Nha Trang with its eighteen-line tape relay center relieved much of the message congestion at the Phu Lam station. To provide additional circuits from Southeast Asia to Hawaii, the Strategic Communications Command rushed a satellite terminal to Saigon from Asmara, Ethiopia, where it had been the primary U.S. overseas station on the African continent, and moved the two Saigon terminals to Korat and Nha Trang.[45]

By mid-January 1966 the reinforcements from the Strategic Communications Command and the deployment of the 69th Signal Battalion had reversed the worrisome situation of previous months. Although the volume of messages continued to rise, backlogs in communications centers had all but disappeared. A campaign for communications discipline, which sought to reduce the quantity of lengthy, high-precedence messages sent out with unnecessarily wide distribution, seemed to have a salutary effect on the work load in message centers.

[43]Joint Logistics Review Board, *Monograph 5*, p. 8, and app. A, pp. 5–6; Ltr, Capt Stephen F. Johnson to Col William M. Spitz, 28 Apr 71, CMH.

[44]Msg, CINCPAC to JCS, 29 May 65, sub: System Plan for Increased DCA Teletype Service Pacific Area, CMH; USARPAC Sig Ofcr, Quarterly Review Rpt, 4th Qtr, FY 64, pp. 26–27, 338–75–1009/53, WNRC; Msg, DCA to CINCPAC, 26 Aug 65, sub: Cam Ranh Bay Communications, CMH; Msg, DCA PAC to DCA, 4 Aug 65, sub: Comm Facility Requirements for RVN, CMH.

[45]Memo, USASCC for CSA and VCSA, 10 Jan 66, sub: Improved Communications in SE Asia, CMH.

Units of the 2d Signal Group, taking advantage of the relaxation of pressures on communicators and the additional resources received during the late fall, finally had the opportunity to begin long-needed improvements and to replace makeshift facilities that had been hastily installed to meet urgent requirements during the early phases of the buildup.[46]

They found much work to be done. In Saigon, for example, years of repairs and additions to the cable plant, by both Americans and South Vietnamese, had left an unfathomable labyrinth of wiring that was impossible to troubleshoot. A well-placed grenade, thrown at one of the many exposed cableheads in the Saigon area, would cast headquarters communications in the capital into complete confusion. Seeking to replace all old cables and consolidate individual wire lines into large multipair cables, Colonel Myer told his companies to give first priority to improving the trunk lines between the nine switchboards that his battalion operated throughout Saigon. While wiremen from the 580th Signal Company tackled the cabling, Colonel Myer's tactical multichannel teams spread throughout the city, parking in alleys and on sidewalks and lashing antennas on rooftops, to provide temporary trunks between the switchboards.[47]

Responding to an order from General Westmoreland that there be secure tactical links directly from the operations center at MACV headquarters to all major combat units in South Vietnam, the 69th Signal Battalion also was to establish a theater-wide radio-teletype net. By early January, twenty-three radio teams, equipped with GRC–26's, had dispersed throughout South Vietnam to install ten separate radio-teletype nets.[48]

Mobile Command Communications

G eneral Westmoreland's desire to have direct communications to all tactical headquarters reflected his desire to emphasize offensive "search and destroy" operations by actively seeking out the enemy and confronting him in his own base areas. Realizing that the fixed backbone system, ideal for an enclave strategy, would be inadequate for the new approach, General Westmoreland emphasized use of mobile command communications, such as those provided by the 54th Signal Battalion and the radio company of the 69th Signal Battalion, for direct support of wide-ranging units conducting search and destroy operations.[49]

Throughout the late winter of 1966, American and South Korean combat units did indeed disperse throughout the countryside in battalion-size task forces. Because the mobile combat units often were too dispersed to maintain their own

[46]MACV History, 1965, p. 394; Operational Report-Lessons Learned (ORLL), USASTRATCOM-SEA-V, 31 Jan 66, p. 3, file 2–05, 69A722/5, WNRC.

[47]Interv, author with Col (ret.) Wilbur A. Scudder, Jr., former staff officer, MACV, 8 Feb 78, Historians files, CMH; Ltr, 69th Sig Bn to USARV, 11 Jan 66, sub: Command Report for Period Ending 31 Dec 65, p. 7, 72A7128/24, WNRC.

[48]69th Sig Bn, Command Rpt, 31 Dec 65, p. 7; USARV Sig Ofcr, Stf Rpt, Oct–Dec 65, par. 3b. Both in WNRC.

[49]Sharp and Westmoreland, *Report on the War in Vietnam*, pp. 97–111.

communications and seldom remained near an access point to the area communications network, they relied on the 54th Signal Battalion to keep them in contact with their parent units or with the field force headquarters in Nha Trang. Supporting the brigade of the 101st Airborne Division as it deployed along 150 miles of coast from Phan Rang to Tuy Hoa, for example, Colonel Whisler's men had to split into several detachments to cover the brigade's main, forward, and rear headquarters. Providing support to South Korean Army and Marine units operating with the 1st Cavalry Division in the Bong Son area, as well as to the principal South Korean headquarters around Qui Nhon, further diffused the 54th Signal Battalion's resources. Were it not for augmentations of the 54th Signal Battalion by Colonel Myer's radio teams, the practice of splitting major tactical units into battalion-size task forces under the control of a forward headquarters of the parent unit would have left some combat units without command communications to their higher headquarters.[50]

To cope with unique demands imposed by American tactics and the South Vietnamese environment, communications officers assigned to the brigades and battalions conducting operations in South Vietnam during the spring of 1966 altered traditional methods of signal tactics and discarded some standard items of communications equipment. Since field wire, formerly the primary implement of the field communicator's trade, was used during operations in South Vietnam only to connect platoons on nightly defensive perimeters and usually was retrieved, companies normally carried only two miles of wire and a few phones to the field; stocks of bulky field wire, cable, and switchboards remained stored in base camps. Radio receivers, assigned to companies throughout the Army since the early days of World War II for monitoring air warning nets, were also consigned to storage at base camps. In South Vietnam, where the enemy posed little threat from the air, the heavy receivers were an unnecessary encumbrance.[51]

The threat of Viet Cong attack did affect communications by messenger, the mode most used by the Communists themselves. While native Viet Cong messengers, acquainted with the terrain and the habits of the local populace, could move relatively safely, American couriers, usually traveling unfamiliar routes, were in constant danger of ambush. Eliminating scheduled messenger runs outside secure enclaves, American communications officers dispatched couriers only when they could join an armed convoy going to their destination, or they sent material with staff officers traveling by helicopter between headquarters. Only to brigade and division headquarters did the 54th Signal Battalion make scheduled helicopter courier runs.[52]

Radio, and more specifically a new family of FM voice radios called the VRC–12 family, was the predominant form of communications at all echelons from brigade

---

[50]Ibid., pp. 123–25; Ltr, 54th Sig Bn to ACSFOR, DA, 14 May 66, sub: Operations Report-Lessons Learned, pp. 3–5, 72A7128/23, WNRC; ORLL, 1st Bde, 101st Abn Div, 30 Apr 66, 72A7128/27, WNRC.

[51]USARV Rpt, Evaluation of U.S. Army Combat Operations in Vietnam (hereafter cited as Combat Operations Evaluation), 25 Apr 66, an. D, Command, Control and Communications, app. 9, pp. 1, 8, ASDIRS no. 1362, Army Library, Pentagon.

[52]Ibid., pp. 5, 9; 54th Sig Bn, Command Rpt, 24 Jan 66, p. 11. The first casualties in the 54th Signal Battalion were two couriers killed when their helicopter crashed on a courier run.

to platoon.[53] Squads normally had no radios until more PRC–25's became available later in the war; most tactical units, finding their assigned squad radios, the
old PRC–6's, too clumsy to carry in the jungle and unsuitable for communicating
through dense foliage, had left them in storage. Since distances between command posts at the different echelons of command often exceeded the range of
the PRC–25, communications officers used specially modified antennas or replaced
the portable radio with a more powerful vehicular model, the VRC–46, to extend
the communicating range. For even longer distances they installed automatic
retransmission sets, called VRC–49's, on centrally located hilltops such as the Hon
Cong Mountain site that supported the 1st Cavalry Division's nets. During important operations, enterprising communications officers often appropriated an
aircraft to carry a radio operator to relay messages between ground stations. In
the 1st Cavalry Division, the two specially outfitted airborne retransmission sets
could perform that relay function automatically. Since almost every brigade and
battalion commander took to the air in a helicopter equipped with FM radios to
control his forces during critical operations, communications officers had less need
for relays when their commanders were aloft in their airborne command posts.[54]

As units dispersed during operations in the spring of 1966, a few began to
rely more heavily on high-frequency radio for its long range. Because high-
frequency equipment had disadvantages—bulkiness, vulnerability to atmospheric
interference, and overheating—communicators in tactical units in South Vietnam
had avoided using their radio-teletype or single-sideband equipment. Finally
forced to employ radio-teletype when FM radio proved inadequate to link units
spread along the entire coast of II Corps, the communications officer of the brigade
of the 101st Airborne Division learned that the deficiencies of high-frequency radio
could be overcome with good results. In the 173d Airborne Brigade, communications officers overcame mobility limitations of the high-frequency set, which had
been built into a truck-mounted shelter, by installing the radio on a tractor-type
vehicle, called a mule, that the airborne troopers used for transport in rough
country. Because the specially modified configuration was also outfitted with FM
radios and other assorted items of communications equipment, it came to be called
the "talking mule."[55]

For most American units, replacement of old high-frequency communications
equipment by FM and single-sideband voice radios presaged a corresponding
atrophy in the ability of radio operators to use Morse code, a primary mode of
transmission for high-frequency radio. Determined that such a fate not befall
Special Forces radiomen, their signal officer, Maj. Anthony J. Scibilia, required
that the net to the A detachments be operated during certain hours with Morse
code equipment; during the remainder of the day, new single-sideband voice
radios could be used. When in March 1966 a large North Vietnamese force attacked
the A Shau Special Forces camp in I Corps, Major Scibilia's concern proved pres-

[53]The VRC–12 series of radios contained a variety of models of compatible transistorized FM voice
radios, of which the portable model, the PRC–25, was most widely used.
[54]Interv, author with Smith, 8 Mar 78; USARV Rpt, Combat Operations Evaluation, an. D, Command, Control and Communications, app. 9, pp. 2–3 and app. 4, pp. 4–6.
[55]ORLL, 1st Bde, 101st Abn Div, 30 Apr 66, pp. 2–4; Interv, author with Peter J. McAteer, former
signal officer with the 173d Airborne Brigade, 12 Mar 78, Historians files, CMH.

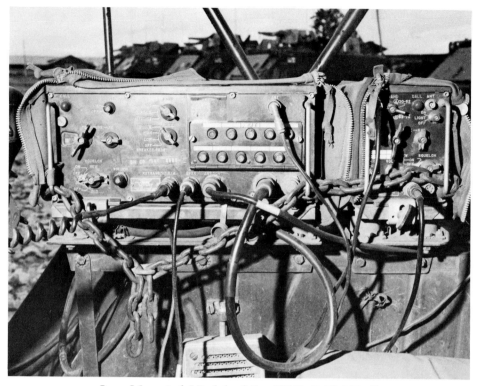

Jeep-Mounted Model of the VRC–12 FM Radio

cient. Having lost communications and power facilities except for a single GRC–109 radio and a hand-cranked generator when the enemy overran a section of the camp, the camp's radioman had to send out his distress call by Morse code. For two days, as relief forces fought their way to the camp, only the uninterrupted reception of Morse code transmissions monitored by the C detachment in Da Nang enabled the relief forces to ascertain that the 200 American and South Vietnamese soldiers in the beleaguered camp were still holding out.[56]

The eventual evacuation of the A Shau camp, located astride a strategic valley corridor leading towards the city of Hue, demonstrated that the North Vietnamese and Viet Cong still held the offensive. Shifting the bulk of the American 3d Marine Division north from Da Nang to Thua Thien Province, General Westmoreland requested additional forces to assume the division's mission to protect the Da Nang enclave. The American buildup in South Vietnam intensified.[57]

Although General Westmoreland stated that communicators had "responded brilliantly" during the first year of the buildup in South Vietnam, many of the actions that signal officers had taken to meet his urgent requests for additional communications were temporary expedients pending completion of the long-delayed Integrated Wideband Communications System. Fifteen months after the

[56]ORLL, 5th SFG, 30 Apr 66, app. 15, 67A5293/8, WNRC.
[57]Sharp and Westmoreland, *Report on the War in Vietnam*, pp. 115–16, 124.

Defense Communications Agency had submitted the plan for that project, it was still far from complete—and would be insufficient even for existing needs whenever it was finished. For the Military Assistance Command's most vital communications, General Westmoreland was still depending on attached contingency teams that could be withdrawn at any time for other crises and on detachments loaned by worldwide Army and Air Force commands. Like men on the satellite terminal team sent from Ethiopia, many of the communicators who had been rushed to South Vietnam for temporary duty had left unfinished work and unprepared families in other areas of the world. With further build-up in South Vietnam imminent, the interim measures of 1965 would have to become the permanent solutions of 1966. Temporary duty would have to become permanent assignment, attached units from other commands would have to be transferred to the U.S. Army, Vietnam, and General Westmoreland would have to find some way to consolidate and manage his vast communications responsibilities.

8

The Genesis of a Signal Command
1962–1966

As signal units poured into South Vietnam during late 1965, there was no single organization or commander to take charge of them. To consolidate control over the rapidly proliferating communications in South Vietnam, in October 1965 General Westmoreland proposed that his J–6, Brig. Gen. Walter E. Lotz, Jr., assume command of all Army signal units in Southeast Asia. When Lotz responded that he thought it inappropriate for a joint staff officer to take command of the units of a service component, Westmoreland pointed out that MACV's Assistant Chief of Staff for Intelligence (J–2), Maj. Gen. Joseph A. McChristian, was commanding several combined intelligence agencies and exercising operational control over Army intelligence units while serving as the MACV intelligence staff officer. With the help of MACV Chief of Staff, Maj. Gen. William B. Rosson, Lotz eventually convinced Westmoreland that such an unorthodox approach would be too facile a solution to the complexities of command and control of Army communications.[1]

Lotz knew that the situation in South Vietnam was the result of changes in signal command arrangements that had taken place over the previous five years. As signal officer of the U.S. Army, Pacific, in the late 1950s, General Lotz had been in a position to maintain tight control over theater signal operations while working within an informal signal chain of command emanating from the Army's chief signal officer in the Pentagon, through his office in Hawaii, down to the signal units and Army Command and Administrative Net stations spread throughout the Pacific. By 1965 there was neither a chief signal officer nor a signal chain of command, and the Army shared its communications responsibilities with its sister services and a powerful Defense Communications Agency. In General Lotz's opinion, inserting a joint staff officer of a subordinate unified command into the Army's signal command structure would only aggravate the confusion caused by those recent changes.

[1]Interv, author with Lotz, 20 Sep 78.

167

Strategic, technological, and organizational developments brewing since the closing days of World War II led to the changes in signal command structure. The advent of nuclear weapons imbued even minor clashes in remote areas with serious global portent. Tactical decisions once made in the field were being made in the Pentagon or even the White House, blurring traditional distinctions between tactical and strategic communications. For example, during an attack on a U.S. Marine Corps regimental command post in I Corps in the summer of 1965, President Johnson called the regimental commander directly for an appraisal of the situation.[2]

The dramatic acceleration in electronics technology, especially the development of transistors and microminiaturization of circuitry, made possible the extension of commercial-quality communications from Washington to the foxhole, but also made it difficult for the Army to keep signalmen qualified to operate and maintain a constantly changing inventory of old and new electronic equipment. Technical difficulties were magnified by the linking of incompatible components from multiple generations of tactical and strategic communications equipment and the common use of equipment from different services. Bringing together signalmen who had formerly worked in relative isolation to operate consolidated networks also bred internal Army conflicts. So great had become the problem of command and control of Army signal units in Vietnam that General Lotz finally had to draft a message for General Westmoreland to General Johnson, the Army chief of staff, requesting "extraordinary measures . . . to resolve fragmentation of command and control of Army signal units to RVN."[3]

Managing Strategic Communications

F oreseeing just such a problem, in the waning days of World War II the Chief Signal Officer, Maj. Gen. Harry C. Ingles, had proposed the consolidation of all nontactical communications into a single network after the war. He felt the Army should turn over its Army Command and Administrative Net, the global system for flow of America's strategic direction throughout the war, to a consortium of commercial companies. He wanted it to be operated as a diplomatic and governmental network during peacetime and transferred to the military during wartime. Although Maj. Gen. Frank E. Stoner, the chief of the Army Communications Service that operated the network, was determined to keep the Army's strategic system functioning until commercial operation was feasible, a less patient Army Chief of Staff, General of the Army Dwight D. Eisenhower, directed Stoner to rid the Army of the strategic networks so that it would have "more energy

---

[2]Ltr, Lotz to Maj Gen Thomas M. Rienzi, 16 Feb 71, w/Incl, CMH.
[3]Quote from Msg, COMUSMACV to CSA, 19 Oct 65, sub: C-E Responsibilities RVN, file 139458, 72A25/2, WNRC.

. . . to devote to strictly military problems."[4] Although General Stoner believed that the Army was making an expensive blunder, he dismantled the network, leaving stations only at major overseas headquarters. Reflecting Southeast Asia's lack of strategic importance, the global ring of American stations was broken between the Philippine Islands and North Africa, leaving Indochina without an American communications link.[5]

True to General Stoner's predictions, at the outbreak of the Korean War international communications were insufficient for military purposes in the Pacific, and each of the services hastily built separate nets to meet its own strategic communications needs. Justifying the continuation of three independent systems even after the cease-fire in Korea, the services argued that the consolidation of strategic communications was no more practical than the "integration of communications facilities of three large industrial companies with separate management."[6]

During the 1950s the development of modern communications went hand in hand with the evolution of nuclear strategy and new weapons systems, becoming an essential part of the nuclear trigger that could be pulled only by the president. National military authorities and the president had to be informed immediately of any event that might precipitate a nuclear confrontation, and they had to have the means of alerting American forces around the world and of directing the launch of the American nuclear response. Communicators devised ways to communicate directly to Washington from remote radar sites on Pacific atolls and in the Arctic and from underground command posts to missile silos and strategic bombers aloft. Those communications circuits had to have a reliability known to nuclear strategists as "fail safe" and a rapidity that signalmen called "real time." The Air Force, the service most responsible for U.S. strategic nuclear forces, received the most money and developed the most sophisticated communications equipment. With costs of military electronic equipment rising at a rate of 25 percent a year, the Army and Navy became concerned that they would be priced out of the competition for new equipment.[7]

In 1958 the chief of the Army Communications Service, Col. George P. Sampson, proposed to end service competition for expensive communications equipment and service by establishing a single strategic network to be managed by the Army. Although the Air Force and Navy promptly opposed the proposal, a drift towards centralization of military functions that had begun with the Defense Reorganization Act of 1958 kept the idea afloat long enough for Secretary of

---

[4]Address of General of the Army Dwight D. Eisenhower to the Army Ordnance Assn, Detroit, Mich., 3 Jun 46, quoted in George Raynor Thompson and Dixie R. Harris, *The Signal Corps: The Outcome* (hereafter cited as *The Outcome*) (Washington, D.C.: U.S. Army Center of Military History, Government Printing Office, 1966), p. 621.

[5]Thompson and Harris, *The Outcome*, pp. 620-23.

[6]Quoted from a report to the secretary of defense in 1953 cited in Lt Col Blaine O. Vogt, The Defense Communications Agency, Single Management of the Defense Communications Systems, 30 Mar 63, Industrial College of the Armed Forces, p. 6.

[7]By 1958 the costs of providing communications to a typical field army had risen from $33 million to $180 million. Memo, Paul R. Ignatius for General Hamlett, 21 Nov 62, sub: Requirements for Communications Equipment, file 2301207, 66A3140/19, WNRC. For a discussion of the influence of nuclear strategy on command and control communications, see Judith A. Merkle, *Command and Control: The Social Implications of Nuclear Defense* (New York: General Learning Press, 1971), pp. 1–13.

Defense Thomas S. Gates, Jr., to ask the Joint Chiefs of Staff to examine Sampson's proposal. When the Joint Chiefs reported in October 1959 that they were unable to agree on a means for consolidating strategic communications, Gates took matters into his own hands. On 12 May 1960, he established the Defense Communications Agency to supervise a single worldwide military communications network to be called the Defense Communications System.[8]

Prior to the establishment of the Defense Communications Agency, the J–6 of the Joint Chiefs of Staff had been responsible for coordinating signal matters between the services. Even after his staff was augmented in 1958 by a Communications-Electronics Directorate manned by forty-six officers drawn from the Army, Navy, Air Force, and Marine Corps, he had little success in controlling competition between the services for their divergent signal enterprises. Seeking to avoid service rivalry, the first head of the new Defense Communications Agency, Rear Adm. William D. Irvin, spent a year planning the consolidation of existing strategic communications systems and the equitable assignment of operational responsibilities for the different parts of the Defense Communications System to the different services. While the technical staff of the 212-man agency did the engineering work to mesh the equipment of the separate service networks into the single Defense Communications System, Admiral Irvin assigned operational missions on a geographical basis. As the Air Force and the Navy jousted for control over communications in such strategic areas as Hawaii and the Mediterranean, responsibility for Southeast Asia, which at the time had only a few small stations serving the advisory missions, passed unchallenged to the Army.[9]

Since the services were to retain control of those communications required for command and control of their own forces within a theater, traditionally identified as tactical communications, Admiral Irvin had first to determine what communications should be classified as strategic communications.[10] While it may have been obvious that the stationary global communications facilities came under the purview of the Defense Communications Agency, its role in day-to-day military operations was less certain. Doctrine for joint communications operations was lacking, and with new high-capacity, mobile communications equipment, distinctions between tactical and strategic communications based on range, sophistication, or mobility were no longer valid. On the very day that the Defense

---

[8]USASCC History, FY–65, pp. 12–13; OCSO, Signal Corps Summary of Major Events and Problems, FY–60, pp. 8–9. Both in CMH.

[9]Memo, Dir, DCA, for JCS, 28 Jun 62, sub: Defense Communications Agency's Mid-Range Plan-1962, Incl to JCS 22/477, JACO (1962), DA/13, NARS; Col Albert Redman, Centralized Management, Integration and Operational Direction of Communications Systems in Southeast Asia and Its Impact on the Overall DOD Communications Posture (hereafter cited as Centralized Management), 23 Mar 67, Industrial College of the Armed Forces, pp. 36–42. This study, written by the first chief of the Defense Communications Agency's field office in Saigon, provides a good background of the development of a management structure for military communications from World War II to the early days of the Vietnam War.

[10]The generally accepted definition for strategic communications at that time was: "Long-haul, point-to-point and channel control facility existing or proposed that could be used by the President, the Secretary of Defense, the Joint Chiefs of Staff, or the unified commanders for essential intelligence and command purposes under survival conditions." From a brochure entitled "Global Communications Program in Support of National Defense," presented by Col. George Sampson to the secretary of defense et al., July 1959, p. 3, and quoted in Redman, Centralized Management, p. 42.

Communications Agency was established, for example, the Army unveiled a new transportable communications terminal, the TSC–18, that could be airlifted into a combat area to serve either as a base station for international communications or for command and control communications within the battle area. When the large MRC–85's were moved to South Vietnam in 1963 and were installed in a fixed configuration on the BACKPORCH network, the Defense Communications Agency made no move to include the network in its Defense Communications System.[11]

During its first years of existence, the agency avoided extending its influence into matters construed as the tactical commander's prerogatives. Seeking instead to solidify control over those parts of the network that were obviously the agency's responsibility, on 14 November 1961, Secretary of Defense Robert S. McNamara revised and strengthened the Defense Communications Agency's charter. To the agency's director he gave the responsibility for operational and management direction of Defense Communications System and precisely defined the scope of that responsibility.[12]

Broadening the responsibilities and functions of the agency beyond the Defense Communications System, McNamara extended the agency's operations to technical support of the military's satellite program and to a complex of high-echelon communications nets and command posts forming the National Military Command System. In November 1962 Lt. Gen. Alfred D. Starbird was appointed head of the strengthened Defense Communications Agency with the principal task of operational direction and management of a growing Defense Communications System.[13]

The Abolition of the Office of the Chief Signal Officer

A s the Defense Communications Agency was consolidating its control over strategic communications, the Army Signal Corps was undergoing the most drastic change in its century-long history. By 1960 the chief signal officer had become one of the most powerful men in the Army. As head of the third largest branch in the Army, he was responsible for all aspects of Army communications:

[11]Ibid. USARPAC, Final Report, Communications Evaluation in Southeast Asia (COMSEA), 30 Jun 69; see an. B, Concepts and Doctrine, 72A2315/14, WNRC, for a thorough discussion on the difficulty in reconciling joint military doctrine and operations of the Defense Communications Agency.

[12]Operational direction is defined as: "The authoritative direction necessary to obtain and effectively operate a single long-line, point-to-point communications system for the Department of Defense. It includes, but is not limited to, authority to direct the operating elements, to prescribe the manner in which tasks will be performed and to supervise the execution of those tasks." Management direction is defined as: "The coordination and review and, within approved programs, the continuing guidance and supervision necessary to accomplish the mission." See DOD Directive 5105.19, 14 Nov 61, p. 5.

[13]For a collection of topical articles concerning the Defense Communications Agency written by senior communicators of each service, see *Signal* 18, no. 1 (September 1963), Army Library, Pentagon. For a more critical study of the development of the Defense Communications Agency, see Col Kenneth E. Shiflet, Reorganization of the Defense Telecommunications Management and Operational Structure, 1966, Industrial College of the Armed Forces.

doctrine, training, personnel, logistics, staffing, and operations. With the technological breakthroughs during the 1950s in electronics and computers, his span of interest embraced such esoteric endeavors as missile guidance, battlefield surveillance, data processing, satellites, and night vision. By 1962 the chief signal officer's budget exceeded $1 billion for the first time. Less than a year later his empire had collapsed, and all of his responsibilities except his duties as a staff officer and his control of strategic communications were parceled out to others.[14]

The pervasiveness of sophisticated electronic gear throughout the Army, which had made the chief signal officer so powerful, was also a cause of his downfall. Other branches, especially the Artillery and Ordnance Corps, resented the intrusion of signalmen into "everything that contained electrons," and sought curtailment of the chief signal officer's influence over endeavors that had traditionally belonged to them. An opportunity to curb the protean electronics empire came in 1962 when Assistant Secretary of the Army (Installations and Logistics) Paul R. Ignatius criticized Army planners for the excessive quantity and complexity of communications being programmed for the future Army. Besides restricting mobility and increasing rear-echelon maintenance requirements, continued proliferation of communications equipment within eight years would cause the costs of communications for a typical field army to equal the current year's budget for the entire Army. He cited the Signal Corps as an example of why the Army would have to become more austere and more efficient.[15]

The new secretary of defense had already determined how he was going to make the Army more efficient. On 8 December 1961, called Black Friday by many on the Army's staff, Secretary McNamara called together the chiefs of all the technical services and told them that he was recommending to the president that their positions be abolished. For the previous nine months, Project 80, a committee headed by Deputy Comptroller of the Army Leonard W. Hoelscher, had been planning a reorganization of the Army along functional lines and had determined that the chiefs of the technical services should be divested of their operational, training, and logistical functions. Busy with ongoing operations and crises in Berlin and Southeast Asia, the technical service chiefs had largely ignored the proceedings of the Hoelscher committee in the belief that they would have time to study the conclusions and in normal staffing fashion offer their concurrences, objections, and suggested modifications. Apparently they felt that the reorganization fever would run its course as earlier attempts had. Just a few weeks before Black Friday, the chief signal officer had offhandedly explained his lack of involvement in the course of the reorganization study: "I'm sure I can't influence it at all; . . . so far nobody wants my comments."[16] But a resolute Secretary McNamara, who believed that the Army had to be made more efficient and more fiscally responsible to survive in the modern technological era, was not to be stayed by the bureaucratic delays that had diverted his predecessors. On 16 January 1962,

---

[14]DF, DCSOPS to CSO, 25 Jan 63, sub: Reduction of Material Requirements, file 2301207, 66A3140/19, WNRC; Interv, author with Lotz, 20 Sep 78.

[15]Ibid.

[16]Rpt, Signal Officers' Conference, Nov 61, p. X–4, file 201–45, 67A4845/1, WNRC.

President Kennedy approved the reorganization.[17]

Because the chief signal officer had the most to lose, the reorganization affected him most severely. He was to surrender responsibility for signal doctrine to a newly formed Combat Developments Command that had proponency for all Army doctrine. To the Continental Army Command the chief signal officer relinquished his training responsibilities and control over the signal schools. To the new Office of Personnel Operations, subordinate to the deputy chief of staff for personnel, he transferred responsibility for signal personnel management. The huge logistical mission of the Signal Corps was consolidated into an Electronics Command, subordinate to the new Army Materiel Command. When Fort Monmouth, which housed the Signal Corps' laboratories, was made the headquarters of the Electronics Command, the traditional home of the Signal Corps transferred to the control of the Army Materiel Command, which was commanded and staffed by many of the chief signal officer's rivals from the other technical services. Since the Army lacked a functional command that could assume responsibility for strategic communications, the chief signal officer retained that one major operational responsibility.[18]

While staff members of the Office of the Chief Signal Officer were preparing for transfer to new organizations in the spring of 1962, they also had to plan and monitor the deployment of the 39th Signal Battalion to South Vietnam. Personnel officers mustered qualified signalmen from worldwide posts; training officers arranged for instruction for troposcatter operators at the signal school and at manufacturers' plants; and supply experts scoured inventories of signal stocks throughout the country for specialized equipment needed in South Vietnam. The mobilization and dispatch of the 39th Signal Battalion overseas was the last major staff action taken by the Office of the Chief Signal Officer.[19]

About the same time that the last men of the 362d Signal Company (Tropo) arrived in South Vietnam in August 1962, the reorganization in the United States was officially completed. But the Signal Corps was still in turmoil. Experienced civilian staffers found new positions on nonsignal staffs in Washington rather than move to other areas of the country. Even those who remained in signal jobs had to learn new procedures and adjust to new supervisors. Those with newly acquired authority had to find the boundaries of their responsibility and develop relationships for lateral coordination with other newly formed headquarters. For some, careers came to an abrupt end. The first commander of the Electronics Command, Maj. Gen. Stuart S. Hoff, felt that Lt. Gen. Frank S. Besson, Jr., a Transportation Corps officer and commanding general of the Army Materiel Command, was unable to fathom the complexities of highly technical electronic logistics. Hoff resigned after only one year in his job.

---

[17]Thorough accounts of the reorganization of the Army are contained in Martin Blumenson, Reorganization of the Army, OCMH Monograph, 1962, file 2–3.7 AC.J, CMH; and James E. Hewes, *From Root to McNamara: Army Organization and Administration, 1900–1963* (Washington, D.C.: U.S. Army Center of Military History, Government Printing Office, 1975), pp. 299–365.

[18]For a discussion of the implications of the reorganization for the Signal Corps that contains interviews with Signal Corps general officers, see U.S. Army Signal School (USASS), *Tec Tac,* no. 100 (18 December 1962), CMH.

[19]Rpt, Chief Signal Officer's Conference, 1962, p. I–5, file 203–03, 67A4846/1, WNRC.

To guide the Army through the chaotic period, the depleted signal staff remaining at the Pentagon wrote fifty-six new regulations outlining revised policy and establishing new lines of authority and coordination. Each new directive involved an inordinate amount of staff coordination. Where previously a staff member might never have to leave the Office of the Chief Signal Officer to coordinate a staff paper, after the reorganization he had to search out the appropriate individuals in other agencies within the Pentagon or in the newly created field commands and repeatedly explain the meaning and ramifications of a staff paper before he could get the necessary concurrences. When the secretary of defense in late 1962 directed the Army to obtain additional troposcatter radios to expand communications into Thailand, it took the reorganized Army staff and the new Army Materiel Command eighteen months to arrange delivery of the first TRC–90. The Signal Corps had rushed the same set through its initial production in eight months during the previous year. It took over a year for the Continental Army Command and the Army Materiel Command simply to move models of the same set to the signal school to train operators.[20]

The signal staff was so weakened in both prestige and resources that the Chief Signal Officer, Maj. Gen. Earle F. Cook, had to interject himself into Army planning, often to the annoyance of other staff members, lest important communications considerations be neglected. Diffusion of responsibility and neglect of communications in the Army's operational planning almost caused a loss of command and control of contingency forces during the Cuban crisis. When General Cook tried to divert signalmen and equipment from around the world to a task force forming in Florida, he learned that the Army Materiel Command had neglected to include important signal support units on the troop list that had been prepared at emergency planning meetings to which signal representatives had not been invited. The task force was without communications for forty-eight hours while the Army added signal units to its priority troop lists. The headquarters in command of the task force, the Continental Army Command, had eliminated the position of signal officer from its staff during the recent Army reorganization. Thus, even after signal units were assembled, the command was without a qualified staff officer to plan and coordinate communications operations until a Signal Corps officer working on the training staff was hurriedly designated the signal officer. After the crisis abated, the Continental Army Command reinstated a signal office on the permanent staff, but relegated it to a minor branch of the Office of the Director of Plans and Operations.[21]

Retiring in frustration in June 1963, General Cook told General Earle G. Wheeler, the chief of staff of the Army, ''I find after one year's functioning under the 1962 Army reorganization that there is lacking in elements of the Army Staff

---

[20]As Blumenson notes, amidst the post-reorganization confusion the entire Army staff suddenly became aware of the tremendous amount of work performed by the technical services. Reorganization of the Army, p. 125. DA, DCSOPS, AHS, FY–65, an. K, pt. 2, pp. 1–2, CMH. For a detailed view of the new Office of the Chief Signal Officer, see Chief of Staff Regulation (CSR) 10–65, 2 Dec 63, CMH.

[21]General Cook discusses his difficulties during the aftermath of the reorganization in Rpt, Chief Signal Officer's Conference, 1962, file 203–03, 67A4846/1; and MS, George R. Thompson, The Signal Corps Role in the Cuban Crisis, 1962, completed in 1963, file 201–45, 67A4846/1. Both in WNRC.

a proper understanding of Army communications and electronics and the role of the Chief Signal Officer."[22] Agreeing that "tactical communications and electronics for command and control are among the basic elements necessary for success in ground combat," on 12 June 1963, General Wheeler directed his Deputy Chief of Staff for Military Operations, Lt. Gen. Harold K. Johnson, to conduct a study to determine "Army responsibilities, objectives, requirements, commitments and allocation of personnel and resources in the communications and electronics field."[23]

A group of general officers from all the major staffs in the Department of the Army, called the Powell Board, conducted the study. They confronted two major issues: the nature and extent of the chief signal officer's influence on the Army staff, and the chief signal officer's responsibilities for strategic communications. By changing the title of the signal staff from Office of the Chief Signal Officer to Office of the Chief, Communications-Electronics, the board sought to reflect the wide interests of the Army's chief signal officer. They also proposed that the signal staff should function primarily in an advisory capacity. Arguing that the proposal would perpetuate the exclusion of the signal staff from Army planning, General Cook's successor, Maj. Gen. David P. Gibbs, convinced General Wheeler to change the staff's mission to make the new signal office "a focal point for staff advice and coordination." Opposing the board's recommendation that the chief, communications-electronics, "exercise supervision and control" of strategic signal operations, Deputy Comptroller Hoelscher, who had been instrumental in stripping operational authority from the technical services, argued successfully to restrict the chief, communications-electronics, to the exercise of staff supervision over only strategic operations. When the Office of the Chief, Communications-Electronics, was established on 1 March 1964 as a subordinate agency of the Office of the Deputy Chief of Staff for Military Operations, the 357-man signal staff was released from all operational responsibilities except for the Army Photographic Agency. General Gibbs turned over control of Army strategic communications to Maj. Gen. Richard J. Meyer, who was appointed commander of a new functional command, the U.S. Army Strategic Communications Command, which was established the same day.[24]

While General Gibbs lost some authority, the formation of a separate command reporting directly to the chief of staff of the Army conveyed greater importance to Army strategic communications. Although the Army had been the primary advocate of consolidating strategic communications, once the Defense Communications Agency was created for that purpose, the Army had been the slowest of the services to improve the operations and management of its part of the Defense Communications System. As General Cook explained, "The Army Staff to a large extent considers the strategic communications support provided

[22]Memo, Maj Gen Earle F. Cook for CSA, 21 Jun 63, sub: Final Report of the Chief Signal Officer, file CS 319.1, 43027457-166, 66A3140/19, WNRC.

[23]Memo, Maj Gen V. P. Mock for Dep Chiefs of Staff et al., 12 Jun 63, sub: Special Study of Signal Activities, file 4302757, 66A3140/17, WNRC.

[24]DCSOPS, Special Study of Signal Activities, 15 Oct 63; MFR, ODCSOPS, 2 Nov 63, sub: Briefing for Vice Chief of Staff on Special Study of Signal Activities; DA, DCSOPS, AHS, FY-64, an. C, pt. 2, p. 2; DA, DCSOPS, AHS, FY-65, an. K, pt. 2, pp. 2-3. All in CMH.

by the Army to defense and national agencies as a burden. The prevalent attitude in the Army is that the outside support the Army renders is at the expense of combat capabilities. Some senior officers appear willing to relinquish strategic and natural roles and missions of the Army.''[25]

The chief signal officer, although theoretically the lone defender of strategic communications in the Army, actually had controlled only the fixed stations in the United States and the Middle East. The Continental Army Command had possessed all transportable communications sets in the United States, and overseas commanders, reluctant to relinquish control of any communications in their theaters to the chief signal officer in faraway Washington, held tightly to their fixed and transportable communications. There were, in fact, serious doubts at the time concerning the authority of the Army chief of staff to redeploy signal units that had been dispatched to overseas commands in response to military emergencies. After the departure of the 39th Signal Battalion for South Vietnam depleted the radio relay component of the Strategic Army Corps, General Wheeler had considerable difficulty obtaining the return to the United States of two of the eight signal companies that had been deployed to the U.S. European Command during the Berlin crisis. Even though the tensions had subsided, the overseas commanders had become dependent on the recently arrived signal units.

By mid-1963 the Army was able to reconstitute a more readily available signal base to respond to global contingencies without the extensive restructuring that had been required to prepare the 39th Signal Battalion for South Vietnam. In May 1963 the 11th Signal Group was formed at Fort Lewis, Washington. Its one subordinate unit, the 505th Signal Company, was equipped with enough transportable radio and terminal equipment to support a contingency headquarters with austere internal communications and a few overseas circuits. When the Strategic Communications Command was established in 1964, the 11th Signal Group was the first unit assigned to it.[26]

The New Strategic Communications Command

The Strategic Communications Command did not have an easy birth. General Wheeler established the new signal command over the objections of General James F. Collins, the commander of the U.S. Army, Pacific, and with the lukewarm acquiescence of the other theater commanders. As General Meyer established field offices in the overseas theaters to manage his global command, his appoint-

[25]Memo, Cook for CSA, 21 Jun 63, sub: Final Report of the Chief Signal Officer.

[26]Memo, USASCC for CSO, 31 Jul 63, sub: Final Report of the Commanding Officer, U.S. Army Strategic Communications Command (USASTRATCOM), app. B; Address by Maj Gen Richard J. Meyer to the STRATCOM Commanders' Conference, 4 Nov 64, app. D. Both in USASCC History, FY-65, CMH. Summary Sheet, ODCSOPS, 2 Apr 62, sub: Redeployment of Support Units to CONUS, file CS 322, 2204867, 65A3314/2; DF, DCSOPS to DCSPER-AD, 28 Mar 62, sub: Justification and Source of Spaces for Proposed Increase to STRICOM Communications Element, file 250/36, DCSOPS 62, 65A3314/9; Summary Sheet, ODCSOPS, 12 May 64, w/Incl, CSM 64-3, file 201-45, 3400549, 67A4855/6. Latter three in WNRC.

ed regional commanders encountered difficulties in obtaining office space and normal garrison support. Cautioning the regional detachment commanders against seeking assistance from theater signal officers instead of dealing independently with local agencies, General Meyer's deputy, Col. Wallace M. Lauterbach, told them to "cut the umbilical cord." He feared that continued dependence on the theater signal officer would present the overseas commanders with an opportunity to retain control of strategic communications.[27]

In establishing his command's hegemony over the Army's strategic communications, General Meyer moved cautiously. Giving priority to strategic communications in the European theater, Meyer waited several months, until September 1964, to activate the Strategic Communications Command, Pacific, in Hawaii and until November before assuming responsibility for the Phu Lam station. He inherited a complicated situation in Southeast Asia. The STARCOM stations in South Vietnam and Thailand, which were to be operated by the Strategic Communications Command, had been assigned to tactical battalions under the operational control of an advisory rather than operational headquarters but were classified a part of the Army's theater forces. Reflecting General Meyer's lack of resources, signal units under the control of the Continental Army Command, rather than the 11th Signal Group, were alerted during the Tonkin crisis to be prepared to move a contingency station should anything happen to the Phu Lam station. When General Westmoreland requested TRC–90's from the Strategic Communications Command in January 1965 to expand the BACKPORCH network, General Meyer objected to committing any contingency equipment from the 11th Signal Group.[28]

Meyer's caution was prompted in part because he had yet to receive a charter for his command that defined its roles and mission. The Martin Board, formed at the Department of the Army to prepare a charter for the new command, found the critical point of contention to be disagreements concerning the definition of strategic and tactical communications. Rather than resolving the disagreements, the new charter, finally published on 19 February 1965, merely established that responsibilities would be assigned to the Strategic Communications Command on a case-by-case basis.[29]

With approval of the strategic Integrated Wideband Communications System and its incorporation into the Defense Communications System, General Meyer became more concerned about strategic communications in Southeast Asia. Meyer saw the responsibility for operating the network, which was to become part of the Defense Communications System, as basic to the mission of the Strategic Communications Command. But that revived the contention between the Strategic Communications Command and the U.S. Army, Pacific. General John K. Waters,

---

[27]Ltr, Collins to Wheeler, 4 Dec 63, tab J, file 2, OCSO papers, CMH; Address by Lauterbach to the STRATCOM Commanders' Conference, 4 Nov 64, in USASCC History, FY–65, app. D, CMH.
[28]Msg, USARPAC to USASCC, 11 Apr 65, sub: DCS Restoral Capability; Msg, CC-E to CINCUS-ARPAC, 10 Feb 65, sub: Expansion RVN Long Line System. Both in CMH.
[29]DA, Appraisal of U.S. Army Strategic Communications Command and Other U.S. Army Long Range Communications Facilities (Martin Board Report), 31 Mar 65, OCSO papers, CMH.

who had replaced General Collins, believed communications so essential to the daily conduct of the war should be controlled within the theater. Even the Army's Chief Signal Officer, Maj. Gen. David P. Gibbs, opposed transferring BACK-PORCH to the Strategic Communications Command on the grounds that it performed a tactical function. He also did not want to provide an opportunity for the Defense Communications Agency to extend its authority over the network. Although General Waters traveled to Washington to argue his case personally, on 31 May 1965, the Army chief of staff overruled him and General Gibbs; he directed that within sixty days the Strategic Communications Command should take responsibility for all long-haul communications in Southeast Asia.[30]

Critical to the Army's decision was General Westmoreland's support of the Strategic Communications Command's mission. He believed that the U.S.-based command offered the benefit of consolidated planning, engineering, and procurement and expected that the commitment of the new command's equipment would free some of his tactical signal equipment being used by the Army Support Command, Vietnam, for long-haul communications. Voiced by the senior tactical commander in South Vietnam, such support destroyed General Waters' argument that transfer of communications responsibility to the Strategic Communications Command would interfere with the flexibility of tactical commanders.[31]

Planning for the Strategic Communications Command's expanded mission in South Vietnam was carried out in Hawaii during June. Planners attempted to define limits of authority and responsibility to guide relationships between the Defense Communications Agency, the other services, the Strategic Communications Command, and tactical units in South Vietnam. Although all parties agreed to the primary stipulation that the Strategic Communications Command would be responsible for operating all communications classified as part of the Defense Communications System, a new Army policy announced just a few days after completion of the plan caused renewed controversy. Addressing the entire Army portion of the global Defense Communications System, and not specifically the system in Southeast Asia, the Department of the Army stated that it would allow Army component commanders and the Strategic Communications Command temporarily to share responsibility for the operation of strategic communications. Citing this new policy, General Waters tried unsuccessfully to make all agencies of the Strategic Communications Command in the Pacific accountable to the staff coordination of the U.S. Army, Pacific, and its subcommands. Despite confusions in policy, General Meyer ultimately prevailed in his struggle with the U.S.

---

[30]Msg, CINCUSARPAC to USASCC, 24 Mar 65, sub: BACKPORCH FY-66 Contract. An account of the interplay between the U.S. Army, Pacific, and the Strategic Communications Command from the perspective of the Military Assistance Command, Vietnam, is contained in MACV History, 1965, pp. 378-88. The conflict at the Department of the Army during the spring of 1965 is described in a series of memos from the acting secretary of the general staff to General Abrams, vice chief of staff, and the position of the U.S. Army, Pacific, is presented in Msg, CINCUSARPAC to DA, DAIN 628326, 28 Apr 65, sub: Operation and Maintenance of SEASIA Communications Facilities, Incl 3 to Memo, DA, Actg SGS, for General Abrams, 12 May 65, sub: Strategic Communications. All in CMH.

[31]Msg, COMUSMACV to CINCUSARPAC, 8 May 65, sub: SEA Integrated Wideband Communications System, CMH.

Army, Pacific, to gain control over strategic communications in South Vietnam.[32]

Having prevailed in matters of policy, the new command faced still more struggles in obtaining the means to carry out its mission. Facing the continuing uncertainty over command relationships as well as the typical problems of obtaining living space and support in a crowded Saigon, Lt. Col. Jerry J. Enders arrived in early summer with fifty-four men to set up the nucleus of the Strategic Communications Command, Vietnam, and assume control of Backporch by August 1965. Because the 2d Signal Group, which also had just arrived in South Vietnam, was in the midst of reorganizing geographical responsibilities of the 39th and 41st Signal Battalions, Colonel Moran, commander of the 2d Signal Group, was unprepared to transfer any elements of his command to Colonel Enders. While the disputed issues were forwarded to the Department of the Army for a decision, the deadline set for the transfer of Backporch to the Strategic Communications Command, Vietnam, passed with the U.S. Army, Vietnam, still controlling that strategic communications system.[33]

Despite Colonel Enders' intentions to take control of strategic communications even before the personnel issue was resolved, Brig. Gen. John Norton, deputy commanding general of the U.S. Army, Vietnam, had delayed Enders' plans until he could be sure they would not interfere with combat operations then taking place in the Central Highlands. In the meantime, at the behest of Maj. Gen. Stanley R. Larsen, the commander of a newly established corps headquarters in South Vietnam called Task Force Alpha, General Norton in early August asked the U.S. Army, Pacific, to reconsider the decision to transfer control of strategic communications vital to tactical operations to an organization as inadequately staffed as the Strategic Communications Command, Vietnam. Norton's plea put Col. John C. Liggett, the signal officer of the U.S. Army, Pacific, in a difficult position as he had been opposing the transfer of staff officers and engineers from the U.S. Army, Pacific, to General Meyer's command. Moreover, General Westmoreland's prior support of the Strategic Communications Command over General Waters' opposition contradicted Norton's implication that the Strategic Communications Command would impair tactical operations. Reluctant to challenge General Meyer again, General Waters left the matter for Westmoreland's decision. Responding to Norton, he noted that, "Unless COMUSMACV now states positively his wishes to delay or reopen the issue of transfer of responsibilities . . . USARPAC will not support the recommendations."[34] On 19 August

---

[32]Ltr, USARPAC to CC-E, 29 Jun 65, sub: Plan for Transfer of Responsibilities for Army-Operated DCS Designated and Associated Facilities in Southeast Asia from U.S. Army, Pacific, to U.S. Army Strategic Communications Command, p. 12, file 139565, 72A25/6, WNRC; Ltr, DA, OPS OD CC, to Dep Ch of Staff et al., 24 Jun 65, sub: Policy for Assignment of Responsibility for Planning and Operating Defense Communications System (DCS) Facilities, file 228–06 (STRATCOM-PAC 1965), ACC Historians files; Msg, CINCUSARPAC to USASCC-PAC, 14 Jul 65, sub: Operational Relationships Between CINCUSARPAC and COUSASCC-PAC, CMH.

[33]As late as December 1965, the personnel transfer was still being disputed by the two commands. Msg, CINCUSARPAC to USASCC, 18 Dec 65, sub: Communications-Electronics Responsibilities RVN; Msg, USASCC PAC to CINCUSARPAC, 24 Jun 65, sub: Transfer of Communications Responsibilities in SEASIA; Msg, CINCUSARPAC to DA, 17 Jul 65, sub: Transfer of Responsibilities for DCS Designated and Associated Communications Facilities in SEAsia to USASCC. All in CMH.

[34]Msg, CINCUSARPAC to CGUSARV, 20 Aug 65, sub: Transfer of Communications Responsibility, CMH.

1965, General Norton, lacking support from Waters and apparently unwilling to raise the issue again with Westmoreland, abruptly halted his rebellion. The mission, personnel, and facilities for long-haul communications in South Vietnam were transferred to the Strategic Communications Command.[35]

Although General Gibbs, commenting on the transfer, stated that "no specific problems [are] now existing which routine follow-on actions cannot resolve," the continuing buildup of troops in South Vietnam created new communications missions that had not been envisioned when the transfer plan was drafted.[36] Because the Strategic Communications Command had not participated in planning for new projects such as the base at Cam Ranh Bay, General Meyer was inundated with unanticipated missions. Having just fought General Norton for a strategic communications mission, Colonel Enders found himself becoming increasingly dependent on Norton's command for cable and multichannel equipment to carry out his mission, at least until the completion of the long-awaited Integrated Wideband Communications System. Although General Norton was reluctant to divert his hard-pressed tactical equipment, the U.S. Army, Vietnam, together with the Pacific Air Force, provided equipment to augment the long-lines network in South Vietnam.[37]

The Defense Communications Agency, Southeast Asia Mainland

T he Defense Communications Agency was also working to improve the situation in South Vietnam. In June 1965 the director of the agency, Lt. Gen. Alfred D. Starbird, dispatched the first chief of the DCA Saigon Support Agency, Lt. Col. Albert Redman, Jr., with the parting words: "If DCA cannot provide a responsive communications management capability in an active combat area, there then was no requirement for a DCA."[38] Colonel Redman spent the summer months in daily meetings with the MACV signal staff developing reporting procedures and determining circuit priorities. With the help of signalmen detailed from the 39th Signal Battalion, his seven-man staff established a circuit control center at Tan Son Nhut from which they could monitor the Defense Communications System's crisscrossing circuits in South Vietnam and Thailand. Colonel Redman's task was easier because he had the full support of General Westmoreland, who confirmed that the Saigon Support Agency had "the specific

[35]Msg, USASCC-PAC, DC 2429 to USARV, 14 Aug 65; Msg, USARV to CINCUSARPAC, 17 Aug 65, sub: Transfer of Communications Responsibility; Msg, COMUSMACV to USARV and USASCC PAC SEA, 19 Aug 65, sub: O and M of IWCS. All in CMH.

[36]Fact Sheet, Maj Gen David P. Gibbs to Chief of Staff, U.S. Army, 23 Aug 65, sub: Transfer of DCS Responsibility in S.E. Asia to USASCC, file 139565, 72A25/6, WNRC.

[37]Memo, JCS for Secy of Defense, 13 Aug 65, sub: Communications Requirements for Cam Ranh Bay and Expansion of BACKPORCH in RVN, Incl A to JCS 222/873, 7 Aug 65, JACO (1965), DA/4, NARS; Msg, USASCC to CINCUSARPAC, 24 Aug 65, sub: Cam Ranh Bay Communications; Msg, DA to CINCUSARPAC, 31 Aug 65, sub: Cam Ranh Bay–Nha Trang M/W Link; Msg, USASCC-PAC to USASCC, 27 Oct 65, sub: RVN Communications Support. Latter three in CMH. USARV, Quarterly Command Rpt for 1st Qtr FY–66, 15 Nov 65, p. 16, 68A1507/1, WNRC.

[38]Ltr, Redman to Col P. J. McDonnell, 26 Jan 70, CMH.

responsibility for operational direction and restoration of all DCA circuits in Vietnam to include the supervision and restoration down to and including the subscriber's instrument at the 'tactical tails.' "[39]

When the Army's management of the Backporch system faltered, causing outages on vital circuits between Tan Son Nhut and air bases in Thailand in September 1965, General Westmoreland looked to the Defense Communications Agency to rectify the situation. He proposed that Colonel Redman's staff directly supervise the technical controllers of the Army signal units operating Backporch. After exploring this proposal, the agency declined to go as far as Westmoreland suggested, but countered that the Army's Strategic Communications Command, the system operator, should retain the means to control the quality and routing of its circuits. The Strategic Communications Command would continue to apply its own independent technical controls but, in the future, would pass performance data and other technical information to Colonel Redman's control centers, enabling the Defense Communications Agency to improve its monitoring of the strategic communications system in Southeast Asia.[40]

In the fall of 1965 General Starbird traveled to South Vietnam to discuss the changes with General Westmoreland. Upon returning he obtained the approval of the secretary of defense to extend DCA's authority over all long-lines systems and to increase the size of Colonel Redman's agency, which had been renamed Defense Communications Agency, Southeast Asia Mainland, to eighty-nine men. With the assistance of General Lotz, the MACV J–6, Colonel Redman established DCA circuit coordination centers at Tan Son Nhut, Pleiku, Nha Trang, and Da Nang in South Vietnam and at Korat, Thailand. Since Lotz had arranged with General Starbird to have General Westmoreland write Redman's efficiency report, a unique situation within the Defense Communications Agency, Westmoreland obtained tighter control over the Defense Communications Agency at the same time the agency was increasing control over his communications.[41]

Establishing a Composite Signal Command

Westmoreland's growing concern about the fragmentation of Army communications and the threat of DCA's encroachment into Army signal operations prompted General Johnson to send a member of his operations staff, Maj. Gen. John C. F. Tillson, to South Vietnam to find a solution to the problem. In briefing Tillson in Saigon, General Lotz stated his opinion that artificial distinctions between strategic and tactical communications were at the root of the Army's

---

[39]Quote from Msg, COMUSMACV to USASCV, 6 Jun 65, sub: DCA-SAIGON, as cited in Redman, Centralized Communications, p. 19.

[40]Msg, DCA to CINCPAC, 18 Sep 65, sub: Communications System Management SEASIA, CMH.

[41]JCSM 2299/36, Starbird to CJCS, 16 Nov 65, sub: Report of Action of SM 1018–65, 26 Oct 65, "Visit to CINCPAC and South East Asia" (hereafter referred to as the Starbird Report), p. 6, file 139640, 72A25/8, WNRC; Redman, Centralized Communications, pp. 19–24; Memo, JCS for Dir, DCA, 4 Dec 65, sub: Report for Action on SM–1018–65, 26 October 1965, "Visit to CINCPAC and Southeast Asia," file 139640, 72A25/8, WNRC; Interv, author with Lotz, 20 Sep 78.

problem. Despite a growing convergence of the communications systems operated by the Strategic Communications Command and the 2d Signal Group, rifts between the operators of those systems had deepened. On the many sites manned jointly by signalmen from the two commands, differing policies toward guard duty and normal housekeeping chores caused constant friction in day-to-day living. The existence of two commands sharing a single mission offered tempting opportunities for the shifting of responsibilities and accountability. General Lotz warned Tillson that unless the Army consolidated its control over all communications in South Vietnam, the "DCA would have a legitimate basis to take over the network as an operating agent." He proposed that all communicators, regardless of whether they performed strategic or tactical missions, be assigned to a single Army signal command subordinate to the Army's U.S.-based Strategic Communications Command, but under the operational control of the U.S. Army, Vietnam. To ensure that the signal interests of the tactical commanders were not neglected and that Army operational control was preserved, General Lotz suggested that the commander of the signal command should also serve as the deputy chief of staff for communications-electronics on the staff of the U.S. Army, Vietnam, a "dual-hat" relationship that had already been established on a trial basis in Europe.[42]

General Johnson was most concerned that the command's communications be fully integrated into the worldwide Defense Communications System and that they be seen as serving all services, not just the Army. He favored having the commander of the proposed signal command rated by the commanding general of the Strategic Communications Command. Westmoreland thus found his control over his own signal operations being jeopardized. Speaking as the commanding general, U.S. Army, Vietnam—an Army component commander—Westmoreland objected that such a "dilution . . . of the Army commander's control over communications to his subordinate units is contrary to proven command principles and not in the interest of the Army." Stating that, "I agree with his comment. [But] we should not give him his conclusions," General Johnson argued that the Strategic Communications Command could best look out for the interests of the Army.[43]

The Army staff felt that General Westmoreland was attempting to exert influence not warranted to either an Army component or theater commander. The Deputy Chief of Staff for Military Operations, Lt. Gen. Vernon P. Mock, warned General Johnson that the Army should be wary of overstepping its bounds in satisfying Westmoreland because the "incorporation of the major portion of the RVN [Republic of Vietnam] system into the Defense Communications System precludes its being treated in isolation from the rest of the regional and world-

[42]Msg, DA to COMUSMACV and CINCUSARPAC, 30 Oct 65, sub: C-E Responsibilities RVN, Tab 2 to Summary Sheet, OPS OD, 24 Nov 65, file 2516875; Ltr, DA to CINCUSARPAC and USASCC, 27 Nov 65, sub: Communications-Electronics Responsibilities, RVN, file 139458. Both in 72A25/2, WNRC. Ltr, Lotz to Maj Gen Thomas M. Rienzi, 16 Feb 71, w/Incl; Ltr, Lotz to Gibbs, 16 Nov 65; Ltr, Lotz to Gibbs, 11 Dec 65. Latter three in CMH.

[43]Msg, USARV to CINCUSARPAC, 7 Dec 65, sub: Communications/Electronics Responsibility RVN; Memo, Johnson for DCSOPS, 7 Dec 65, Incl to Memo, SGS for General Abrams, 10 Dec 65. All in file 139458, 72A5711/7, WNRC.

Generals Lotz and Terry *(Photograph taken in July 1966.)*

wide system."[44] The Strategic Communications Command, not a theater component command, was supposed to operate the Defense Communications System. The Army staff also was reluctant to allow General Westmoreland to become involved in purely Army matters. He had already tried to influence the restructuring of the 69th Signal Battalion before its deployment, and General Johnson had told his staff: "Services equip their units. Joint Staff and JCS do not get into the act. Pull the rope on this one."[45]

Finally deciding on a compromise that was practically identical to that recommended by General Lotz several months earlier, on 25 February 1966, General Johnson directed that by 1 April 1966 the Strategic Communications Command consolidate into a signal brigade all Army communications units in South Vietnam and Thailand except those organic to tactical units. The commander would be rated by the deputy commander, U.S. Army, Vietnam, for whom he would also serve as assistant chief of staff, communications-electronics. His efficiency report would be endorsed by the commanding general, Strategic Communications Command, who would exercise command and technical control over the

---

[44]Memo, Mock for Chief of Staff, 8 Dec 65, sub: Communications/Electronics Responsibility in RVN, Tab A to Memo, SGS for Abrams, 10 Dec 65, file 139458, 72A5711/7, WNRC.

[45]Quote from Memo, Johnson for DCSOPS, 3 Sep 65, Incl to Memo, OPS OD CC for Chief of Staff, 1 Oct 65, sub: MACV Command and Control, CMH.

brigade.[46] Brigade units in South Vietnam would be under the operational control of the U.S. Army, Vietnam, and those in Thailand under the operational control of the commander, U.S. Military Assistance Command, Thailand. The compromise solution made the brigade directly responsible to the local combat commander, unified tactical and strategic communications, and provided a direct channel to the Army-wide resources and industrial base accessible to the Strategic Communications Command.[47]

To command the new unit, General Gibbs nominated Col. Robert D. Terry, an officer scheduled to be promoted to brigadier general in July. Terry had served ably as the signal officer of the XVIII Airborne Corps during the crisis in the Dominican Republic. For three months after his selection Colonel Terry served as a peripatetic planner-diplomat, shuttling back and forth between Washington, Honolulu, and Saigon, to prepare for the brigade's activation and to resolve the organizational controversy that was impeding its swift birth. On 5 February he obtained two officers—one from the MACV signal staff and one from the 2d Signal Group—to form a brigade planning group that wrote a concept plan and developed policies and procedures for the anticipated brigade. Present at the Pentagon when General Johnson decided to proceed with the compromise solution for the brigade, Colonel Terry cabled the essential features of the final plan to General Westmoreland and expressed his confidence that it gave field commanders in South Vietnam sufficient control over their signal support. He also reassured General Meyer, who remained unhappy over his loss of rating authority over the signal brigade commander, that he was well aware "that the loyalty and integrity required of an officer with respect to his commander must, in this case, apply to two commanders."[48]

Writing to Maj. Gen. Jean E. Engler, who replaced General Norton in March as deputy commander, U.S. Army, Vietnam, Vice Chief of Staff General Creighton W. Abrams, Jr., presented the official interpretation of Colonel Terry's relationship to his two bosses:

CG USARV, in his role of conducting military operations, has authority to assign missions, direct task organizations, and when required under emergency conditions, take other actions within the scope of complete authority. CG USASCC, as manager of DCS (Army) communications system (AR 10–13), has authority to, in coordination with CINCUSARPAC, plan, program, and direct the employment of the brigade to meet assigned missions . . . to assure army responsiveness to the operational direction and management of DCS by DCA.[49]

---

[46]The Army dictionary defines technical control as the specialized or professional guidance and direction exercised by an authority in technical matters.

[47]The initial transfer plan, which was revised by General Johnson, is the Incl to Ltr, USARPAC to CSA, 29 Jan 66, sub: Communications-Electronics Responsibility, RVN. DF, CC-E to DCSOPS, 11 Feb 66, sub: Communications-Electronics Responsibilities in RVN; Ltrs, USASCC to CSA, 3 Feb 66 and 11 Feb 66, same subs; Staff Study, ODCSOPS/OD CC, 15 Feb 66; Ltr, Johnson to CG, USASCC, 25 Feb 66, same sub. All are in file 139355, 72A25/1, WNRC.

[48]Quote from Msg, Terry to Meyer, 16 Mar 66, HWA 0959, Maj Gen Robert D. Terry Papers, Army War College, Carlisle Barracks, Pennsylvania. Interv, author with Lotz, 20 Sep 78; Interv, author with Maj Gen (ret.) Robert D. Terry, former CG, 1st Signal Brigade, 5 Oct 78, Historians files, CMH; Msg, Terry to Seitz, 25 Feb 66, and ibid., 15 Mar 66, HWA 0945, both in Terry Papers.

[49]Msg, Abrams WDC 3439 to Engler, 19 Mar 66, in Terry Papers.

Because Terry was to become a general officer soon after the activation of the signal brigade, General Meyer was unable to assign the brigade to the Strategic Communications Command, Pacific, which was headed by a colonel. Establishing a direct command line from the headquarters of the Strategic Communications Command to the brigade, General Meyer cautioned Terry to coordinate closely with the regional office in Honolulu to ensure that the Strategic Communications Command spoke with a single voice in the Pacific.[50]

On 1 April 1966, the Strategic Communications Command Signal Brigade, Southeast Asia, was formally activated at its new headquarters at Tan Son Nhut. The new unit included all of the 5,855 signalmen spread throughout Southeast Asia who had formerly belonged to the 2d Signal Group, the Continental Army Command, and the Strategic Communications Command, Vietnam. Although General Meyer wanted the brigade to retain its original designation and to have the insignia of the Strategic Communications Command, General Terry convinced him that the men needed to be more closely identified with the theater lest they be treated as outsiders. In May the signal command was renamed the 1st Signal Brigade (USASTRATCOM) and given a distinctive insignia.

By then the Department of the Army had formally issued the brigade its missions, which the Strategic Communications Command promulgated. The U.S. Army, Vietnam, added two additional missions: "Reinforce field signal elements to meet operational requirements as directed; . . . perform other functions as directed." The men in the field were determined that the 1st Signal Brigade would be responsive to tactical commanders.[51]

Better to organize the brigade for its many missions, on 5 April Colonel Terry created a second signal group, the Regional Communications Group, to operate the communications systems specifically identified as part of the Defense Communications System—the troposcatter and microwave radios that were to be included in the Integrated Wideband Communications System, the radios and tape relays at Nha Trang and Phu Lam, and the satellite stations. As the pace of combat activity quickened throughout the spring, stretching the ability of the 2d Signal Group to control the activities of its signalmen supporting tactical units and advisers throughout the 700-mile length of South Vietnam, Terry decided to form another group, the 21st Signal Group, to handle responsibility for the two northern corps areas. In September the 379th Signal Battalion and the Strategic Communications Command Signal Group, Thailand, were consolidated to

---

[50]MFR, USASCC, 21 Mar 66, sub: Interrelationship of STRATCOM's Subcommands in the Pacific Area, file 139355, 72A25/1; MFR, STRATCOM Sig Gp Thailand, 21 Jul 66, sub: STRATCOM Command Relationships Conference, 19–20 Jul 66, file U–113, 72A18/3. Both in WNRC.

[51]Msg, Terry to Meyer, 24 Mar 66, Staff Service 6008, Terry Papers; Msg, DA to USASCC and CINCUSARPAC, 26 Mar 66, sub: Activation of the USASTRATCOM Signal Brigade-SEA; Ltr, DA to CINCUSARPAC and USASCC, 23 Mar 66, sub: Communications-Electronics Responsibilities in Southeast Asia; Ltr, DA to CINCUSARPAC and USASCC, 7 Apr 66, sub: Activation of the Headquarters, USASTRATCOM Signal Brigade-SEA (TOE 11–302T); USASCC Regulation 10–13, Mission of USASTRATCOM Signal Brigade-SEA, 13 Apr 66; Ltr, USARV to USASTRATCOM Signal Brigade-SEA, 23 Apr 66, sub: Letter of Instructions, USASTRATCOM Signal Brigade-SEA. Latter five in file 139355, 72A25/1, WNRC.

form the 29th Signal Group to manage communications in Thailand for the signal brigade.[52]

In earlier wars, communications had been organized on an echelon concept paralleling the chain of command. Terry instead structured his brigade on an area orientation. He assigned to certain commanders the additional responsibility to coordinate the support and defense of all signal units, regardless of parent unit, in their respective areas. Since they were authorized to assume operational control of those units in emergencies, the area commanders frequently took responsibility for coordinating operational communications with local tactical commanders. As areas were subdivided, that authority reached down even to junior signal officers and noncommissioned officers serving as site commanders on lonely hilltops containing the troposcatter radios of the Regional Communications Group and the tactical radio relays of the local area support signal battalion.[53]

The brigade that emerged from Terry's careful molding was a product of the evolution of American military communications that had taken place during the previous two decades. Increased mobility and dispersion mandated by the nuclear threat forced signalmen to despair of keeping wide-ranging units in direct contact with headquarters and support bases, and had spawned a doctrine based on an area communications grid with nodal points at which tactical units could link into the overall network. In South Vietnam, where American bases were islands of safety in disputed territory, such a doctrine was particularly appropriate. While adapting the organization of the signal brigade to that new doctrine, Terry's assignment of command authority on an area basis down to the smallest signal detachments also diminished the command conflicts and diffusion of responsibility that had formerly plagued signal operations in Southeast Asia.

Just as the structure of the entire brigade reflected the merging of tactical and strategic communications within the combat area, the establishment of one functionally organized unit, the Regional Communications Group, demonstrated a recognition of the growing influence of the Defense Communications Agency. The formation of that unit to operate the proposed high-quality strategic Integrated Wideband Communications System was the realization of the concept of a single, completely integrated strategic network proposed during the waning days of World War II and developed amid controversy and conflict over years of unsettling organizational strife and dramatic doctrinal and technological change.

---

[52]Msg, USASTRATCOM Sig Bde SEA to USASCC, 5 Apr 66, sub: Redesignation of Unit, file 139355, 72A25/1, WNRC; Msg, DA to USASCC et al., 15 Sep 66, sub: Communications-Electronics Responsibilities in SEA, CH–IN–178677, CMH; Ltr, USARV to 1st Sig Bde, 20 Nov 66, sub: Letter of Instructions, file 139865, 72A25/23, WNRC; Interv, author with Terry, 5 Oct 78.

[53]1st Sig Bde, Regulation 10–10, Area Communications Commanders, 17 May 66, file 139355, 72A25/1, WNRC. Colonel Terry aptly referred to the position of site commander as ''King of the Hill.''

9

Pushing Out From Saigon

A few days after the 1st Signal Brigade was activated on 1 April 1966 at Camp Gaylor, a small compound on the outskirts of Tan Son Nhut that housed the 69th Signal Battalion, the camp was hit by enemy mortar and recoilless rifle fire. Although the attack caused only minor damage, the boldness of the Viet Cong strike in the heart of South Vietnam's capital district impressed upon Colonel Terry the vulnerability of his signal command deployed throughout the country. In his first letter of instructions to his subordinate signal commanders, he emphasized his determination that signal officers would first and foremost be concerned with the security of their men and equipment. Aware that soldiers preoccupied with communications tasks frequently neglected defensive measures, Colonel Terry cautioned his commanders to do more than simply post routine gate guards. He expected them to coordinate protective fires with neighboring units, conduct alerts and rehearsals, and patrol areas around their sites. He placed primary emphasis on signal installations in the Saigon–Bien Hoa area, formerly considered relatively safe.[1]

General Westmoreland shared Colonel Terry's concern for the security of the area around the capital, the heartland of South Vietnam and the location of the principal American headquarters and bases. Forty percent of South Vietnam's population and almost all its industry were clustered within fifty kilometers of the capital. The Viet Cong had also established some of their most highly developed and well-protected base areas around Saigon. To the east and southeast, the *5th Viet Cong Division* still roamed coastal Phuoc Tuy Province and controlled the Rung Sat mangrove swamp through which the capital's link to the sea, the Saigon River, meandered. To the north and northwest, the *9th Viet Cong Division* moved freely, often within sight of the lights of Saigon, withdrawing into bases in the dense jungles and rubber plantations of Binh Long and Tay Ninh Provinces or across the nearby Cambodian border. In that border area existed the elusive

---

[1]Camp Gaylor was named after the 69th Signal Battalion's first casualty, S. Sgt. Gerald H. Gaylor, who was killed by a terrorist on the streets of Saigon. ORLL, 69th Sig Bn, 30 Apr 66, pp. 1–2; 1st Sig Bde, Letter of Instruction (LOI) 1, 27 May 66, file 2–09 (LOI) (66). Both in 69A722/6, WNRC.

Infantrymen *on a clearing operation in Long An Province.*

headquarters complexes of the National Front for the Liberation of South Vietnam and the Central Office for South Vietnam, the military headquarters through which Hanoi directed the insurgency in South Vietnam. Closer to Saigon, about thirty kilometers north of the capital in a heavily wooded area called the Iron Triangle, the Communists established a headquarters called Military Region 4 to control guerrilla activities in the Saigon area. To the west, where the Cambodian border lay only some forty kilometers from the capital, Hau Nghia Province provided unimpeded access to Viet Cong attacking Saigon from their Cambodian sanctuaries. To the south, strongly entrenched guerrilla units virtually controlled heavily populated Long An Province, the gateway to the rich alluvial rice fields of the Mekong Delta.[2]

Deciding that the South Vietnamese Army needed help to halt the growing Viet Cong threat in the most strategic region of the country, General Westmoreland deployed most of the American combat units that arrived during the winter and spring of 1965–1966 to build a shield around Saigon. To control those forces in the III Corps area surrounding Saigon, on 15 March 1966, he established at Long Binh, twenty-five kilometers north of the capital near Bien Hoa, a corps headquarters, the II Field Force, Vietnam, under the command of Lt. Gen. Jonathan O. Seaman. To the 2d Signal Group, which was responsible for communications in the two southern corps areas, went the tasks of providing the field force with command communications until a corps signal battalion became available and of building an area communications grid for the American units stationed in the region.[3]

Relays on the High Ground

Since the terrain in the 2d Signal Group's area of operations comprised dense jungle in the north and low tidelands in the south, finding locations from

---

[2]George L. MacGarrigle, in The Year of the Offensive, a forthcoming volume in the U.S. Army in Vietnam series, covers the disposition of Viet Cong forces in the southern half of South Vietnam and traces the American operations in the area during the period November 1966 to October 1967.

[3]For a concise summary of General Westmoreland's strategy in III and IV Corps, see Sharp and Westmoreland, *Report on the War in Vietnam*, pp. 113–29.

Radioman *wades through the swampy Rung Sat.*

which to relay line-of-sight radio signals over the horizon and the heavy vegetation was of primary concern. General Lotz convinced General Westmoreland to
designate the few mountaintops in the region as strategic territory to be held at
all costs. Four hills—Nui Ba Den in Tay Ninh Province, Nui Ba Ra in Phuoc Long,
Nui Chua Chan in Long Khanh, and VC Hill in Phuoc Tuy—formed a semicircu-
lar fan around Saigon of relays for multichannel systems connecting lowland bases
and FM voice retransmission stations linking those bases with infantrymen slog-
ging through swamps and jungles. Except for VC Hill, which rose over peaceful
Vung Tau, the communicators on the mountaintops shared their hills with the
Viet Cong, who habitually sought the cover and isolation offered by the steep
wooded slopes of the mountains in the region. All resupply for the isolated signalmen on the mountaintops had to be handled by helicopter. Despite the strategic value and vulnerability of the remote sites, the Viet Cong seemed to ignore
or abide their presence.[4]

East of Saigon, where Nui Chua Chan dominated the northern horizon and
VC Hill that to the south, establishing communications was relatively easy.
Although the *5th Viet Cong Division* had long controlled much of the region and
its *275th Regiment* occasionally located its command post on Nui Chua Chan, the
first U.S. Army unit to arrive in South Vietnam, the 173d Airborne Brigade, had

[4]Interv, author with Lotz, 20 Sep 78.

The VC Hill Signal Site at Vung Tau

secured several bases and had cleared most of the main roads in the region. The 39th Signal Battalion, the oldest signal battalion in South Vietnam, operated regional communications from a well-established base in the security of coastal Vung Tau.

Lt. Col. Donald L. Jenkins, who replaced Colonel Dorney in early 1966 as the commander of the 39th Signal Battalion, controlled all signal operations to the east of Saigon from the top of VC Hill, a crowded promontory that he shared with South Vietnamese and U.S. Air Force communicators. From the site radiated a number of tactical multichannel systems to bases throughout Bien Hoa and Phuoc Tuy Provinces. One unusual VHF system, employing a standard, four-channel tactical GRC–10 set, transmitted to a Navy aircraft maintenance ship anchored off the coast. Using an omnidirectional antenna from a tactical FM voice radio, the link enjoyed high-quality circuits during calm seas when the antenna on the ship remained steady. The Regional Communications Group also operated troposcatter links from VC Hill to Cam Ranh Bay and to Green Hill, Thailand. As the Integrated Wideband Communications System expanded, the hill became the relay point for several additional high-capacity troposcatter and microwave links. Surprisingly, until November 1966 the huge complex at Vung Tau was connected to Saigon only by twelve-channel tactical TRC–24 radio. Only then was Colonel Jenkins able to move his 518th Signal Company, a hard-working unit that had been installing microwave systems between newly established bases

190

throughout South Vietnam and Thailand, to Vung Tau to set up a high-capacity microwave link to Saigon. To carry the many circuits terminating in the radios on the hill down to Vung Tau Air Base, where American aviation and logistical facilities were located and where the Army was installing a 2,000-line dial exchange, the battalion's cablemen installed a 200-pair cable. Using helicopters to haul telephone poles to strategic locations on the steep slopes, the ingenious cablemen installed pulleys on the poles and winched the cable and supporting guy lines up the hill.[5] *(Map 9)*

Australian Communications

Australian troops, who began arriving in South Vietnam soon after the 173d Airborne Brigade, did much of the fighting in Phuoc Tuy Province. Using the signal center on VC Hill as a relay, the 39th Signal Battalion provided the Australians with communications from the II Field Force in Long Binh to their field command post in Nui Dat, about thirty kilometers to the south, and linked the Australian command post to its supporting air and logistical bases in Vung Tau and to the headquarters of Australian Forces, Vietnam, in Saigon. For better coordination with American units in the region, the 39th Signal Battalion also operated secure teletype circuits for the Australians.[6]

Two Australian Army signal units, totaling about 500 communicators, provided tactical and administrative communications for the 7,500-man task force. The 110th Signal Squadron operated a tape relay facility at Saigon as well as a single-sideband station that served as the primary strategic link for both the Australian and New Zealand contingents in South Vietnam. As backup to that radio system, which spanned the disturbance-prone equatorial zone, the Australians operated a tributary station of the Phu Lam relay that gave them access through the Defense Communications System to circuits to Melbourne from Okinawa, Honolulu, and California. At Vung Tau the 110th Signal Squadron manned an alternate overseas radio station and handled all communications for the Australian Army, Navy, and Air Force units located near the busy port city. At Nui Dat the 110th Signal Squadron terminated the long-distance telephone and teletype circuits provided by the 39th Signal Battalion. For field communications, tactical signalmen in the 104th Signal Squadron provided internal communications for the task force headquarters and operated multichannel radio and courier service to subordinate battalions and companies. Wherever possible, those Australian field units also linked up with local signal detachments of the 39th Signal Battalion to gain access

---

[5]USARV Sig Ofcr, Command Rpt, Oct–Dec 65, p. 5; Interv, George R. Thompson with Lt Col William C. Stephens, CO, 39th Signal Battalion, 24 Mar 67. Both in CMH. ORLL, 69th Sig Bn, 31 Jan 67, p. 3, 69A722/6; 1st Sig Bde, Itinerary of Brig Gen Terry, 27 Mar–2 Apr 67, tab H, 72A25/24. Both in WNRC.

[6]A complete description of American communications support to the Australian forces in South Vietnam can be found in Communications Supplement to Working Arrangement Between Commander, USMACV, and Chairman, Chiefs of Staff Committee Australia, 30 Nov 67, file 139657, 72A25/8, WNRC.

Phuoc Binh

Nui Ba Ra

An Loc

BINH LONG

PHUOC LONG

TAY NINH

86th Sig Bn (Spt)

36th Sig Bn (Cbt Area)

Tay Ninh Nui Ba Den

Dau Tieng

LONG KHANH

BINH DUONG

BINH TUY

Phu Cuong

Bien Hoa

Xuan Loc

HAU

Khiem Cuong

Di An

Gia Dinh

Long Binh

Nui Chua Chan

NGHIA

SAIGON

BIEN HOA

PHUOC TUY

Ham Tan

LONG AN

GIA DINH

39th Sig Bn (Spt)

Tan An

Phuoc Le

SOUTH

69th Sig Bn (Army)

Vung Tau

CHINA

VC Hill

CAPITAL SPECIAL ZONE

SEA

III CORPS — AREAS OF RESPONSIBILITY

December 1966

▲ MOUNTAIN RELAYS

MAP 9

to the American area telephone network.[7]

Tying in Division Bases

B y late 1965 American units had begun arriving at staging areas in Phuoc Tuy and Bien Hoa en route to the northern and western approaches to the capital. Soon after the 1st Infantry Division deployed to defend Saigon's northwest approaches, the 25th Infantry Division arrived from Hawaii to take positions in the Viet Cong–infested province of Hau Nghia astride the western corridors. Later the 196th Light Infantry Brigade deployed between the two divisions around the important city of Tay Ninh, and in December 1966 the 3d Brigade of the 4th Infantry Division opened a base thirty kilometers to the east at Dau Tieng to close the northern half of the ring around Saigon. While the divisions had their organic signal battalions and the two separate brigades each had communications platoons, the only area communications available throughout that vast strategic region were those provided by a few signal teams of the 232d Signal Company that were supporting local advisory detachments with relics of the original equipment brought to South Vietnam four years before by Colonel Blackwell's men.[8]

Although the Army signal staff had programmed two signal support companies for each division-size unit, General Westmoreland's decision to rush combat troops to South Vietnam without the necessary support increments had delayed the arrival of signal units. Even after Westmoreland changed his emphasis, the flow of incoming units was not easily altered. Priorities to the Signal Corps for everything from transport space to allocation of recruits had to be raised. In the interim, the combat units had to use their organic resources for base communications. To be prepared to operate base communications should divisional units be required for tactical operations, Colonel Terry assembled men and equipment from the 1st Signal Brigade to form a contingency force in the 69th Signal Battalion.[9]

To provide command communications for the II Field Force, Vietnam, until a corps signal battalion was deployed from the United States, General Westmoreland attempted to get the U.S. Army, Pacific, to send the 999th Signal

---

[7]Interv, Capt Hrair N. Badalian with Lt Col Barry Hockney, chief signal officer, Headquarters, Australian Forces, Vietnam, Nov 69, VNIT 563; Interv, Capt Hrair N. Badalian with Maj Keith Paul Morel, CO, 104th Signal Squadron, Royal Australian Signals, Feb 70, VNIT 605. Both in CMH. Letter of Agreement Between COMAAFV and COMUSMACV, 31 Jul 65, 338–75–1009/61, WNRC. Descriptions of Australian signal support in South Vietnam are contained in USARV Pamphlet 105–4, *Command Communications*, issues dated September 1966, October 1968, and July 1969. This booklet, published every few months from September 1966 through November 1971 to disseminate lessons learned about communicating in South Vietnam, is hereafter cited as *Command Communications*. A full set of booklets is in CMH files.

[8]125th Sig Bn, AHS, CY–66, CMH. Although the brigade's official designation was the 196th Infantry Brigade, it was commonly called a light infantry brigade.

[9]Interv, author with Terry, 5 Oct 78; Fact Sheet, USARV, AVSI-PO, 5 Apr 66, sub: Revised Unit Deployment Capabilities for CY 66, file 139556, 72A25/1; Ltr, USARV to USARPAC, 25 Apr 66, sub: Impact of the Army Force Deployment Capability (24 March 1966 DA Data Base), pp. 8–10, 338–75–1009/59. Both in WNRC.

Company from Okinawa. Because the company had been drained of its resources to meet pressing needs of other Army units already committed to Southeast Asia, it was ill equipped to support a corps-size headquarters and could not be sent. Colonel Terry had to give that mission also to the 69th Signal Battalion.[10]

To assist the overcommitted battalion, which was supporting all the U.S. headquarters in Saigon, in April 1966 the Department of the Army finally squeezed onto the deployment roster the 595th Signal Company, a unit based at Fort Devens, Massachusetts, that had been designated to operate base communications for the 1st Infantry Division. On short notice the entire company was loaded on three aircraft and flown directly to Bien Hoa; equipment followed by ship. When the ship arrived off Vung Tau a few weeks later, it sailed directly up the Saigon River, bypassing an armada of merchant ships waiting for dock space. The men in the company, the first signal reinforcements to reach South Vietnam in almost six months, had relieved the 69th Signal Battalion's overworked operators even before the equipment arrived. When its equipment was unloaded in early May, the company commander, Capt. Arthur P. Chesley, dispatched a platoon east of Long Binh to support units of the 173d Airborne Brigade that were clearing bases for the incoming 11th Armored Cavalry. Within a few weeks another platoon deployed to the west to connect the headquarters of the 1st Infantry Division at Di An and the division's artillery at Phu Loi with II Field Force headquarters. When the 53d Signal Battalion (Corps) arrived in South Vietnam in June to support the field force, Captain Chesley shifted the remainder of his company west to expand area communications for the 1st Infantry Division and the 25th Infantry Division.[11]

The commanders of the two divisional signal battalions in the II Field Force welcomed the arrival of an area support signal unit. In the short time they had been in South Vietnam they had seen their battalions' ability to perform tactical missions eroded by the requirements to support the large base camps springing up in their divisional areas. The 1st Infantry Division's 121st Signal Battalion was deployed in the standard manner for a divisional signal battalion, with its Company A providing support to the division's main and artillery headquarters, the three platoons of Company B each supporting one of the division's three brigades, and Company C handling communications for the division's logistical and administrative elements. But that support had taken on the characteristics of garrison communications. The division's signalmen had unloaded signal equipment from mobile vans and installed it in underground bunkers for protection from enemy mortars and the tropical sun. Field wire and cable that should have been loaded and ready to move to the field was strung on poles throughout the camps. Only after arrival of the 595th Signal Company was some of the equipment in the 121st Signal Battalion and in the 25th Infantry Division's 125th Signal

---

[10]Msg, CGUSARV to CINCUSARPAC, 25 Feb 66, sub: Advance Deployment of 53d Sig Bn; Msg, CINCUSARPAC to CGUSARV, 28 Feb 66, sub: Request for TDY and Advance Deployment to RVN; Msg, CINCPAC to MACV and JCS, 4 Mar 66, sub: Deployment to SVN; Msg, COMUSMACV to CINCPAC, 7 Mar 66, sub: Deployment to SVN. All in file 7, 70A2378/5, WNRC.

[11]Interv, author with Lt Col Arthur P. Chesley, former CO, 595th Signal Company, 2 Nov 78, Historians files, CMH; ORLL, 69th Sig Bn, 31 Jul 66, 69A722/6, WNRC.

The Nui Chua Chan Relay Site

Battalion released for its intended tactical use.[12]

In September 1966 the 86th Signal Battalion relieved the 595th Signal Company of responsibility to assist the 25th Infantry Division and the 196th Light Infantry Brigade, the two units on the westernmost segment of the ring around Saigon. The newest signal battalion in the entire Army, the 86th had been planning from the day of its activation for its commitment to the Viet Cong–infested jungles of Hau Nghia and Tay Ninh Provinces. Later the battalion's mission expanded to include support of the 3d Brigade, 4th Infantry Division, at Dau Tieng and of a Filipino civic action unit working in Tay Ninh. To project radio signals from the 25th Infantry Division's base at Cu Chi to those outlying units, the battalion commander, Lt. Col. Walter G. Ellis, arranged for the 518th Signal Company to build a 106-foot antenna tower at the base camp. When Viet Cong mortarmen began using a red aircraft warning light on the top of the tower as an aiming point during nighttime bombardments, Colonel Ellis had to remove the light and lower the tower below the aircraft flight path. Relays at Nui Ba Den then became indispensible for communicating from the lowlands of Hau Nghia Province.[13]

To support the 1st Infantry Division's units deployed to the north and east

[12]Maj. Gen. Charles R. Myer, *Division-Level Communications, 1962–1973,* Vietnam Studies (Washington, D.C.: Government Printing Office, 1982), pp. 23–48; ORLL, 69th Sig Bn, Oct 66, 69A722/6, WNRC.
[13]Interv, George R. Thompson with Lt Col Walter G. Ellis, CO, 86th Signal Battalion, and with 1st Lt C. W. Sarchet, CO, Company B, 86th Signal Battalion, 26 Mar 67, CMH.

of Tay Ninh, the 595th Signal Company also operated relays on Nui Ba Den. Since the company was already operating a site for the 11th Armored Cavalry far to the east on Nui Chua Chan, it was ill equipped to establish another mountaintop relay at Nui Ba Ra in the northeastern section of the 1st Division's zone to link outlying units with the base camp at Di An near Saigon. Relief came in December with the arrival of the 36th Signal Battalion. Company A of the new unit took responsibility for the 1st Infantry division's base at Di An and the relay on Nui Ba Den, releasing the 595th Signal Company, which was reassigned to the 36th Signal Battalion, to establish a relay on Nui Ba Ra and to support bases in the division's eastern sector. The company also expanded its radio relay and circuit-patching facility on the top of Nui Chua Chan.[14]

The headquarters company of the 36th Signal Battalion remained at Long Binh to establish base support communications for the incoming 199th Light Infantry Brigade, the first combat unit to arrive in South Vietnam to find communications already in place. Due to the late arrival of the brigade's organic communications platoon, the 36th Signal Battalion also provided the brigade with all of its tactical communications for several weeks. Company B of the 36th Signal Battalion was assigned to the 86th Signal Battalion to work in the Tay Ninh area, Company C to the 39th Signal Battalion to operate in the northern delta area, and Company D to the 509th Signal Battalion in II Corps.[15]

Although the cross-attachment of companies caused problems with unit identification and mail delivery, it was preferable to physically moving entire signal units as signal support in a particular area expanded from a platoon to a company and then to a battalion. Signalmen preferred to see the designation of their battalion headquarters change than to give up facilities they had struggled to erect and the communications equipment they had laboriously tuned and perfected. Persistent negotiating with engineers and much back-breaking labor by signalmen were required to build communications facilities during the troop buildup. Since airfields, roads, and hospitals received top priority for construction, at signal sites engineers rarely did more than clear an area with bulldozers and provide building materials for signalmen to construct their own operating and living facilities. Since the engineers frequently were unable to install power for base camps, the local signal officer usually found his signal generators providing the power for all tenant units at a base.[16]

As the platoons and companies of the 1st Signal Brigade became more closely associated with the units they were supporting, tactical commanders, incorrectly treating the brigade's area support units as organic units, began to hold their own staff signal officers responsible for the communications and power service provided by elements of the 1st Signal Brigade. Unhappy with an arrangement making them responsible for the activities of men over whom they had no authority, several division signal officers attempted to obtain operational control over the units of the 1st Signal Brigade that provided them area signal support. Those

---

[14]"Blackhorse Signal," *Command Communications*, March 1967, p. 38, CMH; ORLL, 36th Sig Bn, 31 Jan 67, file 2-05, 69A722/5, WNRC.
[15]Interv, George R. Thompson with Lt Col Lester K. Tate, CO, 36th Signal Battalion, 22 Mar 67, CMH.
[16]Ibid.

attempts faltered when General Terry, in his capacity as the signal officer of the U.S. Army, Vietnam, intervened to convince tactical commanders to respect the integrity of his signal command.[17]

To forestall repetition of that problem, General Terry traveled incessantly and required his commanders to do the same. Many complaints of senior tactical officers, which served only to intimidate or confuse junior officers commanding supporting signal sites, were quickly resolved by the arrival of an equivalent grade signal officer from "headquarters." Most of General Terry's visits involved informal meetings with senior tactical commanders, many of them classmates from West Point or former acquaintances, to hear suggestions, to give advice, and to project future requirements. General Terry's personal influence was considerably strengthened when Lt. Gen. Bruce Palmer, Jr., who had been Terry's commander when he served as the signal officer of the XVIII Airborne Corps task force sent to the Dominican Republic, became commanding general of II Field Force, Vietnam, and later deputy commanding general, U.S. Army, Vietnam. While General Terry traveled, his two deputies, Col. George R. O'Neal and Col. William A. Higgins, performed the day-to-day work of supervising the staff and running the brigade.[18]

As MACV J-6, General Lotz also used to great advantage his personal acquaintance with his contemporaries to ensure that tactical commanders properly employed the communicators assigned to their commands. He lobbied to make the position of communications officer in combat infantry, armor, and artillery battalions a Signal Corps slot. In 1961 the chief signal officer had obtained such a designation for the position of brigade signal officer and by mid-1966 the Signal Corps officers with the brigades had won such reknown in South Vietnam that the combat arms agreed to relinquish a position on all battalion staffs to the Signal Corps. Appealing to division commanders to make full use of their staff signal officers, General Lotz obtained commitments, such as that from the commander of the 25th Infantry Division, to "insure that communications, the means by which command control is achieved, is not shunted aside or neglected."[19] In a post-reorganization Army that had seen the dissolution of the authority of the staff signal officer, such seemingly minor commitments were actually major accomplishments.[20]

After General Westmoreland chose his MACV J-3, Maj. Gen. William E. DePuy, to command the 1st Infantry Division, which was preparing in the spring of 1966 to take the offensive, General Lotz spent several days informally discussing with his fellow staff officer the communications problems he could expect

---

[17]In Chapter 3 of *Division-Level Communications,* General Myer discusses the attempt by the division signal officers to gain control of supporting 1st Signal Brigade units.

[18]Interv, author with Terry, 5 Oct 78. O'Neal and Higgins were later replaced by Col. Jack Hines and Col. John B. McKinney.

[19]Maj. Gen. Frederick C. Weyand, "Communications," *Command Communications,* March 1967, p. 3, CMH.

[20]Interv, author with Lotz, 20 Sep 78. A discussion of earlier efforts by the Signal Corps to obtain officer positions in combat units is in USASS, "Two Generals Write About the Signal Corps," *Tec Tac,* no. 97 (22 December 1961):4–5; and USASS, "Three Signal Officer Assignments Below the Division Level," *Tec Tac,* no. 98 (27 April 1962):3–6. Both in CMH.

Signalman *operates the MRC–34 ½ radio relay.*

to encounter when he led his division into the dense jungles north of Saigon, the location of the Viet Cong's main base areas, called War Zones C and D. As a former signal officer in the Ninth Air Force supporting Lt. Gen. George S. Patton's breakout in France during World War II, General Lotz was convinced of the importance of airborne communications in fast-moving combat operations. Knowing that General DePuy was an aggressive officer in the Patton mold and that the jungles of War Zone C would severely attenuate radio signals as his units moved farther from their bases, General Lotz advised him to make maximum use of heliborne command posts and airborne radio relays. He also tried to accelerate for the 1st Division the dispatch of lightweight signal configurations being assembled at depots in the United States in response to lessons learned in the Ia Drang battle.[21]

The equipment failed to arrive in time. In June, General DePuy's infantrymen, supported by an entire combat aviation battalion, embarked on Operation EL PASO into the far reaches of northern III Corps to dislodge a large force of the *9th Viet Cong Division* that was massing to attack An Loc, the provincial capital of Binh Long. He discovered that his divisional signal battalion was ill equipped to support an airmobile campaign. Multichannel sets were too heavy for lifting by helicopters, the six heliborne command posts assigned to his division were insufficient, and frequencies were too few.[22]

After the operation the 121st Signal Battalion adopted an ingenious expedient, developed by the 125th Signal Battalion to lighten the weight of the multichannel terminals. It involved removing radio and carrier equipment from the MRC–69 VHF van and installing it in a jeep trailer or a truck small enough to be lifted in a sling by a helicopter. Because the makeshift twelve-channel terminal consisted of one-half of the essential components in the standard VHF set, it came to be called the MRC–34 1/2. To improve the accessibility of heliborne command posts, a new laboratory at Fort Monmouth, the Avionics Configuration Control Facility, fabricated a console containing three FM radios for UH–1 helicopters that

---

[21]Interv, author with Lotz, 20 Sep 78; Lt. Gen. John J. Tolson, *Airmobility, 1961–1971,* Vietnam Studies (Washington, D.C.: Government Printing Office, 1973), p. 103; Msg, USARV to CINCUSARPAC, 11 Dec 65, sub: Improved Airmobility for Radio Relay Equipments, CMH.

[22]Ltr, 121st Sig Bn to 1st Inf Div, 24 Sep 66, sub: After-Action Report Operation EL PASO II–III; Ltr, 1st Bde to 1st Inf Div, 24 Sep 66, sub: Combat Operations After Action Report, p. 5. Both in 65A5216/4, WNRC.

could easily be rotated between aircraft. Since infantry battalion commanders were authorized only observation helicopters too small to carry such a heavy communications load, the signal technicians from Fort Monmouth also devised and installed in fifty-one helicopters a sheet-metal rack on which a single FM radio was installed.[23]

Frequency Management

Finding remedies for frequency problems was more difficult. Incompatibilities between the frequency ranges of the radios in aircraft and those carried by ground troops had complicated airmobile operations during EL PASO. While the VRC–12 radio family had 920 channels spaced every 50 kilohertz between 30 and 75.95 megahertz, the ARC–44 radios in aircraft, which belonged to an old series of radios, had only 280 channels available because channel separation was set at 100 kilohertz and frequency range extended only from 24 to 51.9 megahertz. During EL PASO, the Air Force's forward air controllers, who were equipped with the old series of radios, were unable to monitor the communications of the ground units, which were all operating on frequencies above 52 megahertz.

The small number of frequencies common to all FM radios, and the increasing use of aircraft that transported radios beyond a unit's normal operational area and permitted greater transmission range, caused frequency problems in the crowded III Corps area even worse than those experienced by the 1st Cavalry Division in the more remote Ia Drang valley. Transmissions from aircraft in southern III Corps blocked out transmissions from a 1st Infantry Division command net that was assigned the same frequency during a critical phase of Operation EL PASO.[24]

Competition for the 220 frequencies common to both old and new radios, the only frequencies usable by aircraft, was so intense that the Americans had to issue them on a shared basis. When the South Vietnamese Directorate of Posts and Telecommunications, which controlled all frequencies used within the boundaries of South Vietnam, distributed those frequencies, the Joint General Staff took most for the South Vietnamese Army, which had only the old series radios. To ensure that the rest of the military FM band remained available for U.S. use, the MACV signal staff circumspectly suggested to General Westmoreland that provision of the PRC–25 radio to modernize the South Vietnamese Army, as recommended by U.S. Army signal advisers, be delayed.[25]

The Military Assistance Command, Vietnam, assigned the entire list of FM voice and VHF multichannel frequencies reserved for American use to each of the three major tactical headquarters: I Field Force, II Field Force, and III Marine

---

[23]USAECOM, Avionics Configuration Control Facility, Annual Program Review, FY–66, CMH.
[24]Ltr, 3d Bde, 1st Inf Div, to 1st Inf Div, 20 Aug 66, p. 25, 67A5216/4, WNRC; Lt. Col. Kearns, ''Frequency Control—Old Problem, New Environment,'' *Command Communications*, November 1966, pp. 8–9, CMH. See also pp. 3–7 for additional information on frequency management.
[25]MACV History, 1966, p. 314, CMH; Interv, author with Lotz, 20 Sep 78.

Amphibious Force. The headquarters, in turn, allocated them to units through-out their respective operational areas. Except for seven discrete frequencies as-signed to each division, the II Field Force signal officer controlled the use of all his FM frequencies in III Corps to preclude mutual interference. Decentralizing frequency management in II Corps, the I Field Force signal officer assigned an entire block of 442 FM frequencies in each of four regions to be managed by local area frequency coordinators. The two field forces followed similar procedures in assigning VHF frequencies, which they shared with the 1st Signal Brigade, for radio relay systems. Paralleling the procedures of the field forces, the 2d Signal Group in III Corps centralized its frequency management, while the 21st Signal Group in II Corps allowed frequency coordinators within each battalion to assign frequencies from a master list. On some mountain relay sites shared by several units operating a multitude of systems, decentralized management caused fre-quency interference and organizational acrimony that often had to be resolved by the field force signal officer. In early 1968 an investigation by a team of radio frequency experts from the Georgia Technological Institute found that the de-centralized frequency management in II Corps restricted the efficiency of signal officers in resolving interference and left in untrained hands the complicated task of apportioning frequencies to maintain minimum separation. Thereafter the field forces and the 1st Signal Brigade centralized all frequency assignments and dis-tributed monthly computer-prepared lists to show current assignments.[26]

When the South Vietnamese eventually began obtaining the PRC–25 radio, assigning frequencies became increasingly an exercise in diplomatically manag-ing a diminishing resource. Where the 25th Infantry Division once had fifteen frequencies assigned for the sole use of each brigade, by mid-1967 the entire division had only seven dedicated frequencies, and even those were given to other units to use as long as they did not interfere with the division's nets. The re-mainder of the 200 frequencies allotted each division had to be shared with other units on a noninterference basis. Although the field force signal officers tried to assign frequencies on a geographical basis, in a congested area like III Corps, where over 20,000 radios operated in 2,100 FM nets, interference inevitably oc-curred between different voice nets on the same frequency and between voice nets and VHF multichannel sets operating in the same band. Eventually the Mili-tary Assistance Command and the South Vietnamese Joint General Staff agreed to restrict the use of the 120 highest frequencies in the band of the new series of radios for multichannel equipment that operated in that same range of fre-quencies. Of the remaining 800 frequencies available for tactical voice radios, American units received 442 and the South Vietnamese 358.[27]

Signal officers had anticipated having to plan VHF multichannel systems, which

[26]DA, Review and Analysis of the Army Command and Control Structure in Vietnam, 15 May 68, an. C, pt. 2, pp. 44–45, CMH. The report of the team from the Georgia Technological Institute is contained in Trip Rpt, 15 Apr 68, Project A–878, AD 390338, Defense Documentation Center (DDC), Cameron Station, Virginia.

[27]MACV J-6, Briefing Notes, Jan 68, tab K–8, file 139359, 72A4171/1, WNRC; Maj. James F. Lehan, "FM Frequency Problems," *Command Communications*, January 1967, CMH; ORLL, FFV, 31 Jul 67, p. 36, 68A4975/3, WNRC.

requires calculation of directional azimuth and antenna polarization, and to engineer HF frequencies, which involves consideration of diurnal and seasonal propagational influences. Since the new series of FM radios required no tuning and was designed for short-range use with a simple whip antenna, they had expected little need for engineering FM communications. In South Vietnam, where many FM emitters were crowded on a small fire base—often on the same tower—and where signals from aircraft radios spanned the horizon that normally served as the outer limit for line-of-sight FM transmissions, they soon found that engineering was crucial to managing FM communications. To avoid mutual interference between FM radios located close to each other, they had to consider

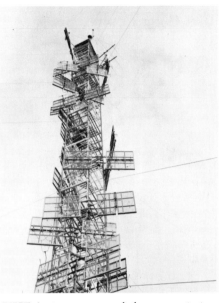

VHF Antennas *crowded on a mast at Di An.*

a relationship between distance and frequency separation as well as harmonic effects. Two PRC–25 radios operating five feet apart had to be operated at frequencies separated by ten megahertz; radios operating on frequencies separated by only one megahertz had to be located 350 feet apart. Distances were even greater for higher-powered vehicular FM radios. Frequencies separated by 5.75 or 23 megahertz, or related frequencies such as 35 and 70 megahertz, caused harmonic interference. Elimination of sources of interference to FM radios was particularly critical; due to a phenomenon called the capture effect, the strongest FM signal received by a radio completely blocked out all other signals.[28]

Besides engineering and distributing frequencies, signal officers also had to enforce their proper use. The presence of communications traffic in several different languages complicated the policing of the communications channels. While the units of the 1st Cavalry Division may have been able to use unauthorized frequencies in the wilds of the western highlands of the II Corps without causing any interference, in the crowded confines of the II Field Force's area of operations bootlegging frequencies had disastrous consequences. Lacking specialized equipment to track down the sources of interference, the signal staff of II Field Force had to turn to electronic warfare units for monitoring assistance. They found that most reports of interference, called meaconing reports, thought to be enemy jamming, were actually cases of mutual interference.[29]

---

[28]Malvin F. Shar, "Reduction of Mutual Frequency Interference," *Command Communications*, May 1969, pp. 26–27; Maj. Duane B. Riggs, "The FM Capture Effect," *Command Communications*, January 1969, p. 39. Both in CMH.

[29]Interv, author with Leon Staskiewicz, former electronic warfare staff officer, 26 Apr 78, Historians files, CMH.

Viet Cong Communications

A lthough by 1966 the Viet Cong were using captured American radios, especially PRC–10's taken from the South Vietnamese Army, for short-range voice communications, the monitoring program uncovered very little interference from Viet Cong radios. Because the Viet Cong habitually used low power settings and employed directional antennas, while the Americans and South Vietnamese tended to use high power and rarely bothered to erect anything more than a standard omnidirectional whip antenna, it was difficult to intercept Viet Cong transmissions. Most enemy transmissions were picked up accidentally by frontline American units operating close to the enemy. During an operation in February 1967 a unit of the 173d Airborne Brigade overheard on its command frequency the Viet Cong plotting an attack. After the unit alerted nearby American and South Vietnamese units to the Viet Cong plans on another net, the Viet Cong, who had apparently monitored the American warnings, transmitted a message announcing that the attack was compromised and warning all stations to use code on the net in the future.[30]

Occasionally the Viet Cong deliberately entered American and South Vietnamese nets to influence or confuse allied communications. They plagued South Vietnamese radio operators with misleading fire support requests and calls for assistance to trap relief forces. Although not bold enough to attempt such deception with the Americans during the early stages of the war, they sometimes entered American nets with crude attempts at psychological warfare. On one instance, the entire command net of a battalion of the 173d Airborne Brigade was shut down by a single radio transmitting repeatedly, "Growing American aggression is costing the U.S. aggressors their freedom." On a few occasions American units also complained of nonverbal interference—whistles, bells, and keying of a microphone—on their radio nets.[31]

Such attempts to interfere with American communications were rare, and probably done without authority. Considering allied communications a fruitful source of intelligence, the Viet Cong high command was wary of warning the Americans of an extensive intercept program directed against those communications. Called technical reconnaissance, the enemy electronic warfare endeavor was controlled directly by the Central Office for South Vietnam and conducted by the *47th Technical Reconnaissance Battalion*. During Operation EL PASO, the 130-man *C1 Company* of the battalion targeted thirty American nets and copied 7,745 messages. A smaller unit of fifty men operating near Nui Ba Den targeted the communications transmitted through the mountaintop relay and from nearby Special Forces outposts that served as bases for allied units reconnoitering Viet Cong bases along the Cambodian border. All intelligence was encrypted and sent to the Central Office for South Vietnam by Morse code radio or messengers on bicycles. Since the Viet Cong knew that Westmoreland had strengthened his

---

[30]II FFV, INTSUM 42, 11 Feb 67, an. B, file 501–04, 69A6621/4, WNRC.
[31]II FFV, PERINTREP 18, 2 May 67, p. 12, file 501–04, 69A6621/4; CICV Rpt, VC/NVA Electronic Warfare Capability (ST 67–061), 1 Jul 67, p. 8, 71A4237/12. Both in WNRC.

forces sufficiently by 1966 to attack the strongholds from which they were directing the insurgency, they were very interested in American intentions.[32]

ATTLEBORO

Although Westmoreland was planning just such an offensive for early 1967,
the unexpected discovery of large caches of materiel just north of Tay Ninh
in November 1966 drew American forces prematurely into the heavy jungles of
War Zone C. Called Operation ATTLEBORO, the main battle began on 3 November when a small task force of the 196th Light Infantry Brigade searching for
storage depots of the Viet Cong's *82d Rear Service Support Group* stumbled onto
the headquarters of the notorious *9th Viet Cong Division.* The Viet Cong fought
furiously, surrounding the three companies in the American task force and foiling attempts to relieve them. The commander of the 196th Light Infantry Brigade,
Brig. Gen. Edward H. de Saussure, Jr., moved his command post thirty kilometers
east from the brigade's base at Tay Ninh to Dau Tieng to be closer to the scene
of the operation. Still, he had difficulty coordinating the movement of his relief
forces, who were operating in foliage so dense that FM signals were severely
attenuated. When a Viet Cong mortar barrage knocked out the communications
equipment operated by the 595th Signal Company at the brigade's base at Tay
Ninh shortly after midnight on 4 November, General de Saussure's communications to his controlling headquarters, the 25th Infantry Division, were also interrupted. The acting commander of the II Field Force, Maj. Gen. Frederick C.
Weyand, responded quickly with support from his corps signal battalion. At first
light, CH–47 helicopters ferried in two lightweight MRC–112 four-channel radios
to relay communications from the brigade's forward command post at Dau Tieng
to the 25th Infantry Division's base at Cu Chi.[33]

Throughout the morning of 4 November, relief forces fought their way a company at a time to the beleaguered task force. Using only a PRC–25 radio, the task
force commander, Maj. Guy S. Meloy, eventually controlled eleven companies
from five separate battalions. While lying pinned down by enemy fire, Sfc. Ray
Burdette had assembled and propped against a tree a large antenna, called an
RC–292, that enabled Major Meloy to maintain contact with the relieving companies as well as with a more powerful vehicular-mounted FM radio at Dau
Tieng.[34]

As Major Meloy's men prepared to spend their second night under the guns
of the *9th Viet Cong Division,* General Weyand decided to commit a brigade from
the 1st Infantry Division, based forty kilometers to the south, to the relief operation. Alerted during the night to move on a fifteen-minute notice, a platoon from

[32]Intel Rpt, 569th MID, 28 Mar 67, no. 20/69; Intel Rpt, CMIC, 8 Apr 67, no. A147. Both in CMH.
Ltr, USARV to Distribution A, 20 Nov 69, sub: Operations Security, 72A6443/26, WNRC.
[33]MacGarrigle covers the ATTLEBORO operation in The Year of the Offensive. Accounts of signal support to ATTLEBORO are in Ltr, 125th Sig Bn to 25th Inf Div, 1 Dec 66, sub: Signal Operations After
Action Report, AD 386106, DDC.
[34]Myer, *Division-Level Communications,* pp. 43–44.

Company B, 121st Signal Battalion, was lifted out by helicopter with the 3d Brigade early on the morning of 5 November to Suoi Da, a village near the base of Nui Ba Den. Soon after, Company C left for Dau Tieng with communications equipment for a division forward command post. At Dau Tieng the signalmen installed a sixty-foot tower with FM and VHF antennas to improve contact with the maneuver units and with Di An, where Company A remained to operate communications for the division headquarters.[35]

After the 1st Infantry Division relieved the pressure on the 196th Light Infantry Brigade long enough for Major Meloy to withdraw his battered command to the safety of Dau Tieng, the battle area widened to the Suoi Da region, where the 3d Brigade had encountered a Viet Cong regiment. On nearby Nui Ba Den, the 121st Signal Battalion installed an FM retransmission station, and the 53d Signal Battalion deployed another MRC–112 relay. The corps signal battalion encountered so much difficulty with frequency interference on its MRC–112 systems, which operated in the same frequency range as the VRC–12 family of radios, that it had to replace them with twelve-channel sets. Although the 121st Signal Battalion had tried to retransmit automatically the six major divisional FM nets by synchronizing twelve frequencies so that they would not cause mutual or harmonic interference, transmission from other nets and from the MRC–112 systems caused radios in the retransmission stations to key and block out regular traffic. To eliminate the problem, radiomen on Nui Ba Den operated each net on a single frequency and personally relayed messages for stations having difficulty maintaining contact.[36]

Because of frequency interference many ground units relied on colored smoke grenades for communicating with aircraft. Green smoke marked friendly positions, and red identified the enemy's location. When a red smoke grenade landed in the midst of the command post of a battalion of the 3d Brigade that was closely engaged with the Viet Cong near Suoi Da, the battalion communications officer, Capt. Euripides Rubio, Jr., scooped up the burning grenade in his bare hands and, running through a hail of enemy fire, threw it into the Viet Cong's positions, which were promptly blasted by air strikes. Killed twenty meters from the Viet Cong trenches, the brave communications officer was posthumously awarded the Medal of Honor.[37]

Although the violence of the battles in ATTLEBORO, the first time that a large Viet Cong force stood and fought, took American commanders by surprise, the 1st Signal Brigade responded quickly to the unanticipated requirements for communications in the battle area. Disregarding procedures established by the Defense Communications Agency for obtaining approval for circuit changes, in two hours the 2d Signal Group installed and rerouted circuits—tasks that would have taken weeks to accomplish using the prescribed procedures. In Viet Cong after action reports, the enemy admitted that his communications were far less responsive

---

[35]Ltr, 121st Sig Bn to 1st Inf Div, 17 Dec 66, sub: AAR Operation BATTLECREEK (ATTLEBORO), 68A75/4, WNRC.

[36]ORLL, 53d Sig Bn, 31 Jan 67, 68A75/1, WNRC; Ltr, 121st Sig Bn to 1st Inf Div, 17 Dec 66, sub: AAR Operation BATTLECREEK (ATTLEBORO).

[37]Myer, *Division-Level Communications*, pp. 44–45.

Company Commander, *pinned down by the Viet Cong, uses the PRC–25 to call for air support.*

to the surprise encounter with the Americans; poor communications especially hampered coordination of a defense against rapid movements by heliborne American units. Although the signal officer of the *9th Viet Cong Division* increased the number of scheduled radio contacts with the division's regiments from three to twenty-four a day, confusion and continuous movement of units disrupted communications severely. Worried that air strikes might home in on the communications complex supporting the Central Office for South Vietnam, the Viet Cong had deliberately interfered with the flow of communications by moving the station transmitting to the *9th Division* twelve kilometers to the east.[38]

CEDAR FALLS

Before pushing deeper into War Zone C, General Westmoreland decided to invade a stronghold just thirty kilometers north of Saigon, called the Iron Triangle, that housed the headquarters of Military Region 4, the organization that directed Viet Cong activities in and around Saigon, and also served as the hub

[38]Interv, author with Vogel, 16 Jan 78; Translation Rpt, MACV, MAJJ214, Log entry 03-3331-67, 6 Apr 67, sub: VC After-Action Rpt Opn ATTLEBORO, CMH.

of the communications-liaison network in III Corps. In January 1967 units of the 1st and 25th Infantry Divisions, the 173d Airborne Brigade, the 196th Infantry Brigade, and the 11th Armored Cavalry sealed off the Iron Triangle and searched for Viet Cong installations believed to be within. In planning for the operation, called CEDAR FALLS, communicators drew on their experiences during ATTLEBORO and experimented with several new techniques.[39]

To expand airborne FM communications, the 173d Airborne Brigade installed an extra antenna and an internal connector on all observation helicopters to enable battalion commanders' radio operators to hook their radios into the aircraft's antenna system while airborne. The 11th Armored Cavalry fabricated from angle iron a console that held three PRC–25 radios, enough to give a battalion staff complete communications while airborne, which could be quickly removed when the aircraft landed. During CEDAR FALLS signalmen introduced a new voice security device, the KY–8, for automatically encrypting FM transmissions. Because it could not be used with aircraft radios and because improper operation increased interference in already troublesome FM nets, they limited its use to the nightly communications between major command posts planning the following day's operations.[40]

General Westmoreland was wary of giving the Viet Cong an opportunity to learn of American plans. Although the 173d Airborne Brigade had swept through the Iron Triangle during the fall of 1965, the Viet Cong had apparently been forewarned and escaped. During CEDAR FALLS Viet Cong communicators reacted to the penetration of their safe haven in the Iron Triangle by halting all radio communications to deny American electronic warfare teams a means to track them down by radio intercept.

Although the Americans were unable to trap the Viet Cong in the Iron Triangle, they did find a large tunnel complex. Soldiers called tunnel rats crawled into the tunnels to investigate. Although each man carried either a hand telephone or had a microphone strapped to the back of his skull, communications were the biggest difficulty encountered by the tunnel rats. Mouthpieces clogged with dirt or cracked from constant jarring. Only a few teams had lightweight Canadian assault wire; for the others, the bulk and weight of American field wire proved an encumbrance in the cramped tunnels. Despite difficulties with communications, the tunnel rats finally discovered the underground headquarters of Military Region 4 and retrieved thousands of documents that were sent back to Saigon for intelligence review.[41]

Among the most valuable documents were the signal directives and frequen-

[39]A thorough discussion of CEDAR FALLS is contained in Lt. Gen. Bernard W. Rogers, *CEDAR FALLS-JUNCTION CITY: A Turning Point*, Vietnam Studies (Washington, D.C.: Government Printing Office, 1974), pp. 30–74; and MacGarrigle, The Year of the Offensive. ORLL, 53d Sig Bn, 31 Jan 67; ORLL, 196th Inf Bde, 30 Apr 67, pp. 18–19; 125th Sig Bn, AAR and Lessons Learned-Operation Cedar Falls, file 101; Ltr, 121st Sig Bn to 1st Inf Div, 26 Feb 67, sub: After Action Report, Operation NIAGARA FALLS/CEDAR FALLS. Latter two in CMH.

[40]Combat Operations After Action Report (COAAR), Operation NIAGARA/CEDAR FALLS, 173d Abn Bde, 25 Feb 67, pp. 37–38, file 10; AAR, 11th Armd Cav Rgt, CEDAR FALLS, 13 Mar 67, file 125, pp. 29–30. Both in CMH.

[41]See Rogers, *CEDAR FALLS-JUNCTION CITY*, p. 67, for a discussion of the tunnel rats.

cies of Viet Cong units operating in III Corps. Although the Viet Cong quickly revised compromised signal plans, American electronic warfare experts learned much about the signal tactics and capabilities of the *9th Viet Cong Division*, which guarded the approaches to the jungle hideout of the Viet Cong's high command. Within War Zones C and D, two major signal organizations provided most communications: the *44th Signal Battalion* supported the Central Office for South Vietnam, and the *102C Signal Company* handled communications for the *9th Viet Cong Division*. The *44th Signal Battalion* was well equipped with American and Chinese Communist equipment and operated well-established radio, switchboard, and courier communications throughout the sprawling headquarters complex. Although the manning and configuration of the battalion changed frequently, it had a permanent cadre of 265 highly trained communicators, many of whom doubled as instructors at a signal school located at the Central Office for South Vietnam. The best communicators in the battalion operated Morse code radio links to Hanoi; the rest manned radio links to the military regions and to the *9th* and *5th Viet Cong Divisions*. Apparently because of the presence of the *44th Signal Battalion*, the Viet Cong deviated from the normal procedure of assigning a signal battalion to each division and assigned only a 140-man signal company to the *9th Division*. Much of the tactical communications load was carried by 100-man signal companies with each of the three regiments in the division and signal platoons of each infantry battalion. For long-distance communications the Viet Cong signalmen depended on Morse code transmissions using captured GRC–9 radios or fifteen-watt Chinese Communist model 102 radios. For short-range voice communications they used captured American FM radios, village and hamlet radios, and Chinese Communist two-watt 72B radios. To enhance security, most communications within the region were handled by wire or courier, a luxury American communicators enjoyed only within the perimeters of secure bases.[42]

JUNCTION CITY

By February 1967 Lt. Gen. Jonathan O. Seaman, the II Field Force commander, was determined to eliminate the major Viet Cong safe haven by positioning forces in a horseshoe shape around War Zone C and sweeping through from the open end with the 11th Armored Cavalry and the 2d Brigade of the 25th Infantry Division. Although he was aware that the battle area for the operation, named JUNCTION CITY, consisted of difficult terrain, from marshy flatlands in the south to dense bamboo forests in the north, he expected the *9th Viet Cong Division* to be weakened by almost a year of continuous warfare. Equipment in the *102C Signal Company* was indeed worn out, the reserve of batteries for radios nearly depleted.[43]

For U.S. units, the recent arrival of the 36th Signal Battalion had released substantial amounts of tactical resources that had been committed to base camp

---

[42]CICV Rpt, VC/NVA Signal Order of Battle Update (ST 67–067), 16 Sep 67, 319–74–053/3, WNRC; II FFV, PERINTREP 23, 12 Jun 67, p. H–1; II FFV, PERINTREP 12, 4 Apr 67, p. 7. Latter two in file 501–04, 69A6621/4, WNRC.
[43]Rogers, *CEDAR FALLS–JUNCTION CITY*, pp. 83–153.

communications; the new area battalion had also built several new signal centers on the fringes of War Zone C. Better to support the separate brigades that were to be under the control of the 25th Infantry Division during JUNCTION CITY—the 3d Brigade, 4th Infantry Division; the 196th Light Infantry Brigade; the 11th Armored Cavalry; and the 1st Brigade, 9th Infantry Division—the 578-man 125th Signal Battalion was reorganized to place similar types of equipment together within companies. Company A, normally assigned to support division main headquarters, assumed responsibility for all teletype and radio communications; the unit that supported the organic brigades, Company B, handled all multichannel communications; and Company C, the unit normally providing rear-echelon and logistical communications, assumed all telephone and cabling support. While the 1st Infantry Division retained the organization it had used during ATTLEBORO and CEDAR FALLS, which was essentially the standard doctrinal configuration for a divisional signal battalion, it had been bolstered since those operations by the release of additional equipment from base camp support. Since the 173d Airborne Brigade was to be under the operational control of the 1st Infantry Division, the II Field Force signal officer, Col. John D. Hartline, advised the commander of the 121st Signal Battalion, Lt. Col. James M. Rockwell, that he would have to relieve the 53d Signal Battalion of support to the separate brigade. The 53d Signal Battalion would be heavily committed to support a forward headquarters that General Seaman planned to establish at Dau Tieng, the first corps headquarters to move from its base camp to the field in the war.[44]

As one of the first elements to deploy on JUNCTION CITY, on 17 February 1967, the 53d Signal Battalion moved an advance party to Dau Tieng. For security reasons the signalmen were not permitted to emplace any equipment until 20 February. Upon arrival they staked areas for the various communications vans and planned the VHF systems that would be emanating from the command post. By nightfall on 20 February the 53d Signal Battalion had installed multichannel communications from Dau Tieng to the forward headquarters of the 1st and the 25th Infantry Divisions and back to the field force base at Long Binh. Except for unexpected delays when the helicopters carrying the communications for the 196th Light Infantry Brigade had maintenance problems, the 125th Signal Battalion rapidly linked the 25th Infantry Division's advance command post at Tay Ninh to the brigades operating under the control of the division. Since the 1st Infantry Division was moving its forward command post into Minh Thanh, an undeveloped base twenty-five kilometers northeast of Dau Tieng, the 121st Signal Battalion had considerably more trouble establishing field communications. To raise antennas for eleven multichannel systems and three FM radio nets above the canopy of the heavy jungle surrounding the base, the battalion had to build a huge 120-foot tower.

With communications established with the major headquarters, on 22 February the combat units closed the ring around War Zone C. In the largest single-day helicopter operation in history, 249 helicopters ferried assault troops of three

---

[44]MacGarrigle, The Year of the Offensive; ORLL, 53d Sig Bn, 30 Apr 67, 68A4975/7, WNRC. See *Command Communications*, March 1967, CMH, and ORLL, 25th Inf Div, 31 Jul 67, pp. 71–83, AD 504136, DDC, for a discussion of communications within the 25th Infantry Division.

Closing the Ring in War Zone C

brigades to form the arch of a horseshoe along the Cambodian border. Once on the ground, the airlifted units were supported by FM and high-frequency radios and lightweight MRC–34 1/2 configurations carried in by cargo helicopters. Other units, accompanied by standard signal vans, moved by ground convoy to form the sides of the horseshoe and attack into the center of the trap.[45]

In the first and only U.S. parachute jump of the war, a battalion of the 173d Airborne Brigade parachuted into the most inaccessible segment of the arch. Among the first parachutists on the ground were the brigade commander, Brig. Gen. John R. Deane, Jr., the brigade signal officer, Maj. Fred Darling, and his assistant, Capt. Peter J. McAteer. Darling and McAteer supervised the rapid installation of communications at the drop zone. Within minutes the brigade's communicators had erected an RC–292 antenna and had FM communications to the 1st Division's base at Minh Thanh. To assist the other jumpers and to guide the cargo drops that followed the airborne troopers into the drop zone, they used smoke grenades and gas-filled colored balloons. A prearranged system of colored parachutes used in the cargo drop made unit equipment easily identifiable; but the brigade's communications equipment had become so mired down in the soft ground of the drop zone that the communicators had to wait for the arrival late

---

[45]AAR, II FFV, Signal Section, Operation JUNCTION CITY, Phase I; AAR, 1st Inf Div Sig Ofcr, Operation JUNCTION CITY–1. Both in file 139806, 72A25/21, WNRC. COAAR, 196th Inf Bde, 4 May 67 (RCS: MACV J3–32), pp. 8–10, file 3, CHB 23; COAAR, 125th Sig Bn, 5 Jun 67. Latter two in CMH.

Brig. Gen. Bernard W. Rogers *directs operations from a helicopter command post in Operation Junction City.*

in the afternoon of armored personnel carriers to tow it to firmer ground. By that time Captain McAteer had already arranged for a cargo helicopter to bring in another load of equipment, and by nightfall the brigade command post was linked by multichannel VHF systems to the forward command post of the 1st Infantry Division in Minh Thanh and by field wire to all the subordinate battalions of the brigade. This marked the first time that all the battalions in the airborne brigade were so close together that they could communicate using telephone wire. When the subordinate battalions later spread out to the west, they once again had to rely on FM voice radio and hastily installed VHF multichannel systems to link temporary battalion fire bases.[46]

Anticipating frequency problems, signalmen avoided using automatic retransmission stations, especially on the top of crowded Nui Ba Den. Airborne relays still caused some interference between widely separated units that were trying to use the same frequencies, but Colonel Hartline was able to shift frequencies before the interference affected operations. Mutual interference caused by inductions through the long coaxial cables leading from the radios in the 1st Division's forward command post to the top of the tower at Minh Thanh was resolved by mounting radios on top of the 120-foot tower and extending them

[46]ORLL, 173d Abn Bde, 30 Apr 67, tab A, p. 38, and tab B, p. 33, 68A4975/8, WNRC.

by field wire to the command post on the ground.[47]

During JUNCTION CITY signalmen exploited the many capabilities of the new series of radios. Although most brigade commanders, fearing FM interference, still shunned use of secure voice on their nets, most important traffic on the corps and division command nets was sent in the secure mode. To preclude continuously operating both a nonsecure and a secure net, signalmen established procedures to permit a station wishing to communicate in the secure mode simply to call the distant station on a nonsecure net and tell him to meet on "net 2." The two would go to a prearranged frequency to carry on their conversation in the secure mode without interference from net stations lacking secure devices that might otherwise have unknowingly transmitted and interfered with the secure conversation.[48]

Another special capability, radio-wire integration, permitted communications between FM radios and telephones by placing a call to a radio-wire integration station, which had both radio contact with the field and a telephone line to the local switchboard. After getting both parties on the line, the operator had only to advise them to use radio procedure and adjust a small electronic device, called a GSA-7, to permit the two parties to converse. Used extensively in the 1st Division, it enabled battalion logistics officers in the field to call back to assistants at the base camps for supplies, and personnel officers at the rear bases to call commanders in the field to coordinate personnel actions. Senior commanders even used radio-wire integration to call from their helicopters flying over the battlefield to coordinate administrative matters with MACV staff offices in Saigon.[49]

Anticipating the heavy use of FM radio, Colonel Hartline had arranged for VHF multichannel systems to interlace the area of operations. To minimize congestion in the FM frequency span, the MRC-34 1/2, rather than the MRC-112, was used whenever possible. With the high antenna towers, the VHF radios performed far beyond planning ranges; one system from Nui Chua Chan to the 25th Infantry Division's base at Cu Chi had a span of ninety-three miles, more than twice the planning range for the radio. That system worked well except for six hours during midday. Communicators had neglected to plan for multichannel systems from forward support bases of the 15th Support Brigade, the logistical unit providing direct support to the operation, to the divisional support bases at Trai Bi and Suoi Da. As a result, combat units overloaded command and operations circuits to relay messages through Long Binh back to logistical units deployed in War Zone C. The 11th Armored Cavalry, which ordered replacement parts for its armored vehicles directly from its base in Long Khanh Province, had to call through four switchboards. Throughout the operation, the 53d Signal Battalion and the divisional signal units had to respond to emergency requests to install new systems or preempt circuits to meet unanticipated requirements for

[47]II FFV, OPLAN 3-67, 15 Feb 67, an. H; AAR, 1st Inf Div Sig Ofcr, Operation JUNCTION CITY-1, p. 1. Both in file 139806, 72A25/21, WNRC. COAAR, 1st Bde, 1st Inf Div, 4 May 67, p. 16; COAAR, 2d Bde, 1st Inf Div, 13 May 67, p. 11; COAAR, 3d Bde, 1st Inf Div, 25 Apr 67, p. 9; COAAR, 1st Inf Div Artillery, 1 May 67, p. 8. Latter four in file 99, CHB 22, CMH.
[48]AAR, II FFV, Operation JUNCTION CITY Phase 1.
[49]AAR, 121st Sig Bn, Operation JUNCTION CITY, Phase I and II, 2 May 67, p. 8, CMH.

Hot Lines in a Brigade Operations Center

logistical communications.[50]

Planners at the field force headquarters had apparently felt that high-frequency radio-teletype nets designated for administrative and logistical communications would be sufficient for such nontactical communications. Yet so long as any circuits over the VHF multichannel systems were operational, those high-frequency radios were seldom used. Because messages had to receive special handling for routing to the radio-teletype van, often located some distance from the main section of the command post, the message centers normally passed traffic directly to the main communications center for transmission by teletype over a VHF circuit. Although Colonel Hartline had directed that important reports be transmitted by both high frequency and VHF, at least one critical report was delivered late to the forward command post of the field force due to a failure to use radio-teletype.[51]

Signal officers mustered all available teletype operators, many of them operators from the underused radio-teletype vans and clerk-typists with security clear-

[50]AAR, II FFV, Operation Junction City Phase 1, p. 6; II FFV, OPLAN 3–67, 15 Feb 67, an. H, app. 3; COAAR, 11th Armd Cav Rgt, 9 Jun 67, pp. 38–40, file 5. Latter two in CHB 23, CMH. Annex L of the II Field Force, Vietnam, After Action Report describes the circuits that were ultimately installed for logistical communications.

[51]II FFV, OPLAN 3–67, 15 Feb 67, an. H, app. 1; Ltr, II FFV to COMUSMACV, 3 Jul 67, sub: Tactical Command Post–Junction City, Incl 7 (Signal), p. 2, CMH.

ances, to poke out messages on teletype tapes. But a jump in message volume and the limited number of circuits available in the field caused message delays that aggravated staff officers accustomed to the better service provided by the fixed equipment used by the 1st Signal Brigade in the base camps. Impatient message originators began assigning unrealistically high precedences, which increased the pressure on overworked teletype operators and disrupted the normal flow of communications. Over 78 percent of the messages handled at the field force's forward command post were Operational Immediate, a precedence normally reserved for urgent messages having a critical bearing on tactical operations in progress.[52]

Because switchboard operators bore the brunt of the complaints of subscribers, they were less fortunate than their comrades isolated in the teletype communications centers. Dealing with impatient local subscribers and other harried switchboard operators created such psychological pressures that the efficiency and diplomacy of many switchboard operators declined so drastically that they had to be transferred to other jobs. To improve the telephone service for the most important staff sections and to take some of the pressure off the switchboards, during JUNCTION CITY signal planners emphasized sole-user service; in the 25th Infantry Division almost half the circuits were point-to-point rather than switchboard trunks. Although that expedient degraded communications available to the mass of subscribers in the division and caused a need for additional multichannel systems, it improved the timeliness of communications between the tactical operations centers controlling the combat operations. To increase the availability of those hot lines, signal officers often terminated them on small switchboards within the operations centers.[53]

From a communications standpoint, the creation of a forward command post for the field force during JUNCTION CITY proved unwise. The need to move communications equipment to Dau Tieng as much as five days before the beginning of the operation to ensure that communications would be available from the start jeopardized the surprise that General Seaman wanted to achieve. Unlike the divisional signal battalions, which were staffed to man an alternate and a tactical command post, the 53d Signal Battalion, which was still providing internal communications for the separate brigades, was ill equipped to operate a major command post in two locations. Since all teletype communications between the forward command posts of the field force and divisions flowed through a tape relay at Long Binh, the location of the field force main headquarters, little advantage accrued from establishing a forward command post for the field force. As expected, most traffic flowed directly between the main headquarters in Long Binh and the forward command posts of the divisions; the message volume at the teletype center in Long Binh was eventually fifty times greater than at the forward command post of the field force. Although multichannel systems between the forward command post and each division permitted direct telephone circuits between the field command posts, just as many phone lines were available from

---

[52]AAR, II FFV, Operation JUNCTION CITY Phase 1, ans. J and K.
[53]Ibid., ans. C, D, E, F; 125th Sig Bn, AAR and Lessons Learned-Operation Cedar Falls, p. 2, CMH; Myer, *Division-Level Communications*, pp. 34–35.

Long Binh to the divisions in the field. Only for secure FM communications, for which retransmission equipment was unavailable in South Vietnam, was there an advantage to moving the field force command post closer to the divisions. When General Seaman finally closed his forward command post and the 53d Signal Battalion removed its equipment from Dau Tieng, staff officers at the divisions noted little change in communications service to the field force.[54]

As JUNCTION CITY moved into its second month, signalmen expanded their support and fine-tuned their communications. To replace the four-channel MRC–34 1/2 sets that had been airlifted in with the original attacking units, heavier equipment with greater capacity was moved in by road. Where territory could be secured, wiremen ran cable between fire bases and installed carrier equipment on the cable, obtaining multichannel communications without the interference and noise experienced on VHF radio systems. Unlike the Americans, Viet Cong radiomen handled less traffic than normal during JUNCTION CITY. Soon after American B–52 strikes began, most stations reverted to a rarely interrupted radio silence. As in ATTLEBORO, the terminals supporting the Central Office for South Vietnam split about eighteen kilometers apart.[55]

Although JUNCTION CITY failed to uncover the Central Office for South Vietnam, the operation did blunt the Viet Cong's military threat to the heartland of South Vietnam. General Westmoreland had gained breathing room to expand his defense of Saigon from the confines of the capital and to embark on a campaign to neutralize the more subtle threat of the Viet Cong's political and psychological influence over the population of South Vietnam. For signalmen, JUNCTION CITY was an opportunity to refine techniques developed during earlier campaigns. Some concepts, such as the establishment of a forward command post of the field force, and some new developments, such as the MRC–112, proved unsatisfactory. On the other hand, the operation demonstrated the flexibility of the conventional divisional signal battalion and the versatility of the FM radio when frequencies were tightly controlled. It also showed signalmen that a base communications grid built with tactical equipment installed in a semifixed configuration was effective during combat operations.

The pattern of signal operations established around Saigon followed traditional Army doctrine. Signalmen moved into new base camps with tactical units, sought the nearest high ground for relays to adjacent units, and set up an area system as the principal means of communications. Some equipment and teams were always held in reserve, ready for emergency use or for deployment on brief operations. As the Americans pushed out their span of control, those teams then became new semipermanent stations in the area system and new units assumed the reserve deployment mission. It was a pattern that had to be maintained by tactical communications until a permanent, fixed system could be installed.

---

[54]Ltr, II FFV to COMUSMACV, 3 Jul 67, sub: Tactical Command Post–JUNCTION CITY, Incl 7 (Signal), Incl 4 (G–2), and Incl 5 (G–3).
[55]AAR, 121st Sig Bn, Operation JUNCTION CITY, Phase I and II, 2 May 67; 125th Sig Bn, AAR and Lessons Learned-Operation Cedar Falls.

10

Expanding the Base in the III and IV Corps

With the northern and western approaches to Saigon secured, General West-moreland moved American headquarters and bases away from the congestion of Saigon into the open country north of the capital. During 1967 the headquarters of the Military Assistance Command, Vietnam, moved from downtown Cholon to Tan Son Nhut; several major Army headquarters—including the U.S. Army, Vietnam, the 1st Logistical Command, the 1st Signal Brigade, and the 2d Signal Group—relocated north to the Long Binh–Bien Hoa area. Those moves involved the realignment of many communications circuits and helped to temper the adverse psychological and economic effects of a large American presence in South Vietnam's capital. Having concentrated initially on the enemy threat from the north and west, Westmoreland then turned his attention to South Vietnam's richest agricultural region just south of Saigon and to the densely populated Mekong Delta in IV Corps.[1]

Operations in the Delta

A merican signalmen welcomed the move from the teeming city, where a labyrinth of cable hung from rooftops and window sills and vehicular ignition caused constant crackling on radios. They were less pleased with the prospect of operating in the delta. There the encroachment of the horizon limited the range of line-of-sight radio paths just as in the lowlands of III Corps, but the delta lacked hills like Nui Ba Den for relaying signals. Ground firm enough to bear the weight of heavy communications equipment was usually already occupied. The soil, leached by heavy monsoons and seasonal flooding, provided a poor electrical ground. Rust and rot quickly corroded delicate electronic components. Unwilling to relinquish a primary source of food and recruits, the tenacious Viet Cong contributed to the region's inhospitality. Controlling most of the countryside and the few major roads in the delta, the Viet Cong forced the allies to take to helicopters or boats.

[1]Sharp and Westmoreland, *Report on the War in Vietnam*, pp. 146–47.

To bolster the three South Vietnamese Army divisions in the delta, the U.S. Army's newest division, the 9th Infantry Division from Fort Riley, Kansas, became the first American combat unit to operate full time in the delta. When alerted, the commander of the 9th Signal Battalion, Lt. Col. John H. Reeder, had a cadre of only 150 noncommissioned officers and enlisted men to prepare for a sudden influx of enlisted men recently graduated from basic training and young officers shifted from staff and school assignments. Profiting from the experiences of earlier units, the battalion quickly obtained antenna towers and air conditioners for signal vans. The entire division was issued the new family of FM radios and the first production models of the Army's new series of high-frequency radio, the GRC–106, the replacement for the GRC–19 series. Planning to conduct joint operations with the Navy on the 2,400 kilometers of rivers and 4,000 kilometers of canals in the delta, Colonel Reeder sent one of the division's brigade signal officers, Maj. Nathan Plotkin, to arrange for the installation of Army communications equipment on U.S. Navy ships being prepared to operate in the delta.[2]

At Bear Cat, thirty kilometers east of Saigon, Company C, 36th Signal Battalion, installed a 200-line switchboard, a communications center, and a multichannel link to the II Field Force for the incoming division. In late 1966 when Bear Cat became the base for a Thai regiment that arrived in South Vietnam without its communications, General Terry sent additional support, including a transportable 600-line dial exchange, making the 9th Division the first combat unit to have dial telephone service.[3]

Separated from Bear Cat by the impassable Rung Sat swamp, the division's 2d Brigade was located ninety kilometers to the south on a man-made island of solid ground at Dong Tam in Dinh Tuong Province, and the 3d Brigade was seventy kilometers southwest of Bear Cat in Long An Province. Through relays on VC Hill at Vung Tau and at an old French fort in the Rung Sat, Colonel Reeder's men operated twelve FM and multichannel radio links into the delta. To reach the many units dispersed over the 4,225 square miles encompassing the division's area of operations, Colonel Reeder made full use of aircraft. Logging over 15,000 miles a month, the signal battalion's air courier visited each brigade daily. Airborne relays or airlifted retransmission stations extended FM communications to units on operations. For air-transportable multichannel communications, the division relied on the airmobile MRC–34 1/2 radio expedient that had been developed earlier by the 25th Infantry Division.[4]

The 9th Signal Battalion soon developed its own techniques of coping with the peculiarities of communicating in the delta. To improve grounding conditions, the battalion's maintenance men collected a large quantity of scrap metal, buried it deep below the water table, and welded it to a large rod that became a com-

[2]Myer, *Division-Level Communications,* pp. 16–22; Msg, USARV to USARPAC, 25 Sep 66, sub: Radio Relay Requirements, and Msg, DA to USARPAC, sub: Requirement for Microwave Tower AB216, both in file 13, 70A2328/6, WNRC.

[3]Fact Sheet, USARV CE, 31 Dec 66, sub: 1st Signal Brigade Communications Support, 9th Infantry Division; Ltr, 1st Sig Bde to USARV, 30 Dec 66, sub: Critical Signal Matters; Fact Sheet, USARV AVHSI-CS, 2 Jan 67, sub: Local Telephone Service Bear Cat. All in file 139867, 72A25/23, WNRC.

[4]"9th Infantry Division," *Command Communications,* November 1967, pp. 5–25; Interv, author with Lt Col John A. Hedrick, former S-3, 9th Signal Battalion, 5 Dec 78, Historians files. Both in CMH.

Soldier Calls Home *from the 9th Infantry Division's mobile MARS station.*

mon grounding point for all signal components at Bear Cat. In a less successful experiment, the signal battalion tried using a balloon to lift a radio antenna to increase transmission range, a concept first tested three years earlier by the Army Concept Team in Vietnam. Using a large 4,000-cubic-foot balloon to elevate an entire FM radio transmitter, the battalion greatly extended the range of the radio, but as in the earlier experiment the high winds of the monsoon season made balloons impractical.[5]

The 9th Infantry Division had more success exploiting an amateur radio network, the Military Affiliate Radio System (MARS), instituted in 1965 when Deputy U.S. Ambassador William J. Porter, himself an amateur radio operator, convinced the reluctant South Vietnamese to authorize frequencies for it. Converting two old ambulances to mobile MARS stations, the 9th Signal Battalion provided a means for soldiers at remote camps to call their families in the United States. To complete a call, a MARS station called an amateur radio operator in the United States who in turn called the soldier's family on the telephone and patched the radio into the phone system, allowing the two to talk. Although the MARS

---

[5]ACTIV, Balloon Borne Radio Communication System, 10 Apr 65, JRATA Project 1A–103.0, 70A868/5, WNRC; Msg, CINCPAC to JCS, 26 Jul 65, sub: Final Report . . . (JRATA Project 1A–103.0), CMH; Ltr, ACTIV to USARV, 10 Feb 69, sub: Letter Report of Evaluation—Balloon Borne Radio Relay, AD 848980, DDC.

The USS Benewah *with boats of the Mobile Riverine Force.*

program was well established throughout South Vietnam by the time the 9th Infantry Division arrived, the unique mobile service instituted by the division resulted in over 1,800 calls to the United States during its first three months of operation and had a dramatic effect on sustaining the division's high morale.[6]

The most important and in many ways the most unique mission of the 9th Signal Battalion was its support of the Mobile Riverine Force, a joint waterborne endeavor comprising an assault squadron of U.S. Navy ships carrying the 2d Brigade of the 9th Infantry Division. From a command post in a large barracks ship, the USS *Benewah,* the brigade commander and the Navy flotilla commander used two parallel communications systems to command their respective subordinates. Each of the brigade's battalions had a small command and communications boat equipped with FM and high-frequency radios for the battalion commander. Since those radios were compact and used omnidirectional antennas, they were ideal for the riverine force.

Establishing multichannel communications from the *Benewah* to the riverine

---

[6]Interv, author with Hedrick, 5 Dec 78; "9th Infantry Division," *Command Communications,* November 1967, p. 25; Msg, COMUSMACV to 2d Air Div et al., 4 Dec 65, sub: Establishing MARS Stations in RVN, CMH. When the 9th Division arrived, eighteen MARS stations were operating in South Vietnam. Msg, USARV to CINCUSARPAC, 4 Oct 66, sub: USARV MARS Phone Patching, file 13, 70A2328/6, WNRC.

VHF Boat *with the 2d Brigade, 9th Infantry Division.*

Command Post *of the 2d Brigade, 9th Infantry Division.*

force's base at Dong Tam was more difficult. While the ship was moving or shifting with the tide at anchor, radio operators on the ship had continuously to turn a hand crank to orient the directional VHF antenna to maintain the strongest signal from the transmitter at Dong Tam. There, two men atop a 204-foot tower, linked to the ground by field telephone, manually turned the antenna on the command of radio operators monitoring the incoming signal from the ship. This inefficient and hazardous expedient, which required signalmen to work dangerously close to antennas radiating high signal voltages and in full sight of Viet Cong snipers, was eventually discontinued when the 9th Signal Battalion obtained heavy-duty commercial rotors to crank the antennas from the ground.[7]

When another brigade joined the riverine force in the early spring of 1968, the 9th Infantry Division, which had moved its headquarters from Bear Cat to Dong Tam, began penetrating deeper into the delta along waterways too narrow for the *Benewah*. Because the ship transporting the forward command post was too small to carry any multichannel or switchboard equipment, the 9th Signal Battalion sent along a second ship with a VHF van lashed to its deck. By rotating antennas on the deck, radiomen in the van maintained radio contact with Dong Tam. As soon as the ships cast anchor, they used field wire to connect the command post ship to the van's multichannel system.[8]

Because the 9th Infantry Division was the first major American unit committed to the delta, the 1st Signal Brigade's area communications network in the IV Corps was austere. Mistakenly assuming that the commercial Southern Toll would handle military needs, early signal officers had failed to extend the BACKPORCH system to the delta. Not until late 1964 did the 39th Signal Battalion form the provisional Delta Company to handle area communications in the delta and to relieve the overextended 232d Signal Company, which also had responsibility for the III Corps Tactical Zone and the capital. Redesignated the 581st Signal Company in 1965 and augmented by two microwave teams from the 518th Signal Company to operate a system from Can Tho to Vinh Long, the company was equipped only to provide small signal centers to support the advisory detachments at the South Vietnamese corps headquarters in Can Tho, at the command posts of the 7th, 9th, and 21st South Vietnamese Divisions, and at the headquarters of the 13th Aviation Battalion (Combat) at Soc Trang. Not until the activation of the 52d Signal Battalion at Can Tho in late 1966 did the 1st Signal Brigade begin to pro-

---

[7]Comprehensive studies of the Mobile Riverine Force are contained in Maj. Gen. William B. Fulton, *Riverine Operations, 1966–1969*, Vietnam Studies (Washington, D.C.: Government Printing Office, 1973); and MS, Lt Col Thomas C. Loper, The Mobile Riverine Force or the Marriage of the Brown Water Navy and the Rice Paddy Army, 9 Mar 70, U.S. Army War College. Communications for the force are described in "Communications in a Riverine Environment," *Command Communications*, November 1967, pp. 26–31, CMH; Myer, *Division-Level Communications*, pp. 49–59; and 9th Inf Div, Riverine Communications Concepts, 7 Feb 69, file U–351, 72A18/6, WNRC. See also Capt. John A. Hedrick, "Developing and Testing a Rotatable VHF Antenna," *Command Communications*, October 1968, pp. 20–22, CMH.

[8]9th Inf Div, Riverine Communications Concepts, 7 Feb 69; Msg, 9th Inf Div to USARV, 8 Apr 68, sub: Added Requirement for Mobile Riverine Forces MRF, and Msg, USARV to CINCUSARPAC, 19 Apr 68, sub: Added Requirement for Mobile Riverine Forces MRF, both in file 201–46.1, CMH SC No. 56951, CMH.

vide full-scale area signal support to the IV Corps.[9] *(Map 10)*

Managing the Expansion

The 52d Signal Battalion had been formed in response to General Terry's proposal that the Army establish a battalion in each corps area to handle communications for advisers at every level down to battalions and subsectors. Approving the concept in principle in October 1966, the Department of the Army gave Terry permission to establish cadres for those battalions and promised to fill out the battalions later. During the fall of 1966 the 1st Signal Brigade took the first steps to establish the advisory support battalions.[10] By the time the new battalions were manned, their principal mission had shifted to supporting American units. In the III Corps, for example, the 44th Signal Battalion had become so involved with signal support to American units relocating from Saigon to the Bien Hoa–Long Binh area that advisers received less support from the entire battalion than they had formerly received from the 232d Signal Company. Although the 1st Signal Brigade continued to provide the larger advisory teams at corps and division level with radio-teletype, switchboard, and communications center support, just as the 39th Signal Battalion had been doing since its arrival, advisers at subsectors and infantry battalions continued to rely on South Vietnamese communications channels backed up by portable single-sideband radios.[11]

Delays in constructing fixed signal facilities forced General Terry to divert tactical equipment intended for the advisory battalion to the support of other American headquarters. To link Bien Hoa with Saigon, for example, the 44th Signal Battalion installed several multichannel systems intended as extensions to advisory teams assigned to district headquarters. Although Bien Hoa was included in the original plans for the Integrated Wideband Communications System, by the spring of 1967 only a portion of the contractor's excavation work for the microwave site there had been completed. After many delays in approving the contract for the overall network and several modifications to blueprints to expand the size of the facility to meet new requirements, the subcontractor hired by Page to construct the signal buildings at Bien Hoa proved incapable of doing the job and was fired. Even telecommunications projects being constructed by Army engineer units suffered delays. A U.S. Army engineer unit that had been build-

---

[9]Incl to Ltr, 581st Sig Co to 2d Sig Gp, 13 Jun 66, sub: Unit History, file 2–05 (66), 69A54/4, WNRC.

[10]The 178th Signal Company in I Corps became Company A, 37th Signal Battalion; the 586th Signal Company in II Corps became Company A, 43d Signal Battalion; the 232d Signal Company in III Corps became Company A, 44th Signal Battalion; and the 581st Signal Company in IV Corps became Company A, 52d Signal Battalion.

[11]Msg, 1st Sig Bde to USASTRATCOM, 16 May 66, sub: Weekly Summary, Backchannel file, CMH; 1st Sig Bde, Organization and Doctrine, Aug 67, pp. 16–17, file 11, 69A5363/11; ORLL, 1st Sig Bde, 31 Oct 67, p. 9, file 228–07, 1st Sig Bde (1967), 72A7128/5; ORLL, 52d Sig Bn, 31 Jul 67, 68A4975/7. Latter three in WNRC. MACV J–6, Radio Equipment for MACV Advisers, Mar 68, file U–267, and USARV C-E, Adviser Communications, 30 Dec 68, file U–223, both in 72A18/4, WNRC. Msg, USARV to CINCUSARPAC, 28 Oct 65, sub: Radio Set AN/PRC–74 (HC–162D), CMH.

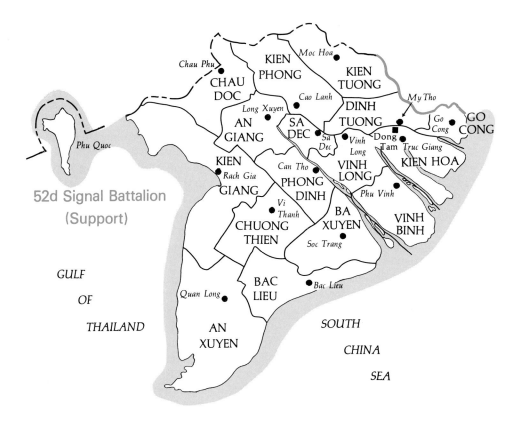

IV CORPS — AREAS OF RESPONSIBILITY

1966-1968

Map 10

ing a new communications center at Bien Hoa since July 1966 had to stop work in September while the blueprints were changed to increase the size of the facility. Only five days after resuming work in November, the engineers shifted to a higher-priority project. Construction was resumed in mid-December by a South Vietnamese contractor who completed the shell of the building by mid-May 1967. The project then was held up for several more months while Army engineers unsuccessfully tried to locate electrical power items and insulating material.[12]

The relocation of major Army headquarters to the suburbs of Saigon made other communications projects in III Corps particularly susceptible to frequent changes and delays in construction support. Through a Communications Coordinating Office within the 1st Signal Brigade, General Terry managed the installation of communications facilities at the new headquarters locations and ensured that communications remained functioning in both old and new locations during the move. He also activated the 160th Signal Group to control two signal battalions supporting the major American command complexes in the region: the 69th Signal Battalion for Saigon and Tan Son Nhut and the 44th Signal Battalion for the Long Binh area. By October 1967, when the relocation of headquarters was complete, the 44th Signal Battalion was the busiest in South Vietnam. Formed less than a year earlier to provide communications to field advisory detachments, the 44th Signal Battalion by October was operating four radio-teletype nets; a teletype relay at the headquarters of the U.S. Army, Vietnam; dial exchanges for Long Binh Post and the II Field Force; a teletype communications center for the 1st Signal Brigade; and a data terminal for the 1st Logistical Command's automated supply facility, the 14th Inventory Control Center. The shift in missions to the 44th Signal Battalion decreased the size of the 2,374-man 69th Signal Battalion to a more manageable 1,500 soldiers.[13] *(Map 11)*

The establishment of the Long Binh base, which quickly grew to a population of almost 75,000 troops, took a prodigious effort by Army engineers and signalmen. Besides clearing land and constructing buildings, the engineers had to install water and power systems, build roads, and erect defensive barriers. The precise requirements of commercial signal equipment for a steady power source and a dust-free, temperature-controlled environment made the installation of signal equipment a particularly onerous and exasperating mission for the engineers. Rigid procedures and detailed justifications required for construction of fixed facilities, called Class IV projects, hindered both civil and military communications engineers. The Signal Corps reacted to those emergency needs by joining tactical units and commercial contractors in installation efforts and by rushing in transportable equipment to operate interim systems during the construction of fixed facilities. Communications engineers provided the bond that held the

[12] 1st Sig Bde, Fact Sheets on III Corps, 25 Apr 67, file U–513, 72A18/9, WNRC.
[13] ORLL, 1st Sig Bde, 30 Apr 67, pp. 9–14, 72A7128/5; 2d Sig Gp, OPORD 1–67, 15 May 67, w/chg 2, 8 Jun 67; 2d Sig Gp, OPORD 2–67, 1 Jul 67, in ORLL, 2d Sig Gp, 31 Jul 67, 68A4975/3; 1st Sig Bde, Command Progress Rpt, 4th Qtr, FY–67, pp. 2–27, 68A4975/2; ORLL, 44th Sig Bn, 31 Oct 67, 68A4975. All in WNRC.

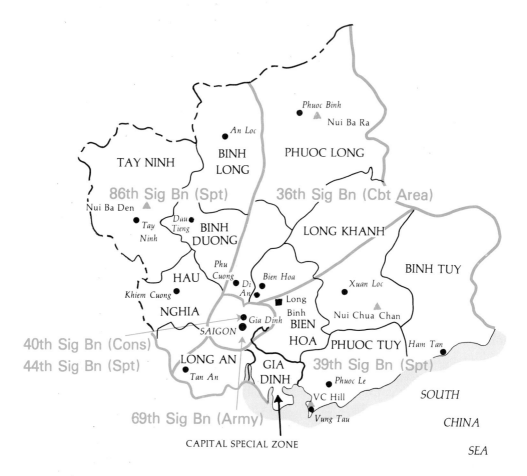

III CORPS — AREAS OF RESPONSIBILITY

December 1967

▲ MOUNTAIN RELAYS

Map 11

disparate organizations and technical facilities together.[14]

Responsibilities for communications engineering nevertheless were unclear and confused. After the Strategic Communications Command received the mission for the Integrated Wideband Communications System in August 1965, the responsibility for communications engineering in Southeast Asia was divided between the U.S. Army, Ryukyu Islands, which had performed the task since the late 1950s, and the Strategic Communications Command's Pacific field office in Hawaii.[15]

For some projects, duplicate engineering plans were prepared and two sets of materiel requisitioned; for others, work was never begun. Not until 9 February 1966, when the two commands signed an interim memorandum of understanding providing for the transfer of all engineering in Southeast Asia to the Strategic Communications Command, did the stalled signal engineering and installation programs get started. Although General Meyer assigned the engineering mission to the Pacific field office, Colonel Terry also used the 1st Signal Brigade's engineering staff to ensure that the installation of vital "nontactical" projects, which were actually the backbone of tactical communications in South Vietnam, were progressing to his satisfaction. Eventually the Pacific field office became primarily an installation agency, providing teams to assist in setting up facilities engineered by the 1st Signal Brigade.[16]

On 25 May 1966, Terry established the Communications-Electronics Engineering and Installation Agency in the signal brigade, assigning as its chief Lt. Col. Clarence R. Driscoll, the former head of the engineering team at the U.S. Army, Ryukyu Islands. To manage the installation of the wideband network and a new teletype and data system, the Automatic Digital Network (AUTODIN), Terry formed a special agency under Lt. Col. Patrick F. Kearins called the Integrated Wideband Communications System Management Office. In the summer of 1967 Terry consolidated the two organizations into the Communications Systems Engineering and Management Agency under the control of the brigade's director of operations. As the 206-man agency assumed an increasingly larger burden of engineering projects from the Pacific field office in Honolulu, General Meyer augmented it with engineers from his headquarters on temporary duty.[17]

---

[14]Interv, author with Col (ret.) Clarence R. Driscoll, former chief, Communications-Electronics Engineering and Installation Agency, 5 Jan 79, Historians files, CMH; Rienzi, *Communications-Electronics*, pp. 70–75.

[15]Msg, USARYIS to CINCUSARPAC, 14 Jan 66, sub: Responsiveness of Communications Engineering Support of USARV, file 10, 70A2328/6, WNRC.

[16]Msg, CINCUSARPAC to CGUSASCC, 8 Feb 66, sub: Assignment of Responsibility for Fixed Telecommunications Class IV Project System, file 10; Msg, USASTRATCOM PAC to CINCUSARPAC, 5 May 66, sub: Conference-Implementation of Class IV Sig Dev Projs in Vietnam, file 11. Both in 70A2328/6, WNRC. Memo, Gen Terry for Col Gordon B. Cauble et al., 23 Apr 66, sub: Plant Engineering and Installation Functions, 1st Sig Bde file, ACC Historians files; Ltr, USASCC to 1st Sig Bde and USASCC PAC, 10 Aug 66, sub: Engineering for Fixed Plant Communications in Southeast Asia, file U–113, 72A18/3, WNRC.

[17]A complete summary of the development of communications engineering within the Strategic Communications Command and the 1st Signal Brigade is contained in Bruno J. Rolak, History of U.S. Army Communications-Electronics Engineering Installation Agency and Communications Engineering from Origin to 1976, Jul 78, ACC Historians files; 1st Sig Bde, Organization and Doctrine, Aug 67, p. 10; "CSEMA," *Command Communications*, January 1968, pp. 40–42, CMH; ORLL, 1st Sig Bde, 31 Oct 67, p. 13.

Building the Telephone System

To perform traffic engineering for telephone systems in the Saigon area, in the spring of 1966 Colonel Terry directed the 2d Signal Group to establish the Saigon-Cholon Telephone Management Agency. He staffed it with officers who had recently attended a one-year commercial telephone course sponsored by the American Telephone and Telegraph Company. When the telephone management agency was formed, the city's telephone plant was composed of an unmanageable conglomeration of American, French, and South Vietnamese facilities of disparate vintage and quality: the Postes, Telegraphes, et Telephones operated two large, but ancient, manual switchboards; the South Vietnamese Army had four small dial exchanges that had been installed in 1957; the U.S. embassy operated several small switchboards throughout the city; the Air Force had a 600-line dial exchange at Tan Son Nhut; and the Army operated one long-distance and nine local manual switchboards. A failure to engineer subscriber lines and interconnecting trunks caused excessive signal losses when calls were switched from one exchange to another. Each organization operating the exchanges maintained separate circuit records, and there were no cable records for South Vietnamese tactical cables and old French lines. This lack of coordination made correcting technical problems or installing new interconnecting trunks practically impossible.[18]

The switchboards in Saigon were so busy that it often took operators five minutes to answer a call from a subscriber. Invariably angry when the operator finally responded, subscribers sometimes further aggravated the operator's problems by demanding an explanation for the slow service. When a call was for a subscriber of another switchboard, the operator frequently had to tell the irate subscriber that all the trunks lines were busy and that he would need to call back. Even when the operator found an open trunk, he had time only to plug into the circuit and ring. The subscriber might have to wait another five minutes for the distant operator to respond, never knowing whether he would be cut off in the meantime. The switchboards were not equipped with a feature called plug supervision, which showed operators when a call was finished. Thus, busy operators searching for an available line and hearing a quiet circuit, might ask, "Are you working?" and pull the plug before the unsuspecting subscriber could reply that the distant switchboard had not yet answered. Only rehabilitating the cable plant and eliminating the need for operators by installing automatic dial equipment would resolve the chaotic situation. In May 1965 General Westmoreland sent an urgent request for dial switchboards for the bases in South Vietnam. For the first time dial service would be installed throughout a combat zone.[19]

[18]ORLL, 1st Sig Bde, 31 Oct 66, 72A7128/5, WNRC; Ltr, USASTRATCOM, Sig Bde, SEA, to 2d Sig Gp, 9 Apr 66, sub: Establishment of Saigon/Cholon Telephone Management Agency (Prov), and Memo, USARV Sig Ofcr for Chief of Staff, 22 Apr 66, sub: Saigon Telephone Communications, both in SEA file, ACC Historians files.
[19]Interv, author with Col (ret.) Wilbur A. Scudder, Jr., former MACV staff officer, 20 Dec 78, Historians files; Msg, CINCUSARPAC to CC-E and USASCC, 22 May 65, sub: Emergency Project USARPAC–Vietnam–SIG–099–65–DEV. Both in CMH.

To modernize the telephone system, the Army awarded a contract to the Stromberg Carlson Company to build fixed dial exchanges at major bases around the country and arranged for the Lexington-Bluegrass Army Depot in Kentucky to install three 600-line dial central offices in trailers for interim use. The U.S. Army Signal School increased the enrollment in the commercial communications course conducted by the American Telephone and Telegraph Company. Staffed with recent graduates of that course, the new telephone management agency was soon running the Army portion of the capital's telephone system like a commercial telephone company. The agency processed all requests for new service, printed a revised telephone directory every quarter, and even billed American subscribers for service received from the Postes, Telegraphes, et Telephones. To adjust to demands for service, the agency closely watched developments within the major headquarters and continuously analyzed traffic. In August 1967, after similar agencies had been formed at other major American bases, a consolidated Southeast Asia Telephone Management Agency was established subordinate to the Directorate of Operations of the signal brigade.[20]

Telephone service improved most rapidly in the Saigon area. By January 1967 the 580th Signal Company had installed 160 miles of 600-pair cable throughout the city, and civilian contractors had completed the first dial exchange at the headquarters of the Military Assistance Command. General Terry was able to move the temporary transportable dial exchanges to other locations where construction of fixed dial exchanges was proceeding more slowly.[21]

Insufficient engineer support and transportation delays hindered signal installation in outlying locations more than in the Saigon area. While well-supplied construction crews completed an exchange at Tan Son Nhut in less than two months, at Long Binh, where competition for engineer support was great, the dial facility took eight months to finish. Installation of a dial exchange at Phu Bai was delayed when civilian installers refused to live in the tents provided for them. They eventually had to use the building in which they were installing the dial exchange as their living quarters. When air-conditioning equipment was late in arriving at the An Khe exchange, contractors tried leaving the doors to the stifling building open while installing equipment, but had to stop work when dust settled in the electronic components. Technicians assembling the dial central office at Qui Nhon had to stop and move on to another site when they discovered thirty-one boxes of components missing. Trying to avoid a similar waste of man-hours, signalmen left the shipment for the dial exchange at Can Tho unpacked when they discovered that eleven boxes listed on the manifest were missing. Only after futilely searching for the missing boxes did they unpack the shipment to discover that the boxes had been included in larger crates and the entire exchange was intact. Despite such frustrating delays, by the end of 1967

---

[20]ORLL, 69th Sig Bn, 30 Apr 66 and 31 Oct 66. Both in 69A722/6, WNRC. Capt. Lawrence J. Schumann, "Telephone System Management in Saigon," *Command Communications*, April 1967, pp. 25–27, CMH; 1st Sig Bde, Organization and Doctrine, Aug 69, p. 13; 1st Sig Bde, Functional Guide Packet, SEA TELMA, 20 Mar 69, file U–480, 72A18/8, WNRC.

[21]ORLL, 1st Sig Bde, 30 Apr 67, pp. 11–12.

The MACV Switchboard at Tan Son Nhut

eleven dial exchanges were operating and four more were nearing completion.[22]

Thinking that installing cable from the dial exchanges to subscribers and to multichannel terminals would be relatively simple, the Army mistakenly made no attempt to obtain contractor assistance. Signal units in the mid-1960s were ill prepared for any cable construction, especially for installing a complex cable plant for modern telephone and teletype systems. Anticipating a fluid battlefield in which multichannel radio relay would be the primary means of handling long-distance communications for mobile forces, Army signal doctrine had excluded cable systems from its concept of future signal operations. Faced with tight budgets and dwindling manpower, the Signal Corps in 1961 halted all classes on cable installation and splicing, and Army logisticians ignored requests to replace stocks of World War II–vintage, lead-covered cable with new polyethylene cable compatible with the transmission standards of modern commercial telephone and teletype equipment.[23]

Although in early 1965 signalmen in South Vietnam had forecast a need for

[22]1st Sig Bde, Dial Central Office Program for Southeast Asia, 11 Aug 67, file 10; ORLL, 1st Sig Bde, 31 Jan 68, pp. 6–7, file 12. Both in 69A5363/11, WNRC.

[23]ORLL, 1st Sig Bde, 31 Jan 67, p. 2, 72A7128/5, WNRC; Interv, Joseph T. Jordan with John T. Holleran, former assistant chief of plans and doctrine, U.S. Army Southeastern Signal School, 31 Jan 75, Historians files, CMH.

The Mobile Dial Switch at Long Binh

a more sophisticated cable plant, the Department of the Army, apparently preoccupied with mobilizing the 2d Signal Group for deployment, failed to alert the Army Materiel Command to obtain the necessary materials or to inform the schools to begin training cablemen once again. When the 1st Signal Brigade was formed a year later, Colonel Terry, facing the installation of approximately five million feet of cable to support the American buildup, had only thirteen cable splicers assigned to his new command. Except for a few men having prior experience with civilian companies, most of the splicers had trained years before to work with the old style, lead-sheathed cable. Although Army contracts were being issued by that time for large quantities of cable supplies, the American cable industry, geared to production with long lead times, was slow to fill the Army's orders. The most urgent needs were filled by purchasing cable in Japan.[24]

Signalmen, moreover, were unfamiliar with new types of cable, installation hardware, and splicing materials. Lacking technical specifications indicating the moisture resistance required of buried cable, weight limitations for aerial installation, or shielding resistance from power sources, Army signal planners were unable to determine the proper type of installation. Not until the spring of 1966,

[24]Msg, USARV to CINCUSARPAC, 1 Apr 66, sub: Availability of Cable Splicers, file 11; Msg, CINCUSARPAC to DA, 3 Aug 66, sub: Cable Construction Experience in Vietnam, file 12. Both in 70A2378/6, WNRC.

Installing a 300-Pair Cable to Vung Tau Mountain

when a team from the Western Electric Company visited Saigon and prepared a list of supplies required to improve the cable system there, could signalmen project their cable needs accurately. While waiting for supplies, officers from the signal groups and the Communications-Electronics Engineering and Installation Agency began detailed planning for the upcoming installation projects. An enterprising signal officer on the staff of the 2d Signal Group, 1st Lt. Elisha W. Erb, even corresponded with cable manufacturers to obtain manuals, ordered special installation kits, and wrote his own guide containing installation procedures and specifications.[25]

When in February 1966 the Pentagon alerted the 40th Signal Battalion at Fort Bragg, the only cable construction battalion in the entire Army, to go to South Vietnam to install the outside plant for the dial exchanges and teletype communications centers, the battalion had only 44 percent of its authorized personnel. The best equipment and most experienced men had been transferred during the previous fall to the 580th Signal Company when it left to join the 69th Signal Battalion in South Vietnam. Although little could be done about the unit's obso-

[25]Msg, USARV to USARYIS, 10 Oct 65, sub: Dial Telephone Exchange for Saigon-Cholon; Msg, COMUSMACV to CINCPAC, 1 Jul 65, sub: Telephone Cable Supplies; Msg, CINCUSARPAC to CC-E et al., 21 Jul 65, sub: Telephone Cable Supplies. All in CMH. Msg, DA to USAMC et al., 24 Aug 66, sub: Signal Construction and Splicing Equipment and Training, file 12, 70A2378/6, WNRC.

lete equipment, much of it relics of the Korean War, the Army quickly assigned recruits fresh from basic training to fill out the ranks of the battalion. Cadres from the battalion conducted advanced individual training, the specialized training normally completed at a training center before a man is assigned to a unit. The battalion arrived in South Vietnam in September 1966, a cohesive unit with high morale that had been nurtured during the predeployment period.[26]

Sending two companies to work in the coastal enclaves of II Corps, the battalion commander, Lt. Col. Kirby Lamar, moved his headquarters and Company A to Long Binh, where the battalion was assigned to the 2d Signal Group and worked under the operational control of the Communications-

40th Signal Battalion *lays under-ground cable at Cam Ranh Bay.*

Electronics Engineering and Installation Agency. Long days of hard manual labor clearing virgin jungle and erecting barracks and warehouses were interspersed with classes in splicing and installing polyethylene cable, which most men saw for the first time when they reached South Vietnam. On 2 October 1966, a platoon from Company A embarked on the battalion's first operational mission, the installation of 3 1/2 miles of aerial cable through the busy streets of Saigon from the old MACV headquarters in Cholon to port facilities on the Saigon River. Other teams soon spread throughout the Long Binh area to prepare a cable plant for the new base and headquarters there. In January 1967 a platoon moved to the delta to construct the outside plant for the dial central offices under construction at Soc Trang, Vinh Long, and My Tho.[27]

Wherever the cablemen went in the two southern corps, soil conditions hindered installation of cable. In the delta, signalmen had to place underground cable in very shallow trenches to keep it from being inundated by the high ground-water level. But when heavy vehicles sank through the thin earth cover, they damaged the buried cable. To keep poles for aerial cable from sinking into the soft ground, cablemen had to set them in wide cans that were put into holes filled with gravel and cement. In the hard laterite soil of Long Binh, the cablemen required special equipment for digging. Until February 1967, when the 40th Signal Battalion finally located critical missing accessories for its cable plow believed lost

---

[26]An excellent history of one of the companies of the 40th Signal Battalion is contained in 23d MHD, Company A, 40th Signal Battalion: A Signal Construction Company in Support of Operations in Vietnam (hereafter cited as History of Co A, 40th Sig Bn), Jun 67, 69A5363/11, WNRC. See also "The 40th Signal Battalion (Construction)," *Command Communications*, April 1967, pp. 40–45, CMH.

[27]23d MHD, History of Co A, 40th Sig Bn, pp. 3–7; 1st Sig Bde, LOI 42–66, Command Relations, 40th Signal Battalion (Construction), Sep 66, file 2–09 (LOI) (66), 69A722/6, WNRC.

Cableman *operates VA–10 hole digger.*

in shipment to South Vietnam, the cablemen had to wait for engineer units that were seldom available or to tackle the hard ground themselves with pick and shovel.

The laying of telephone cable was also slowed by the lack of a vehicular-mounted reel for large drums of 600-pair polyethylene cable. Standard Army cable trailers were too small for the drums, which measured eight feet in diameter and weighed over seven thousand pounds. One of the battalion's cablemen, Sfc. Juan Cifuentes-Alvarez, solved the problem by building a reel from scraps of dunnage and mounting it on the bed of a 2 1/2-ton truck.[28]

Although the linemen installing cable could work faster with the new reel and plow, splicing crews following the linemen to interconnect cable sections and to install junction boxes worked slowly. Splicing 600-pair cable was tedious and time-consuming. Each interior wire had to be individually connected and tested to preclude cross-connection of circuits. The light pastel color of wire insulation in Japanese cable made working with that cable particularly difficult at night. Because of the extreme heat, humidity, and moisture in South Vietnam, cable splicers had to take extra precautions, using moisture-proof and heat-resistant tapes and conduits specially developed for use in South Vietnam by the Electronics Command Laboratories.[29]

Even when proper equipment was available, logisticians had difficulty maintaining a reliable flow of cabling materiel to South Vietnam. When supply depots rejected the first requisitions for installation kits for lack of a detailed listing of the parts included, signalmen in South Vietnam were unable to determine the nomenclature or quantities of the hundreds of types of brackets, wires, sheaths, and other small items classified as cable hardware that they would need. Even after the team from the Western Electric Company provided a list of required supplies, the 1st Signal Brigade had to hold requisitions until 200 nonstandard items on the list were assigned military nomenclatures and federal stock numbers. Although representatives from the Communications-Electronics Engineering and Installation Agency went to Fort Monmouth to obtain item identifications for their requisitions, when the materiel ordered arrived in South Vietnam it was often misplaced by supply handlers who had not received any information concerning

---

[28]23d MHD, History of Co A, 40th Sig Bn, pp. 14–53; Msg, USARV to CINCUSARPAC, 27 Jan 66, sub: Request for Cable Burying Equipment, file 10, 70A2328/6, WNRC.

[29]23d MHD, History of Co A, 40th Sig Bn, pp. 7, 41; Schumann, "Telephone System Management in Saigon," p. 26; ORLL, 41st Sig Bn, 31 Oct 66, p. 11, 69A722/6, WNRC.

the newly catalogued signal parts. Despite periodic meetings between General Terry and the commander of the 15th Support Brigade, signal officers had to make weekly trips to warehouses throughout South Vietnam to liberate cable hardware shelved as "Identity Unknown." Even a shipment of cable hardware sent at the special direction of the commander of the Electronics Command, Maj. Gen. William B. Latta, who returned from a trip to South Vietnam determined to resolve the supply problem, was lost. Technicians in the Communications-Electronics Engineering and Installation Agency found that the most reliable means of obtaining unique parts was by having them mailed by an associate in the United States.[30]

Complicating the supply problem, the Communications-Electronics Engineering and Installation Agency frequently updated cable plans and adjusted installation priorities. At Can Tho, where cable could not be buried as deep in the marshy ground as blueprints directed and where the South Vietnamese would not approve the right of way for an alternative aerial cable route, the engineering agency had to redesign an entire cable plant. At An Khe and Di An, cables had to be rerouted around structures recently constructed in the proposed cable path. Looking forward to eventually tying together all the telephone exchanges in South Vietnam into a direct-dial system, the agency tried to design cable plants and devise numbering systems compatible with a future consolidated network, but the physical movement of so many major headquarters during the construction of the dial exchanges made such comprehensive planning especially difficult.[31]

By late 1967 the 40th Signal Battalion had installed almost 1.25 million feet of cable. Repair of damaged cable, rather than new construction, had become its primary mission. Enemy action caused only 12 percent of the damage to cable, accidents the rest. Trucks sideswiping telephone poles on the shoulders of narrow roads or dump trucks driving with beds raised under cable crossing toppled aerial cables. The bulldozers and entrenching machines of the Army engineers and cablemen themselves chewed up buried cable.[32]

As base construction tapered off in the III and IV Corps areas in late 1967, the frenzy to install communications facilities diminished and the urgent calls to rush cablemen around the region to restore damaged cables or to install new lines became less frequent. With automatic telephone service at most important headquarters, the lot of the switchboard operator, who then had to be concerned only with inter-base calls, also improved. A 240-line microwave network, the first portion of the Integrated Wideband Communications System to be completed, provided sufficient trunks for long-distance calls between the switchboards in Saigon and Long Binh.

The experience of Army signalmen in III and IV Corps had shown the importance of both innovation and tradition. In the delta the expedients of imagina-

---

[30]Msg, CINCUSARPAC to CC-E, 21 Jul 65, sub: Telephone Cable Supplies, CMH; Incl 1 to ORLL, 69th Sig Bn, 31 Oct 66, 69A722/6, WNRC; Interv, author with Driscoll, 5 Jan 79; Msg, Terry to Myer, 12 Jul 66, Staff Service 50703; Msg, Terry to Myer, 20 Jul 66, Staff Service 50709. Latter three in CMH.

[31]1st Sig Bde, Dial Central Office Program for Southeast Asia, pp. 3–9; 1st Sig Bde, Organization and Doctrine, Aug 67, pp. 51–52.

[32]MACV J-6, Summary of Remarks by the J6 at the Senior Communicators' Tactical Planning Conference, Dec 67, par. 8, file 139685, 72A25/9, WNRC.

tive communicators overcame the obstacles posed by the watery terrain and lack of elevation for relays. Soldiers proved that they could adapt well to the challenges of communicating from shipboard.

In III Corps, on the other hand, the Signal Corps learned that it had erred badly in the early 1960s when it turned away from cable communications. It had appeared then that modern military forces had become too mobile for cable. Thus the Army had replaced cable with multichannel radio. In Vietnam the Army found that modern weapons were indeed mobile, but for that very reason they also required more logistical support and more efficient and extensive command and control. Only cable could provide the large quantity of circuits between headquarters and support bases needed to satisfy the voracious appetite of a modern army in the field. And only dial exchanges could handle the volume of traffic transmitted by those cable systems. The network in South Vietnam rapidly grew to be as extensive as many regional systems in the United States which, even under ideal conditions, would take as long as a decade to build. Setting up the dial system in South Vietnam under difficult environmental conditions and the ever-present dangers of combat was an unparalleled feat. Without that system the expansion of the American base would have been impossible.

11

Into the Killing Zone

By mid-1967 the II Corps Tactical Zone was assuming an increasingly important role in the strategy of both the North Vietnamese and the Americans. Easily defended coastal enclaves at Qui Nhon, Nha Trang, Cam Ranh Bay, and Phan Rang provided the Americans with ideal central locations for ports, logistical bases, and airfields from which to expand operations into the highlands. Inland from the narrow coastal plain, in the sparsely inhabited mountains and plateaus, the full effect of superior American firepower could be brought to bear on Communist forces without fear of causing civilian casualties. For the Communists, the rugged highlands of the northern half of South Vietnam reduced American mobility and provided them access to sanctuaries and logistical bases in nearby Cambodia and Laos. Mechanized forces were restricted to the few available roads in the highlands, and few landing zones or airfields existed to support air operations. The scene of the ambush and destruction of several French mobile groups during the early 1950s, the Central Highlands were known to the North Vietnamese as the "killing zone."[1]

Expanding the II Corps Network

American and North Vietnamese troops met in battle for the first time in the Ia Drang valley of the Central Highlands in late 1965. After the battle the 1st Cavalry Division moved east to Binh Dinh Province to fight the Viet Cong in their long-held mountain sanctuaries overlooking the fertile coastal rice lands of northern II Corps. General Westmoreland then sent the newly arrived 4th Infantry Division to Pleiku Province in the Central Highlands.

Working in the rugged terrain of the II Corps posed particularly difficult problems for communicators. The 4th Infantry Division, operating in mountains

[1]MACV History, 1966, pp. 20–21, CMH; Sharp and Westmoreland, *Report on the War in Vietnam*, pp. 138–39.

that blocked even short-range communications and assigned an area larger than the entire III Corps, depended heavily on the area support provided by the 21st Signal Group in Nha Trang. This group also supported the 1st Cavalry Division, the 1st Brigade of the 101st Airborne Division, the 173d Airborne Brigade, and two Korean divisions as well as other nondivisional Army units in the II Corps. The 54th Signal Battalion (Corps) at Nha Trang provided command-oriented communications from the I Field Force to major tactical units in the II Corps.

Although over 1,200 Korean signalmen accompanied the two South Korean divisions to South Vietnam, the 21st Signal Group and the 53d Signal Battalion had to augment the ill-equipped Korean units. The 1st Signal Brigade allocated channels on its long-lines systems to the Koreans and turned over to them equipment replaced in U.S. units by new models. In September 1968 the Strategic Communications Command installed for the Korean Army a single-sideband radio system from South Vietnam to its army headquarters in Korea. Whenever the Koreans received service from American communications facilities, their signalmen worked alongside and received training from their American contemporaries. They proved to be professional and resourceful communicators who did much to improve communications in the II Corps.[2]

The absence of hills along the coast on which to put relays and difficulties in obtaining an electrical ground in the dry, sandy soil were the only technical obstacles faced by American and Korean signalmen working in the coastal region of II Corps. Ingenious signalmen resolved their grounding problem by connecting ground rods to steel plates buried in holes filled with ash and salt or by simply installing ground rods in earth near urine sumps or dripping air conditioners.

Extending communications from the coastal enclaves to the interior highlands presented the real challenge for signalmen in eastern II Corps. The first major expansion to the west followed the valley and road from Qui Nhon to Pleiku. The 586th Signal Company operated a teletype communications center and a nine-position switchboard at the 1st Cavalry Division base at An Khe, midway between the coast and Pleiku, and manned smaller signal centers at airmobile brigade base camps in the valley. The company operated VHF systems from Hon Cong Mountain near An Khe to nodes of the BACKPORCH system at Pleiku and Qui Nhon and a radio-teletype net from the An Khe depot to the large logistical complex at Qui Nhon on the coast. Lest the Viet Cong disrupt the VHF network by attacking the relay site on Hon Cong Mountain as they had in February 1966, the signal company also operated a backup VHF system directly from Camp Radcliffe at An Khe to Qui Nhon.

Area communications support to the 4th Infantry Division in the highlands was not as comprehensive as that provided to the 1st Cavalry Division. Company A of the 41st Signal Battalion in Pleiku was already fully committed to supporting the II Corps advisory team and Army helicopter units at nearby Camp Holloway. To set up initial communications at the 4th Division's base, Camp Enari

---

[2]Msg, CINCUSARPAC to USARV, 30 Nov 66, sub: ROKFV Radio Requirements, file 14, 70A2328/6; Ltr, ACofS, CE, USARV, to ACofS, CE, USARPAC, sub: Summary of Significant Activities, 10–16 Aug 68, file 139800, 72A25/20. Both in WNRC.

U.S. and Korean Operators *at a joint switchboard in Saigon.*

near Pleiku, an entire signal company of the division's 124th Signal Battalion had to accompany the division's advance party to South Vietnam.[3]

The 41st Signal Battalion had responsibility for all of the I and II Corps, over 40,000 square miles stretching from Dong Ha south to Phan Thiet. As headquarters detachments of new signal battalions began arriving in the late summer of 1966, the commander of the 21st Signal Group, Col. Hunter L. Sharp, gradually reassigned some of the 2,200-man battalion's nine companies to other battalions. In mid-August the 46-man headquarters detachment of the 73d Signal Battalion at Nha Trang received three companies to cover the seven southernmost provinces in II Corps. The 41st Signal Battalion also transferred to the 73d Signal Battalion the 362d Signal Company, whose troposcatter teams were spread throughout the country. Then the 41st Signal Battalion relinquished area support of I Corps to the 178th Signal Company, which was later expanded and redesignated Company A of the 37th Signal Battalion. By October, the 41st Signal Battalion was a more manageable 800 men with responsibility reduced to support of Army units in the coastal areas of Binh Dinh and Phu Yen Provinces. That mission still in-

[3]The 586th Signal Company (Support) in Support of Operations in An Khe, Vietnam, Incl to Ltr, 1st Sig Bde to OCMH, 26 Feb 67, sub: Special Report 586th Signal Company (Support), CMH; Msg, USARV to USARPAC, 20 Jul 66, sub: Deployment of Forward Communications Company, 124th Signal Battalion; Msg, DA to USCONARC et al., 4 Aug 66, sub: Deployment of Composite Signal Company, 124th Signal Battalion. Latter two in file 12, 70A2328/6, WNRC.

Dak To

KONTUM

Kontum

509th Sig Bn (Spt)

41st Sig Bn (Cbt Area)

BINH DINH

Pleiku

An Khe

Qui Nhon

Ia Drang Valley Area

Hau Bon

PHU
YEN

PLEIKU

PHU BON

Tuy Hoa

43d Sig Bn (Spt)

DARLAC

459th Sig Bn
(Cbt Area)

Ban Me Thuot

KHANH
HOA

QUANG
DUC

Nha Trang

TUYEN DUC

Cam Ranh

Gia Nghia

Da Lat

SOUTH

NINH
THUAN

73d Sig Bn (Spt)

Bao Loc

Phan Rang

CHINA

LAM DONG

BINH
THUAN

SEA

Phan Thiet

II CORPS — AREAS OF RESPONSIBILITY

1966

MAP 12

cluded the many logistical installations in the Qui Nhon enclave. *(Map 12)*

Farther inland, the cadre of the newly arrived 509th Signal Battalion took control of the 586th Signal Company and a company of the 36th Signal Battalion (the remainder of the 36th Signal Battalion was in III Corps) to operate fixed telephone and communications center facilities being constructed at An Khe. The 43d Signal Battalion was formed in Pleiku in mid-October 1966 from Company A, 41st Signal Battalion, to handle advisory support for II Corps. That specialized mission was soon superseded by the pressing needs for communications of the American units moving into the Central Highlands with the 4th Infantry Division.[4]

In late fall 1966 the first full-strength battalion, the 459th Signal Battalion, arrived in II Corps after having been on alert for overseas movement for the previous six months at Fort Huachuca, Arizona. The long delay in deploying to Vietnam upset men who had left their families at home in anticipation of an imminent departure. By the time the reinforcements arrived in South Vietnam, they were anxious to begin real operations. Colonel Sharp, commander of the 21st Signal Group, attached companies of the 459th to the 41st and 43d Signal Battalions and gave the remainder of the unit the communications mission for northern Khanh Hoa Province, which included the important city of Nha Trang.[5]

Prior to the arrival of the 459th Signal Battalion, the 73d Signal Battalion had been responsible for the area communications around Nha Trang, the site of the headquarters of the I Field Force and the principal hub of the long-lines system. It also provided service to Cam Ranh Bay, which was becoming one of the world's busiest ports. The battalion's wiremen were hard pressed. They had to dig trenches along the busy streets of Nha Trang to connect the many headquarters springing up in the city. In the burgeoning port complex of Cam Ranh Bay, construction teams expanding the base were accidently cutting cables as fast as the signalmen could repair them. Even new telephone exchanges proved to be too small before they could be put in service.[6]

Perhaps the biggest crisis for the battalion commander of the 73d, Lt. Col. Louis F. Dixon, occurred over the hasty installation of a public address system, a much neglected and poorly supported mission of the Signal Corps that traditionally has been an embarrassment to signal officers at the most inopportune times. Notified on the morning of 26 October 1966 of a surprise visit by President Johnson to Cam Ranh Bay in two hours, Colonel Dixon had to collect additional microphones, amplifiers, and cords from the Red Cross, chapels, and recreation centers to install public address systems at the three places the president was going to visit. They were put in operation minutes before the president arrived; just before one ceremony was to begin, a signalman set up his amplifying and recording equipment on top of a nearby silver suitcase. While a South Vietnamese dignitary was introducing President Johnson, the president asked his aide for

---

[4]ORLL, 21st Sig Gp, 31 Oct 66, pp. 1–5; ORLL, 41st Sig Bn, 31 Oct 66, pp. 1–3. Both in 69A722/5, WNRC. Msg, 1st Sig Bde to USASTRATCOM, 26 Sep 66, sub: A and D Companies, 41st Signal Battalion, file 13, 70A2328/6, WNRC; "41st Signal Battalion (CA)," *Command Communications*, January 1969, pp. 6–30, CMH.

[5]ORLL, 459th Sig Bn, 31 Jan 67, p. 2, 69A722/5, WNRC.

[6]ORLL, 73d Sig Bn, 31 Oct 66, par. 2e, 69A722/5, WNRC.

his eyeglasses: they were in the silver suitcase.[7]

Tactical Troposcatter Systems

A lthough only three troposcatter sites of the 362d Signal Company's fourteen operational installations were in the 73d Signal Battalion's zone, Colonel Dixon was assigned the troposcatter unit. General Terry previously had tried several means of maintaining control of the far-ranging troposcatter and microwave operations of the brigade. In May 1966 he attempted to reduce the geographical span of control of the 362d Signal Company (Tropo) and the 518th Signal Company (Microwave) by exchanging equipment between the companies to enable them to operate on an area rather than a functional orientation. The 362d Signal Company, which was to handle all troposcatter and microwave missions in the two northern corps areas of South Vietnam, was transferred to the 41st Signal Battalion; the 518th Signal Company remained assigned to the 39th Signal Battalion to perform the dual mission in the two southern corps areas. When the transfer caused confusion in the distribution of spare parts and difficulties for maintenance men unacquainted with both types of equipment, General Terry eventually restored the companies to their original organizational structure and reassigned the 362d Signal Company to the 73d Signal Battalion.

Receiving additional microwave and troposcatter equipment in mid-1967, General Terry was finally able to reduce the geographical responsibilities of the 362d and 518th Companies. He formed the 337th Signal Company (Troposcatter/Microwave) for I Corps and the 327th Signal Company (Troposcatter/Microwave) for III and IV Corps. The 21st Signal Group at Nha Trang then took direct control of the 518th Signal Company (Microwave) and 362d Signal Company (Tropo) to provide long-lines support in II Corps only.

During the buildup in 1965 Lang Bian Mountain in the southern highlands of the interior and Vung Chua Mountain on the coast in the northern section of the corps area were the primary relay points for multichannel and tactical troposcatter systems in II Corps. Since Lang Bian Mountain was a poor location for relaying troposcatter systems to the east, the 362d Signal Company had to establish another relay hill in the southern section of II Corps to provide a route from Saigon to coastal bases at Phan Rang, Phan Thiet, and Cam Ranh Bay. The best area appeared to be in the hills around Da Lat, a resort town. The South Vietnamese were wary about allowing soldiers in the region around Da Lat, which had as yet been unscathed by the war. After extensive negotiations they finally allowed the company to establish a relay site atop a mountain eleven miles southeast of Da Lat that came to be called Pr' Line. To be nearer to the two relay centers of Pr' Line and Lang Bian, which together housed 254 American signalmen, the headquarters of the 362d Signal Company moved from Nha Trang to a small compound in Da Lat that had been built by American prisoners of war

---

[7]Ibid., par. 6a.

during World War II to serve as a Japanese hospital.[8]

Since 1962 the number of tactical troposcatter terminals in South Vietnam had grown from fourteen to forty-four. Each augmentation resulted in the installation of improved models of the TRC–90 (TRC–90A, –90B, –132, –129). Because the original TRC–90's were still on the air, and few had ever been shut down for scheduled maintenance, technical problems abounded. The terminal at Cam Ranh Bay, moved from Ban Me Thuot when the CROSSBOW network was discontinued, was in poor condition. Typhoons had so eroded the sand dune on which it was sitting that the shelter was tilting. The ocean spray had rusted and rotted the shelter, and sand blew freely into the equipment. Yet until the completion of new facilities for the Integrated Wideband Communications System at Cam Ranh Bay in late 1967, the terminal remained a primary communications gateway for the important port.[9]

Attempting Innovations

T he I Field Force was responsible for a region four times more vast than that normally assigned to a U.S. corps. When the VHF equipment belonging to the 53d Signal Battalion (Corps) proved insufficient in range to maintain command communications from Nha Trang to the combat units moving about the mountainous terrain of II Corps, in late 1966 General Terry requested that light troposcatter TRC–97 terminals mounted in small 3/4-ton trucks be issued to support the field forces. Having obtained thirty sets from the Air Force, the Army had training and logistical problems reminiscent of those encountered when the 39th Signal Battalion took over the Air Force MRC–85's on BACKPORCH in 1962. Although a few Army signalmen trained on the equipment at Clark Air Base in the Philippines before it was deployed and the Air Force agreed to maintain the sets temporarily, the Army procrastinated in developing an inventory of spare parts and in training operators and mechanics until in the summer of 1968 the Air Force announced it was withdrawing its support. The Electronics Command then hurriedly contracted with the manufacturer of the set, Radio Corporation of America, to send two technicians to South Vietnam to build a repair facility and to establish a supply system for spare parts. The Electronics Command sent instructors, who had first been trained at the Air Force's signal school at Keesler Air Force Base, Mississippi, to train the Army signalmen already operating the radios. Just after the training and logistical problems were resolved for the elec-

---

[8]ORLL, 39th Sig Bn, 31 Oct 66, p. 3, 69A722/5, WNRC; 362d Signal Company (Tropo), Incl to Ltr, 23d MHD to 362d Sig Co, 25 Apr 66, sub: Special Report, 362d Signal Company (Tropo), 68A75/11, WNRC; Msg, General Terry (Saigon) 40506 to General Meyer (Washington), 30 May 66, CMH.

[9]23d MHD, 362d Signal Company (Tropo): The Employment of Tactical Tropospheric Scatter Equipment and Units in Support of Operations in Vietnam [hereafter cited as 362d Signal Company (Tropo)], 25 Apr 66, 68A75/11, WNRC; Msg, General Terry (Saigon) 50709 to General Meyer (Washington), 20 Jul 66, CMH; Msg, USARV to CINCUSARPAC, 28 Jul 66, sub: Communications Capability RVN August–December 1966; Msg, COMUSMACV to CINCPAC, 29 Jul 66, sub: Communications Requirement; Msg, DA to CINCUSARPAC, 11 Aug 66, sub: Communications Support, Southeast Asia. Latter three in file 12, 70A2328/6, WNRC.

tronic components of the sets, the generators that powered the equipment began to wear out, and the radios had to be taken off the air for overhaul of the aging power equipment. By midsummer of 1969, almost three years after the U.S. Army, Vietnam, had first requested the troposcatter equipment for I Field Force's command and control communications, the unique equipment was still proving more a hindrance than a help.[10]

Without adequate light troposcatter sets, the tactical communicators in I Field Force, Vietnam, experimented with their standard VHF equipment. Using MRC–69 radio relay sets, the workhorse of tactical multichannel communications, they learned to alter the line-of-sight path of VHF radio by tilting antennas and bouncing signals over mountain barriers, a phenomenon called obstacle gain. Even if a map showed a barrier between two planned stations in a VHF system, systems planners first sent out teams to attempt a direct link using the obstacle-gain expedient to curve signals over the blocking mountains. Experimentation with the siting of antennas and the frequency of the radios often produced a system stronger than one that "profiled," that is, than an unobstructed transmission path. The technique worked best when the obstacle was a sharply defined peak in the middle of the transmission path and when radios were operating on the low portion of the VHF band with antennas horizontally polarized so as to radiate waves perpendicular to the earth. The main problem in establishing those extended systems was that the FM radios normally used by crews while establishing multichannel systems could not bounce over obstacles. For that reason, radio relay crews deploying into the mountains always carried commercial KWM–2A single-sideband sets.[11]

Communicators in II Corps were the first to receive new MSQ–73 technical control vans in late 1966. They provided the 1st Signal Brigade with a means to bridge the gap between the Integrated Wideband Communications System and tactical equipment and to distribute and control the quality of the hundreds of circuits converging on the mountaintop relays. Since the MSQ–73 was developed specifically for use in South Vietnam, the 1st Signal Brigade had to establish a school in that country to train operators on the equipment. Manufacturers' representatives offered two weeks of practical instruction, and officers of the 1st Signal Brigade presented thirty hours of instruction in general systems control procedures. Soon after the first class graduated in October 1966, the first van went into operation on Vung Chua Mountain; in succeeding months the signal brigade moved the transportable technical control vans to mountaintop relays and major

---

[10]Msg, USARV to CINCUSARPAC, 8 Oct 66, sub: Lightweight Tactical Tropo, file 9, 70A2328/5; Msg, USARV to DA, 13 Dec 66, sub: Lightweight Tactical Tropo (ENSURE), file 14, 70A2328/6; Ltr, Dep ACofS, CE, USARV, to ACofS, CE, USARPAC, sub: Summary of Significant Activities, 13–19 Jan 68, file 139800, 72A25/20. All in WNRC. Msg, Van Harlingen (Long Binh) ARV 3514 to Latta (Fort Monmouth), 31 Dec 66, sub: RCA/AN/TRC–97B Maintenance Contract, CMH; ORLL, 1st Sig Bde, 31 Jul 69, pp. 13, 19, file 228–07, 1st Sig Bde (1969), 72A7128/5, WNRC.

[11]Ever since installing the first MRC–85's on BACKPORCH, troposcatter crews had found the reliable and easily operated single-sideband radios to be indispensable for installing and troubleshooting multichannel systems. ORLL, 459th Sig Bn, 31 Jan 67, p. 14; ORLL, 73d Sig Bn, 31 Oct 66, p. 5; ORLL, 21st Sig Gp, 31 Oct 66, p. 3. All in 69A722/5, WNRC. Capt. Richard E. Griffin, "Obstacle Gain VHF Systems," *Command Communications*, April 1967, p. 8, CMH.

Communicator Checks *circuits in the MSQ–73 with a TA–312 field phone.*

nodal points throughout South Vietnam. When fixed technical control facilities for the Integrated Wideband Communications System were completed, the vans were moved to smaller tactical bases.[12]

Defending the Sites

While the signal brigade tackled the equipment's technical weaknesses, vulnerability to attack and sabotage remained a vexing problem. Although the signal brigade's Directorate of Intelligence and Security had staff supervision for such matters, that office had been preoccupied with extensive paperwork and lengthy investigations to process security clearances for the many replacements arriving with incomplete clearances. Attention to physical security was left primarily to local commanders.[13]

[12]Msg, Terry (Saigon) 40506 to Meyer (Washington), 30 May 66, CMH; F. A. Graham, "A New Dimension for Tech Control," *Command Communications*, November 1966, pp. 27–28, CMH; Msg, USASTRATCOM to 1st Sig Bde, 23 Jun 66, sub: AN/MSQ–73 Tech Control Vans, file 12, 70A2328/5; 1st Sig Bde, LOI 25–66, AN/MSQ–73, Operator Training School, 27 Jul 66, file 2–09 (LOI) (66), 69A722/6. Latter two in WNRC.

[13]ORLL, 1st Sig Bde, 31 Oct 66, p. 5, and ibid., 31 Jan 67, pp. 4–6, 16–17, both in 69A722/5, WNRC.

The Pr' Line IWCS Site. *Note the fighting trenches (foreground) outside the Montagnard huts.*

Signalmen in the units, untrained in infantry tactics and fatigued after long hours manning their equipment, were proving unskilled and lax in security matters. General Terry finally obtained the 235-man 194th Military Police Company, later designated the U.S. Signal Security Force, to inspect signal sites and advise signal technicians how to improve defenses. At each site they taught classes on laying mines, establishing fields of fire, designing bunkers, adjusting artillery and close air support, and firing mortars. At the more remote sites, teams from the security force remained to provide the nucleus of guard details; at others, South Vietnamese paramilitary units performed that duty. At Pr' Line, for example, the huts of a ninety-man Montagnard force led by the U.S. Special Forces ringed the hilltop, providing a stark contrast with the modern buildings being erected to house a relay of the Integrated Wideband Communications System. As most physical security still had to be handled by signalmen, the commanders of the battalions responsible for Lang Bian and Vung Chua located company headquarters detachments on the hilltops to increase the size of the force available for defense, and General Terry sent uncommitted communicators to help construct bunkers, fences, and minefields.[14]

---

[14]Interv, Maj Fremont E. Binder, CO, 23d MHD, with Col John B. McKinney, Dep CO, 1st Signal Brigade, 22 Jan 68, VNIT 112, CMH; ORLL, 21st Sig Gp, 31 Jan 67, p. 2, 69A722/5, WNRC.

As site security improved, the principal hazards occurred while signalmen were traveling between sites. Although General Terry tried to keep his men off the roads to avoid mines and ambushes, the fifteen aircraft in the 1st Signal Brigade were too few to respond to all the transportation needs of the more than two hundred sites in the brigade. Combat damage, maintenance overhauls, and a shortage of pilots usually left less than half that number of aircraft available. Faced with failure of a critical communications system for lack of repairmen or fuel, most commanders simply formed small convoys to relieve a site rather than wait for an aircraft or scheduled convoy that benefited from preplanned air or artillery cover. Since American combat units were not available to protect convoys in the mountains of southern II Corps, the dangers were greatest for signalmen manning the relays near Da Lat. Civilian contractors building a site for the Integrated Wide-band Communications System at Pr' Line were unwilling to remain on the hill overnight, and signal soldiers had to run a daily convoy back and forth to Da Lat. On 26 November 1966, the morning work convoy was ambushed; eight Page employees and one soldier were killed and eleven other soldiers and technicians wounded. Thereafter the civilians lived on the hilltop.[15]

Flexibility Through Contingency Forces

With the almost total commitment of signal equipment and men, the 1st Signal Brigade's capacity to respond to destruction of a signal site or loss of a large number of soldier technicians was limited. Although the 69th Signal Battalion maintained a contingency force for the brigade and each signal group had its own reaction forces, those standby units were often committed to new missions or their personnel assigned to fill in at understaffed operational facilities. Most emergencies were met by drawing assets from other units or reinforcement from outside South Vietnam. Delay in construction of a planned fixed tape relay at Da Nang, resulting in the overload of the relay at Nha Trang with traffic from I Corps, forced General Terry in mid-December 1966 to deploy to Da Nang from his contingency force a transportable communications center that was soon handling over 5,000 messages daily for units in the northern corps. When Viet Cong rockets destroyed that indispensable teletype relay on the night of 26 February 1967, the 1st Signal Brigade had not yet replaced the equipment in its contingency stocks and had to wait ten days for the Strategic Communications Command to send a replacement from the United States. Meanwhile the Defense Communications Agency, Southeast Asia Mainland, tried to reroute traffic from I Corps through the relays at Nha Trang and Phu Lam. Because it had difficulties reconciling disagreements between the services over which circuits had priority for restoral, the Military Assistance Command asked each service to identify its twelve most vital circuits. Technical controllers at every nodal point in Southeast

---

[15]ORLL, 73d Sig Bn, 31 Oct 66, par. 4, and 2d Ind to Ltr, 1st Sig Bde to USARV, 8 Dec 66, sub: ORLL For Quarter Ending 31 Oct 66, both in 69A722/5, WNRC. 23d MHD, 362d Signal Company (Tropo), 25 Apr 66.

Relay Site *in Quang Ngai Province supporting Task Force Oregon.*

Asia were instructed that they were to rectify outage of any one of those priority circuits by preempting any other circuit. In addition, the 1st Signal Brigade directed each site commander to prepare a site restoral plan for each type of communications outage and to establish a reaction team to execute that plan. The brigade also expanded and dispersed its contingency reaction force to enable it to respond more quickly to emergencies in the northern sections of the country.[16]

The two troposcatter detachments assigned to the contingency force, the 544th and 545th Signal Detachments, were stationed at Nha Trang near where they most likely would be needed—in the mountains of II Corps. But a few weeks later the two troposcatter detachments were deployed to install a system from Vung Chua Mountain to Cu Lao Re, an island twenty-five miles off the coast of Quang Ngai Province in I Corps, to support a buildup of Army troops, called Task Force Oregon, in the southern area of I Corps. After communications were rerouted to Chu Lai through Da Nang, the teams returned to the contingency force at Nha Trang.[17]

The creation of an Army division-size unit to replace U.S. Marine Corps units moving north to the Demilitarized Zone provided a test of the decision to give operational control of Strategic Communications Command units to the theater

[16]ORLL, 1st Sig Bde, 31 Jan 67, p. 7; ibid., 30 Apr 67, pp. 7–15, 68A4975/1, WNRC.
[17]23d MHD, 362d Signal Company (Tropo), 25 Apr 66; ORLL, 1st Sig Bde, 30 Apr 67, pp. 1, 10.

tactical commander. Using contingency stocks and units of the signal brigade, General Terry formed a tactical signal unit that ultimately became the division signal battalion to the 23d Infantry Division (Americal), the unit formed from Task Force Oregon. The 21st Signal Group provided most of the signal support to Task Force Oregon (Company A, 36th Signal Battalion; Company D, 459th Signal Battalion; and Headquarters and Headquarters Detachment, 509th Signal Battalion). General Terry therefore adjusted battalion support areas in II Corps to give the 43d Signal Battalion at Pleiku the 509th Signal Battalion's responsibilities for An Khe and support of the 1st Cavalry Division. As fixed signal facilities gradually replaced tactical equipment on the interim network established in southern I Corps, equipment was returned to Nha Trang so that the 1st Signal Brigade could rebuild its contingency force.[18] *(Map 13)*

The Battle for Dak To

As events soon demonstrated, signalmen in II Corps needed all the backup tactical equipment they could muster. In early October 1967 a large enemy force began crossing the Laotian border into II Corps. Adhering to standard Communist practice of maintaining radio silence while moving, the enemy units remained relatively invulnerable to attempts by American and South Vietnamese electronic intercept units to determine their exact identity and destination. Although enemy activity and shelling around Duc Co, a Special Forces camp southwest of Pleiku City, indicated an attack in Pleiku Province, communications intercepted in late October by the Army Security Agency's 374th Radio Research Company revealed enemy military intelligence teams farther to the north near the Dak To Special Forces camp in Kontum Province. Since the presence of such teams usually presaged an attack, the 4th Division commander, Maj. Gen. William R. Peers, decided to send his 1st Brigade to reinforce a battalion protecting engineer units building another Special Forces camp at Ben Het, a few kilometers west of Dak To near the Laotian border.[19]

The division's 2d Brigade remained in position west of Pleiku, prepared to respond to any movement against Duc Co; the 3d Brigade was in I Corps with the Americal Division. The field force commander, Lt. Gen. William B. Rosson, attached to the 4th Division a battalion of the 173d Airborne Brigade that had fought in the Dak To area just a few months earlier. Besides the radio-teletype set and FM voice radios in each infantry battalion and the communications pla-

[18]Interv, author with Maj Gen Robert D. Terry, former CG, 1st Signal Brigade, 4 Oct 78, Historians files, CMH; 1st Sig Bde, Communications Expansion Plan, 27 Dec 67, vol. 1, pp. M–1 and M–2, file 139556, 72A25/5; MACV J–6, Briefing Notes, 15 Feb 68, sub: Contingency Communications, file 139591, 72A25/6; ORLL, 1st Sig Bde, 31 Oct 67, p. 3, file 228–07, 1st Sig Bde (1967), 72A7128/5. Latter three in WNRC.

[19]Msg, Rosson to Westmoreland, 9 Nov 67, sub: Evaluation and Assessment in II CTZ, October 1967; Msg, Abrams MAC 11239 to Wheeler, 22 Nov 67. Both in CMH. Col. Hoang Ngoc Lung, *Intelligence,* Indochina Monograph Series (Washington, D.C.: U.S. Army Center of Military History, Government Printing Office, 1982), pp. 210–11.

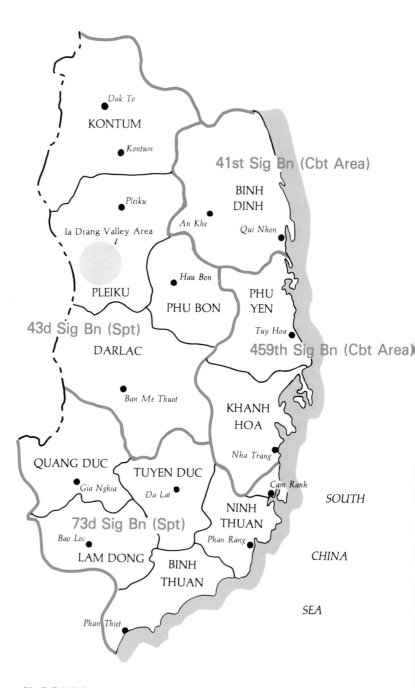

Dak To

KONTUM

Kontum

41st Sig Bn (Cbt Area)

BINH
DINH

Pleiku

An Khe

Qui Nhon

Ia Drang Valley Area

Hau Bon

PHU
YEN

PLEIKU

PHU BON

43d Sig Bn (Spt)

DARLAC

459th Sig Bn (Cbt Area)

Tuy Hoa

Ban Me Thuot

KHANH
HOA

Nha Trang

QUANG DUC

TUYEN DUC

Cam Ranh

SOUTH

Gia Nghia

Da Lat

NINH
THUAN

73d Sig Bn (Spt)

Bao Loc

Phan Rang

CHINA

LAM DONG

BINH
THUAN

SEA

Phan Thiet

II CORPS — AREAS OF RESPONSIBILITY

1967

Map 13

toon organic to the brigade, the 4th Division signal officer, Lt. Col. William M. Spitz, dispatched the platoon from Company B, 124th Signal Battalion, that normally supported operations of the 1st Brigade. Other communications in the area included the standard single-sideband nets of the U.S. Special Forces, the radio-teletype set of each engineer battalion, and the multichannel system normally provided by the 54th Signal Battalion to engineer battalions operating in remote areas. Colonel Spitz anticipated few problems supporting a one-brigade task force.[20]

Ominous intelligence obtained by the division during the first days of November caused the size of the task force to grow rapidly. A captured member of an enemy reconnaissance force revealed that four regiments of the *1st North Vietnamese Division* were converging on Dak To. The 374th Radio Research Company observed the communications pattern of the *1st Division* change from complete radio silence during the move, to normal, twice-a-day contacts, to an hourly schedule indicating the beginning of intense combat activity. The North Vietnamese rear support unit operating in Laos, the *559th Transportation Group,* moved a station into western Kontum Province where it would be close enough to provide logistical communications during an operation in the Dak To area. On 5 November 1967, General Rosson reinforced the 4th Division with the 173d Airborne Brigade, and General Peers established a division tactical command post at Dak To.[21]

After the signal officer of the 173d Airborne Brigade, Maj. Philip H. Enslow, Jr., moved all his available communications to Dak To, he still required considerable additional support. Divisional signal battalions normally provided direct support to divisional brigades, as Company B, 124th Signal Battalion, had done for the 1st Brigade. Nondivisional brigades like the 173d had only their organic communications: a 34-man communications platoon with a small switchboard, a teletype center, and single-channel radios. Corps battalions helped with whatever support they could.

Providing communications support to the separate brigades—the 173d Airborne Brigade and the 196th and 199th Light Infantry Brigades—and the 11th Armored Cavalry had so strained the corps signal battalions that General Terry eventually arranged for another platoon to be assigned to each brigade. The platoon was similar to the forward support platoon normally provided divisional brigades by each divisional signal battalion. When the newly formed 173d Signal Company (Provisional) moved to Dak To, it had not yet received any additional equipment. Having to support the 4th Infantry Division's headquarters at Camp Enari, eighty-eight kilometers south of Dak To, and two other brigades stationed even farther away, Colonel Spitz's 124th Signal Battalion could not spare any signal equipment for the airborne brigade. Thus the corps signal battalion had to assist the

---

[20]Journal, I FFV, Sig Ofcr, 6 Oct 67, item 2; 29 Oct 67, item 5; and 1 Nov 67, item 3. All in file 206–07, Daily Journal 67, 70A478/33, WNRC. For communications normally available to engineer units, see Ltr, AVHGG-PP, USARV, to CG, U.S. Army Engineer Command, 29 Aug 67, sub: U.S. Army Engineer Command Communications Requirements Plan, file U442, 72A18/8, WNRC.

[21]Msg, Abrams MAC 10931 to Westmoreland, 15 Nov 67, CMH; Journal, I FFV, Sig Ofcr, 1 Nov 67, item 3.

separate brigade at Dak To.[22]

When the battle at Dak To began in early November 1967, the 54th Signal Battalion was dispersed at twenty-four locations throughout II Corps. The battalion was most heavily committed to radio relay missions, using the very equipment that separate brigades like the 173d Airborne Brigade lacked. With less than half his authorized 346 radio relay operators, the battalion commander, Lt. Col. Robert M. Springer, Jr., had to fill out his relay teams with soldiers possessing less critical skills. While radio technicians operated electronic equipment, other soldiers erected antennas, operated generators, and performed guard duties.[23]

Although Colonel Springer tried compensating for the shortages of multi-channel equipment by emphasizing the use of radio-teletype, the slowness of handling large volumes of traffic on a single-channel radio and the inconvenience of routing messages to a radio park rather than to a message center perpetuated the reliance on multichannel radio relays. The two radio-teletype stations operated at Dak To rarely had any traffic. While shorthanded multichannel crews were overworked, radio-teletype operators were relegated to hourly communications checks.[24]

The platoon from Company B of the 124th Signal Battalion supporting the 1st Brigade at Dak To had only to install a short multichannel system to the 54th Signal Battalion's local terminal to obtain service to the provincial capital of Kontum, where the 54th Signal Battalion operated a patch panel and teletype relay to switch circuits into the countrywide system. When the 4th Division sent reinforcements to Dak To later in the week, the 124th Signal Battalion sent additional radio relay terminals to establish direct systems to Camp Enari.[25]

The normal path for a VHF system from the tactical headquarters at Dak To to the division main command post at Camp Enari, eighty-eight kilometers to the south, would have been through a relay about midway between the two locations. But the lack of a secure relay site and the location of both headquarters in depressions masked by surrounding hills forced signalmen to route systems south through a relay at the adviser's compound in Dak To to another relay on Dragon Mountain, a high hill just outside Camp Enari, and then through a short system to a terminal at the division headquarters. Besides being a waste of equipment, that path relied on a leg between Dak To and Dragon Mountain twice as long as the normal 45-kilometer range of the equipment and impeded by mountains. Having experimented with the system previously, signalmen in the 124th

---

[22]Journal, I FFV, Sig Ofcr, 6 Oct 67, item 2; Ltr, 124th Sig Bn to CG, 4th Inf Div, 9 Dec 67, sub: COAAR, Battle for Dak To, p. 5, Tab I to 29th MHD, Battle for Dak To, 71A2312/1, WNRC. For the restructuring of signal support to separate brigades, see Ltr, Capt Richard J. Meyer, Jr., to Lt Gen Ben Harrold, 28 Jun 66; "Separate Brigade C-E Operations," *Command Communications*, September 1967, pp. 46–48; and Capt. Charles M. McCracken, "Communications in the 173d Airborne Brigade (Separate)," in ibid., pp. 38–40. Latter three in CMH.

[23]For an account of the difficulties experienced by the signal schools in meeting the demand for radio relay operators, see Chapter 18.

[24]124th Sig Bn, AHS, 1967, p. 4, CMH; ORLL, 54th Sig Bn, 31 Jan 68, pp. 1, 10, and ibid., 31 Oct 67, p. 3, both in 73A3330/35, WNRC.

[25]ORLL, 54th Sig Bn, 31 Oct 67, p. 3; Ltr, 1st Bde, 4th Inf Div, to 4th Inf Div, 9 Dec 67, sub: AAR, p. 28, Tab A to 29th MHD, Battle for Dak To, 71A2312/1, WNRC.

Signal Battalion knew the precise siting of antennas and frequency settings to capitalize on the phenomenon of obstacle gain to make the seemingly impossible system work well. They were unable to find such an ideal combination for routing systems into Kontum, less than half as far from Dak To. Masked by obstacles, Kontum was located in such a "dead area" for line-of-sight propagation that even FM voice communications over short distances were poor.

To conserve radio relay equipment, the 54th Signal Battalion terminated all systems from Kontum and Pleiku at the advisory compound near Dak To so that the circuits could be routed through a patch panel and consolidated for distribution to the tactical units operating in the area. An attempt to eliminate the need for VHF systems by running wire lines to those units, some only five kilometers away from the advisory compound, failed because the lines were repeatedly cut by incoming rounds, pulled up by engineer vehicles repairing roads and sweeping for mines, or burned in brush fires started by the flares used to illuminate defensive perimeters at night. A cable line hastily installed from the top of Dragon Mountain to the signal complex at Camp Enari did remain in operation, enabling the 124th Signal Battalion to conserve radio relay equipment at that end of the system.[26]

By 9 November the 124th and 54th Signal Battalions, having committed all their communications equipment, requested help to support a forward logistical base being established at Dak To to handle the ammunition, petroleum, and other supplies being assembled for the task force. Although difficulties with logistical communications during Operation JUNCTION CITY had resulted in the requirement for one teletype and two voice circuits from each forward support area to the 1st Logistical Command, all circuits on the 54th Signal Battalion's system from Dak To had been preempted for tactical use. The commander of the 21st Signal Group, Col. Charles H. Burr, Jr., assigned the support of the logistical units at Dak To to the 43d Signal Battalion, the unit operating area communications in Pleiku and Kontum Provinces. Indirectly the 43d Signal Battalion was already supporting the operations around Dak To. Its 278th Signal Company provided base communications at Camp Enari and an access to the node of the Integrated Wideband Communications System at Pleiku. Company A handled communications for Kontum, which had become a staging area and supporting air facility for units in the Dak To operation. The 586th Signal Company, transferred to the 43d Signal Battalion when the 509th Signal Battalion headquarters moved north with Task Force Oregon, operated communications systems from Pleiku and Kontum to An Khe, the 173d Airborne Brigade's base, and to the depots at Qui Nhon on the coast. Within a few hours after receiving the logistical communications support mission, Lt. Col. Edwin B. Gentry, the commander of the 43d Signal Battalion, assembled equipment from several locations at Pleiku; there he waited

---

[26]COAAR, 124th Sig Bn, Battle for Dak To, p. 6, Battle for Dak To file 71A2312/1, WNRC; 124th Sig Bn, AHS, 1967, p. 5; Journal, I FFV, Sig Ofcr, 7 Nov 67, item 4, file 206–07, Daily Journal 67, 70A478/33, WNRC; Ltr, 4th Inf Div to I FFV, 3 Jan 68, sub: COAAR, Battle for Dak To, pp. 58–59, Battle for Dak To file 71A2312/1, WNRC. For a list of VHF systems installed during the battle, see file U–442, 72A18/8, WNRC.

The Dragon Mountain Relays

over a day for clearance to convoy his contingent to Dak To.[27]

Lack of communications between the 43d Signal Battalion and forces providing road security was the principal cause for the delay of convoys moving along Highway 14 from Pleiku to Dak To. Unlike the enemy, the Americans relied heavily on radio communications during convoy movements, especially to coordinate security with covering aircraft and security detachments at bridges and road junctions. Even before the operation in the Central Highlands began, the field force signal staff had been trying to establish a single highway net for the entire corps area to eliminate the confusion of using several local nets as convoys moved through different jurisdictions along their route. While the signal officer, Col. Jack A. Milligan, met with the intelligence and operations staffs of the field force to coordinate netting procedures for security and fire support units along the main supply routes, his deputy, Col. Lawrence J. Kunkel, had been discussing movement schedules and communications needs with the logistical units that normally traveled the strategic corridor from Qui Nhon through An Khe to the Central Highlands. The buildup for Dak To interrupted those negotiations before they produced a satisfactory convoy communications plan. The 2d Squadron, 1st Caval-

[27]USARV, AVHSI-PP, 1st Logistical Command Communications Requirements Plan, 20 May 67, file U–442, 72A18/8, WNRC; AAR, 1st Bde, 4th Inf Div, p. 29, CMH; COAAR, 4th Inf Div, p. 58, Battle for Dak To file, 71A2312/1, WNRC; ORLL, 54th Sig Bn, 31 Jan 68, p. 2; 43d Sig Bn History, p. 4, CMH; Journal, I FFV, Sig Ofcr, 9 Nov 67, item 3, file 206–07, Daily Journal 67, 70A478/33, WNRC.

ry (4th Infantry Division), responsible for security of the Kontum–Dak To road, a hazardous route passing within sight of North Vietnamese guns in the hills south of Dak To, was having its own difficulties with communications. Since the armored cavalry unit had just been issued new radio equipment, its communicators had insufficient time to install and become familiar with their equipment by the start of the Dak To operation. Communications for control and security of convoys were in disarray as U.S. units moved into the Dak To area.[28]

Fortunately for the Americans, the North Vietnamese ignored the convoys moving within range of their guns. They were more interested in drawing U.S. troops onto the ridge lines where they could engage them from well-prepared positions ringing the crests of the hills. There they connected trenches and bunkers by telephone lines to coordinate their defense and counterattacks without fear of being monitored by American intercept teams.[29]

When a patrol of the 173d Airborne Brigade found one of those wire lines and followed it to a Communist strongpoint on 6 November, the first major skirmish of the Dak To battle erupted. Realizing how strongly entrenched the North Vietnamese were, the patrol pulled back, and the forward observer with the patrol called for artillery. Communications for artillery support at Dak To were typical of artillery communications throughout Vietnam. Forward observers maintained contact with the fire direction center of supporting artillery units by backpack PRC–25 radio. From the fire direction centers, artillerymen forwarded firing instructions to the gun crews by telephone or FM radio, depending on their proximity. The forward observer, who had to adjust the artillery fire on the target after the first salvoes, was the key to accurate fire support. During that first battle at Dak To, the forward observer was killed shortly after the fight began on the ridge line. His radioman, Sp4c. Ernest Fulcher, continued to direct artillery on the North Vietnamese positions throughout the day as the airborne troopers and the North Vietnamese defenders battled it out.[30]

As in earlier operations in the rugged terrain of the Central Highlands, almost the full load of communications in the infantry battalions during battle fell on the radioman. Although every battalion had an organic communications platoon with wiremen, switchboard operators, and radio-teletype operators, during actual combat the battalions rarely stayed in one place long enough for those men to install their communications. Most were drafted to be messengers or radiomen. Called radio-telephone operators (RTOs), the signalmen carrying radios for battalion and company commanders, platoon leaders, and artillery forward observers had one of the most important and most dangerous jobs in the combat units. To the infantrymen fighting an elusive enemy in unfamiliar terrain, the operator was the link with civilization that kept fear and isolation at bay; to commanders trying to control platoons and companies in jungle so thick that even five-man fire teams had difficulty maintaining cohesiveness and visual contact, he was the bond that held the command together; to the enemy, the soldier with the radio

[28]Journal, I FFV, Sig Ofcr, 29 Oct 67, item 2, file 206–07, Daily Journal 67, 70A478/33, WNRC.
[29]COAAR, 173d Abn Bde, Battle of Dak To, Operation on 6 Nov 67, 7 Dec 67, p. 1, Battle for Dak To file, 71A2312/1, WNRC.
[30]Ibid., pp. 1–3.

Fire Mission *is radioed on the PRC–25.*

was the man to be cut down in the first volley. Radio-telephone operators knew how vulnerable they were and frequently even packed their radios upside down to hide the telltale antenna from the enemy. Still, they fell in alarming numbers.[31]

Because the PRC–25 radio was so simple to use, anyone could take it from a fallen signalman and continue to operate it. But if the radio itself was hit, combat leaders had to turn to messengers and visual signals to control their men and summon help. On 13 November, in a fight for Hill 823 overlooking Dak To, that was exactly what happened. The leader of the first platoon to encounter the enemy was wounded, his radio-telephone operator killed, and the platoon radio destroyed. Using runners to carry messages to the company commander's radioman, the wounded platoon leader adjusted artillery on the enemy positions to his front. When the company radio operator was also killed, the company commander, Capt. James P. Rogan, continued the coordination of fire support. With only a few radios left operating, the surrounded Americans on Hill 823 used visual signals to communicate with helicopters resupplying them and evacuating casualties and with Army helicopter gunships and Air Force fighter bombers providing close support. Because every man carried pyrotechnics, each pocket of Americans around the hill was able to mark its position for supporting aircraft with colored smoke grenades during the day and flares and flashlights at night. By prearrangement certain colors identified friendly positions, and others marked the locations of the enemy for striking aircraft.

American infantrymen fought well in the most remote areas with full confidence that if they fell they would be quickly evacuated to a place where they would be given the best of care; their faith was borne out by the high rate of recovery from wounds that in other wars had been fatal. Brave helicopter pilots and rapid battlefield communications made medical evacuation the most responsive operation of the Vietnam War. When Captain Rogan reported on the battalion command FM net that there were critically wounded soldiers on Hill 823, the radio-telephone operator at the battalion command post forwarded the message with map coordinates to the 173d Airborne Brigade command post on a special emergency evacuation net, called a Dustoff net. Usually by the time the brigade forwarded the mission to the supporting aviation unit over a telephone hot line, the aviators had monitored the request on the Dustoff net and already had a

[31]Ibid.

Radio-Telephone Operator *equipped with PRC–25 and smoke grenades.*

helicopter on the way. Arriving in the general area of the map coordinates, the evacuation helicopters contacted the men on the ground on the DUSTOFF net to determine the color of the smoke or lights that would mark the landing zone where the casualties were waiting. Having also monitored the DUSTOFF request, Company B of the 4th Medical Battalion, the direct support medical unit at Dak To, used a single-sideband radio to alert the hospital at Kontum to expect incoming casualties and to notify the division headquarters at Camp Enari of the losses.[32]

Although pyrotechnics were primarily used for air-ground signaling, they sometimes were used to signal between dispersed units on the ground. A flare of one color might trigger the launch of an attack, while another announced a withdrawal. Lacking a suitable radio for squad communications, infantrymen had found a variety of ingenious ways to signal visually.

Shortly before the Dak To operation, the 173d Airborne Brigade and the 4th Infantry Division had received prototypes of a radio that also promised to improve low-level communications. Developed to replace the old PRC–6, which had proven too cumbersome in the rugged terrain of South Vietnam, the new squad

[32]Ltr, 4th Inf Div to I FFV, 3 Jan 68, sub: COAAR, Battle for Dak To, p. 51, Battle for Dak To file, 71A2312/1, WNRC. For a description of communications available to the 44th Medical Brigade, see Ltr, USACDC to CDCCS-L, 12 Apr 68, sub: Trip Report-Medical Communications and Electronics Equipment, AD 851736, DDC; Ltr, 44th Med Bde to USARV, 1 Aug 68, sub: Senior Officer Debriefing Report, CMH.

Using Smoke *to call for a medical evacuation helicopter.*

radio consisted of two separate components: an eighteen-ounce PRT–4 transmitter that was easily carried in the palm of the hand and an eleven-ounce PRR–9 receiver that clipped onto the helmet near the ear. In a few months of use prior to the Dak To battle, the radios improved communications between squad leaders, who carried both a transmitter and receiver, and their men, who wore only the helmet receivers. But the tiny sets required careful handling to stand up to the wear and tear of combat in South Vietnam. In the 4th Infantry Division, soldiers wrapped the radio in a waterproof plastic bag and taped the receiver antenna to the helmet liner to protect it from being snapped off by branches. Communications officers ensured that each radio set was packed in an ammunition can when not in use to protect the small components from being mislaid or stepped on. Those units in the division that used the radio at Dak To found that it worked well.[33]

In the 173d Airborne Brigade electronic gear was not as well cared for. Many of the brigade's radios were inoperable by the time the brigade deployed to Dak

---

[33]"Squad Radio Expedients, 4th Infantry Division," *Command Communications*, July 1968, pp. 51–52, CMH. By September 1969, few of the squad radios were still in use. Infantrymen had found them "too much like a toy" and had rejected a means of communications in which there was no way to acknowledge messages. USASESS, Trip Rpt of Lt Col Dean B. Dickinson to South Vietnam from 9 Sep 69 to 3 Oct 69, 10 Oct 69, pt. 2, p. 28, CMH.

Squad Leader *uses squad radio to direct his men during operations in Pleiku Province.*

To. Spare parts for the new squad radio, still a nonstandard, developmental item, were especially difficult to obtain. A vast array of snapped antennas, cracked handsets, and waterlogged radios made many of the brigade's PRC–25's inoperable. When combat damage began taking a heavy toll of the radios at Dak To, the 173d Airborne Brigade had to request emergency resupply of PRC–25's from the depot at Qui Nhon.[34]

Administrative and logistical communications from the highlands to the coastal logistical base at Qui Nhon and to the 173d Airborne Brigade's rear headquarters at An Khe could not cope with the heavy demand of supply and personnel actions during the battle at Dak To. Radio-teletype nets designated for such communications had fallen into disuse and were not employed during the battle. Instead, communicators continued to use the overloaded multichannel systems. Most logistical communications traffic thus had to compete with higher priority operational traffic. As the number of Flash messages, the precedence normally used for critical battlefield emergencies, rose during the battle to eighty times normal levels, administrative messages piled up in the communications centers waiting for open lines. Logisticians and personnel officers, despairing of ever having their

[34]ORLL, 173d Abn Bde, 31 Jan 68, Ind 3, p. 1, 73A3330/51; 2d Bn, 503d Inf, Unit History, 1 Jan–31 Dec 67, p. 20, 69A591/9. Both in WNRC.

traffic sent by teletype until after the battle, tried to communicate with rear bases by telephone, only to find that the common-user circuits to the east, many of which were routed through the relay at Kontum, were too noisy for long-distance calls. The best circuits had been preempted for teletype channels and for hot lines to control air operations.[35]

On 8 November Colonel Spitz requested a troposcatter system for better long-distance communications from Dak To to Pleiku. As the 21st Signal Group readied two contingency troposcatter teams for airlift from Nha Trang, a typhoon with winds of eighty miles an hour hit the coast. Not only did the storm delay the departure of the aircraft bearing the signal reinforcements, but it knocked off the air existing equipment linking the coast with the Central Highlands. Huge waves crashing over sea walls in Nha Trang forced the 54th Signal Battalion to evacuate its high-frequency radio park near the beach. Up and down the coast, VHF antennas were blown down, smashing electronic equipment, entangling guy wires, and wrenching signal cables from nearby telephone poles. When the antenna tower on Hon Cong Mountain toppled, An Khe was left without communications. High winds continuing throughout the day and night of 10 November made the repair of antennas dangerous and futile; washed-out roads and grounded helicopters frustrated attempts to rush replacement equipment to the sites. Not until 13 November were all the VHF systems back on the air and the troposcatter teams dispatched to the Central Highlands.[36]

Although the troposcatter system improved communications from the battlefield to the 4th Division's main headquarters near Pleiku, it did not improve communications to the rear base of the 173d Airborne Brigade at An Khe or to the coastal logistical bases. When General Rosson, responding to heightened hostilities, sent the 1st Brigade of the 1st Cavalry Division to Dak To, communications to the east became even more critical. The air cavalrymen needed communications lines to their division headquarters in Binh Dinh Province and to the division rear base at An Khe. Because the rest of the division was heavily committed, the cavalry division's 13th Signal Battalion could send only a single radio-teletype set to the brigade's base at Kontum. The 4th Infantry Division provided the brigade a small multichannel set, airlifting it four times during the following week to keep the units fighting at Dak To in constant contact with the command post at Kontum. But that multichannel system, as most communications from Dak To to Kontum, was poor. Often single-sideband radio was the only means of linking the brigade command post with tactical units at the scene of the battle.[37]

Moving new units from the cavalry division into Dak To in the midst of the battle caused FM radio problems. Because the new units were assigned frequencies already being used by the 4th Division, frequencies had to be reshuffled and

[35]COAAR, 4th Inf Div, p. 59; COAAR, 1st Bde, 4th Inf Div, p. 29; COAAR, 124th Sig Bn, p. 7; COAAR, 1st Bde, 1st Cav Div, p. 11. All in Battle for Dak To file, 71A2312/1, WNRC.

[36]Journal, I FFV, Sig Ofcr, 8 Nov 67, item 4; 9 Nov 67, items 2, 3; 10 Nov 67, item 2. All in file 206–07, Daily Journal 67, 70A478/33, WNRC.

[37]Ltr, 1st Bde, 1st Cav Div, to 1st Cav Div et al., 1 Dec 67, sub: Combat Operations After Action Report-1st Brigade Participation in Operation MACARTHUR , pp. 10–11 and Incl 1, p. 3; Ltr, 124th Sig Bn to 4th Inf Div, 9 Dec 67, sub: COAAR, Battle for Dak To, p. 7. All in Battle for Dak To file, 71A2312/1, WNRC.

daily amendments made to the Signal Operating Instructions. The routine weekly changing of frequency and call sign assignments became extremely difficult to coordinate. On 7 November, just a few hours before the scheduled weekly change, the signal officer of the 1st Brigade, 4th Division, requested permission temporarily to retain his old frequencies and call signs to avoid disrupting communications with two battalions heavily engaged in combat with the North Vietnamese. Forward observers were engrossed in directing artillery fire, and radio-telephone operators were talking to helicopters shuttling in and out of the battlefield on resupply and evacuation missions. A change in frequencies threatened to turn an already hectic situation into chaos. Agreeing to postpone the change, Colonel Spitz then had to notify all other units in the

CH–54A Flying Crane *moves an antenna tower from An Khe to Hon Cong Mountain.*

division to continue using their old frequency assignments.

The change was finally made a few days later; but then an aviation unit reported the loss of one of its helicopters with the new edition of the Signal Operating Instructions on board. Since Colonel Spitz had to presume the enemy had recovered the signal documents, his staff notified all holders of the Signal Operating Instructions to revert to a reserve edition already distributed for just such an eventuality. Before the signal staff could publish and distribute another reserve edition, a patrol found the body of an American radio-telephone operator, whom the North Vietnamese had stripped of his radio equipment and Signal Operating Instructions. With fighting at such close quarters taking place in the hills around Dak To, more such losses were expected. The signal officer suspended the replacement of compromised signal documents, and units continued to use the compromised codes. Even if there had been a way to publish a new edition quickly and enough helicopters to distribute copies to every unit, the constant changing of frequencies and call signs threatened to cause a complete breakdown in communications nets at critical moments during the battle. Loss of a cryptographer assigned to the headquarters of the *1st North Vietnamese Division* and his code books created a similar problem when the North Vietnamese tried to change codes during the battle. For an entire day, the division headquarters was unable to decode messages from its *32d Regiment*.[38]

As more and more American, South Vietnamese, and North Vietnamese units

---

[38]Journal, 1st Bde, 4th Inf Div, 7 Nov 67, item 73, 2–06 Daily Journal Files (Nov 67), CMH; Journal, I FFV, Sig Ofcr, 8 Nov 67, item 4; Journal, 1st Bde, 4th Inf Div, 19 Nov 67, item 99, 2–06 Daily Journal Files (Nov 67), CMH.

with radios converged on the Dak To area during mid-November, complaints of frequency interference multiplied. The division signal staff was able to resolve most complaints of mutual interference by American units and some interference caused by South Vietnamese units, but was helpless to do anything about those frequencies being used in common with North Vietnamese communicators. In desperation, American signal officers monitored the entire frequency band in search of unused channels for their own units.[39]

Management of FM frequencies used by supporting aircraft at Dak To became complicated as the number of aircraft committed to support operations increased. Besides helicopters of the air cavalry brigade that had joined the battle late, forward air controllers with FM radios were flying over every skirmish to guide Air Force and Marine fighters providing close air support. Many of those high-performance jet aircraft were coming from distant fields in other frequency assignment areas.

To control the activities of the numerous aircraft supporting the battle, the 4th Division established an Air Control Operations Center at Dak To from which hot lines linked each aviation unit and each ground unit receiving air support. Over that communications web flowed emergency requests, alerts to the airfields, and warnings to artillery units to halt firing in areas where aircraft were firing. The staff of the center also monitored the radio nets of ground units and forward air controllers to obtain advance notice of requests and to divert aircraft to places where they were most needed.[40]

Forward air controllers who were flying in the vortex of the air-ground maelstrom had the most critical communications role in the air support war at Dak To. They directed aircraft streaking in at speeds of hundreds of miles an hour to targets completely hidden by the jungle canopy and marked only by a thin wisp of colored smoke or by the confusing directions of a bewildered radioman fighting for his life down below. Fighting at Dak To was at such close quarters that pilots had to respond to terror-filled radio calls such as, "They're still coming, put the next one right on top of me." Forward air controllers not only had to guide sorties in on the very troops they were supporting, but also to take care not to interfere with artillery support to the troops. To keep the enemy at bay as long as possible, they waited until the last minute, until fighters were ready to start their bombing runs, to radio CHECKFIRE, the command to stop all artillery fire to ensure that aircraft were not hit. Forward air controllers bore a heavy responsibility for the safety of the fighter pilots and the men on the ground; flying low over the battlefield in slow, single-engine observation planes exposed to both ground fire and artillery, they risked their own safety as well. Because of their perilous situation and critical mission, when they gave the call sign TONTO, the radio identifier at Dak To, other stations cleared the net.[41]

On 19 November, when the 173d Airborne Brigade's 2d Battalion, 503d Infantry, assaulted the well-entrenched troops of the North Vietnamese Army's *174th*

[39]Journal, 1st Bde, 4th Inf Div, 25 Nov 67, item 56, 2–06 Daily Journal Files (Nov 67), CMH.

[40]Ltr, 4th Avn Bn to 4th Inf Div, 10 Dec 67, sub: Combat Operations After Action Report, p. 6, Battle for Dak To file, 71A2312/1, WNRC.

[41]PACAF, Battle for Dak To, Project CHECO, 21 Jun 68, CMH.

Regiment on Hill 875 southwest of Dak To, the delicate balance of safety maintained by good air-ground coordination tipped against the Americans. The enemy trapped the battalion on the slopes of the hill with murderous fire from three sides. American radio nets became an indistinguishable cacophony of commanders shouting directions and besieged pockets of soldiers calling for assistance. Forward air controllers warned the Air Control Operations Center of their inability to enter the noisy nets to determine target information from the infantrymen and to avoid collisions between the helicopters and tactical fighters providing air support. A short time later, at 1758 hours, one of those fighters accidentally dropped a 750-pound bomb in the center of the battalion's position. All contact with the battalion on the hill was lost.[42]

After twenty minutes of silence, the commander of Company D, Capt. Bart O'Leary, restored radio contact with the brigade command post and confirmed the worst—the accident had added almost one hundred casualties to those already caused by the North Vietnamese. Later that night a second fatal accident was averted when one of Captain O'Leary's platoon sergeants heard a radio-telephone operator calling for artillery directly on the company position. Rather than allow untrained and shell-shocked soldiers to adjust artillery and air strikes, the seriously wounded Captain O'Leary, the only company commander on Hill 875 still living, operated the radio himself until the remnants of the battalion's three companies were rescued over a day later.[43]

When Colonel Milligan, the field force signal officer, visited Dak To soon after the remnants of the 2d Battalion, 503d Infantry, were rescued, he found that the combat of the previous days and the crash of a helicopter carrying replacement PRC-25 radios had left the airborne brigade critically short of radios. Milligan immediately arranged for the 1st Logistical Command to dispatch a shipment of radios directly from the depot at Qui Nhon to the embattled airborne brigade.[44]

By the time Colonel Milligan visited Dak To, the battle was drawing swiftly to a close. The Americans had frustrated the attempt of the North Vietnamese to capture a Special Forces camp and to gain a foothold in Kontum Province, but in retreating, the North Vietnamese had been successful in foiling a vigorous American pursuit by the stand of the *174th North Vietnamese Regiment* on Hill 875.

Both the strength and weaknesses of American communications had affected the outcome of the battle. Despite a destructive typhoon and the difficulties of coordinating communications for a task force of three brigades from different commands, the network installed throughout the difficult terrain of II Corps by the 1st Signal Brigade, the field force, and the divisions enabled commanders to con-

---

[42]Interv with Capt Carl L. Leggett, forward air controller, 173d Airborne Brigade, 18 Nov 67, Incl to PACAF, Battle for Dak To, Project CHECO, 21 Jun 68, CMH; Journal, 2d Bn, 503d Inf, 19 Nov 67, item 124, 2–06 Daily Journal Files (67), 69A591/9, WNRC.

[43]173d Abn Bde, 10 Dec 67, sub: COAAR-Battle of DAK TO (17–19 Nov 67), Incl 4, Battle for Dak To file, 71A2312/1, WNRC.

[44]Losses to the 173d Airborne Brigade totaled 61 PRC-25's, 22 PRT-4's, 19 PRR-9's, and 21 field telephones. The 1st Brigade of the 4th Infantry Division lost 28 PRC-25's and 11 field telephones during the battle. COAAR, 173d Abn Bde, 7 Dec 67, p. 37; COAAR, 1st Bde, 4th Inf Div, p. 36; Journal, I FFV, Sig Ofcr, 20 Nov 67, item 2, and 21 Nov 67, item 2; Journal, I FFV, G-4, 21 Nov 67, item 10. Latter two in file 206–07, Daily Journal 67, 70A478/31, WNRC.

trol the maneuver of ground forces, artillery fire support, and close air support by tactical aviation units. The sheer quantity and high precedence accorded operational message traffic hindered administrative and logistical communications of the 173d Airborne Brigade and the 1st Brigade, 1st Cavalry Division. The heavy volume of radio traffic occasionally caused breakdowns and frequency interference, but the ingenuity and bravery of the radio-telephone operators with the infantrymen in the hills around Dak To enabled commanders fighting in difficult terrain, often against overwhelming odds, to keep their units together and to marshal effectively the American superiority in fire support.

Forsaking hopes of destroying the Americans in the "killing zone," by the summer of 1968 the North Vietnamese division had moved all but one regiment out of II Corps. The Americans also shifted forces. To counter the move of several North Vietnamese divisions across the Demilitarized Zone, the 1st Cavalry Division moved to the northern regions of I Corps. The 173d Airborne Brigade replaced the air cavalrymen in the populated coastal region of II Corps, and the 4th Infantry Division garrisoned a much quieter Central Highlands. Signalmen expanded the relay sites on Lang Bian, Hon Cong, and Dragon Mountains to improve communications across the vast mountainous region. Against the obstacles of terrain and enemy action, the 1st Signal Brigade had built by late 1968 a reliable network throughout II Corps.

12

Tet and the Border Battles

Dak To had been a bloody battle fought under trying circumstances; but it had been a relatively uncomplicated military operation. Army infantry units, backed by standard artillery and air support, fought conventional North Vietnamese Army units for key terrain in an isolated region of the Central Highlands. The respective allies of the two adversaries—the South Vietnamese and the Viet Cong—played a lesser role in the action. Nor did fighting occur in a populated area where concern for civilian casualties or damage to civil facilities affected tactics.

Army units were not soon to have another opportunity to meet the North Vietnamese in such a set-piece battle. The next Communist offensive was waged by the Viet Cong in the cities and towns of South Vietnam. That offensive was followed by a general shift in major Army operations to the I Corps, where Army units shared the responsibility for ground operations with American marines and even obtained fire support from naval ships offshore. With the move north and later to the western borders and into Cambodia, Army operations became more fluid. Flexibility became the overriding goal, and communicators found themselves constantly adapting to new and unexpected situations.

Communications During the Tet Offensive

Hoping to spark a popular uprising against the Saigon regime, the Communists decided to mount a concerted, countrywide offensive by main force and guerrilla units against American bases and South Vietnamese cities. Seeking surprise, they launched the offensive during Tet, the Vietnamese lunar new year and traditionally a time when fighting slackened. Early on the morning of 31 January 1968, when the holiday cease-fire was only hours old, the phones and intercoms in the Army Communications Operations Center at Tan Son Nhut suddenly became busy with calls from technical controllers throughout the country reporting attacks on their signal sites. When Tan Son Nhut itself came under heavy assault at 0300, a 28-man reaction platoon from the 69th Signal Battalion rushed

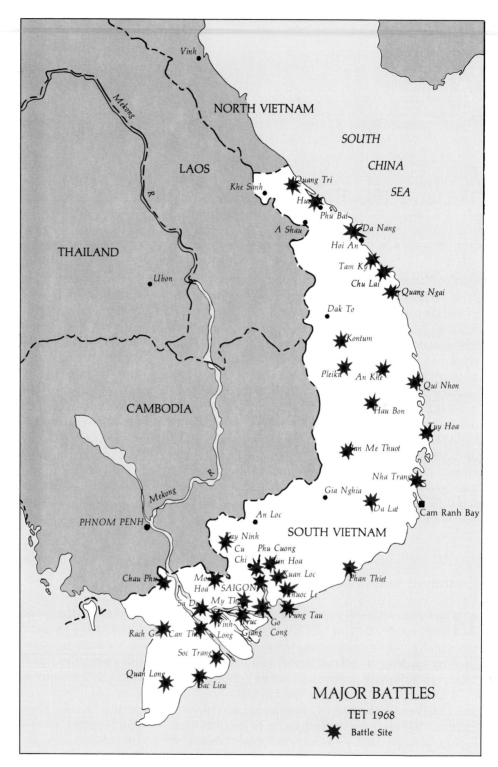

Vinh

NORTH VIETNAM

SOUTH

Mekong

CHINA

LAOS

Quang Tri

Khe Sanh

Hue

SEA

Phu Bai

THAILAND

A Shau

Da Nang

Hoi An

Tam Ky

Ubon

Chu Lai

Quang Ngai

Dak To

Kontum

CAMBODIA

Pleiku

An Khe

Qui Nhon

Hau Bon

Tuy Hoa

Ban Me Thuot

Nha Trang

Mekong

Gia Nghia

Da Lat

Cam Ranh Bay

PHNOM PENH

An Loc

SOUTH VIETNAM

Tay Ninh

Cu

Phu Cuong

Chi

Bien Hoa

Chau Phu

Xuan Loc

Phan Thiet

Moc

Hoa

SAIGON

Sa Dec

My Th

Phuoc Le

Vinh

Truc

Vung Tau

Rach Gia

Can Tho

Long

Giang

Go

Cong

Soc Trang

Quan Long

Bac Lieu

MAJOR BATTLES

TET 1968

 Battle Site

MAP 14

Signalmen Repair *damaged cable in Can Tho during the Tet offensive.*

to a section of the air base perimeter being stormed by the Viet Cong. Although the enemy cut down the platoon's machine gun crew in the first minutes of the fight, the signalmen repulsed the attack. Safe, but cut off from reinforcement, the small night crews on duty at the Army Communications Operations Center and other signal facilities on the base continued to man their equipment for two days until a relief crew of communicators could break through the Viet Cong siege of the air base.[1]

The simultaneous outbreak of fighting throughout South Vietnam caused a surge in communications, especially calls for assistance and battle reports. General Westmoreland imposed a moratorium called Minimize on all but the most essential communications; the volume of traffic immediately dropped by 31 percent, but the number of high-precedence messages rose dramatically. Amid the pressures of handling traffic to be communicated at extraordinary speeds, signal crews already depleted by casualties and by the diversion of communicators to secure perimeter defenses also had to restore communications destroyed during the attacks.[2] *(Map 14)*

---

[1] Rpt, The TET Offensive, Its Impact on the 1st Signal Brigade (hereafter cited as The TET Offensive), Incl to Ltr, 23d MHD to OCMH, 11 Oct 68, 69A5356/11, WNRC; Briefing, 1st Sig Bde, Operations at the 1st Signal Brigade, Incl to Ltr, 23d MHD to OCMH, 27 Dec 68, sub: Operations of the 1st Signal Brigade, VNIT 374, CMH.

[2] MACV History, 1968, vol. 2, p. 726, CMH.

Helicopter Resupply *helps signalmen rebuild the site at Nui Ba Den.*

The enemy damaged many communications facilities and temporarily captured commercial power plants in several cities, disrupting radio service until military generators were put into operation. The worst disruption of communications occurred on cable trunks connecting military radio terminals with local switchboards and teletype centers and on circuits to local subscribers. Viet Cong sappers cut wire and cable lines outside perimeters, and shell fragments and bullets tore into overhead cables within compounds. With many airfields and roads closed during the initial heavy fighting, couriers could not compensate for the loss of electrical communications. As during the coups of earlier years when military communications were disrupted, radio broadcasts became a primary means of communicating instructions to beleaguered garrisons. In Qui Nhon, where the Viet Cong seized the local radio station, the 41st Signal Battalion even provided broadcasting facilities for South Vietnamese civil authorities.[3]

In many locations, especially those where signalmen were the only American military present, personal security and survival overshadowed communications

---

[3]Ltr, ACofS, CE, USARV, to ACofS, CE, USARPAC, 21 Feb 68, sub: Summary of Significant Activities 10–16 Feb 68, file 139800, 72A25/20; Brig Gen W. M. Van Harlingen, Debriefing Rpt (hereafter cited as Van Harlingen Debriefing Rpt), 18 Jan 69, pp. 9–10, file 139772, 72A25/19. Both in WNRC. For accounts of the courier service instituted after the Tet offensive, see Ltr, USARV to MACV, 21 Feb 68, sub: Status of Communications, Brig Gen William M. Van Harlingen Papers, and "USARV Courier Service: 69th Signal Battalion," *Command Communications*, May 1968, pp. 44–48, both in CMH.

A More Austere, *but stronger, Nui Ba Den signal site.*

problems. In Kontum a platoon of the 41st Signal Battalion fought an entire day and night to rescue survivors of an embattled American military police outpost. At many South Vietnamese Army camps American signal teams supporting advisers fought alongside South Vietnamese soldiers and arranged for medical evacuation and air support by American aviation units. Krause Compound, the headquarters of the 362d Signal Company in Da Lat, became a haven for American missionaries, civilian technicians, and South Vietnamese politicians living in the area. Besides housing and feeding a large influx of refugees swelling the compound, the signal company commander, Maj. William R. Crawford, formed his men into security platoons that ventured out into the city to repel the Viet Cong. The signalmen rescued American civilians from villas, guarded convoys transporting food, water, and ammunition to the compound, and fought off repeated Viet Cong attacks on the local airstrip, the besieged town's only link with the outside world.[4]

Conditions were worst in the northern city of Hue, which the North Vietnamese tenaciously held for three weeks against repeated counterattacks by American marines, soldiers from the 101st Airborne Division, and South Vietnamese infantrymen. The U.S. adviser's compound and the 1st Signal Brigade's site were

[4]Ltr, 362d Sig Co to 73d Sig Bn, 3 Mar 68, sub: Attack on Dalat, After Action Report, VNI 168, CMH; Col. John D. McKinney, "They Communicate and Shoot," *Army,* September 1968, pp. 55–60.

the only American installations in the city not overrun. Forty-one signalmen at the site held out against repeated attacks and even captured the commander of the attacking Viet Cong unit. Every few days a Marine unit opened a temporary corridor from the adviser's compound to the site to resupply the signalmen and to evacuate their wounded. Making a bold foray by boat up the Perfume River and into a canal circling the citadel of the city, other signalmen from the 1st Signal Brigade fought their way into the city with a communications terminal for the American fire support coordinator directing air and artillery fire.[5]

As the last battles of the enemy offensive sputtered out in late February, all facilities of the 1st Signal Brigade were still operating, but communications support was tenuous. In four weeks of fighting the signal brigade had suffered more casualties than in the entire previous year: 22 killed, 160 wounded, and 1 missing. Fatigued by weeks of sleepless nights, communicators were beginning to make careless errors. The attacks had caused damage of $2.5 million to signal facilities and equipment, and sites still operating were badly in need of repair. Supplies were low and few of the brigade's aircraft were still in good enough condition to shuttle repairmen and equipment between sites. Only the establishment of an air courier service, begun with the assistance of the U.S. Air Force during the offensive, kept the Army's communications network from breaking down.[6]

Attacks on signal installations continued after the Tet offensive. On the night of 13 May 1968, the Viet Cong attacked the remote signal relay on Nui Ba Den, killing twenty-three communicators and destroying most of their equipment. The few men who survived took refuge in a Buddhist shrine on which the Viet Cong were reluctant to fire. Two weeks later a patrol from the Pr' Line site clearing the road to Da Lat suffered eleven casualties. In August the Viet Cong killed the gate guards at the Vung Chua site near Qui Nhon but were driven out of the perimeter by alert signalmen before they could harm the communications gear. Attacking Nui Ba Den again in mid-August, the Viet Cong destroyed five generators and once more put the strategic site off the air temporarily.[7]

The increase in enemy actions against signal installations, which by the summer of 1968 were occurring at a rate of eighty a month, took its toll on communications service. As equipment was taken out of operation for repairs, channels were rerouted to keep high-priority circuits in service. Lower-priority common-user channels were preempted to replace disrupted sole-user circuits. Even after full radio or cable service was restored, busy circuit controllers normally lacked the time to reinstall the common-user circuits so vital to logistical and administrative operations.[8]

[5]DA, General Order 66, Valorous Unit Award, 513th Signal Detachment, file 139566, 72A25/6, WNRC; Rpt, The TET Offensive, Incl to Ltr, 23d MHD to OCMH, 11 Oct 68.

[6]Interv, Maj Fremont E. Binder, CO, 23d MHD, with Col Charles H. Burr, CO, 12th Signal Group, 10 Apr 68, VNIT 76, CMH; ORLL, 1st Sig Bde, 30 Apr 68, pp. 1–2, file 228–07, 1st Sig Bde (1968), 72A7128/5, WNRC.

[7]Ltr, ACofS, CE, USARV, to ACofS, CE, USARPAC, 18 May 68, sub: Summary of Significant Activities, 11–17 May 68, file 139800, 72A25/20; ORLL, 1st Sig Bde, 31 Oct 68, pp. 1–2, file 228–07, 1st Sig Bde (1968), 72A7128/5. Both in WNRC.

[8]ORLL, 1st Sig Bde, 31 Jul 68, p. 15; ibid., 30 Apr 68, pp. 23–24. Both in file 228–07, 1st Sig Bde (1968), 72A7128/5, WNRC.

Emerging from the Tet offensive, the 1st Signal Brigade had exhausted its reserves of high-capacity transportable equipment to replace damaged fixed facilities. Other units were also finding themselves shorthanded, and in the spring of 1968 President Johnson authorized a selective call-up of reserve and National Guard units. The Army mobilized the 107th Signal Company (Support) of the Rhode Island National Guard to assist the signal brigade in South Vietnam. When the company arrived in October 1968, Brig. Gen. William M. Van Harlingen, Jr., assigned it to the newly arrived 972d Signal Battalion, designated the brigade's contingency unit. A few months later, the Army augmented the small signal battalion with six eight-man teams equipped with new 24-channel TRC–129 microwave-troposcatter terminals. The 972d's contingency mission was shortlived. The 1st Signal Brigade soon committed four of these teams to install a double system of 48 channels from Cam Ranh Bay to Lang Bian Mountain as an alternative east-west axis to augment systems emanating from Pr' Line and alleviate concerns that loss of the remote Pr' Line would cripple communications in southern II Corps; the other two terminals were rotated with operational terminals to permit the long overdue overhaul of fixed equipment. By March 1969 the Army had only two troposcatter sets in reserve at Cam Ranh Bay; all the rest of the long-distance troposcatter, microwave, and single-sideband equipment available in the Pacific for use in contingencies belonged to the Air Force.[9]

Moving North

S ince late 1966 the 1st Signal Brigade had been using reserve contingency equipment to keep pace with the expansion of American bases. In December 1966 General Terry deployed the brigade's contingency tape relay station to Da Nang to support U.S. Marine units moving north toward the Demilitarized Zone. When General Westmoreland formed Task Force Oregon in April 1967 to fill the void left in southern I Corps by the departing marines, General Terry exhausted his contingency stocks and deactivated some operational facilities to support the task force with a divisional signal battalion and to augment the 37th Signal Battalion, the sole Army signal unit in the northern corps. The brigade's contingency troposcatter teams installed a system from Nha Trang through Cu Lao Re Island in the South China Sea to the task force headquarters at Chu Lai.[10] *(Map 15)*

In January 1968, nine months after all the brigade's contingency reserves had been committed to Task Force Oregon, General Van Harlingen deactivated twenty-

---

[9]Ltr, USARV to MACV, 21 Feb 68, sub: Status of Communications, Van Harlingen Papers. Ltr, ACofS, CE, USARV, to ACofS, CE, USARPAC, sub: Summary of Significant Activities, 12–18 Oct 68, file 139800, 72A25/20; ORLL, 1st Sig Bde, 31 Jul 69, p. 8, file 228–07, 1st Sig Bde (1969), 72A7128/5; MACV J–6, Briefing Notes, 10 Mar 69, sub: Contingency Communications, tabs E–7 and E–8, file 139865, 72A25/23. All in WNRC.

[10]Sharp and Westmoreland, *Report on the War in Vietnam*, p. 134; Van Harlingen Debriefing Rpt, p. 8; ORLL, 509th Sig Bn, 30 Apr 67, CMH; ORLL, 1st Sig Bde , 31 Oct 67, p. 9, file 228–07, 1st Sig Bde (1967), 72A7128/5, WNRC; Capt. Robert McGowan, "523d Signal Battalion, AMERICAL's Voice of Command," *Command Communications*, July 1968, pp. 16, 32–35, CMH.

DEMILITARIZED ZONE

Quang Tri ●

QUANG TRI

SOUTH

CHINA

SEA

Hue ●

Phu Bai ●

THUA THIEN

Da Nang ●

Hoi An ●

37th Sig Bn (Spt)

QUANG NAM

Tam Ky ●

QUANG TIN

Quang Ngai ●

QUANG NGAI

I CORPS — AREAS OF RESPONSIBILITY

1966-1967

Map 15

one multichannel links and transferred ninety-four pieces of equipment to the northern corps of South Vietnam. To provide a signal staff for a forward headquarters of the Military Assistance Command being formed at Phu Bai in northern I Corps, twenty-five experienced officers and noncommissioned officers were transferred. With less than a week's notice, General Van Harlingen had to assemble over 600 men as well as tons of signal equipment from forty different signal sites in South Vietnam to provide area support for two Army divisions moving to the region. To command the signal force, he transferred the headquarters detachment of the 459th Signal Battalion from Nha Trang and two company headquarters from other signal battalions in II Corps. He also augmented the composite battalion with Company B of the 37th Signal Battalion, which had been supporting advisers in the northern sections of I Corps, and with the 588th Signal Company, which moved from the Mekong Delta. Signalmen installed the first circuits from the new command post to the Military Assistance Command in Saigon late on the evening of 29 January, only a day before rockets and mortars signaling the start of the Tet offensive began raining down on Phu Bai. Despite especially violent assaults in the Hue–Phu Bai area, the command post remained on the air throughout the offensive.[11]

When the fighting slackened, General Westmoreland converted his forward command post to a headquarters called Provisional Corps, Vietnam, a subordinate command of the III Marine Amphibious Force with responsibility for all operations in the two northern provinces. At the same time, the Headquarters and Headquarters Detachment, 63d Signal Battalion, arrived from the United States to relieve the 459th Signal Battalion of responsibility for communications in the new sector. *(Map 16)* The battalion commander, Lt. Col. Elmer H. Graham, had a difficult and dangerous mission. His northernmost unit, the 588th Signal Company, linking Marine outposts along the Demilitarized Zone with Army artillery positions, was within range of North Vietnamese guns in the Demilitarized Zone. In the early summer of 1968, when the 1st Brigade, 5th Infantry Division (Mechanized), the last Army combat unit to deploy to South Vietnam, established a base camp at Dong Ha, just south of the 17th Parallel, the 588th provided it with support also. Company B, 37th Signal Battalion, operated communications at the 1st Cavalry Division's base at Camp Evans near Quang Tri. The newly arrived 596th Signal Company performed a similar mission at Camp Eagle near Phu Bai for the 101st Airborne Division, which was committed to the I Corps to help in retaking Hue during the Tet offensive. In October 1968 the 17th Signal Platoon (Construction) arrived from the United States to install underground cable at those fast-growing bases.[12]

Besides the challenges posed by mission and enemy, the 63d Signal Battalion faced organizational challenges. Lacking an organic corps signal battalion, the provisional corps relied on the 63d Signal Battalion to provide tactical command communications. Having to perform an area support mission and provide command and control communications for the corps put the 63d Signal Battalion in

---

[11]Van Harlingen Debriefing Rpt, pp. 6–8; Interv, Binder with Burr, 10 Apr 68, VNIT 76; Ltr, 23d MHD to OCMH, 27 Dec 68, sub: Operations of the 1st Signal Brigade, VNIT 374, CMH.

[12]"63d Signal Battalion," *Command Communications*, September 1970, pp. 2–50, CMH.

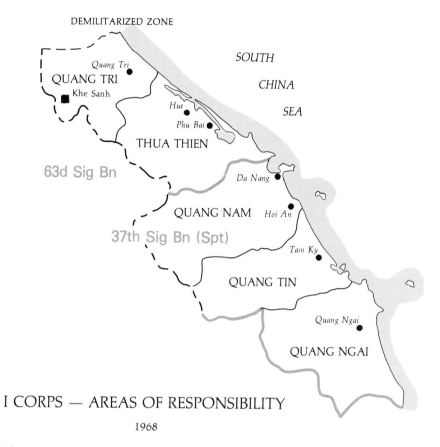

DEMILITARIZED ZONE

SOUTH

CHINA

SEA

Quang Tri

QUANG TRI

Khe Sanh

Hue

Phu Bai

THUA THIEN

63d Sig Bn

Da Nang

QUANG NAM   Hoi An

37th Sig Bn (Spt)

Tam Ky

QUANG TIN

Quang Ngai

QUANG NGAI

I CORPS — AREAS OF RESPONSIBILITY

1968

MAP 16

the awkward position of serving two commands. Only a close working relationship between Colonel Graham and the corps signal officer, Lt. Col. Gerd S. Grombacher, made this arrangement work. The divided responsibilities were alleviated in October 1968 when General Van Harlingen assigned the 270th Signal Company, the last signal unit to arrive in South Vietnam, to the operational control of the corps, which had been redesignated XXIV Corps. The 270th Signal Company relieved the 63d Signal Battalion of most of its corps support missions. On 1 December 1968, the new I Corps Tactical Zone Group (Provisional), later redesignated the 12th Signal Group, assumed from the 21st Signal Group at Nha Trang the responsibility for the 37th and 63d Signal Battalions. That transfer completed a series of adjustments to both area and tactical signal support in I Corps that had begun eighteen months earlier with the deployment of Task Force Oregon to southern I Corps.[13]

The signal units deployed to I Corps from II Corps found the terrain to be much like that which they left—coastal lowlands and rugged interior—but with few high hills suitable for relay sites in friendly hands. The concentration of headquarters and units of the four services around the city of Da Nang created unique demands for cooperation between communicators in I Corps. Until late 1966, when General Terry moved a contingency tape relay station to Da Nang, coordination of interservice communications was weak. Teletype messages transmitted between Army and Air Force units just miles from each other in the Da Nang area had to be routed over the BACKPORCH system through a communications center at Tan Son Nhut, over 400 miles away.[14]

When Terry first visited Da Nang in 1966 after taking command of the 1st Signal Brigade, he predicted that indistinct service lines of responsibility for communications support in I Corps would eventually interfere with communications service and contribute to interservice conflicts in the northern corps. Although the Department of Defense had given the Army responsibility for long-haul and common-user communications throughout South Vietnam, the Army's authority over the network in I Corps stopped at the troposcatter terminals at Hue and Da Nang. From there, marines assigned to the 5th and the 7th Communications Battalions, the two U.S. Marine Corps area signal battalions in South Vietnam, extended circuits to their tactical units in the field. At Da Nang the Air Force provided telephone service to subscribers within five miles of its dial exchange, and the 1972d Communications Squadron on Da Nang Air Base installed and operated most American telephone communications in the vicinity of the city. The 178th Signal Company, the local Army signal unit and the oldest American communications unit in Da Nang, provided communications only to local advisory detachments.[15]

By early 1968 the American force around Da Nang had grown beyond the Air

---

[13]Interv, Maj Ronald W. Schuette, CO, 23d MHD, with Lt Col Gerd S. Grombacher, signal officer, Provisional Corps, Vietnam, 18 Jul 68, VNIT 183, CMH; ORLL, 1st Sig Bde, 31 Oct 68, p. 12; Col. Gerd S. Grombacher, ''Corps Signal Communications in Vietnam,'' *Signal*, April 1969, pp. 23–29.

[14]Ltr, CINCPAC to JCS, 26 Aug 68, sub: PACOM Communications-Electronics Experiences, an. C, app. 1, 02K712.03/74, OAFH.

[15]Msg, Terry SCC VCG 50702 to Meyer, 5 Jul 66, CMH; Briefing, 1st Sig Bde, 6 Jan 69, file U–315, 72A18/6, WNRC.

Force base to include major Army, Navy, and Marine logistical bases, Army and Marine airfields, and an entire Marine division, as well as various American and South Vietnamese military facilities. Air Force cablemen accustomed to working within the confines of an air base were unable to keep pace with the demand for service to outlying camps. Soon a hodgepodge of tactical multichannel radio systems and cables belonging to several American and South Vietnamese signal units emanated from the air base. Scores of cables and wire lines hung from the railings of the single bridge crossing the Da Nang River. As cables were damaged by monsoon storms or by the rocket attacks that frequently struck Da Nang, there was no central authority to coordinate restoral of service. Instead, cablemen would go out to one of the many cable heads or junction boxes where the various cables intersected and "ring down" pairs of cable with a field phone. If the pair was serviceable and no one answered the ring, they would appropriate the circuit. With the constant turnover of American cablemen on one-year tours, eventually only wiremen from the I Corps Signal Battalion, the local South Vietnamese communications unit, knew enough about the haphazard American cable plant to be able to troubleshoot circuits.[16]

Air Force, Navy, and Marine Communications

Throughout South Vietnam, six battalion-size Air Force signal units belonging to the 1964th Communications Group—the 1876th, 1877th, 1878th, 1879th, 1882d, and 1972d Communications Squadrons—provided a variety of communications services in addition to air base dial exchanges. Teletype centers and manual switchboards at every Air Force installation handled standard administrative and logistical communications and more specialized communications for air traffic control, weather reporting, and navigational assistance. To manage tactical air support, Air Force communicators operated the Tactical Air Control System, a network of single-sideband radios and dedicated telephone and teletype circuits that linked air bases, the Seventh Air Force's Air Operations Center at Tan Son Nhut, and Direct Air Support Centers at each corps. Single-sideband radio and telephone connected the Direct Air Support Centers with Tactical Air Control Parties at each Army division. The Tactical Air Control Parties used telephone and FM voice radios to coordinate the activities of the Air Force air liaison officers with the brigades and battalions in the field. The entire system depended upon efficient FM communications with the forward air controllers who directed the aircraft providing close air support.[17]

Although well-coordinated air support was vital to the success of ground oper-

---

[16]Interv, author with My Cao-Huy, former CO, I Corps Signal Battalion (ARVN), 15 Mar 79, Historians files, CMH.

[17]Interv, Maj Charles C. Pritchett, CO, 20th MHD, with Col Robert L. Leuchtmann, USAF, CO, Direct Air Support Center, IV Corps, 20 Sep 68, VNIT 298, CMH; Ltr, Dir of Telecommunications, PACAF, to J–6, MACV, 15 Jan 69, sub: COMSEA Study-Request for Info-Data and Documents, file 139768, 72A25/19, WNRC.

ations, the Army and the Air Force often competed for the same communications circuits, particularly on the strategic long-haul systems operated by the 1st Signal Brigade. In the early 1960s the Air Force shared BACKPORCH circuits only with advisory detachments and was able to obtain enough channels on the countrywide network to have circuits dedicated for its own use between its operations centers and bases. When American combat forces arrived in 1965, the Air Force was reluctant to relinquish those dedicated channels to the new Army units or to permit its dedicated, sole-user circuits to be converted to more efficient common-user trunks between switchboards. Air Force communicators felt they required the speed and continuous accessibility of dedicated circuits to handle the large mass of perishable information—weather reports, target lists, flight plans, frag orders, damage reports—required for their air operations. As late as January 1968, the Air Force still had 432 high-priority, sole-user circuits on the BACKPORCH system while the Army had only 180. Only after the Pacific Air Force installed automated digital teletype and data terminals in its headquarters, operations centers, and airfields throughout the Pacific, which made more efficient use of circuits than slower voice or manual teletypewriter terminals, was the Air Force able to reduce its requirements for sole-user service.[18]

Although improvement in communications services relieved some of the interservice competition, a fortuitous association between the two officers holding the two most powerful signal positions in South Vietnam helped also. In mid-1967, Brig. Gen. John E. Frizen, U.S. Air Force, became the MACV J–6 and Brig. Gen. William M. Van Harlingen, Jr., succeeded General Terry as commander of the 1st Signal Brigade. In their former assignments at the North American Air Defense Command in Colorado, the roles of the two officers had been reversed: General Van Harlingen had been the signal officer of the Air Force–dominated headquarters, and General Frizen had commanded the Air Force signal unit operating its communications. The harmonious working relationship between the two men did much to alleviate conflicts between Army and Air Force communicators. To stay abreast of the requirements of the Air Force, General Van Harlingen also assigned a liaison officer to the Seventh Air Force.[19]

To a lesser degree than the Air Force, the U.S. Navy also obtained service from the Army-operated long-haul network. When naval support activities were established at Da Nang and Cam Ranh Bay in 1965, most Navy communications were routed over BACKPORCH to the teletype relay and switchboard operated by the Army at Phu Lam, where they were rerouted to other addressees in South Vietnam or to the Navy's master communications station at San Miguel in the Philippines. From there, messages were broadcast to the Seventh Fleet in the South China Sea. By late summer of 1967 the Navy had installed dial exchanges, teletype tape relays, and secure-voice switchboards at its task force headquarters

---

[18]For a discussion of the Air Force's weather communications, see MACV J–6, Briefing Notes, 9 Apr 69, sub: Weather Communication Circuit Requirements in Vietnam, tab J–2. Ibid., 18 Apr 69, sub: PACAF Integrated Automated Command and Control System, tab J–10. Both in file 139865, 72A25/9, WNRC. Interv, Maj Fremont E. Binder, CO, 23d MHD, with Brig Gen William M. Van Harlingen, CO, 1st Signal Brigade, 26 Jan 68, VNIT 72, CMH.

[19]Interv, Binder with Van Harlingen, 26 Jan 68, VNIT 72; MACV J–6, Briefing Notes, 4 Apr 69, sub: Dial Central Offices (DTE), tab F–1, file 139865, 72A25/23, WNRC.

at Cam Ranh Bay and logistical support base at Da Nang. Navy-operated microwave systems connected those facilities to the Army's long-lines system.[20]

Supporting operations in Indochina, the Seventh Fleet had 200 ships with 60,000 men stationed throughout the South China Sea and the Gulf of Tonkin. Ships from the fleet mounted an air campaign against North Vietnam with carrier-based aircraft, interdicted Communist seaborne infiltration of South Vietnam, conducted riverine operations in the delta and Rung Sat, and provided fire support to ground operations in coastal regions. To maintain continuous contact from the communications stations in South Vietnam and the Philippine Islands to the far-ranging ships of the naval force, the fleet operated two communications relay ships equipped with twenty-four transmitters and sixty receivers. Because the Joint Chiefs of Staff monitored the air campaign against North Vietnam from Washington, reliable and rapid communications with the aircraft carriers in the Gulf of Tonkin were most essential. Besides maintaining links through San Miguel to the United States, the Navy also operated radio nets from the carriers to Da Nang and Tan Son Nhut to coordinate naval air operations with the Marine Corps and Air Force. During actual strikes the carrier task force also operated over twenty voice nets with the attacking pilots.

Along the coast and inland waterways of South Vietnam, the Navy and U.S. Coast Guard relied primarily on short-range high-frequency and FM voice radios to conduct their seaborne interdiction and riverine operations. To coordinate and adjust naval fire support, naval gunfire liaison officers located in the fire support coordination centers of tactical ground units used direct high-frequency voice links with supporting cruisers, destroyers, and the battleship *New Jersey* firing from offshore. The proximity of many combat operations in I Corps to the coast, and the frequent smuggling of materiel by boat from nearby North Vietnamese ports, required Army units and Navy ships in I Corps to support each other. In one such joint endeavor on the morning of 1 March 1968, a naval reconnaissance plane spotted a North Vietnamese trawler off the coast of Quang Ngai Province. The Navy communications station at Da Nang broadcast an alert on a single-sideband coastal surveillance net monitored by naval liaison officers working in the tactical operations center of the 23d Infantry Division (Americal). Navy swiftboats launched from the small port at Chu Lai near the division headquarters and helicopter gunships from the division's 11th Infantry Brigade quickly spotted the trawler and fired on it to drive it towards shore. The trawler exploded just as it reached the sandy beach; infantrymen from the Americal Division captured the crew and salvaged the huge cargo of weapons. The entire operation was controlled by FM and single-sideband voice radio from the Army division's tactical operations center.[21]

The marines, who normally conducted such littoral operations, were committed

---

[20]MACV J–6, Briefing Notes, 10 Mar 69, sub: Communications Facilities for Da Nang (Sea Anchor) and Cam Ranh Bay (Bow Line), tab E–6; and ibid., 18 Apr 69, sub: Communications with Seventh Fleet, tab K–1. Both in file 139865, 72A25/23, WNRC. Lt. Gene R. Will (USN), "Navy Communications Station in Vietnam," *Signal*, April 1967, pp. 27–29; Rear Adm. Robert H. Welks, "Naval Communications in Southeast Asia Operations," *Signal*, April 1968, pp. 12–19.

[21]"The Effectiveness of Communications," *Command Communications*, July 1968, p. 26, CMH.

The 588th Signal Company *provides support to the Navy at Cua Viet in the I Corps.*

instead to the hills around Da Nang and along the Demilitarized Zone. Although both Army field forces kept radio-teletype equipment ready to communicate with a Marine amphibious force should one be committed ashore in the southern or central sections of the country, the marines remained in their landlocked role in the north. Prior to the arrival of the 63d Signal Battalion in I Corps in early 1968, the Marine Corps' 5th and 7th Communications Battalions and signal units of the two Marine divisions provided communications support to Army artillery and combat support units operating in the north.[22]

After Army signal units began moving into I Corps, the 1st Signal Brigade extended its service to the marines. In January 1968 a troposcatter team from the brigade's contingency force, the 544th Signal Detachment, moved to Khe Sanh near the Demilitarized Zone with the 26th Marines, whose mission was to block a major North Vietnamese infiltration route. When two North Vietnamese divisions besieged the camp, the troposcatter system between Khe Sanh and Hue was the primary link to the outside world. President Johnson was so interested in the fate of the besieged base at Khe Sanh that he arranged for reports sent out over the troposcatter system to be forwarded directly to the White House.

[22]Msg, USARPAC to STRATCOM, PAC, 24 Dec 66, sub: ARG/SLF Communications, file 14, 70A2328/6, WNRC.

Rather than abandon this important communications lifeline, when the Communists invaded Hue during the Tet offensive General Van Harlingen refused to accept the recommendation of the local senior adviser to evacuate the tropo-scatter terminal. Although the signalmen were able to hold out in their small enclave in enemy-occupied Hue, the team at Khe Sanh was less fortunate. On 2 February an enemy rocket struck the team's bunker, killing the officer in charge and three radio operators. Assisted by two Marine communicators, the single surviving team member, Sp4c. William Hawkinson, who had been on duty in the undamaged van nearby, kept the power generators and communications equipment operating for three days until relief arrived.[23]

During the course of the siege of the Khe Sanh garrison, Marine radiomen developed techniques to assist in countering North Vietnamese artillery. From an isolated outpost on a promontory jutting out into enemy-held territory, called Hill 881S, the radiomen observed the three main enemy firing positions. When they saw muzzle flashes or heard the whistling of rounds arching overhead, they broke into the regimental command net, announcing "Arty, Arty" and the designation of the hill from which the artillery was fired. A man assigned to monitor the radio for the warnings then activated the base warning system, a truck horn mounted in a tree. The radio operators perfected their alert system to give as much as eighteen seconds' warning before the rounds struck the base. To silence the enemy guns, they then directed air strikes on the muzzle flashes. One signalman with a UHF radio capable of communicating directly with fighter pilots acquired the nickname "Mightiest Corporal in the World" after he personally directed over 200 air strikes from his lonely observation post on Hill 881S.[24]

Fighting in the Mountains of I Corps

To assist the marines in the two northern provinces, General Westmoreland sent the 1st Cavalry Division and the 101st Airborne Division. Having been in South Vietnam over two and a half years, the air cavalry division's 13th Signal Battalion had a reputation as an efficient unit able to communicate with the bare minimum of equipment. Although the 501st Signal Battalion of the 101st Airborne Division joined the battle in I Corps in late February after only two months in South Vietnam, it also had already proven itself a capable outfit. The unit was first committed to Song Be (Phuoc Binh) northwest of Saigon to fight the Viet Cong in their strongholds along the Cambodian border. The battalion commander, Lt. Col. Lennart N. Nelson, had barely completed setting up communications for the division command post when the division moved to Bien Hoa to protect the air base during the Tet offensive. When fighting abated in III Corps, General

---

[23]Rpt, The TET Offensive, Incl to Ltr, 23d MHD to OCMH, 11 Oct 68; Lt. Gen. Willard Pearson, *The War in the Northern Provinces, 1966–1968,* Vietnam Studies (Washington, D.C.: Government Printing Office, 1975), p. 71.

[24]Capt. Moyers S. Shore, USMC, *The Battle for Khe Sanh* (Washington, D.C.: Government Printing Office, 1969), p. 59.

Westmoreland sent the airborne troopers to fight the North Vietnamese still tenaciously holding out at Hue.[25]

To break the siege of Khe Sanh, an attempt called Operation PEGASUS, the provisional corps commander, Lt. Gen. William B. Rosson, chose the more experienced 1st Cavalry Division. In a deception operation to cover the westward move of the cavalrymen to Khe Sanh, Colonel Nelson sent FM radio detachments to the eastern sector of the Demilitarized Zone to operate command, intelligence, and administrative nets to simulate movement of the 101st Airborne Division toward the coastal Dong Ha area. Meanwhile, the 1st Cavalry Division sent combat units to secure hilltops on which the 13th Signal Battalion and the 63d Signal Battalion established relay sites to ensure continual communications with Camp Evans and with a regional air control facility at Quang Tri. Apparently the deception plan worked. Leapfrogging from one critical terrain feature to another along the route to Khe Sanh, the cavalry division reached the Marine base with little resistance, breaking the siege.[26]

Taking advantage of good flying weather, General Rosson then ordered the cavalrymen to move south to join with the 101st Airborne Division in a sweep through the A Shau valley, a major North Vietnamese infiltration route into the northern coastal plain. The 3d Brigade of the cavalry division seized an abandoned airstrip at A Luoi deep in the mountains along the Laotian border from which it conducted air assaults against enemy bases throughout the valley. The 101st Airborne Division fought its way westward along the two major roads transiting the region. The 1st Signal Brigade found the country so rugged that it had to use large cargo helicopters. Even that expedient did not always work. The first MRC–54 radio relay shelter lifted to a mountaintop overlooking the low-lying A Luoi airstrip slipped out of its sling and fell several thousand feet. By the time a twelve-channel radio relay system was installed to connect the A Shau with Phu Bai and Camp Evans, the air cavalrymen had adjusted to working with the fewer channels provided by their own lighter tactical radio sets.[27]

Except for twelve-channel systems installed by the 63d Signal Battalion to the main bases on the eastern end of the valley, Fire Base Bastogne and Landing Zone Veghel, the 501st Signal Battalion also depended primarily on its tactical voice communications during the operation. Spread out at seventeen different locations in the A Shau, the airborne communicators relied heavily on FM and single-sideband radios. Wiremen from one of the airborne brigades installed field wire between several bases using a small hand-held dispenser mounted in a light observation helicopter, the first recorded instance of wire-laying from an aircraft in the war. For multichannel communications the 501st Signal Battalion used with great success a new four-channel set, the GRC–163, consisting of the VRC–12 series radio and a newly developed multiplexer. Small enough to be loaded into

---

[25]Ltr, Col Lennart N. Nelson to Col Joe Finley, 12 May 75; ''501st Signal Battalion 101st Airborne Division (AM),'' *Command Communications*, July 1969, pp. 2–20. Both in CMH.

[26]Ltr, Nelson to Finley, 12 May 75; Pearson, *The War in the Northern Provinces*, pp. 81–92; Briefing, 1st Sig Bde, Operations at the 1st Signal Brigade, Incl to Ltr, 23d MHD to OCMH, 27 Dec 68, sub: Operations of the 1st Signal Brigade, VNIT 374.

[27]ORLL, 1st Sig Bde, 31 Jul 68, p. 2; Van Harlingen Debriefing Rpt, pp. 10–11.

Battalion Command Post *near Khe Sanh during Operation Pegasus.*

a jeep or helicopter, it was carried into landing zones with the assaulting troops. On the crowded knolls that served as fire bases in the mountains of the A Shau, the compact radios took up far less room than standard multichannel sets. Communicators had difficulty only in keeping antennas from being blown off their azimuth by the downdraft of choppers and in having repeatedly to realign equipment disturbed by the blast of artillery firing nearby.[28]

Although using the VRC–12 series radios for multichannel communications reduced the frequencies available for FM voice radios, frequency interference at A Shau was less of a problem than in previous major battles because alternatives to FM radios were available. Unlike communicators in many other units, signalmen in the 101st Airborne Division and the 1st Cavalry Division maintained their proficiency with high-frequency radio. When FM nets became overcrowded they used single-sideband voice radios and radio teletype. At critical times, even the airborne division's MARS station was pressed into service to handle administrative and logistical traffic with the division's rear base at Bien Hoa, 400 miles to the south.[29]

To increase FM frequencies for Army units moving into the I Corps, the Mili-

---

[28]Ltr, Nelson to Finley, 12 May 75. ORLL, 501st Sig Bn, 31 Oct 68, Incl 8, and ibid., 31 Jul 68, pp. 2–3, both in CMH.

[29]Ltr, Nelson to Finley, 12 May 75.

Antennas Rise *above Fire Base Bastogne in the A Shau Mountains.*

tary Assistance Command released thirty-two frequencies reserved for VHF multichannel systems, and the signal officer of the III Marine Amphibious Force obtained from the I South Vietnamese Corps signal officer the loan of 117 frequencies assigned to the South Vietnamese armed forces. When the Tet offensive and the siege of Hue caused an unanticipated influx of Army units to I Corps, the additional frequencies proved invaluable. Americans in Saigon were not as fortunate when the Tet offensive broke out. The task force assembled to rout the Viet Cong from the city was assigned only a single discrete frequency, and service on the overcrowded task force command net was chaotic until frequencies were withdrawn from other units for the task force.[30]

Air-to-Ground Communications

O f far greater concern to signalmen in I Corps than managing frequencies were problems with communicating and navigating in the crowded air space above the northern battlefields. The 1st Cavalry Division and the 101st Airborne Divi-

[30]MACV History, 1968, vol. 2, pp. 726–27; Historical Source Material file, Notes on the Composition of Task Force Ware, 31 Jan–13 Feb 68, VNI 156, CMH.

sion, which was being made the Army's second airmobile division, each had more helicopters than any other Army division in South Vietnam. Besides swarms of Army helicopters flying over the battlefield, Air Force strategic bombers from bases in Guam and Thailand dropped their heavy bombs on North Vietnamese troop concentrations around Khe Sanh and the A Shau valley while Air Force and Marine fighter bombers provided close air support to troops on the ground. The effective marshaling of air support and the control of air space required dependable and rapid radio service linking pilots, air traffic controllers, radar and weather stations, and the ground troops receiving the air support. Target information had to be transmitted quickly and pilots warned of increasingly accurate North Vietnamese antiaircraft fire. Pilots came to expect hostile fire whenever they flew over certain areas, especially in the A Shau valley. Equally important to pilots were reports of friendly fire—long-range gunfire from Navy ships offshore, 750-pound bombs dropped by Air Force B–52's flying unseen high overhead, and Army and Marine heavy artillery rounds arching through the sky.[31]

Unlike Air Force and Navy jet aircraft with their sophisticated navigational and radar equipment, lighter and smaller Army aircraft did without bulky and expensive flight control and avionic equipment. Prior to 1965 most Army pilots in South Vietnam navigated with an open map on their laps to orient them to landmarks seen from the air. At advisory compounds and remote Army airstrips only small omnidirectional radio beacons served as lighthouses marking islands of safety for the pilots. By the time the 1st Cavalry Division arrived in South Vietnam, the Army and Air Force were using a rudimentary navigational system, called DECCA, for small aircraft. Using special receivers installed in aircraft and powerful ground-based transmitters, the DECCA network, called a hyperbolic navigational system, permitted pilots to find their location by matching signal readings with charts containing flight paths. To improve operations at Army airfields, the Army formed the 125th Air Traffic Control Company and arranged with the Federal Aviation Administration to design commercial-quality control towers and ground approach systems at many airfields. But they proved expensive and difficult to build and were installed at only two Army airfields. Most airfields relied on portable towers and guidance systems fabricated in Army depots.[32]

In the skies above remote battlegrounds in northern I Corps, beyond the range of DECCA and the radios and radar of the 125th Air Traffic Control Company, pilots relied on verbal communications with other aircraft by VHF radio, the one mode of voice communications common to the aircraft of all services flying in South Vietnam. Using a new portable UHF/VHF radio, the PRC–71, ground troops could also talk with pilots on the common very high frequencies. Despite im-

[31]Tolson, *Airmobility*, pp. 169–92; MS, USAF, Col Bert Anton, A Shau Valley Campaign, December 1968–May 1969, Project CHECO, 15 Oct 69, K717.0413–139; MS, USAF, Capt Kenneth J. Alnwick, Direct Air Support in I Corps, Project CHECO, 31 Aug 69, K717.0413–106. Latter two in OAFH.

[32]"Navigation—The DECCA Way," *Command Communications*, June 1967, p. 21, CMH; MS, USAF, Lt Col Robert A. MacDonough and Melvin F. Potter, Air Traffic Control in SEA, 14 Feb 69, K717.0413–95, OAFH; "ATC—The Voice of the Skies," *Command Communications*, June 1967, pp. 19–20, CMH; Msg, DA to CGUSAMC, 31 Aug 65, sub: Additional DECCA Chain for RVN, CMH; Ltr, Maj Gen William B. Latta to Brig Gen Robert D. Terry, 21 Mar 67, ECOM Historians files.

proved equipment, traditional means of guiding pilots to landing zones and targets—smoke, flares, panel markers, and even hand-held mirrors—continued to be used by small units lacking the new radios. Pilots even learned to locate a well-concealed enemy by following the path of tracer rounds fired by friendly troops on the ground. But those methods could easily be misinterpreted, particularly by pilots of fighters streaking in on a target at hundreds of miles an hour. To avoid errors from haphazard, confusing signaling at landing zones during air assault operations, troops called pathfinders frequently infiltrated into a proposed area of operations to prepare and secure landing zones and to establish radio beacons and visual signals to guide helicopters to a safe landing.[33]

Air Assault Communications

During the 1st Cavalry Division's air assault operations around Khe Sanh and in the A Shau valley, the air cavalrymen employed signaling techniques and means of command and control that they had been refining since the Ia Drang campaign. As one of the division's two aviation battalions flew the 2d Brigade from Khe Sanh to assault and occupy an airstrip at A Luoi in the western region of the A Shau, radios in the helicopters were used by aviators for navigation and traffic contol and by infantry commanders to command and control their heliborne units. In preparing for the assault, members of each commander's staff, wearing earphones and connected by intercoms, attended to their duties as if they were in a command post on the ground. Using the FM command net, the operations officer coordinated operations with subordinate commanders. The air liaison officer, using the FM or VHF air control nets, communicated with the Air Force forward air controller guiding air strikes against the enemy in the objective area. The artillery liaison officer talked to the supporting fire direction center on the FM fire control net. When informed by aviation company commanders that they were three minutes' flying time from the landing zone, the air liaison officer notified the forward air controller to clear fighter aircraft from the air space above the landing zone, and the artillery liaison officer requested a final volley of white phosphorus. Guiding on the smoke from the phosphorus rounds, the aerial rocket platoon of the aviation battalion, flying one minute ahead of the main body of the assault fleet, swept low over the landing zone firing rockets. As the assault helicopters followed them into the landing zone, machine gunners, firing guns mounted in the doors of the choppers, provided protective fire for the vulnerable hovering helicopters and for disembarking troops scrambling across the exposed landing zone. The success of such operations depended on the surprise of infantrymen assaulting the objective before the smoke of air and artillery strikes lifted. Rapid, dependable communications made possible such procedures of split-second timing and accuracy.[34]

---

[33]MS, Alnwick, Direct Air Support in I Corps, Project CHECO, 31 Aug 69.

[34]Tolson, *Airmobility*, pp. 169–92; Col. Robert S. Kellar, "Heliborne Command Post," *U.S. Army Aviation Digest*, January 1969, pp. 18–21.

Pathfinders Use PRC-25 Radios *to direct an airmobile assault in the A Shau.*

Reliable helicopter radios, the key to the success of air assault tactics, were the product of years of experimentation. In 1962, six years after French commanders in Algeria began experimenting with the concept of commanding ground forces from the air, a study of air mobility in the Army prepared by the Howze Board proposed installing "flying command posts" in Army helicopters.[35] The Army Concept Team in Vietnam examined the idea as a way to improve command and control by South Vietnamese commanders, and the Army's Electronics Command at Fort Monmouth developed a radio console for a heliborne command post. The console contained two FM voice radios, one for the South Vietnamese commander and one for his American adviser; a UHF radio for an air liaison officer; and a single-sideband radio set for entry into the corps air support operations net. This console worked so well in actual operations that the director of the Joint Research and Testing Agency in Vietnam, the organization charged with evaluating all new equipment tested in South Vietnam, declared, "The Heliborne Command Post is the single piece of new materiel which should have the most influence on improving the conduct of the war in Vietnam."[36]

The configuration of the heliborne command post changed to conform to new missions and to improvements in radio and security equipment. The original radio console was altered in 1964 to make room for door gunners in helicopters. During tests in the United States of the air assault division later that year, the Army decided that combat units needed FM radios more than VHF or UHF radios. The helicopters of the 1st Cavalry Division deployed to South Vietnam with the ASC-5, a three-radio, all-FM console. Enterprising signalmen whose units were not issued the ASC-5 fabricated a myriad of radio consoles for use on heliborne command posts. With improvements in radios and new voice security devices, the Army Electronics Command continually refined the design of the heliborne radio console. So important was the project that the Electronics Com-

---

[35]Headed by Lt. Gen. Hamilton H. Howze, the Tactical Mobility Requirements Board convened in the spring of 1962 to address the function of aviation in the Army.

[36]Rpt, ACTIV, Heliborne Command Post, 31 Mar 65 (JRATA Project 1A–102–.0), file 8, 70A4868/5; U.S. Army Tactical Mobility Requirements Board, 20 Aug 62, an. R, p. 6, ACSI files, 66A3138/87. Both in WNRC. DF, ECOM, Comm Dept to Technical Dir, 14 Apr 64, sub: Heliborne Command Post, CMH.

mand used a special grant of funds from the Army Materiel Command's Vietnam Laboratory Assistance Program to develop a new radio, the ASC–15, which was capable of secure transmission on three FM nets. Although the ASC–15 was not installed on every helicopter, signalmen mounted wire antennas between helicopter skids and built mounts for portable radios to make every helicopter capable of being a command post.[37]

The 1st Signal Brigade also experimented with using standard heliborne FM retransmission sets to relay telephone circuits from the four-channel GRC–163. Although this expedient worked well technically, the 1st Signal Brigade did not have enough aircraft to sustain the project. Even after the signal brigade received nine U–21 aircraft to carry the ARC–149, a set capable of retransmitting three FM voice nets in the secure mode, the high cost of maintaining the airborne retransmission stations—over $150 an hour—doomed the experiment. The airborne retransmission sets were used only as temporary FM relays while units were setting up ground relays or during major operations.[38]

With the Americans continually on the offensive in I Corps, there was a great need for airborne retransmission sets. The 63d and 501st Signal Battalions moved GRC–163's and single-sideband radios from fire base to fire base throughout the A Shau; but FM radio remained the primary means of communication. Fighting was furious in the northern battles. In a battle for a peak called Hamburger Hill, the din of battle was so loud that it was impossible to use radios.[39]

By late summer of 1968, despite stiff enemy resistance, reinforcement of I Corps by the 1st Cavalry Division and the 101st Airborne Division removed the threat that the North Vietnamese Army would overrun the northern provinces. The air-mobility and superior firepower of the Americans kept the Communists on the defensive in I Corps. Thereafter American strategy was to wear down the enemy by frequent forays into his base areas along the Laotian border. General Creighton W. Abrams, Jr., who succeeded General Westmoreland on 2 July 1968 as the commander of the Military Assistance Command, Vietnam, turned his attention to the Communist base areas farther south along the Cambodian border. In October 1968 the 1st Cavalry Division moved south to Phuoc Vinh in III Corps on the fringes of War Zone D.

---

[37]DF, ECOM, Avionics Lab to Admin Ofc, 17 May 68, sub: Historical Coverage of the Army Role in Southeast Asia, file 139611, 72A25/6, WNRC; Ltr, Maj Gen William B. Latta to Lt Gen Bruce Palmer, 20 May 68, ECOM Historians files; "Innovations from the 1st Cavalry Division (AM)," *Command Communications,* May 1970, pp. 31–37; Maj. William L. Corley, "AN/ASC–10 Communications Central" and "Comm Central AN/ASC–11," *Command Communications,* June 1967, pp. 24–25, 27. Latter two in CMH.

[38]Maj. William L. Corley, "U–6A Airborne Relay," *Command Communications,* June 1967, p. 26, CMH; USARV, CE, Approved Topics for FY–69 Major Decisions and Primary Accomplishments in USARV, sec. 5, file 139860, 72A25/23, WNRC; Maj Gen Thomas M. Rienzi, Debriefing Rpt (hereafter cited as Rienzi Debriefing Rpt), 4 Jun 70, pp. 51–52, file HRC 314.82, CMH; DF, USARV, ASEW, to Dep CofS, CE (P&M), 3 Jan 68, sub: Airborne Radio Relay, file 139748, 72A25/18, WNRC.

[39]Guenter Lewy, *America in Vietnam* (New York: Oxford University Press, 1978), p. 144.

In the Cambodian Borderlands

By late 1968 American units in the III Corps had a comprehensive communications network. Expansion of the long-lines network provided hundreds of channels between major bases in the region. The base camps of the 1st and 25th Infantry Divisions even had dial telephone service. The 1st Signal Brigade had improved its tactical area network by replacing old MRC–69 multichannel sets with new GRC–50 UHF radio relay equipment that had greater channel capacity and better circuit quality. In the western area of the corps, the 36th and 86th Signal Battalions operated the area system, while the 121st and 125th Signal Battalions handled tactical communications. Along the coast, the 39th Signal Battalion operated the area network for the Australian, New Zealand, and Thai units, which by that time had a full complement of tactical communications. The armored assault vehicles and tanks of the 11th Armored Cavalry that kept open the main roads from the coast to the Cambodian border operated convoy security nets. Only in the northern sector of the corps were communications sparse, for in October 1967 radiomen from the 1st Infantry Division had been driven off the critical relay hill of Nui Ba Ra in a surprise attack. Only single-sideband radio linked the U.S. Special Forces camps and advisory detachments remaining in the region.[40]

It was to that northern sector that the 1st Cavalry Division moved, spreading its brigade base camps along the Cambodian border. The 13th Signal Battalion reoccupied Nui Ba Ra, installing a relay on the hill. The 36th Signal Battalion, commanded by Lt. Col. Clarence E. McKnight, Jr., extended the area network to the 1st Cavalry Division. Since damage to exposed cables during the Tet offensive had underscored the need for buried cable, the 40th Signal Battalion installed a complete underground cable plant at the cavalry division's base camp. The 13th Signal Battalion, about one-half the size of an infantry division signal battalion, needed help providing command communications to its units while in garrison, and General Van Harlingen's signal brigade provided the division with contingency signal equipment from the 972d Signal Battalion. By the summer of 1969 the 1st Signal Brigade was providing the air cavalrymen with service equal to that received by Army units in well-established bases to the south.[41] *(Maps 17 and 18)*

The experience acquired by the division's 13th Signal Battalion in its frequent moves proved fortuitous. In May 1970 the air cavalrymen, in concert with the 25th Infantry Division, the 11th Armored Cavalry, and units of the South Vietnamese airborne brigade, launched an attack against Communist bases in Cambodia, the first U.S. ground operation of the war outside the borders of South Vietnam. Although the attack was made on short notice, the 13th Signal Battalion moved out quickly. The 125th Signal Battalion, on the other hand, took over a week to prepare its equipment. It was delayed while signalmen searched for

---

[40]Daily Staff Journal, 1st Inf Div, G–2, 9 Oct 67, items 4, 6, 36, and 42, file 206–07 (Oct 67), 69A6597/8, WNRC.

[41]MS, Lt Col Norman E. Archibald, Tactical Communications, 1st Cavalry Division (Airmobile), Vietnam, October 1969–July 1970 (hereafter cited as 1st Cavalry Division), 14 Mar 75, chs. 1–5, CMH.

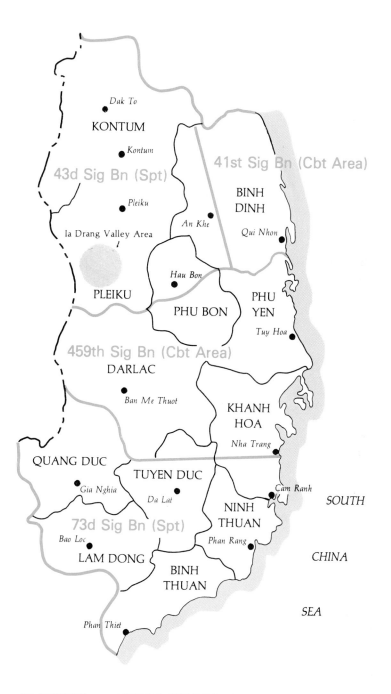

Dak To

KONTUM

Kontum

43d Sig Bn (Spt)

41st Sig Bn (Cbt Area)

Pleiku

BINH
DINH

la Drang Valley Area

An Khe

Qui Nhon

Hau Bon

PLEIKU

PHU
YEN

PHU BON

Tuy Hoa

459th Sig Bn (Cbt Area)

DARLAC

Ban Me Thuot

KHANH
HOA

Nha Trang

QUANG DUC

TUYEN DUC

Gia Nghia

Da Lat

Cam Ranh

SOUTH

NINH
THUAN

73d Sig Bn (Spt)

Bao Loc

Phan Rang

CHINA

LAM DONG

BINH
THUAN

SEA

Phan Thiet

II CORPS — AREAS OF RESPONSIBILITY

1968

Map 17

III CORPS — AREAS OF RESPONSIBILITY

December 1968

▲ MOUNTAIN RELAYS

MAP 18

discarded transportable components and equipment racks to restore mobile sets—over the years much of the signal equipment in the 25th Infantry Division had been modified and dismounted for ease in communicating between static command posts. The division relied entirely on its tactical FM radio nets during the initial week of the attack, and insufficient communications disrupted operations. Because administrative and logistic communications within the 25th Infantry Division depended heavily on fixed telephone and teletype communications, the division's progress into Cambodia stalled until multichannel links could be established. While messages awaited pickup by couriers, radio-teletype sets which had fallen into disuse remained idle in the division's garrison. Only after the 25th

Signalmen Install *an antenna at a 1st Cavalry Division fire base.*

Infantry Division had been in Cambodia for several weeks did the division's signalmen become accustomed to providing signal support under mobile and field conditions.[42]

With its lighter equipment, the 13th Signal Battalion reacted more swiftly to changes of plans and rapid moves. On seventy-two hours' notice, the battalion commander, Lt. Col. Norman E. Archibald, modified the division's nets to support a task force of air cavalry division troops moving into Cambodia. Using jeep-mounted GRC–163 four-channel radios, his signalmen installed links between the division base at Phuoc Vinh, the task force headquarters at Quan Loi, and the command post of the 3d Brigade at Katum in War Zone D. A portable, eleven-line SB–22 switchboard handled all telephone communications for the task force. When the air cavalrymen struck deeper into Cambodia in mid-May, the 13th Signal Battalion took only a few hours to extend telephone communications from the forward command post near O Rang, Cambodia, to Phuoc Vinh, 140 kilometers away. With the forward command post located at an elevation of almost 1,000 meters, obtaining a line-of-sight system to the relay station on Nui Ba Ra was relatively simple.[43]

Maintaining FM voice communications from field positions in Cambodia to bases in South Vietnam was more difficult because the portable antennas of the FM equipment were less effective than stationary VHF antennas. Colonel Archibald occasionally used an airborne relay station to retransmit FM signals.

---

[42]MS, Archibald, 1st Cavalry Division, 14 Mar 75, ch. 6; Ltr, 25th Inf Div to MACV, 19 Jul 70, sub: Combat Operations After Action Report, p. 14 and Incl 6, pp. 4–6, file 228–03, CMH.

[43]MS, Archibald, 1st Cavalry Division, 14 Mar 75, ch. 6; 1st Cav Div, Recommendation for Presidential Unit Citation, file 228–03, 72A403/24, WNRC.

With over 100 radio nets operating from the vicinity of the task force command post at Quan Loi, interference was bad. On one tower at Quan Loi there were 9 VHF, 1 UHF, 7 HF, and 36 FM antennas. During the early stages of the fighting, frequency interference problems were common and were aggravated by the secrecy surrounding the planning for the operation, which prevented an early issuance of Signal Operating Instructions. By carefully managing frequencies and making extensive use of high-frequency radios, the 13th Signal Battalion quickly resolved the initial radio problems and maintained reliable communications until the withdrawal in late June 1970 of all American units from Cambodia.

The Tet offensive and the battles in I Corps and Cambodia tested the resiliency of American communications. Where tactical units had become too dependent on fixed communications and commercial power sources, they had difficulty passing that test when the Viet Cong infiltrated cities and bases during the Tet offensive. On the other hand, the Army communicators who moved north with the two airmobile divisions and the new corps headquarters readily adapted to the fluid situation they found in I Corps. Tactics, equipment, and organizations proved to have the flexibility necessary to react to the different challenges faced by signalmen.

The signal support enjoyed by American units operating in Cambodia rested heavily on the development and expansion over the previous two years of an extensive base communications network in Southeast Asia. As Army divisions moved from corps to corps, the 1st Signal Brigade likewise expanded its area communications support. When Army units operated in Cambodia, the 1st Signal Brigade was operating the Tay Ninh terminal of the Integrated Wideband Communications System, providing combat units in nearby Cambodia with direct access to the Defense Communications System. Messages transmitted from field command posts in Cambodia went directly to the White House. From the Dong Ha terminal, the final station to be installed in the wideband network and whose antennas could be seen from North Vietnam, Army units on the northern borders enjoyed similar support from the 1st Signal Brigade. From the delta to the Demilitarized Zone, from the coast to the Cambodian border, modern communications technology had spread throughout South Vietnam.

13

Strategic Communications

When American units moved into Cambodia, they were supported by the most extensive strategic communications network ever constructed. Secure-voice conversations and encrypted teletype messages flowed between field units, Saigon, and Washington. Communications were so efficient that the Air Force's B–52 bombers dispatched from bases throughout the Pacific could provide direct close air support to the tactical units fighting in Cambodia.

The strategic communications serving American forces fighting in Southeast Asia in the summer of 1970 consisted of automatic telephone and teletype facilities rivaling those found in many communities in the United States. Data networks linked computers at major bases in Southeast Asia with depots throughout the Pacific and logistical headquarters in the United States. With undersea cables and satellite links, raw intelligence could be flashed in encrypted form to agencies in the United States, where it was processed and analyzed and sent back to the tactical units in South Vietnam. Besides permitting an unprecedented compression of space and time, the strategic network enabled communicators to handle the huge volume of messages generated during American air, land, and sea operations throughout the region.

The different pieces of the vast strategic network were designed during the 1960s in response to the requests of various headquarters in the United States and throughout the Pacific. The basic configurations of the facilities in Southeast Asia were determined in mid-1965 when the Joint Circuit Allocation and Requirements Group met in Bangkok to prepare a list of equipment to support the buildup of troops in Southeast Asia. For fixed telecommunications facilities at each major base camp, air base, and logistical installation in Southeast Asia, the group requested high-quality telephone, teletype, and data equipment similar to that found in commercial facilities in the United States.[1]

---

[1]Msg, CINCUSARPAC to CINCPAC and COMUSMACTHAI, 2 Aug 65, sub: SEASIA C-E Shopping List, CMH.

107th Signal Company Member
checks power panel of the dial telephone exchange at Long Binh.

The Telephone Network

For telephone communications up to that time, the military had relied on five dial exchanges serving customers around the major air bases and a hodge-podge of tactical switchboards at head-quarters and advisory compounds. Using proposed troop locations, sketchy cable distribution plans, and estimates of subscriber requirements, during the summer of 1965 the MACV signal staff designed an automatic telephone system to support the impending American buildup. The Joint Chiefs of Staff and the Army's Strategic Communications Command endorsed the proposed dial telephone network. Submitted to the secretary of defense in January 1966, the Army's proposal to install the first dial telephone network in a war zone received McNamara's approval in April 1966. He authorized the Army to build dial exchanges at major installations and to set up nine relays, called tandem switchboards, to tie the local dial exchanges into a regional direct-dial long-distance network.[2]

To provide long-distance dial telephone service while the local dial exchanges and the tandem switchboards were being installed, the Defense Communications Agency, Pacific, used modified transportable manual MTC–9 switchboards to connect with the Air Force's dial exchanges in order to transfer long-distance trunks to regional dial exchanges and local manual switchboards. By 15 April 1967, an interim long-distance network was in operation; dial exchanges at major bases were assigned trunk lines to a regional switch that gave them access to the entire long-lines network. The telephone network quickly became the primary means of coordinating the construction of new bases and logistical support for Americans moving into the Central Highlands and I Corps.[3]

The first dial exchanges installed by the Army were 600-line transportable central offices, called TTC–28's, consisting of commercial telephone equipment hastily

[2]Ltr, ECOM to USASTRATCOM, Pacific, 16 Feb 71, w/Incl, p. 6, CMH; Telecommunications Program Order (TPO) 71–66, Jan 66, file 139439, 72A4171/2, WNRC; CINCPAC History, 1965, pp. 525–26, CMH.

[3]DA, OCC-E, IWCS Progress Report, 25 Jan 66, tab D, CMH; 1st Sig Bde, Communications Expansion Plan, 27 Dec 67, vol. 1, an. E, file 139556, 72A25/5, WNRC; Msg, CINCPAC to MACV et al., 25 Aug 65, sub: Direct Distance Dialing (DDD) SE ASIA, CM–IN–96500, and Msg, CINCPAC to CINCUSARPAC, 7 Oct 65, sub: Automatic Telephone Service Vietnam, CM–IN–119208, both in CMH. Msg, DCA, PAC, to DCA, 13 Aug 66, sub: Phased Implementation of Auto Tele Service SEA, CM–IN–157972, file 11A; Msg, COMUSMACV to USARV et al., 27 Sep 66, sub: Phased Implementation Automatic Telephone Switching System, SEASIA, CM–IN–185264, file 13. Both in 70A2328/6, WNRC.

installed in 38-foot vans at the Lexington-Bluegrass Army Depot in Kentucky. The Army rushed the transportable exchanges to South Vietnam in early 1966 to provide dial service to the burgeoning military population of the Saigon–Long Binh area. Meanwhile, the Army contracted with a major telephone company in the United States, Stromberg Carlson, to supply additional fixed dial exchanges. A subcontractor, the Gustav Hirsch Company, began installing them in September 1966, activating the first dial exchange on 21 January 1967 at the headquarters of the Military Assistance Command in Saigon. By the time of the Tet offensive in January 1968, twenty-nine locations throughout South Vietnam had dial service, and in many cities commanders used the dial system to coordinate the U.S. response to the Viet Cong attacks.[4]

Plans for telephone exchanges had presumed that major headquarters would remain stable or fixed. When troops began shifting around the country for tactical operations, time-consuming adjustments to the dial telephone project became necessary. For example, construction of an exchange at Bear Cat in III Corps halted when the 9th Infantry Division moved to the delta. Then the exchange planned for the division's new base at Dong Tam had to be canceled several months later, after President Richard M. Nixon decided to withdraw the 9th Division from South Vietnam. Farther north, as American troops deployed to confront new North Vietnamese threats during 1968, eight additional exchanges were built.

The tandem switches that permitted direct long-distance dialing took considerably more time to install than the local exchanges. Meanwhile, subscribers using most exchanges still had to dial an operator to make a long-distance call. Awarded the contract for the tandem switches on 10 September 1967, Stromberg Carlson was plagued by a variety of delays. Since it was paying its technicians $145 a day, the company tried to schedule precisely the work of its installation crews. But it was stymied by the vagaries of conditions in South Vietnam. Boxes of material were lost in shipment; technicians were unable to find billeting space; construction crews and engineers erecting access roads and buildings were shifted to higher priority projects. Technicians had to modify dial exchanges to operate with the tandem switchboards at the same time that the dial exchanges were being expanded to serve shifting troop populations. Not until December 1968 was the first tandem switchboard—at Bang Pla in the Bangkok area—put into operation. *(Map 19)* Two months later the Can Tho tandem switchboard, serving five dial exchanges in the delta, went into service. In December 1969, fourteen months late, the final tandem board was activated at Pleiku.[5]

Although completed so late that it could be used only during the withdrawal

---

[4]Interv, 23d MHD with Maj Aaron E. Wildins, CEEIA, 11 Aug 67, file 10, 69A5363/11, WNRC; MACV History, 1968, vol. 2, pp. 716–18; ibid., 1969, vol. 2, ch. 9, pp. 126–27; Msg, USASTRATCOM to USASTRATCOM SIG BDE, SEA, 7 May 66, sub: Dial Central Telephone Offices for Southeast Asia. A series of articles about the installation of dial exchanges in South Vietnam can be found in *Command Communications*, March 1967, pp. 25–32. Latter four in CMH.

[5]Stromberg-Carlson, 17th Program Progress Report (Contract DAAB07-67-C-0580), Sep 69, file 20; 1st Sig Bde, Systems Plan: Pleiku Tandem Switching Center, 1 Nov 69, file B. Both in 72A2315/14, WNRC. Ltr, USARV, AVHGG, to ACofS, C-E, 13 Sep 68, sub: Summary of Significant Activities, 7–13 September 1968, file 139800, 72A25/20; USARV, CE, List of Topics, 8 Apr 69, Incl 8, file 139860, 72A25/23. Both in WNRC. USASCC History, FY-70, p. 55, CMH.

HAINAN

NORTH

VIETNAM

SOUTH

CHINA

SEA

Mekong

R

LAOS

DEMILITARIZED ZONE

● Dong Ha

Phu Bai ●

THAILAND

Da Nang ●

I CORPS

Chu Lai ●

II CORPS

Pleiku ●   An Khe   Phu Cat ●

■   ●   ●

Camp Enari   Qui Nhon

Phu Tai

CAMBODIA

Tuy Hoa ●

SOUTH

VIETNAM

Mekong

R

Nha Trang ●

Cam Ranh Bay ■

III CORPS

Phan Rang ●

Cu Chi   Lai Khe

●   ■

Bien Hoa AFB

SAIGON ●

Bear Cat ■

Vung Tau

Binh Thuy ●

● ■ Dong Tam

Vinh Long ●

Can Tho ●

Soc Trang ●

IV CORPS

AUTOMATIC DIAL
CENTER OFFICES

December 1968

☐   Center locations

MAP 19

of American troops, the direct dial network was impressive. The nine tandem switches linked fifty-four dial exchanges ranging in size from 100 to 5,000 lines. By dialing seven digits a subscriber could reach any dial phone in the network. From the nearest tandem board, a call was routed automatically over one of the specially conditioned circuits connecting each tandem to the other eight. If those circuits were busy, calls were switched to the most direct route available. Calls could be routed through three of the widely dispersed tandem boards and still remain within minimum standards of signal quality.

The automatic dial network also permitted more efficient use of the long-lines system. By designing the network to accept long-distance calls from only certain telephones, called Class A phones, signalmen eliminated the situation in which everyone with a telephone, privates as well as generals, competed for the limited number of long-distance trunk lines. Certain long-distance trunk lines were set aside as hot lines for those key commanders and staffs requiring instantaneous communications for command and control. Special automatic switchboards, emergency action consoles, provided direct access to the common-user and hot line network for members of the staff at the Military Assistance Command and U.S. Army, Vietnam, headquarters.[6]

Functioning much like a civilian telephone company in the United States, the 1st Signal Brigade's Telephone Management Agency, established in early 1966, guided the evolution of the system and managed its operation. The agency processed requests for service, published a telephone directory semiannually, compiled traffic data, and engineered new installations and improvements. Based on weekly reports of equipment installation and counts of line and trunk usage at ninety-four manual switchboards and dial exchanges in South Vietnam, the telephone agency prepared a profile of telephone communications. Using that profile, the Joint Cutover Integrated Working Group, a planning group in Bangkok, performed the circuit engineering of over 800 circuits to tie together the direct-dial system.[7]

The Defense Department also operated a worldwide network, the Automatic Voice Network (AUTOVON) System. In 1967 only two subscriber lines were extended from the AUTOVON switch in Hawaii to the American embassy and the Military Assistance Command in South Vietnam. In the spring of 1969 six more circuits were installed from the joint overseas switchboard at Phu Lam to the Hawaii AUTOVON switch, and late that year several trunk lines were installed from the tandem switches at Phu Lam, Nha Trang, and Bangkok to the AUTOVON switches in the Philippines and Hawaii. Because of the limited number of overseas circuits, only a few subscribers in South Vietnam were permitted

---

[6]"Dial Telephone Service and the Tandem Switch," *Command Communications*, October 1968, pp. 45–48, CMH; Rienzi Debriefing Rpt, pp. 55–58.

[7]Capt. Lawrence J. Schumann, "Telephone System Management in Saigon," *Command Communications*, April 1967, pp. 25–27, CMH. For the records of the Telephone Management Agency, see Record Group 338, 70A6175/1, WNRC. 1st Sig Bde, Briefing for Maj Gen Walter E. Lotz, Jr., on Personnel and Training, 9 Sep 68, tab 1, file 228–03, ACC Historians files; ORLL, 1st Sig Bde, 31 Jan 69, pp. 7–8, 72A7128/5, WNRC.

direct dialing service to the United States.[8]

The Teletype Network

Since sixteen teletype circuits could be transmitted over a single voice chan-nel, the quantity of available circuits had less of an effect on building a teletype network than on a telephone system. On the other hand, the disruptive effect of noise left teletype and data communications far more dependent on high-quality circuits. For example, incompatability of signal equipment and propaga-tional disturbances during the Tonkin crisis caused urgent teletype messages assigning missions to American reconnaissance aircraft based in Thailand to be garbled or lost. That failure provided the impetus for General Westmoreland to request the construction of the high-quality system that ultimately became the Integrated Wideband Communications System.

At that time, in August 1964, the teletype network in Southeast Asia consisted of Air Force–operated fixed station equipment in communications centers at each air base and tactical teletypes operated by the Army's 39th Signal Battalion at advisory detachments and major headquarters in Saigon. Most teletype circuits fed into a manual tape relay operated by the 39th Signal Battalion at Site Octopus at Tan Son Nhut or into an automatic tape relay at Phu Lam operated by the Strategic Communications Command as South Vietnam's gateway to the world-wide Defense Communications System.

At the 39th Signal Battalion's field sites most teletype equipment had been moved into buildings or underground bunkers to escape the unbearable heat in teletype vans that caused fatigue in men and machines. Even so, operating the tactical teletypes continuously at the speed of the fixed equipment in the relays—100 words per minute—was causing them to overheat and their mechan-ical parts to wear out. Low-quality transmission carried on teletype circuits from the field also caused interference that degraded the performance of expensive equipment in the major relay. Moreover, since operators in field communications centers were unacquainted with the procedures, formats, and routing and ad-dress indicators used by the Defense Communications System, up to 25 percent of the message traffic from the field was rejected at the tape relay.

In requesting an expansion of the teletype network to support the buildup of combat troops in 1965, General Westmoreland specifically asked for commu-nications centers equipped with commercial teletype equipment. In the same proposal that included dial exchanges and long-distance tandem switches, the Army requested improved teletype communications centers. Approved in April 1966 by Secretary of Defense McNamara, the concept envisioned having the 1st Signal Brigade operate fixed teletype communications centers similar to local Western Union telegraph offices in the United States to provide service on an

---

[8]ORLL, 1st Sig Bde, 31 Jul 69, pp. 15–16, file 228–07, 1st Sig Bde (1969), 72A7128/5, WNRC; MACV J-6, Briefing Notes, 8 Apr 69, sub: AUTOVON-Pacific, tab F-3, file 139865, 72A25/23, WNRC; 1st Sig Bde, Communications Expansion Plan, 27 Dec 67, vol. 1, an. F.

area basis. That arrangement would free tactical units to use their own organic equipment for establishing command and control nets, transmitting flight plans and weather data between air bases, and sending intelligence information between tactical operations centers.[9]

The start of construction of a large logistical and air base at Cam Ranh Bay and the deployment of the 1st Cavalry Division to the Central Highlands in the summer of 1965 increased the need for teletype service in II Corps. The capacity of teletype circuits between Nha Trang and the tape relay at Phu Lam over the BACKPORCH system was overtaxed. In September 1965 the Strategic Communications Command sent a transportable tape relay to Nha Trang to serve as a gateway to the Defense Communications System for units in the I and II Corps, thus eliminating the Nha Trang–Phu Lam bottleneck. After a permanent tape relay facility was built at Nha Trang in the summer of 1966, the 1st Signal Brigade transferred the transportable relay equipment to Da Nang to serve as a third major teletype relay for the I Corps area. When a rocket attack destroyed the transportable relay at Da Nang in February 1967, the Strategic Communications Command rushed another set to South Vietnam to continue providing teletype service to the northern corps until the opening of a fixed tape facility at Da Nang in May 1967.[10]

The temporary loss of the teletype relay station at Da Nang in 1967 revealed the vulnerability of the DCS teletype network. Traffic normally handled at Da Nang had to be shifted to teletype relays at Nha Trang and Phu Lam, causing an unexpected strain on those stations. At Phu Lam messages were backlogged for three days. Concerned that the DCS network depended entirely on three facilities, General Terry decided to build a parallel teletype system using some of the equipment being installed in the fixed area communications centers and some transportable equipment belonging to the 1st Signal Brigade. The new system would divert some of the message load from the three relays of the Defense Communications System and serve as a backup system in the event of the destruction of the three principal stations. The parallel system would have only a few stations with access to the Defense Communications System's overseas network; by minimizing connections to the long-haul system it would alleviate the technical and procedural problems that had been caused by connecting tactical teletype subscribers directly to the worldwide system at the major relays.[11]

Putting the area teletype network into operation went slowly. Installation of communications centers was subject to the same delays hampering the construction of the dial telephone systems. Even when facilities were ready, overworked teletype operators and technical controllers, preoccupied with handling traffic on

[9]Fact Sheet, USARV, AVHSI-CO, 24 Mar 67, sub: Area Communications Centers, file U–442, 72A18/8; TPO 71–66, Jan 66, file 139439, 72A4171/2. Both in WNRC.

[10]Msg, CINCPAC to MACV and USASCC, PAC, 3 May 66, sub: Interim Relay Da Nang, CH–IN–91831; Msg, CINCPAC to JCS, 21 May 66, sub: Da Nang TTY Relay, CH–IN–105910. Both in CMH.

[11]For several articles concerning teletype communications in South Vietnam, see *Command Communications*, May 1967, pp. 26–46, CMH. Fact Sheet, USARV, AVHGG-CO, 15 Mar 68, sub: Reconfiguration of the In-Country Teletype Network, file 139870, 72A25/24, WNRC; 1st Sig Bde, Communications Expansion Plan, 27 Dec 67, vol. 1, an. H; 361st Sig Bn History, Sep 69, pp. 24–25, CMH.

The U.S. Army, Vietnam, Teletype Center. *Men wear special slippers to retard dust and dirt.*

active teletype circuits, found little time to put new circuits in service and take the pressure off the DCS relays. By the spring of 1967 Phu Lam was handling 27,000 messages daily, making it the busiest tape relay station in the world. Six months later the daily traffic volume on the fifty-nine circuits at Phu Lam had increased to 42,000 messages, and the average length of messages had doubled to 300 words.[12]

During a visit to South Vietnam in the fall of 1965, the director of the Defense Communications Agency, Lt. Gen. Alfred D. Starbird, warned of the unfavorable trend toward longer messages, multiple addressees, and frequent recourse to high precedences. By 1968 teletype communications were caught in a disruptive cycle worse than that envisioned by General Starbird. As the number of messages increased, delivery times took longer and precedences became meaningless. At some communications centers, half of the messages transmitted were assigned Flash or Immediate precedence, the two highest precedences. Although Immediate messages were supposed to be in the hands of addressees within thirty minutes, communications centers were regularly receiving sixty-page Immediate messages that took teletype operators eight hours simply to type on teletype tape.

[12]*Command Communications*, May 1967, pp. 26–46; MACV J-6, Briefing Notes, 6 Dec 67, sub: DCS Teletype Relay Facilities, tab D–3, file 139865, 72A25/9; Van Harlingen Debriefing Rpt, pp. 13–14, file 139772, 72A25/19. Both in WNRC.

Working under unrelenting time pressures in hectic communications centers, teletype operators inevitably made errors that resulted in requests for retransmission of garbled messages. Those corrections, called service messages, further delayed the smooth operation of the network. With misuse of precedences so widespread, the Joint Chiefs of Staff instituted a new precedence, Red Rocket, with an even higher priority than Flash, for use in South Vietnam. Red Rocket messages could be sent by only a few designated individuals, with transmission and delivery taking no more than twenty minutes. Although teletype equipment was kept on standby for the special precedence messages, they too were delayed in hectic communications centers in South Vietnam.[13]

The causes of the teletype glut were many and varied. The rapid troop build-up in South Vietnam and the fragmentation of units on widely dispersed fire bases meant that messages had to be sent to many addressees at constantly changing locations. As highly mobile combat forces moved farther from their static logistical depots and rear bases, message traffic increased. When combat units of the 1st Cavalry Division embarked in the spring of 1966 on a three-year odyssey that eventually took them throughout most of South Vietnam, signalmen remaining at the division's rear base at An Khe struggled to keep track of the widely dispersed units and to maintain the communications so essential to keeping the airmobile soldiers paid and their equipment operating.

The intense scrutiny of all operations by higher echelons of command and a centralization of authority that required many tactical decisions to be made in Saigon or Washington also affected the volume of message traffic. To ensure that everyone was kept informed of daily operations and intelligence, staff officers at field headquarters regularly sent out reports to as many as 100 addressees, including several staffs at the Pentagon and the White House. Even some senior officers stationed in Europe and Korea requested copies of messages to keep informed should they be assigned to South Vietnam in the future.[14]

Data Communications

All Army units requisitioned supplies through an automated system tied to National Inventory Control Points in the United States. The 1st Cavalry Division even maintained its pay records at the U.S. Army Finance Center at Fort Benjamin Harrison, Indiana. Although the centralization of accounting operations at a facility well supported by computers facilitated the work of Army logisticians and finance officers, permitting them to store and retrieve data automatically and to make rapid calculations, it increased the burden on Army communicators. Every personnel action affecting a man's pay, from a promotion to the purchase of sav-

---

[13]Memo, Dir, DCA, for CJCS, 16 Nov 65, sub: Report of Action on SM 1018–66, 26 October 1965, Visit to CINCPAC and South Asia, p. 5, file 139640, 72A25/8, WNRC; Interv, Binder with Van Harlingen, 26 Jan 68, pp. 50–51, VNIT 72, CMH; MACV History, 1968, vol. 2, p. 727.

[14]Interv, Binder with Van Harlingen, 26 Jan 68, pp. 50–51.

ings bonds, had to be transmitted from his company headquarters on a remote fire base in South Vietnam to the division rear base at An Khe and then to the finance center in the United States. There each soldier's pay was recomputed and transmitted to South Vietnam for preparation of the monthly payroll.[15]

Computers in centralized automated systems performed many of the functions of signalmen, theoretically reducing the burdens on communicators in the field. At some posts in the United States, fiscal, supply, and personnel information was fed into a single computer and automatically transmitted to computers at the finance, inventory control, or administrative centers. There it was processed and retransmitted to the field as a pay invoice, supply document, or personnel replacement order. With a trained, stable civilian work force and sophisticated, high-quality commercial communications such on-line computer systems could be made to work in the United States.

Because neither civilian assistance nor adequate communications were available in South Vietnam in 1965, data communications were slow and inefficient. Adapting to the military's automated administrative and logistical communications systems in South Vietnam meant laboriously keypunching data on IBM cards and feeding the cards into transceivers that were frequently jammed by cards swollen by heat and humidity. Often information from the cards was transmitted over unreliable high-frequency radio systems operating at the slow rate of 3 to 100 cards per minute and repunched at Phu Lam, Okinawa, and the Philippines for transmission on circuits to the United States. Frustrated by the uncertainties and delays of electronically communicating keypunched data, signalmen frequently packed data cards into boxes and suitcases and sent them by air courier to their destinations in Okinawa or the United States.[16]

Data communications suffered both from the poor quality of transmission systems initially available in Southeast Asia and from the long-standing neglect and low priorities accorded logistical communications. As early as 1960, signal advisers noted that "inadequacy of communications . . . inhibits the maintenance of up-to-date stock records . . . at a central point and slows down distribution and re-supply."[17] Even after the WETWASH cable was completed to the Philippines in 1964, making possible high-speed data transmission, lack of a cable link to Okinawa, the location of the principal offshore logistical support for South Vietnam, still left communicators with only the unreliable high-frequency radio system for logistical traffic. Because priorities for circuits on the wideband systems in South Vietnam went to communications for command and control, operations, or intelligence, logisticians within Southeast Asia also had to be content with slow and unreliable radio-teletype links. An assessment of logistical operations during the buildup of American troops in 1965 reported that a "lack of reliable and adequate communications . . . was a contributing factor to the logistic problems

---

[15]Van Harlingen Debriefing Rpt, pp. 13–14.

[16]MS, USAF, Project Corona Harvest, Communications in Southeast Asia, 8 Oct 70, pp.137–42, K143.50103-3, OAFH; CINCPAC History, 1965, p. 253.

[17]Rpt, MAAG, Vietnam, Sep 60, sub: Visit of General Williston B. Palmer to MAAG Vietnam, I–16273/60, ISA file 333, 64A2170/11, WNRC.

The Data Relay at Phu Lam

that had developed."[18]

Neglect of logistical and administrative communications stemmed in part from the Army staff's failure to establish firm control over the Army's automatic data processing needs. This lack of control had made it difficult for signalmen to keep track of the communications needs of the many computers and data systems fielded during the early 1960s. Although the special assistant, Army Information and Data Systems, had been supervising the Army's use and development of computerized equipment, he had failed to determine from the chief signal officer whether available communications could support new computer systems or to request that the signal staff engineer communications with the new systems in mind. Once new computer and data systems were fielded, signalmen were faced with urgent and unprogrammed demands to develop expensive special communications on an emergency basis.[19]

The Automatic Digital Network (AUTODIN), a worldwide high-speed data

---

[18]Quote from Joint Logistics Review Board, *Logistic Support in the Vietnam Era* (hereafter cited as *Logistic Support*), 3 vols., 1969, 2:153–54, 71A2351/6, WNRC. Several documents pertaining to data communications in support of logistics are contained in file U–356, 72A18/6, WNRC. See also USARV, The Logistics Review, 1965–1969, vol. 2, pp. A–26 through A–37 and vol. 8, an. Z, CMH.

[19]The issue of engineering and developing communications for automated equipment is discussed in inclosures and background papers attached to Memo, DA, Asst Dep CofS for Mil Opns, for Actg Dep CofS for Mil Opns, 29 May 65, sub: Appraisal of U.S. Army Strategic Communications Command and Other U.S. Army Long Range Communications Facilities, Martin Board files, CMH.

network, was born when the Defense Communications Agency in February 1963 combined fledgling digital communications programs of the Army and the Air Force. The first nine AUTODIN switches were built in the United States. When the Defense Communications Agency, Pacific, convened a meeting of communicators from headquarters throughout the Pacific in October 1964 to determine how to improve the primitive data network in the Pacific, uncertainties concerning the future availability of the high-quality circuits required for digital communications precluded any consideration of expanding the AUTODIN system to Indochina. Once the Integrated Wideband Communications System was approved in the summer of 1965, data nets were quickly requested. In December 1965 the secretary of defense approved a two-phase plan providing for the immediate establishment of a manual data net with relays at Phu Lam and Nha Trang and at Korat, Thailand, and the eventual installation of automatic switches at those same locations to connect to a worldwide AUTODIN network.[20]

By June 1967 the manual relay at Phu Lam was operating four overseas data links—to Okinawa, the Philippines, Hawaii, and California—and ten data circuits to local subscribers. After the opening two months later of the relay at Nha Trang with one overseas trunk to Okinawa and eleven circuits to local subscribers, all the major depots in South Vietnam were connected to the 14th Inventory Control Center in Long Binh, the hub of the Army's supply system in South Vietnam. With data circuits operating at speeds of from 10 to 200 cards per minute, the Phu Lam relay was soon handling 500,000 punch cards per day and the Nha Trang relay 330,000 punch cards per day.[21]

In September 1967 the first overseas AUTODIN switch opened at Clark Air Base in the Philippines. The activation in 1968 of automatic switching centers at Phu Lam, Nha Trang, and Korat inaugurated the conversion of both data and teletype communications in Southeast Asia to the digital mode. Digital communications use the presence or absence of electrical current, rather than a constant supply of current on assigned frequencies as in standard analog communications, to convey signals and data. Each occurrence of a pulse or no pulse, called a bit, when combined with other bits in a binary-code computer, replicates information directly from computer to computer, eliminating the keypunching that makes data transmission by cards so cumbersome. Since teletype pulses are easily translated into a binary code, the same transmission and switching equipment can be used for both teletype and data communications. The capability to store digital information on magnetic tape for later transmission at different speeds enables the switches to relay traffic between terminals operating at varying speeds without slowing the faster circuit. Parity checks, format reviews programmed into the com-

---

[20]For good discussions of the evolution of automatic telephone and digital networks, see "AUTOVON/AUTODIN Development," *Command Communications*, June 1967, pp. 30–33, CMH; and Joseph Rose, "AUTOVON and AUTODIN: Past, Present and Future," *Signal*, April 1968, pp. 13–18.

[21]Memo, Dep Secy of Defense for Secys of Mil Depts, 6 Dec 65, sub: System Plan for Expansion and Upgrade of the Interim Defense Communications System AUTODIN Pacific, Southeast Asia, JCS 222/869–3, JACO (1965), DA/3, NARS; MS, USAF, Project Corona Harvest, Communications in Southeast Asia, 8 Oct 70, pp. 139–46; "Data Communications in Vietnam," *Command Communications*, September 1967, pp. 57–60; DA, OCC-E, IWCS Progress Report, 25 Jan 66, tab E. Latter two in CMH.

puters controlling digital switches, detect errors before transmission, thereby reducing service messages. Encryption of the already encoded signal also is far simpler than the encryption of an analog signal.[22]

Because military data terminals and teletype control units for converting normal teletype signals to digital signals were not available when AUTODIN high-speed switches were completed, the signal brigade contracted for commercial computers and teletype message-processing equipment. The first terminal was installed at Long Binh in May 1968. It communicated with the Phu Lam AUTODIN relay at 1,600 words per minute and immediately reduced the glut of message traffic at that important Army headquarters and logistical base. After a new digital terminal at Cam Ranh Bay was connected to the Nha Trang AUTODIN switch in December 1968, teletype traffic volume at the tape relay in Nha Trang decreased so much that the Defense Communications Agency removed the relay from the Defense Communications System. By February 1969 enough teletype traffic had been routed over the forty-five digital circuits at the automatic switching center at Phu Lam that the remaining eighteen circuits at the tape relay handled only 8,000 messages a day. Later that year the Defense Communications Agency removed the Phu Lam and Da Nang tape relays from the Defense Communications System.[23]

The new Automatic Digital Network operated at a far greater speed than the previous teletype tape and manual punch card networks. Teletype control units and newly fielded military digital subscriber terminals poured out paper tape at the rate of 3,000 words per minute. For data communications the speed of the system depended on the format of the data. Card data moved at the slow rate of 200 cards per minute. Far more efficient were magnetic tapes, operating at the rate of 2,400 bits per second. Even so, General Van Harlingen viewed the Automatic Digital Network as "a mixed blessing, creating nearly as many problems as it has solved."[24]

Trying to bridge the gap between an automatic digital system operating at an average of 1,500 words per minute and tactical teletype circuits passing traffic at 60 or 100 words per minute, the men in the 1st Signal Brigade's communications centers experienced maintenance problems with overextended tactical machines. In a typical situation that occurred during the summer of 1970, the Army tape relay at Da Nang received twenty Flash messages in a twenty-minute period on its digital circuit from the AUTODIN switch. It had to relay the messages to tactical subscribers on circuits operating at 100 words per minute, taking twenty minutes to process each message. When the subscribers' tactical equipment began overheating, the speed of transmission had to be reduced to sixty

---

[22]The following articles contain discussions of the technical characteristics and advantages of military digital communications: "Panel on the Next Decade in Digital Communications," *Signal*, July 1964, pp. 50–69; Lt. Col. Robert A. Bourcy (USAF), "AUTODIN Worldwide Automatic Digital Network," *Signal*, March 1966, pp. 14–20; Stanley M. Schreiner, "Technical Progress in Military Digital Communications," *Signal*, May/June 1969, pp. 107–12.

[23]Van Harlingen Debriefing Rpt, pp. 14–15; 1st Sig Bde, Briefing for Maj Gen Walter E. Lotz, Jr., on Personnel and Training, 9 Sep 68, Incl 3; ORLL, 1st Sig Bde, 31 Jan 69, pp. 4–5; MACV J–6, Briefing Notes, 10 Mar 69, sub: DCS Teletype Relay Facilities, tab D–2, file 139865, 72A25/23, WNRC; USARV, CE, List of Topics, 8 Apr 69, Incl 1.

[24]Quote from Van Harlingen Debriefing Rpt, p. 15.

words per minute. Besides such technical problems, tactical operators lacking special training on the operation of the new Automatic Digital Network were bewildered by its formats and procedures. The 1st Signal Brigade had to keep troubleshooting teams constantly on the road to help inexperienced operators. Buildings housing the sensitive equipment had to be kept at a constant 73 degrees and 54 percent humidity; operators had to wear rubber athletic shoes to avoid scuffing dust into the air and into the sensitive equipment.[25]

Unwilling to rely completely on the Automatic Digital Network, the 1st Signal Brigade retained a comprehensive teletype tape network in South Vietnam with access to the digital system at seven relay points. Similarly, the National Security Agency felt the AUTODIN system provided insufficient security for certain special types of encrypted intelligence and retained its own discrete worldwide high-speed teletype network, called CRITICOMM. Other special-purpose teletype and data nets also remained separate from the Automatic Digital Network. The Pacific Air Force's Interim Automated Command and Control System, a digital network installed throughout the Pacific in mid-1969 to provide direct command and control of air operations, became the principal backup to the AUTODIN net within the Defense Communications System in the Pacific theater.[26]

Overseas Transmission Links

C onnecting the Southeast Asian mainland with theater and worldwide telephone and digital networks had been impossible when high-frequency radios were the sole means of overseas communications. The Torrid Zone, in which Indochina is located, had the world's worst atmospheric interference with high-frequency propagation. To obtain the few good frequencies available in the two- to nine-megahertz range, the only suitable high frequencies in the region, American signalmen had to abide by the rules of the International Telecommunications Union, a regulatory body that sought worldwide to avoid the confusion that occurred when frequency management broke down. Except for those frequencies universally reserved for aircraft use, the International Telecommunications Union recognized the sovereign right of every nation to control the use of the frequency spectrum as it would any other natural resource within its borders.[27]

Obtaining frequencies from the South Vietnamese Directorate of Posts and Telecommunications, the governmental body charged with managing frequencies, was particularly frustrating. Poor record keeping and inadequate monitoring equipment hampered the directorate's ability to regulate frequency use. An

---

[25]Interv, Maj Ronald W. Schuette, CO, 23d MHD, with Lt Col Leonard J. Riley, CO, Phu Lam Signal Battalion, Apr 69, VNIT 483; "Phu Lam Signal Battalion," *Command Communications*, March 1970, pp. 23–28. Both in CMH. ORLL, 1st Sig Bde, 31 Oct 70, p. 10, file 228–03 (1970), 72A7128/5, WNRC.

[26]MACV J–6, Briefing Notes, 10 Mar 69, sub: DCS AUTODIN, SEASIA (Final), tab J–3, and 18 Apr 69, sub: PACAF Integrated Automated Command and Control System, tab J–10. Both in file 139865, 72A25/9, WNRC.

[27]MACV, Senior Communicators Tactical Planning Conference, Summary of Remarks by ACofS, J6, MACV, 14 Sep 67, p. 3, file 139865, 72A25/9, WNRC.

assigned frequency might be found to be already in use by the South Vietnamese military, which usually neglected to request frequency assignments from the governmental agency. American signal officers, on the other hand, also had to obtain permission from the Pacific Command in Hawaii to use frequencies authorized by the South Vietnamese. Processing requests through both the South Vietnamese government and the Pacific Command usually took several months. Having gone to the trouble of obtaining authorization for a frequency, Americans tended to continue using it even when seasonal propagational changes dictated otherwise. Investigations of the causes of unreliable service at the Phu Lam station invariably concluded that improper frequencies rather than faulty equipment caused most technical difficulties on the overseas strategic systems.[28]

Until the activation of a high-frequency radio station in Bangkok in 1958, the Saigon station had been the sole American gateway to Indochina. In the early 1960s the two stations were moved from cramped urban quarters and upgraded with new single-sideband radios which required less power to operate and were less susceptible to noise interference. In 1965 the Strategic Communications Command established another station at Nha Trang. By 1967 the encroachment of American compounds around the stations was causing interference. The 1st Signal Brigade moved its receiver for the Phu Lam station from Ba Queo to Long Binh and relocated the entire Nha Trang station at Dong Ba Thin, an isolated area halfway between Nha Trang and Cam Ranh Bay. By then the Army's high-frequency radios were used only as backup to more reliable, high-quality undersea cable and satellites. Only a high-frequency system between Saigon and Seoul, installed and operated by the 1st Signal Brigade for the forces of the Army of the Republic of Korea in South Vietnam, and several Navy ship-to-shore high-frequency nets operated regularly in Southeast Asia. In September 1970 the Army began dismantling its high-frequency radio systems.[29]

High-frequency radio was used for nonmilitary purposes. For example, the South Vietnamese Postes, Telegraphes, et Telephones operated circuits on several high-frequency international systems to California that it leased to the U.S. Agency for International Development to allow soldiers in hospitals in South Vietnam to call their homes. As another morale service, the Military Affiliate Radio System (MARS) employed high-frequency radios to enable American soldiers to make phone calls or send messages, called MARSGRAMS, to their families in the United States. At the peak of the MARS program in April 1970, forty-seven MARS stations located at military bases throughout South Vietnam made a record 42,325 phone patches in one month to stations in the United States manned by amateur radio operators.[30]

Although originally hailed by the military as a breakthrough in international communications, ionoscatter and troposcatter radio proved an unsatisfactory

[28]Msg, CINCUSARPAC to DCA, PAC, 25 Feb 64, sub: Low Reliability Trunks—Jan 64, CMH.

[29]DCA, SAM, Commander's Report: 1 Jul 66–1 Jul 67, tab II (G), DCA files, CMH; ORLL, 1st Sig Bde, 31 Oct 70, p. 9.

[30]Fact Sheet, USARV, AVHGG-CS, 15 Mar 68, sub: Commercial Telephone Service, RVN to CONUS "Call Mom," tab T, file 139870, 72A25/24, WNRC; "Call Home," *Command Communications*, October 1968, p. 53, CMH; Rienzi Debriefing Rpt, p. 49.

replacement for high-frequency radio. Despite years of work, the 471-mile system from Vung Tau to Green Hill provided only low-quality voice circuits. The 7,800-mile troposcatter and ionoscatter network along the island chain from Hawaii to Okinawa provided satisfactory service, but was expensive and inefficient. To keep the system's two channels in operation for six years required maintaining and manning ten terminals, some located on deserted atolls, at a cost to the Army of $40 million. Susceptible to jamming by either the Soviet Union or the People's Republic of China, the system's utility was marginal for military emergencies. On 31 May 1967, the Army closed down the Pacific scatter system between Hawaii and the Philippines.[31]

By then the military had cable connections from South Vietnam to the United States via WETWASH undersea cable and leased circuits on a commercial cable recently installed between Hawaii and the Philippines. Circuits were also extended to Okinawa over a contractor-operated troposcatter system connecting the Philippines, Taiwan, Okinawa, and Japan. Enthusiastic about the quality and reliability of undersea cable, the Army also tried to obtain permission from the Joint Chiefs of Staff to connect to a British undersea cable system extending from Singapore to Hong Kong to Guam. Because the proposal required a troposcatter link from Thailand to Singapore, with a costly relay in Malaysia, Deputy Secretary of Defense Cyrus R. Vance on 30 September 1965 disapproved the proposal.[32]

Although the cost of installing undersea cable was greater than the cost of buying and installing high-frequency or troposcatter radios, the operation and maintenance cost of undersea cable was minimal. The U.S. Underseas Cable Corporation, the same company that had installed WETWASH, was also commissioned to install a coastal cable between Da Nang and Sattahip, Thailand. After receiving the contract for the coastal system in the spring of 1966, the company sent its cable ship *Neptun* to survey the route. Returning to the United States in December to load cable for the project, the *Neptun* in January sailed back to the South China Sea, where it transferred some of the cable to a second ship, the *Omega*. By May 1967 the two ships had laid 1,567 nautical miles of cable and installed ninety-three submerged repeaters, devices that maintained the strength of the signal as it was carried along the undersea cables. The installation time had been shortened by the use on the *Neptun* of a computer that permitted technicians to position repeaters precisely and to set equalizers to compensate for deviations in the strength of the signal caused by environmental or electrical characteristics of the cable.

The *Neptun* remained in the South China Sea to be ready to repair any breaks in the coastal cable or WETWASH. On 4 October 1967, it was called out on its first

---

[31]Maj. Frederick Eisele, "The End of an Era in Communications," *Trends*, June 1970, p. 27, first printed at U.S. Army Signal School, in CMH files; USASCC, Press Release 67-24-M, 31 May 67, file 228-06, ACC Historians files; USASCC History, FY-67, p. 26, CMH; 1st Sig Bde, Communications Expansion Plan, 27 Dec 67, vol. 1, an. B; Memo, DCA for Dir, C-E (J-6), JCS, 4 Feb 65, sub: Pacific Ionospheric Scatter System, JCS 222/837, JACO (1965), DA/3, NARS.

[32]Rpt, J-6 to JCS, 20 Jul 65, sub: Systems Plan for Increased DCA Teletype Service, Pacific Area, JACO (1965), DA/2; Memo, Dir, DCA, for JCS, 8 Jun 66, sub: Troposcatter System, Philippines to Japan, JCS 222/765-11, JACO (1966), DA/1; Memo, Dep Secy of Defense for CJCS, 30 Sep 65, sub: Thailand-Malaysian Communications, JCS 2339/184-2, JACO (1965), DA/55. All in NARS.

repair mission, a break in the coastal cable about fifty miles off the coast of Sattahip, Thailand. Because most of the strategic links between air bases in Thailand and the Military Assistance Command in Saigon were severed, the Defense Communications Agency, Southeast Asia Mainland, sent an officer on the ship to advise signalmen in Saigon of the progress of the repairs. When inadequate restoral plans delayed the rerouting of those circuits over land-based systems, the Defense Communications Agency reviewed all restoral plans. Having learned by that experience, technical controllers were able quickly to reroute circuits a few months later when a ship dragging its anchor in a storm cut the cable between Da Nang and Qui Nhon.[33]

Although overland segments of the Integrated Wideband Communications System could be used to back up the strategic coastal cable, there was no comparable alternate route for cable circuits to the United States. When a junction box malfunctioned on the commercial cable at Guam in August 1967, the Defense Communications Agency, Southeast Asia Mainland, had to reroute high-priority overseas transmissions over high-frequency radio and satellite systems. Because most of the circuits required high-quality wideband channels, the high-frequency circuits were unsuitable. By February 1969, when the WETWASH cable was severed fifteen miles offshore from Nha Trang, enough satellite circuits were available to restore all high-priority circuits. The Defense Communications Agency had leased thirty channels linking Bangkok with Hawaii on the first commercial satellite system serving Southeast Asia, installed in late 1966 by the Communications Satellite Corporation (COMSAT).[34]

Satellite Links

Problems with the development and operation of military satellites had forced the Defense Communications Agency to lease commercial circuits. To augment the military satellite terminals operating since 1964 from Saigon and Bangkok in the Synchronous Communications Satellite (SYNCOM) System, a program that was actually intended only for research and experimentation, Secretary McNamara directed the Defense Communications Agency to expedite a new satellite program, the Defense Communications Satellite System (DCSS), to get stations

---

[33]MACV J–6, Briefing Notes, 8 Apr 69, sub: Wetwash Cable, tab E–3, and ibid., sub: Submarine Cable, Project 439L SEED TREE, tab E–4, both in file 139865, 72A25/23, WNRC. Herbert H. Schenck, "Ocean Cable Links Southeast Asia," *Signal*, November 1967, pp. 42–44; 1st Sig Bde, Regional Communications Group, IWCS Orientation, Apr 68, ch. 15, in VNIT 458, CMH.

[34]Ltr, DCA, SAM, to USARV, 4 May 69, sub: Recommendation for Award of the Meritorious Unit Commendation, CMH; DA, OCC-E, IWCS Progress Report, 25 Jan 66, tab F; 1st Sig Bde, Communications Expansion Plan, 27 Dec 67, vol. 1, an. C; Msg, CINCPAC to JCS, 6 Nov 65, sub: Wideband Communications Restoral in PACOM, file 139887, 72A25/24; Msg, DCA, PAC, to PACAF et al., 23 Dec 66, sub: Cable Restoral by HF Radio, CM-IN-234533, file 14, 70A2328/6. Latter two in WNRC. JCSM 903-65, JCS for Secy of Defense, 22 Dec 65, sub: Employment of Communications Satellite Capability in the Pacific, JCS 222/910-1, JACO (1965), DA/5; Memo, Dep Secy of Defense for Secys of Mil Depts et al., 21 Jan 66, sub: Employment of Satellite Communications Circuits in the Far Pacific, JCS 222/910-2, JACO (1966), DA/3. Latter two in NARS.

to Southeast Asia as soon as possible. After a satellite for the new system was launched in the summer of 1966, two terminals, called MSC–46's, were rushed to Ba Queo and Nha Trang. They underwent ten months of testing and adjustments before they were put into operation. In the meantime, the SYNCOM terminal at Ba Queo and five circuits routed to South Vietnam from the commercial terminal in Bangkok were the only satellite communications available to the Military Assistance Command.[35]

By the time the last link of the SYNCOM network between the Philippines and Hawaii closed down in 1969, the Defense Communications Satellite System had grown to fourteen ground stations—seven of them in the Pacific—communicating through twenty-seven satellites. Each satellite, weighing 100 pounds and measuring 36 inches in diameter, revolved around the earth in a nonsynchronous orbit between 18,200 and 18,500 miles above the equator. Because the nonsynchronous satellites had no fixed location in relation to the earth, ground stations communicating with each other used whatever satellites were mutually visible as relays. The MSC–46 terminals were housed in three vans and used a forty-foot antenna covered by an inflatable protective dome. They proved their adaptability to combat conditions when rocket fragments hit the antenna at Nha Trang. The dome deflated, but the terminal continued to operate.[36]

The quality of communications provided by the new military system was disappointing. Even after the Defense Communications Agency, Pacific, reduced the number of channels on the two systems to South Vietnam from eleven to five, the links failed to meet the quality and transmission standards of the Defense Communications System. Rather than being used for the digital and secure-voice circuits for which the systems were intended, they handled only voice, teletype, and low-speed data circuits. A smaller TSC–54 satellite terminal, installed in a single van and using an eighteen-foot antenna, proved no better. Deployed to U Tapao Air Base in Thailand in early 1968 to link Guam, it was inoperable 25 percent of the time.[37]

Organizational confusion and the premature fielding of experimental equipment hindered the development of reliable satellite communications from Southeast Asia. After the National Aeronautics and Space Administration completed its experiments with the SYNCOM system in 1965, it turned the entire

[35]Interv, author with Sgt Maj (ret.) Frank W. Hedge, former satellite terminal chief, 6 Dec 78, Historians files, CMH; Memo, Secy of Defense for Secy of Army and CJCS, 16 Apr 66, sub: Employment of Satellite Communications Capability in the Pacific, JCS 222/910–4, JACO (1966), DA/3; Memo, Dir, DCA, for Secy of Defense, 8 Dec 66, sub: Utilization of IDCSP Resources, JCS 222/999–2, JACO (1966), DA/6. Latter two in NARS. U.S. Army Satellite Communications Agency (SATCOM), SATCOM 1966, 1966, an. E, file 139571, 72A25/6, WNRC; 1st Sig Bde, Regional Communications Group, IWCS Orientation, Apr 68, ch. 16, in VNIT 458; DA, OCC-E, IWCS Progress Report, 25 Jan 66, tab H; Msg, SATCOM to DCA, 16 Nov 66, sub: AN/MSC–46 Satellite Communications Terminals, Serial No. 6 and 7, CM–IN–217581, file 14, 70A2328/6, WNRC.

[36]DOD, Press Conference, Harold Brown, Secy of Air Force, and Lt Gen Alfred Starbird, Dir, DCA, 17 Jun 66, file 228–06 (STRATCOM-PAC 1966), ACC Historians files; 1st Sig Bde, Communications Expansion Plan, 27 Dec 67, vol. 1, an. A. MACV History, 1967, vol. 2, pp. 783–84, and ibid., 1969, vol. 2, ch. 9, pp. 124–25, both in CMH.

[37]USASCC History, FY–69, pp. 69–74, CMH; MACV J–6, Briefing Notes, 8 Apr 69, sub: Satellite Communications-Pacific Area, file 139865, 72A25/23, WNRC.

system over to the Department of Defense. Responsibility for the system passed from the Satellite Communications Agency, a developmental organization, to the Army unit operating the ground stations, the Strategic Communications Command. Finding it impossible logistically to support an experimental system for which repair parts were unavailable in the regular inventory, the Strategic Communications Command returned responsibility to the Satellite Communications Agency, which managed the SYNCOM network for the remainder of its life. Although the Defense Communications Satellite System had been planned as a standard system to be operated and maintained by the Strategic Communications Command, its accelerated development left signalmen with technical deficiencies to correct and an inadequate supply base for repair parts. Only after those problems were finally resolved in the early 1970s did the satellites of the Defense Communications Satellite System eliminate the United States' dangerous dependence on undersea cables for all wideband communications to South Vietnam.[38]

Secure-Voice Communications

A primary justification for obtaining a satellite terminal during the Tonkin crisis, and later for leasing channels from the Communications Satellite Corporation and installing terminals for the Defense Communications Satellite System, was the inability of the high-frequency overseas net to handle the secure telephone transmissions needed for communications between leaders in Saigon, Hawaii, and Washington. Similarly, the Joint Chiefs of Staff approved the installation of an overseas secure-voice network because they expected to have high-quality satellite channels for its transmission.[39]

For good fidelity, secure telephone communications required a clear transmission channel of fifty kilohertz bandwidth, far wider than a normal three kilohertz speech circuit. Although the first satellite system installed in August 1964 had the requisite bandwidth, the poor quality of transmission and the lack of sophisticated security equipment prevented the operation of secure-voice circuits from the Military Assistance Command to Hawaii and the Pentagon. Signalmen in Saigon installed direct secure lines only between the ambassador, General Westmoreland, the MACV war room, and the 2d Air Division headquarters. With the completion of undersea cables to Southeast Asia and access to high-quality circuits, the Defense Communications Agency designed a manually switched network, TALK QUICK, that by June 1966 included thirty-eight subscribers, a switchboard in Southeast Asia, and trunk lines over the undersea cable system

---

[38]SATCOM, SATCOM 1966, an. E.

[39]Msg, CINCPAC to JCS, 6 Nov 65, sub: Wideband Communications Restoral in PACOM; Msg, CINCUSARPAC to CC-E, DA, 12 Apr 65, sub: Secure Voice Capability, CMH; Rpt, J-6 to JCS, 24 Sep 65, sub: DCA Plan for PACOM Secure Voice Requirement, JCS 222/751-4, JACO (1965), DA/1, NARS.

to another switchboard in Hawaii.[40]

In July 1967 a new 100-line automatic dial switchboard, the FTC–31, provided secure dial communications in the Saigon area. Twelve small regional secure-voice cordless switchboards (SECORDS), each capable of servicing sixteen subscribers and five trunks, completed the new secure telephone system that replaced TALK QUICK. The new secure telephone system was then connected to a worldwide network, the Automatic Secure Voice Communications (AUTOSEVOCOM) System, that the Defense Communications Agency had developed based on the experience of signalmen in South Vietnam with TALK QUICK. By mid-1969, 216 subscribers in South Vietnam, at headquarters in Saigon and command posts down to division levels, had AUTOSEVOCOM service.[41]

Forming three battalions—the Phu Lam, Nha Trang, and Da Nang Signal Battalions—the 1st Signal Brigade's Regional Communications Group operated the switches for the new AUTOSEVOCOM, AUTODIN, and direct-dial networks, as well as the overseas high-frequency radio stations and satellite terminals in South Vietnam. In Thailand, the 29th Signal Group and Air Force communications units performed similar missions. Because the other signal groups in South Vietnam—the 2d, 12th, and 21st Signal Groups—were not adequately staffed to operate and maintain the dial exchanges and AUTODIN and AUTOSEVOCOM subscriber terminals assigned to them, the Regional Communications Group also provided technical assistance and conducted training for those tactical signal units. Since the new networks were activated or perfected just as the United States began making plans for a gradual withdrawal from South Vietnam, the 1st Signal Brigade was unable to obtain additional personnel to staff new facilities and had to transfer men from tactical units to the Regional Communications Group as new facilities went into operation. *(Map 20)*

From a technical perspective the visionary plans conceived in the mid-1960s for exploiting communications technology in South Vietnam had been met; only their time schedules had been proved wrong. By the time that many of the ambitious projects were finished, the United States had already begun withdrawing from the war. But those facilities that were available early proved indispensable. Better telephone and teletype networks and undersea cables made possible more effective large-scale air operations, especially the B–52 support flown from Guam and Thailand. Automatic teletype and data nets permitted commanders to obtain control of the huge logistical effort required to sustain a large, well-equipped force halfway around the world just as the logistical system appeared about to collapse from the volume of supplies flowing into South Vietnam. Satellite links and secure voice permitted key military and political leaders in Washington to exercise direct

---

[40]MACV History, 1965, pp. 390–92, CMH; MACV, TALK QUICK Secure Voice System, Oct 68, file 139620, 72A25/7, WNRC; DA, OCC-E, IWCS Progress Report, 25 Jan 66, tab G.

[41]Memo, Dir, DCA, for JCS, 13 Jun 66, sub: Defense Communications Agency System Plan for a World-Wide Secure Voice Network, JCS 222/898–3, JACO (1966), DA/3, NARS. A comprehensive summary of the AUTOSEVOCOM project is contained in USASCC, AUTOSEVOCOM Phase 1, Implementation/Installation, Final Report, 2 vols., 20 Jun 70, CMH. For its implementation in South Vietnam, see USARV, C-E LOI 4, 3 Apr 68, and 1st Sig Bde, LOI 1–68, 6 Nov 68. Both in file 139804, 72A25/20, WNRC. USARV, CE, List of Topics, 8 Apr 69, Incl 6.

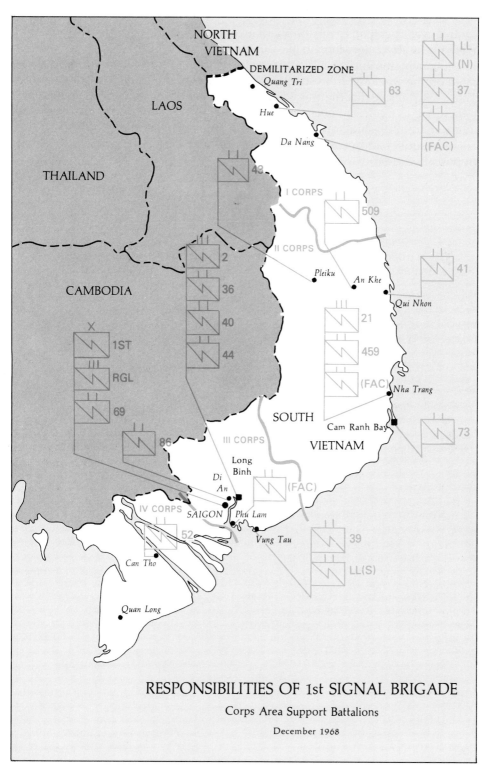

RESPONSIBILITIES OF 1st SIGNAL BRIGADE

Corps Area Support Battalions

December 1968

MAP 20

control over operations in South Vietnam and caused day-to-day events in South Vietnam to affect decisions in Washington.

Ultimately, the impact of U.S. strategic communications on the war was predicated on the wisdom of the strategy that those communications made possible. Those who believe that the war was to be fought and won as a counterinsurgency rather than as a conventional conflict, feel that B–52's, huge logistical bases, and direction from Washington were the wrong approach. For them, the PRC–25 had far more utility in defeating the Viet Cong and North Vietnamese than any troposcatter radio or satellite terminal.

14

The Integrated Wideband Communications System

The effectiveness of sophisticated automatic telephone, teletype, and data networks depended upon a high-quality transmission system. Meeting in Hawaii in 1964 to determine ways to correct signal problems uncovered during the Tonkin crisis, signalmen decided to build a transmission system that could accommodate those sophisticated strategic communications networks while also serving as a tactical area system. They assumed that designing a system to the rigorous technical specifications of strategic systems would also satisfy tactical requirements.

Those early planners failed to recognize that tactical communications imposed demands that technical sophistication alone could not satisfy. Nor did they anticipate that building an integrated fixed system would involve agonizingly slow bureaucratic and fiscal procedures, innumerable technical complexities, and the sheer physical difficulties of transporting, installing, and erecting sophisticated communications equipment in an undeveloped land amidst the confusion and hazards of war.[1]

Building an IWCS Site in Quang Tri

In I Corps, for example, the fixed system never fulfilled its intended mission. The heaviest fighting in the northern provinces was over for American forces by the time the Integrated Wideband Communications System reached Quang Tri, the site of the principal airfield and the forward staging area for the U.S. forces fighting along the Demilitarized Zone. In the spring of 1967, as General

[1]The best discussion of the difficulties encountered in constructing the Integrated Wideband Communications System is contained in MS, Col Frank K. Gardner, A Study of the Delays Experienced in Providing the Integrated Wideband Communications System, SEASIA (IWCS), August 1964–January 1969, 3 Mar 69, U.S. Army War College, CMH. (Hereafter cited as Gardner Study.)

Westmoreland was planning to send Task Force Oregon to I Corps, the Pentagon authorized the system between Phu Bai and Quang Tri. It took two years to complete.

The delays surrounding the construction of that link were typical of those that plagued the installation of most of the links in the wideband system. Soon after receiving approval for the new system, General Terry sent a team to survey a site at Quang Tri. At Phu Bai, the southern terminal equipment had only to be added to an existing facility. Based on technical and security considerations, the team recommended use of land adjacent to the Quang Tri advisory compound for the northern terminal. When the province senior adviser disapproved of the location, General Terry sent his project officer for the Integrated Wideband Communications System, Lt. Col. Thomas P. Pomeroy, to Da Nang to convince the I Corps deputy senior adviser to overrule the local adviser. Then, months of inconclusive negotiations between the signal brigade and the province chief and local landowner ensued without lease of the desired property. Not until September 1967 did the brigade finally obtain permission from the I Corps commanding general to begin construction during negotiations, an exception granted only when contested land contained no houses, crops, or graves.[2]

While the 3d Naval Construction Battalion (Seabees) was stocking construction material at the site in anticipation of building access roads, foundations, and fencing for the facility, the III Marine Amphibious Force proposed relocating the terminal to a new airport being built several miles from the original site. Survey and engineering of the new signal path from Phu Bai to the Quang Tri airport showed that the site change entailed major modifications to the contract with Page. General Van Harlingen, who by that time had replaced General Terry, convinced the marines that the original plans were best. In the meantime, the Navy construction battalion had been directed to another project, and not until December was it able to return to Quang Tri to build an access road, grade the land, and lay foundations. With the foundation work started, the Page contractors responsible for construction of the building and installation of equipment predicted the site would be ready for operation by July 1968. Although Brig. Gen. Samuel L. Huey (USAF), the MACV J-6, pressed for earlier completion to serve the MACV forward headquarters being established in Phu Bai, the unanticipated disruptions caused by the Tet offensive made even Page's timetable overly optimistic.

After the fighting ended in Hue, construction of the Quang Tri site moved ahead rapidly. Giving the site top priority, Page moved twenty technicians from a project in the delta to assist the team installing equipment at Quang Tri. The 1st Signal Brigade assigned an officer full time to solve supply problems and arrange for construction support to expedite completion of the Quang Tri terminal. Food and tents were provided to the civilian installers, and a platoon of Seabees was found to help Page complete its construction and to repair the braces

---

[2]Detailed accounts of the progress and problems involved with the construction of every IWCS site can be found in memos and notes in 1st Signal Brigade files marked, IWCS Weekly Status Reports, 25 Aug 66 to 23 Nov 67, and IWCS Weekly Status Reports, 23 Nov 67 to 27 Nov 68, files 139621 and 139622 (hereafter cited as IWCS Weekly Status Rpt), 72A25/7, WNRC. Data concerning the construction of the Quang Tri site has been extracted from those files.

of an antenna damaged in transit.

After the installation was completed in August, the 1st Signal Brigade began thirty days of system testing required before the government formally accepted the equipment from Page. When a severe monsoon storm disrupted Marine tactical communications between Phu Bai and Quang Tri, the 1st Signal Brigade suspended the tests and installed operational circuits over the new IWCS link. Resuming testing once the tactical systems were restored, the government finally accepted the system from the contractor on 11 October 1968. By that time, the 1st Cavalry Division was leaving its bases and landing zones around Quang Tri for its new home in III Corps. The terminal had not been ready in time to support the many military operations in the region during the Tet offensive, the relief of Khe Sanh, or the assault into the A Shau.

Similar problems beset the construction at most other sites. While some difficulties and delays were attributable to the fortunes of war, the attempt to bring modern communications technology to a remote, relatively undeveloped area of the world had set in motion an unforeseen concatenation of technical, logistical, and management problems.

The Original Plan

C haracterizing long-lines military communications in Southeast Asia as "a heterogeneous structure with an uneconomical use of tactical equipment," in 1964 the original DCA architects of the Integrated Wideband Communications System planned to upgrade the existing BACKPORCH network in Southeast Asia to the standards of the Defense Communications System in one year. They intended to position technical controls at every nodal point of the BACKPORCH system to permit messages of all types to travel from one link of the system to another without the delay of reprocessing or degradation of signal. The architects wanted large billboard antennas to obtain circuits with signal strength and absence of noise sufficient to meet the standards of the Defense Communications System. To improve communications in the Saigon area, they planned new, fixed microwave terminals for Phu Lam, Tan Son Nhut, and major headquarters in the city. Some system redundancy would be obtained by moving MRC–85 terminals from Nha Trang and Phu Lam to Pleiku and Vung Tau and installing a microwave system from Vung Tau to Saigon as an alternate route from the capital to stations in the north. The original plan also provided for expansion of the austere signal base in Thailand by diverting equipment from a canceled project in Indonesia. Having exhausted military stocks of transportable communications terminals meeting DCS specifications, the Defense Communications Agency prescribed the use of commercial equipment installed in prefabricated buildings for all new strategic communications sites constructed in South Vietnam.[3]

---

[3]The systems plan developed at the conference in Hawaii is contained in Memo, Dir, DCA, for CJCS, 28 Dec 64, sub: SAA, App. B to JCSM 124–65, 70A3717/28, WNRC. For the first draft of the systems plan, see file 139439, 72A4171/2, WNRC.

Technical Controller Checks Circuits at Phan Rang

As the director of the Defense Communications Agency was reviewing plans for the expanded system, communications engineers from the Defense Communications Agency, Pacific, inspecting the BACKPORCH terminals cast doubts on the feasibility of upgrading the three-year-old system. They found that several BACKPORCH terminals had been situated with security rather than engineering considerations in mind. Adjacent buildings blocked antennas, and sensitive equipment was vulnerable to vehicular ignition and electrical interference. Although the terminals were nominally transportable, the expense of moving billets for operating personnel, setting new concrete pads for antennas, and installing new security facilities anchored them to their existing locations. Compensation for poor siting and external interference required even more sophisticated technical controls and equipment to filter out noise and improve connections between systems than originally anticipated by military planners.[4]

The diversity of equipment forming the BACKPORCH network created unique problems. Combining light, highly mobile gear such as the TRC–24 VHF multichannel, TRC–29 microwave, and TRC–90 troposcatter radios with heavier, fixed troposcatter and microwave equipment built to commercial standards caused a variety of power and signaling imbalances. The lighter tactical gear operated on

---

[4]A summary of the inspection team's findings is contained in DCA, PAC, Communications-Electronic Experiences SEASIA, 13 Jan 69, app. 1 to an. C, file 139822, 72A25/22, WNRC.

twenty milliamps of current while heavier troposcatter equipment required sixty milliamps of current. Special isolation relays had to be installed at juncture points to balance the currents and make the two types of equipment compatible. Filters had to be installed to shield sensitive equipment on the BACKPORCH system from the background noise of electrical interference induced by lower-quality tactical components and by the use of field cable extensions to subscribers, which the Page engineers called "the barbed wire on the end of the line." Mountains and jungles frequently attenuated signals transmitted over tactical extensions, necessitating their amplification before transmission over the long-haul troposcatter system. When tactical circuits were noisy to begin with, amplification then induced noise on connecting or adjacent channels.

Of all the problems in connecting tactical and strategic equipment, the diversity of frequencies used to transmit signal tones alerting distant subscribers to a call was most aggravating. Equipment installed on the Defense Communications System used a 2,600-hertz signaling frequency compatible with the commercial circuits in the United States. Tactical equipment used a 1,600-hertz signal. To adjust one signal with the other, a pulse link repeater was installed on the BACKPORCH equipment. Even more problems were encountered converting the 20-hertz signal tone emitted by tactical switchboards to the 1,600-hertz signaling frequency for transmission by tactical carriers connecting with BACKPORCH. Channels on the BACKPORCH system experienced a constant tone, requiring modification of signal converters used on every circuit interconnecting with the long-haul network.[5]

Some expedients worked satisfactorily to alleviate interference over voice and regular teletype communications, but they were inadequate when transmitting data, which was very sensitive to noise. Secure voice also required perfectly tuned circuits to transmit pulses that were scrambled by security devices. Admiral Sharp had explicitly asked for those sophisticated means of communication, and the engineers planning the Integrated Wideband Communications System included special circuits for them. Those circuits required special conditioning to reduce electrical interference, to maintain the strength of signal impulse, and to suppress echoes. Conditioned circuits required special technical controls, test equipment, and alarms to alert controllers when a circuit fell below standard. Special circuits, called order wires, had to be installed to notify distant terminals and computer facilities of any problem.[6]

While the investigators from the Defense Communications Agency, Pacific, got a firsthand view of the problems entailed in upgrading BACKPORCH to their proposed integrated wideband long-haul network, a Viet Cong attack on the American advisory compound at Pleiku on 7 February 1965 caused the abrupt termination of their visit and signaled the beginning of a hasty American buildup that would complicate even further the establishment of an improved strategic

[5]A discussion of interface problems and their resolution in the Integrated Wideband Communications System is contained in 1st Sig Bde, Reg Comm Gp, IWCS Orientation, Apr 68, ch. 9, VNIT 458, CMH. See also "Interfacing of Tactical and Strategic Communications," *Command Communications*, April 1967, pp. 9–11, CMH.

[6]DCA, PAC, Communications-Electronic Experiences SEASIA, 13 Jan 69, app. 2 to an. C.

network. In the succeeding months a variety of new signal equipment poured into South Vietnam. The Pacific Command sent heavy troposcatter sets to expand and back up the BACKPORCH network. The 11th Signal Group sent light troposcatter sets to establish a communications link from Saigon to the threatened Central Highlands city of Pleiku. The 2d Signal Group introduced additional tactical VHF sets to extend lines from the BACKPORCH network to new American bases. The interim systems were all combined with the completed facilities of the Integrated Wideband Communications System to form the Southeast Asia Wideband System, the designation for the transmission network of the Defense Communications System in Southeast Asia.[7]

In Washington, consideration of the plan for the Integrated Wideband Communications System had proceeded far too slowly for it to be ready to meet the needs of the buildup. On 23 February 1965, two weeks after the attacks at Pleiku, the Joint Chiefs of Staff validated the Defense Communications Agency's draft plan and recommended that the Army manage and operate the proposed network. *(Map 21)* After two months of deliberation, Deputy Secretary of Defense Cyrus R. Vance approved the network in concept but deferred funding or manpower allocations pending submission of a "telecommunications program objective," a detailed accounting of costs, personnel considerations, and technical specifications. The Department of Defense used the telecommunications program objective to determine and control the costs of major fixed telecommunications facilities; for the first time, it was being applied to the construction of communications projects in a combat situation. The task of preparing the telecommunications program objective fell to the Army's Strategic Communications Command. On 29 June 1965, after coordinating with the Air Force staff and hurriedly preparing engineering surveys, the Strategic Communications Command submitted Telecommunications Program Objective 53–65. On 4 August 1965, exactly one year after the incidents in the Gulf of Tonkin that precipitated the request for the improved network, Deputy Secretary Vance approved the program objective and authorized the expenditure of $26.5 million by the Army and $9.3 million by the Air Force to build the system. However, he deferred the expenditure of additional funds the Army had requested to build a training facility at Fort Monmouth to teach soldiers to operate the commercial equipment.[8]

With large numbers of troops deploying to Southeast Asia by that time, military planners began questioning the adequacy of the proposed long-haul system. The Commander in Chief, Pacific, Admiral U. S. G. Sharp, wanted to avoid repe-

---

[7]Msg, CINCUSARPAC to DA, DAIN 628326, 28 Apr 65, sub: Operation and Maintenance of SEASIA Communications Facilities, Incl 3 to Memo, DA, Actg SGS, for General Abrams, 12 May 65, sub: Strategic Communications; Msg, CINCPAC to MACV, 19 May 65, sub: IWCS Routing and Terminal Locations. Both in CMH. See Chapter 6 for an account of the measures taken to establish interim communications for the Integrated Wideband Communications System.

[8]Memo, Dep Secy of Defense for Secy of Army et al., 21 Apr 65, sub: Integrated Wideband Communications System in Southeast Asia, Incl 1 to Memo, DA, Actg SGS, for General Abrams, 12 May 65, sub: Strategic Communications, CMH; DCA, PAC, Communications-Electronic Experiences SEASIA, 13 Jan 69, app. 1 to an. D; TPO 53–65, 29 Jun 65, file 139439, 72A4171/2, WNRC; DOD Directive 4630.1, Processing of Telecommunications Requirements and Program Objectives, 12 Dec 61. (Later superseded by DOD Directive 4630.1, Programming of Major Telecommunications Requirements, 24 Apr 68, file U–180, 72A18/3, WNRC.)

318

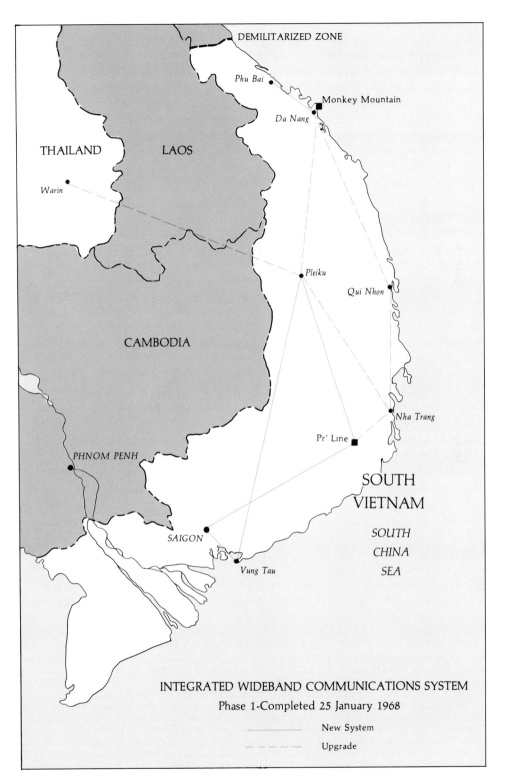

DEMILITARIZED ZONE

THAILAND

LAOS

Warin

CAMBODIA

PHNOM PENH

Phu Bai

Monkey Mountain

Da Nang

Pleiku

Qui Nhon

Nha Trang

Pr' Line

SOUTH
VIETNAM

SAIGON

SOUTH

CHINA

Vung Tau

SEA

INTEGRATED WIDEBAND COMMUNICATIONS SYSTEM

Phase 1-Completed 25 January 1968

New System

Upgrade

MAP 21

tition of time-consuming peacetime procedures involved in planning and funding communications projects. He asked the Joint Chiefs of Staff to obtain a waiver of Department of Defense Directive 4630.1 for projects in Southeast Asia and sought to establish a $25 million Defense Department contingency fund for General Westmoreland's unforeseen communications requirements. Although the Joint Chiefs of Staff rejected Admiral Sharp's request, Undersecretary of the Army David E. McGiffert proposed a modification of the restrictive Department of Defense regulations. He wanted to raise the threshold for application of those regulations from $100,000 to $5 million and to allow General Westmoreland to submit future requests simultaneously to the Pacific Command, the Joint Chiefs of Staff, the Defense Communications Agency, and the appropriate military department to eliminate time-consuming sequential staffing. Unless the Joint Chiefs responded to the contrary within five days, requests from South Vietnam would be considered validated. McGiffert also proposed convening a panel to consider simultaneously all facets of a project—technical, budgetary, procurement, and manpower—to speed up decision making in Washington.[9]

While the policy changes were being considered, contracting for already approved projects proceeded. Within a month after Deputy Secretary Vance had approved the building of the Integrated Wideband Communications System, the Army Materiel Command awarded noncompetitive contracts to Page and Philco for construction of portions of the network in South Vietnam and Thailand, respectively. Their contracts specified government payment of a fixed price and reimbursement for all additional costs incurred in engineering and installing the network to government specifications, a "cost plus fixed fee" contract. Awarding noncompetitive contracts shortened by six months the time it would have taken to solicit bids and award contracts through competitive procurement. Despite this savings in time, the Army had to advance the anticipated completion date of the Integrated Wideband Communications System from December 1965 to April 1966, a timetable that still proved overly optimistic.[10]

Changing Plans

E ven if the system could have been completed on time, it would have been inadequate in quantity of channels and area coverage to support the large

[9]Msg, CINCPAC to JCS, DAIN 391345, 1 Aug 65, sub: Command and Control Communications for SEASIA; Msg, JCS to CINCPAC, 6 Aug 65, sub: Command and Control Communications for SE Asia, CM–IN–86199; Msg, CINCPAC to JCS, 12 Aug 65, sub: Contingency Funds for Communications SEASIA, CM–IN–88567. All in CMH. Memo, Under Secy of Army for Dep Secy of Defense, 1 Mar 66, sub: Flexibility in Execution of Telecommunication Programs in Southeast Asia, App. 2 to An. D of DCA, PAC, Communications-Electronic Experiences SEASIA, 13 Jan 69.

[10]The best discussion of the outlook for the Integrated Wideband Communications System at the time of the signing of the original contract can be found in USASCC, Briefing for Lt Gen Alfred D. Starbird, 25 Aug 65, Tab C to Fact Sheet, SCCPD, 30 Oct 65, sub: USASCC Command Relationships in Southeast Asia, file 139565, 72A25/6, WNRC. See also USASCC AHS, FY–66, p. 20; DA, OCC-E, 25 Jan 66, IWCS Progress Report, tab 1 (Contingency and Restoral Equipment, Southeast Asia, TPO 72–66); 361st Sig Bn, AHS, Sep 68, pp. 21–22. Latter three in CMH.

number of troops already in South Vietnam. Vance permitted the Army to add new links to the system connecting coastal enclaves at Cam Ranh Bay with Vung Tau and Nha Trang and a relay at Pr' Line Mountain near Da Lat with links to Phu Lam and Nha Trang. Additional links were needed to serve new air bases in Thailand and additional channels to increase the capacity on existing links. Soon after the 1st Cavalry Division ended its operations in the Ia Drang, General Westmoreland asked for an extension of the system from the coastal enclaves to the Central Highlands. To improve communications in the northern portion of II Corps, Westmoreland also sought construction of a relay site similar to that being built at Pr' Line Mountain on Vung Chua Mountain overlooking Qui Nhon. The additional projects, approved on 8 February 1966 by the Department of Defense, came to be known as Phase 2 of the Integrated Wideband Communications System; the original project authorized in August 1965 was Phase 1.[11] (*Map 22*)

Even as the Military Assistance Command was trying to enlarge the radio network, communications engineers were seeking still more reliable transmission by long-distance cable. Since exposed surface cables connecting coastal enclaves could be easily severed, General Westmoreland requested undersea cable to connect them. The reliability and quality of communications over the recently installed WETWASH cable connecting Vietnam and the Philippines supported the idea of underwater cable. Over the objections of the Pacific Command, the MACV J–6, Brig. Gen. Walter E. Lotz, Jr., convinced General Starbird, visiting South Vietnam in November 1965, to support the installation of a sixty-channel undersea cable connecting Da Nang, Qui Nhon, Cam Ranh Bay, and Vung Tau, and on 17 December Deputy Secretary Vance approved the project. When tests of the direct troposcatter link between Vung Tau and Thailand provided only marginal communications, General Lotz obtained approval to extend the coastal cable from Vung Tau to Sattahip, Thailand, an important air and sea port 100 miles southeast of Bangkok. From there microwave service was provided to Bangkok and northern Thailand.[12]

The undersea cable project was included in Phase 3 of the Integrated Wideband Communications System. Phase 3 also involved installing a complete system in the delta, expanding microwave service in the two northern corps zones,

[11]Memo, Dep Secy of Defense for Secys of Mil Depts, 3 Sep 65, sub: Communications Requirements for Cam Ranh Bay and Extensions of BACKPORCH Systems in RVN, JCS 222/828–34, JACO (1965), DA/3, NARS; Msg, CINCPAC to JCS, 11 Oct 65, sub: Upgrading and Extension of the Integrated Wideband Communications System SEASIA (IWCS), CM–IN–121245, CMH; Memo, JCS for Secy of Defense, 26 Oct 65, sub: Upgrading and Extension of the Integrated Wideband Communications System for Southeast Asia (IWCS), JCS 22/873–2, JACO (1965), DA/4, NARS; Msg, CINCPAC to JCS, 28 Dec 65, sub: Southeast Asia Communications, file 139885, 72A25/24, WNRC; DA, OCC-E, IWCS Progress Report, tab B (TPO 53–65, Addendum, 20 Dec 65), and tab C (TPO 53–65, 2d Addendum, Jan 66), file 139439, 72A4171/2, WNRC.

[12]MACV History, 1965, pp. 387–88; ibid., 1966, p. 309; Incl to Ltr, Maj Gen Walter Lotz to Maj Gen Thomas M. Rienzi, 16 Feb 71, pp. 5–6. All in CMH. Incl 3 to Memo, Dir, DCA, for CJCS, 16 Nov 65, sub: Visit to CINCPAC and Southeast Asia; Memo, JCS for Dir, DCA, 4 Dec 65, sub: Report of Action on SM–1018–65, 26 October 1965, "Visit to CINCPAC and Southeast Asia." Latter two in file 139640, 72A25/8, WNRC. Msg, CINCPAC to MACV, 7 Dec 65, sub: Extension of Coastal Submarine Cable, CH–IN–153146; Msg, CINCPAC to JCS, 10 Feb 66, sub: Vung Tau–Green Hill Tropospheric Scatter, CH–IN–28597. Both in CMH.

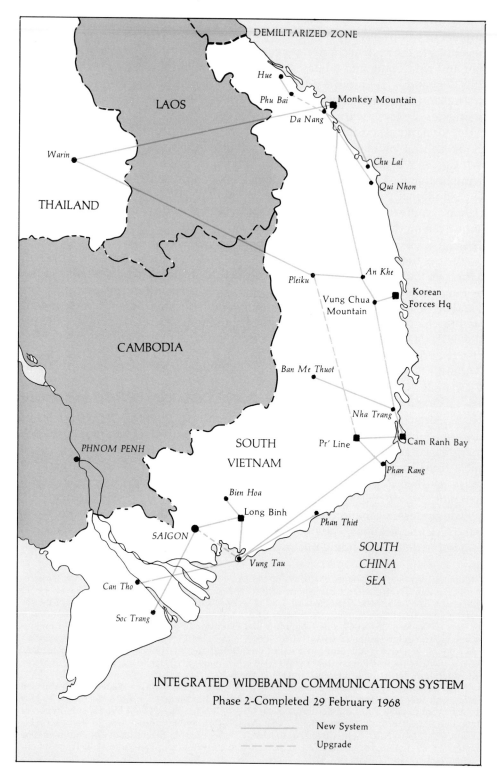

DEMILITARIZED ZONE

LAOS

Hue

Phu Bai

Monkey Mountain

Da Nang

THAILAND

Warin

Chu Lai

Qui Nhon

An Khe

Pleiku

Vung Chua
Mountain

Korean
Forces Hq

CAMBODIA

Ban Me Thuot

Nha Trang

Pr' Line

Cam Ranh Bay

PHNOM PENH

SOUTH
VIETNAM

Phan Rang

Bien Hoa

Long Binh

Phan Thiet

SAIGON

SOUTH
CHINA
SEA

Vung Tau

Can Tho

Soc Trang

INTEGRATED WIDEBAND COMMUNICATIONS SYSTEM

Phase 2-Completed 29 February 1968

—————————— New System

– – – – – – – – Upgrade

Map 22

and adding new channels on previously approved systems, especially those link-ing I and II Corps. The Joint Chiefs of Staff validated the proposed expansion of the system in the spring of 1966, and the Defense Department approved the Army's third major revision of the IWCS program on 2 August 1966. But Secre-tary of Defense McNamara released only $42 million of the $65 million the Army had requested.[13]

McNamara's withholding of funds was a sign of his growing concern about the scope and management of communications projects in Southeast Asia. In plan-ning telecommunications projects, engineers had used theoretical calculations and engineering estimates, called desk-top surveys, to determine the costs of each project. On-site surveys and unforeseen difficulties encountered during construc-tion and operation of the long-haul system's initial phases produced substantial additional costs. Even as the Department of Defense was giving the Army $16.4 million to cover added costs for Phase 2 in December 1966, engineers conducting on-site surveys for Phase 3, which were being hampered by floods in the delta and the remoteness of many new sites, reported a funding deficit of $70 million for Phase 3. Supporting the need for more funds, General Westmoreland re-quested that "futile attempts" to keep to an arbitrary monetary ceiling cease and that agencies providing him with communications "turn to the primary task of providing a communications system that is responsive to MACV validated re-quirements and which has flexibility essential to the environment in Vietnam."[14]

In response to General Westmoreland's plea, the Department of the Army and the Defense Communications Agency convened a joint working group in Washington during March 1967 to review the survey data and contractors' proposals and to revalidate requirements from commands in Southeast Asia. The working group pared Phase 3 to only those systems judged absolutely necessary, but not until November 1967 did the Department of Defense approve an addi-tional $50.5 million sought by the Army to complete the revalidated Phase 3.[15] (*Map 23*)

Uncertainty about the amount or continuation of funding for the fixed net-work forced the Army to release funds piecemeal, losing the savings inherent in large-volume purchases and occasionally idling highly paid construction crews until contractors received additional funds to continue work. Because funds were not allocated for overbuilding to handle possible future needs, the eventual in-crease in channel requirements caused frequent changes of specifications. This meant higher costs and delays as existing facilities were enlarged and power and air-conditioning plants reengineered. The high priority accorded to certain projects

---

[13]TPO 53–65, 3d Addendum, Mar 66, file 139439, 72A4171/2, WNRC. A good compendium of the actions leading to the approval of the three phases of the Integrated Wideband Communications System is contained in MS, USAF, Project Corona Harvest, Communications in Southeast Asia, 8 Oct 70, pp. 57–82, K143.50103–3, OAFH. For a detailed chronology of IWCS actions through 12 December 1967, see USASCC History, FY–67, app. D, CMH.

[14] Quote from Msg, MACV to CINCPAC et al., 25 Feb 67, cited in USASCC History, FY–67, p. 37. MS, USAF, Project Corona Harvest, Communications in Southeast Asia, 8 Oct 70, p. 80; Memo, Maj Wix for Brig Gen Huey et al., 21 Nov 66, file 139621, 72A25/7, WNRC.

[15]USASCC History, FY–67, pp. 35–38; USARPAC, Final Report, Communications Evaluation in Southeast Asia (COMSEA), 30 Jun 69, see an. D, Communications Requirements, pp. 84–86, 72A2315/14, WNRC.

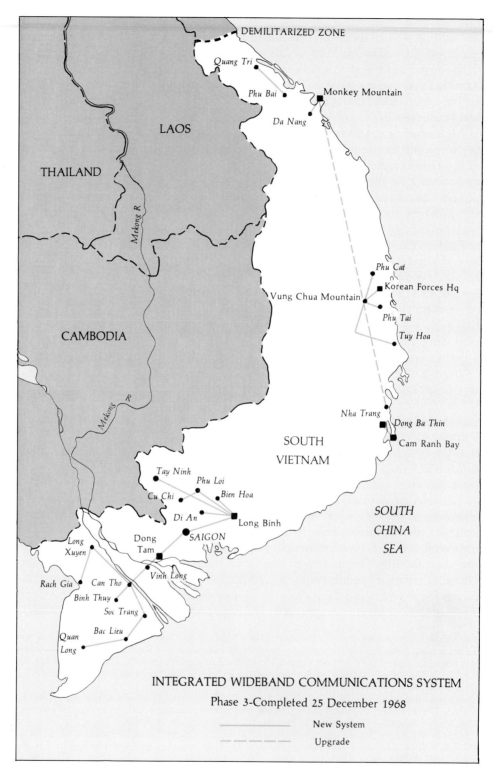

DEMILITARIZED ZONE

LAOS

THAILAND

Mekong R.

CAMBODIA

Mekong R.

Quang Tri

Phu Bai

Da Nang

Monkey Mountain

Phu Cat

Vung Chua Mountain

Korean Forces Hq

Phu Tai

Tuy Hoa

Nha Trang

Dong Ba Thin

Cam Ranh Bay

SOUTH
VIETNAM

SOUTH

CHINA

SEA

Tay Ninh

Phu Loi

Cu Chi

Bien Hoa

Di An

Long Binh

Dong
Tam

SAIGON

Long
Xuyen

Rach Gia

Can Tho

Vinh Long

Binh Thuy

Soc Trang

Bac Lieu

Quan
Long

INTEGRATED WIDEBAND COMMUNICATIONS SYSTEM

Phase 3-Completed 25 December 1968

————————— New System

– – – – – – – – – Upgrade

Map 23

of Phase 3, especially the microwave connections to the coastal cable, also disrupted work on uncompleted portions of the earlier phases.[16]

Lacking any precedent to project construction schedules for a sophisticated communications system in a war zone, overly optimistic signal planners and contractors had doomed themselves to perpetual extensions of deadlines, or slippages, by agreeing in advance to unrealistic schedules. Completion of Phase 1 had been set originally for April 1966, but it was November 1966 before Philco, the contractor in Thailand, completed the first link there and another month before Page activated the first link in South Vietnam. Propagational difficulties encountered after moving the MRC–85 console from Nha Trang to Pleiku to complete a Pleiku–Vung Tau link delayed completion of that final segment of Phase 1 until 25 January 1968. Although Phase 2 had originally been scheduled for completion by October 1966, not until March 1967 was the first portion of Phase 2 on the air. Phase 2 was completed on 29 February 1968. Concerned that similar delays would slow completion of important links of Phase 3, already set back over a year by the debate over supplemental funding, General Westmoreland warned that the management of the project by both the contractor and the military would have to be improved.[17]

Managing the Project

Poorly defined lines of responsibility and confusing and complex command relationships, the legacy of earlier reorganizations within the Army and the Department of Defense, had adversely affected the planning and construction of the Integrated Wideband Communications System. Although the DCA regional office drafted the original plan for the system in the fall of 1964, thereafter the Defense Communications Agency had little to do with the planning or installation of the network until the Defense Communications Agency, Southeast Asia Mainland, upon acceptance of completed segments of the system from the contractor, issued orders to activate circuits. While the Joint Chiefs of Staff and the secretary of defense were considering the original plan during the spring of 1965, the Army and the Air Force—and within the Army, the U.S. Army, Pacific, and the Strategic Communications Command—competed for the mission of executing the plan. Receiving the mission in May 1965, the Strategic Communications Command, in existence only a year, had hurriedly to prepare detailed technical and financial plans. Engineers from the Strategic Communications Command had to travel to Southeast Asia to perform site surveys and obtain information needed to prepare specifications for contracts. Even after the establishment of the 1st Signal Brigade in early 1966, the Strategic Communications Command retained engineers in Southeast Asia to revise specifications and to design system

---

[16]Gardner Study, p. 21.
[17]DCA, PAC, Communications-Electronic Experiences SEASIA, 13 Jan 69, an. D; Gardner Study, p. 15; MACV History, 1967, vol. 2, p. 780, CMH.

modifications.[18]

As the Strategic Communications Command became increasingly involved in making technical changes to the plans for the Integrated Wideband Communications System, it came into conflict with the agency administering the contract, the Army Materiel Command. The Army Materiel Command gave the mission to contract for the network to the Office of the Program Manager, Universal Integrated Communications/Strategic Army Communications (UNICOM/STARCOM), an agency established at Fort Monmouth in July 1962 to handle development of nontactical communications. Using specifications developed by the Strategic Communications Command, the UNICOM/STARCOM program manager procured supplies and contractors' services to fulfill those specifications. The primary conflict between the Strategic Communications Command and the Army Materiel Command concerned the scope of technical changes that could be allowed within the strict confines of the contract. The Army Materiel Command reserved authority to make changes affecting "quantity, quality, time, method or place of delivery." Signal engineers from the Strategic Communications Command, on the other hand, felt they needed authority to make technical changes to preclude delaying the project.[19]

An Army survey team assessing the progress of Phase 1 agreed with the Strategic Communications Command's engineers that inefficient contract management by the Army program manager was causing delays in completing the long-haul system. The team recommended that the Army Materiel Command establish a field procurement office in South Vietnam to make on-the-spot adjustments to the contract to incorporate technical modifications. Arguing that contract administration did not impede the completion of the project, the commander of the Army Materiel Command, General Frank S. Besson, Jr., saw the real problem as the division of administrative and technical responsibilities between his command and the Strategic Communications Command. General Lotz, who had left the Military Assistance Command to become the assistant chief of staff for communications-electronics at the Department of the Army, proposed giving complete responsibility to the Strategic Communications Command. Instead, the Army Chief of Staff, General Harold K. Johnson, directed the two organizations to consolidate their responsibilities for the engineering and procurement of all major communications systems in a single organization, the Communications Systems Agency, that would report to both the Army Materiel Command and the Strategic Communications Command.[20]

The establishment of the Communications Systems Agency resolved a long-

---

[18]Gardner Study, pp. 23–24, 46, 57. Gardner concludes that the primary cause of delays in the construction of the Integrated Wideband Communications System was the lack of a project manager at the DOD level.

[19]Quote from Msg, AMC to DA, OCC-E, DAIN 629273, 18 Nov 66, sub: DA Survey Team Visit to SEA, CMH. Communications Systems Agency (hereafter cited as Comm Sys Agency), IWCS History, 1 Jul 65–30 Jun 66, pp. 43–51; ibid., 1 Jul 66–28 Feb 67, pp. 19–39. Both in file U–193, 72A18/3, WNRC.

[20]Memo, DA, Ch, OCC-E, for CSA, 23 Nov 66, sub: Management of the Integrated Wideband Communications System, w/Tab B, Msg, DA to AMC, 27 Oct 66, sub: DA Survey Team Visit to SE Asia, file CS 091 Southeast Asia (2 Nov 66), 72A5711/7, WNRC.

standing dispute over the responsibility for engineering and installing all world-wide fixed communications. Until April 1964 the chief signal officer had administered most contracts for the installation of fixed communications as part of his responsibility for strategic communications. When he was divested of that mission, the UNICOM/STARCOM program manager took over contract administration for the Army Materiel Command. When General Besson tried to obtain control of operational engineering as part of his responsibility for all Army materiel development, the chief, communications-electronics, at the Department of the Army, Maj. Gen. David P. Gibbs, countered that the Army Materiel Command should have the mission for developmental engineering for new equipment, but that the new Strategic Communications Command should do the operational engineering. Wanting to avoid further controversy at a time when the Strategic Communications Command was having difficulty taking over its operational mission from the theaters, Army Chief of Staff Johnson left the mission for contract administration with the Army Materiel Command and the technical design and engineering with the Strategic Communications Command. The establishment of the Communications Systems Agency in 1967 finally created a clear line of responsibility extending from the officers and noncommissioned officers monitoring construction at each Army fixed communications site to the military contracting officers and technical representatives negotiating with contractors and checking production of communications equipment in the factories.[21]

Headed by Brig. Gen. Hugh F. Foster, Jr., the Communications Systems Agency merged elements of the Communications Engineering Department of the Strategic Communications Command and the former Office of the Program Manager, UNICOM/STARCOM. Systems engineering was to be done at Fort Huachuca, Arizona, where the Strategic Communications Command had moved in the spring of 1967. Equipment engineering, procurement, financial management, and production and logistic support remained the responsibility of the project managers at Fort Monmouth. The system in Southeast Asia was the most important project managed by the new agency.

General Foster appointed Lt. Col. Emmett Paige, Jr., to be the deputy project manager for the Integrated Wideband Communications System. Colonel Paige had been the special assistant for the system in the Office of the Program Manager, UNICOM/STARCOM. As a staff officer in the Signal Training Command at Fort Monmouth in the spring of 1962, Paige had been associated with the training of the first contingent of troposcatter operators sent to South Vietnam with the 39th Signal Battalion. In 1965, while assigned to the field office of the Defense Communications Agency, Southeast Asia Mainland, in the Philippines, Paige had helped the MACV J–6 staff prepare circuit requirements and systems plans for the new network. By the summer of 1967 Colonel Paige was the most qualified individual in the Army to manage the development of the Integrated Wideband

---

[21]DA, Appraisal of U.S. Army Strategic Communications Command and Other U.S. Army Long Range Communications Facilities, 31 Mar 65, an. H, app. 2, tabs C, D, F, OCSO papers, CMH. File 2 (Special Study of Signal Activities), tab R, Historians files, CMH, contains all correspondence relating to the dispute between Generals Besson and Gibbs.

Communications System.[22]

Although pleased with the resolution of differences between the Strategic Communications Command and the Army Materiel Command, General Terry wanted to ensure that the 1st Signal Brigade retained responsibility for field construction and installation of equipment. While assuring Terry that the brigade would continue to manage the everyday work of installing the network, General Meyer explained that the Communications Systems Agency would retain centralized management of the project. The Communications Systems Agency would require the 1st Signal Brigade to provide detailed channel requirements to enable engineering of multiplexing equipment and would review major modifications recommended by the brigade's engineers.[23]

Colonel Paige *(Photograph taken in 1976.)*

To manage the brigade's responsibilities for the IWCS network, General Terry established the Integrated Wideband Communications System Management Office, headed by Lt. Col. Patrick F. Kearins. Although the Strategic Communications Command frequently sent engineers to perform site surveys and resolve special problems, the 1st Signal Brigade's project management office was responsible for every phase of the installation of the system except final testing and acceptance from the contractor of completed systems. Wanting engineers not involved with construction of the system to test it, the Strategic Communications Command contracted directly with Lockheed Aircraft Corporation to do all testing. In Phase 3, the 1st Signal Brigade assumed the testing responsibility. Responsible for a multitude of diverse tasks at each site—from the first negotiations with the South Vietnamese for use of real estate to the posting of guards—the staff of the signal brigade's management office relied heavily on signal officers stationed near proposed sites. They helped to arrange transportation, construction, and other logistical support as work continued at the various neighboring sites.[24]

[22]Comm Sys Agency, IWCS History, 1 Mar–30 Jun 67, pp. 38–41; ibid., 1 Jul 67–30 Jun 68. Both in file U–193, 72A18/3, WNRC; USASCC History, FY–67, an. E, CMH; Interv, Capt Hrair N. Badalian, CO, 23d MHD, with Lt Col Emmett Paige, CO, 361st Signal Battalion, 16 Aug 69, VNIT 469, CMH.
[23]Ltr, 1st Sig Bde to SCC, 28 May 67, sub: Program Management in USASTRATCOM, file U–105; Ltr, SCC to 1st Sig Bde, 28 Jun 67, sub: Program Management in USASTRATCOM, file U–106. Both in 72A18/3, WNRC. Interv, Badalian with Paige, 16 Aug 69.
[24]An excellent discussion of the 1st Signal Brigade's management of the installation of the Integrated Wideband Communications System is contained in Interv, Binder with McKinney, 22 Jan 68, VNIT 112, CMH. ORLL, 1st Sig Bde, 31 Jul 67, p. 26, 72A7128/5, WNRC.

Obtaining Support for the System

S ome delays in completion of the project during its first two years stemmed from difficulties signalmen found in competing for the support and services essential to the construction of the Integrated Wideband Communications System. Other branches of the military also wanted precious cargo space on ships and aircraft bound for South Vietnam; production facilities and raw materials, especially copper, were in great demand by both the military and a burgeoning civilian industry. Not until General Westmoreland began complaining about the slowness of the development of the Integrated Wideband Communications System did the project begin to get the attention and priorities needed to obtain support in the competitive military marketplace. When the official most able to influence that support, the Director of Materiel Acquisition in the Office of the Assistant Secretary of the Army (Installations and Logistics), Maj. Gen. Roland B. Anderson, asked for a monthly report beginning on 1 August 1967 on the problems causing delays, Colonel Paige personally briefed him on the difficulties that signalmen were experiencing. General Lotz also began reporting monthly on the problems and progress of the Integrated Wideband Communications System to the Vice Chief of Staff, General Ralph E. Haines, Jr. With such high-level concern, signalmen in the Communications Systems Agency and the 1st Signal Brigade finally began to resolve the complex combination of problems of materiel acquisition, production, transportation, site acquisition, and construction that had been plaguing them.[25]

Other delays resulted from difficulties contractors had in procuring equipment for the system. To avoid competing with each other, Page and Philco dealt with different subcontractors; but Page's 150 subcontractors and Philco's 100 subcontractors often found themselves dealing with the same vendors for scarce parts. Since those vendors were selling to a lucrative international market for transistorized consumer goods and computers as well as supplying parts for sophisticated sensors and guidance systems for South Vietnam, subcontractors frequently were unable to find a source of parts to build the components ordered by Page and Philco. A strike against the Lenkurt Company, a manufacturer of several major components, further aggravated the situation. As production of equipment for the Integrated Wideband Communications System fell behind schedule, the criterion for award of subcontracts became the promised delivery date rather than quality or price. Even so, delivery rarely was made by the promised dates stipulated in the contract. Since few companies operating in the volatile electronics market would accept contracts with penalty clauses, Page and Philco were powerless to hold subcontractors to deadlines.[26]

To help contractors pressure their suppliers or to assist them in finding other sources of materiel, the project manager sometimes drew on the influence and resources of the Army Materiel Command and the Department of Commerce.

---

[25]USASCC History , FY–67, app. D, CMH; Gardner Study, pp. 12–21.

[26]Project Manager, UNICOM/STARCOM, AHS, 1 Jul 66–28 Feb 67, pp. 30–39, Comm Sys Agency files, Fort Monmouth, New Jersey; Gardner Study, pp. 35–38.

329

To resolve conflicts among military projects competing for scarce supplies, the project manager worked closely with the Vietnam Support Expediting Task Force, an organization established in the Department of Defense to assist in obtaining high-priority materiel, called FLAGPOLE items, for use in South Vietnam. When in mid-1966 the FLAGPOLE list grew to unmanageable size, the program manager was told to identify only the most critical components for inclusion on the list. With four tiers of subcontractors providing parts for the system, identifying the individual parts that were in short supply and causing delays became extremely difficult.[27]

Examining the Army's heavy reliance on contractors to establish the long-haul network, the General Accounting Office subsequently asserted that the Department of the Army should not have contracted with Page and Philco to procure equipment for the network. By purchasing equipment directly from vendors, the government could have obtained about 89 percent of the $60.3 million worth of equipment purchased by Page and Philco from subcontractors. The General Accounting Office estimated that the Department of Defense spent approximately $69 million in fixed fees and overhead expenses for Page to purchase equipment the government itself could have procured. Defending its use of contractors, the Department of Defense explained it had rejected direct government purchase of components because "the risks of procurement delays or incompatible systems could not be chanced." While it is debatable whether direct purchase by the government rather than Page and Philco would have caused even greater delays in delivery dates than those actually experienced, the necessity to deal with hundreds of vendors for the fixed system probably would have detracted from the Army's capability to manage the procurement of tactical communications equipment.[28]

Transportation Problems

A n overtaxed transpacific transportation network, inadequate port facilities in Southeast Asia, and a primitive road net under constant threat of Viet Cong interdiction hindered the completion of the IWCS project. Reviewing the causes of delays in the construction of three sites in the late summer of 1966, the IWCS Management Office discovered that the FBI was investigating the theft of cable from a warehouse in the United States destined for one site; that generators for another site sat on the beach at Qui Nhon where they had been left awaiting a crane to load them onto a truck; and that, at the order of the U.S. ambassador, fuel tanks for the third site had been unloaded from a barge at a Saigon dock to make room for the priority shipment of 10,000 tons of rice. Rarely did equipment arrive in the projected delivery time—three weeks accorded for air

---

[27]Gardner Study, p. 65; 1st Sig Bde, IWCS Weekly Status Rpts, for Weeks Ending 5 Dec 66, in file 139621, and 2 Jun 68, in file 139622, both in 72A25/7, WNRC.

[28]Quote from GAO Report B–168097, *Problems in Acquiring, Installing, and Operating A Communications System in A Theater of Operations,* 5 Jun 72, p. 25. See also pp. 21–26.

shipment and eight weeks for sea.[29]

The Electronics Command took every possible measure to expedite the movement of equipment for the network. In October 1966 personnel went to the assembly plants of Page and Philco to recommend better packaging and shipment procedures. From the Pentagon, General Lotz wrote to his successor in the post of MACV J–6, Brig. Gen. Samuel L. Huey, asking the Military Assistance Command to give the Integrated Wideband Communications System higher airlift priorities to enable signalmen to compete with the "shippers of beans, bullets, and medical supplies." In late 1966 the project received an allowance of 500 tons a month for shipment under the most urgent category of transport, called RED BALL. The Military Airlift Command flew fifty-nine special missions, some comprising five aircraft each, over a period of several months in support of the Integrated Wideband Communications System.[30]

Transshipment within Southeast Asia proved far more difficult to expedite. Although the MACV transportation officers promised movement from air and sea ports within seventy-two hours of unloading, weather and combat frequently caused delays and diversions of cargo lasting as long as six weeks. The 1st Signal Brigade moved the most critical cargo in its own fifteen aircraft, accounting for 300 tons during one busy three-month period in early 1967; but most equipment was carried in convoys vulnerable to ambush, in air transports frequently diverted to combat missions, or in Navy landing craft that unloaded cargo on congested beaches for lack of available docking space. In Thailand, elephants and porters had to carry equipment to several sites on remote mountaintops. Even that mode of transportation proved difficult when elephants, apparently in response to some primal instinct, refused to climb above 6,000 feet.[31]

The unique technical requirements of each site complicated the shipment of equipment. Different propagational and range conditions, channel capacities, and connecting links dictated variations in antennas, amplifiers, multiplexers, and ancillary gear. Some sites required complete power and living facilities while others shared neighboring facilities. Rather than shipping components in bulk to depots in South Vietnam where equipment could be broken down for distribution to each site, components had to be packaged separately at the factory and shipped direct to each site.

Inadequate transportation also delayed visits of engineers and technicians responsible for building the system. To transport teams to survey new sites and to install equipment required making reservations for space on Air Force shuttles seven days in advance and reconfirming them daily. Remaining at a site an extra day or encountering problems with aircraft maintenance or weather might strand a highly paid crew of survey engineers or installer technicians at an isolated site for several days. Only after the Army received supplemental funds for the Integrated Wideband Communications System in the spring of 1967 did Page con-

[29]1st Sig Bde, IWCS Weekly Status Rpt, Week Ending 3 Sep 66, file 139622, 72A25/7, WNRC; Gardner Study, pp. 31–33.
[30]Ibid.
[31]1st Sig Bde, IWCS Weekly Status Rpt, Week Ending 24 Oct 67, file 139621, 72A25/7, WNRC; USASCC History, FY–67, p. 30, and ibid., FY–68, p. 34, both in CMH.

The Isolated IWCS Site at Lang Bian Mountain

tract with a civilian airlines, Air Saigon, for air ferry service.[32]

Transportation problems forced engineers to perform much of the design and planning of the system based on theoretical calculations and map surveys done at the headquarters of the Strategic Communications Command. The MACV signal staff then reviewed the Strategic Communications Command's survey data to uncover potential frequency or siting conflicts with other units.

Locating Sites

A s at Quang Tri, locating terminals on existing bases frequently incurred the opposition of installation commanders who were reluctant to add to the congestion within their camps. In planning sites on South Vietnamese military installations, signalmen also found their allies to be hard bargainers. Permission to build was usually contingent on a promise to share site improvements, power facilities, or antenna towers. Even if plans later changed, the South Vietnamese held the 1st Signal Brigade to its commitments. On military bases, negotiations

[32]Msg, USASTRATCOM, SEA, to USASTRATCOM, PAC, 27 Jan 66, sub: Aircraft for USASTRATCOM-SEA, CH–IN–17817, file 12, 70A2328/6, WNRC; Gardner Study, pp. 34–35; 1st Sig Bde, IWCS Weekly Status Rpt, Week Ending 2 Apr 67, file 139621, 72A25/7, WNRC.

A 60-Foot Tropo Antenna at Vung Tau

over the sharing of the frequency spectrum could be just as difficult as those for physical space.[33]

In seeking to build sites outside the defensive perimeters of military installations, signalmen became involved in complex leasing negotiations with provincial authorities and landowners. In I Corps the 1st Signal Brigade found that it had opened a delicate subject in applying for leasing agreements for signal sites since that formality had been neglected by other American units already holding real estate. In the delta, where firm land was scarce, local consent often depended on a promise to fill in an equal amount of land for the owner. Final approval usually depended on the whims of politics and diplomacy. Since province chiefs, jealous of their prerogatives, habitually ignored approvals granted by the Joint General Staff, signalmen usually depended on local advisers for help with negotiations and indemnifications. When negotiations and political pressure failed to obtain complete agreement on use of real estate or frequencies, signalmen had to plan for a new site.[34]

The most expensive change of plans involved relocation of a site in Thailand

---

[33]MACV Directive 105-17, Communications-Electronics Site Development Responsibilities, Republic of Vietnam, 3 May 67, file U-442, 72A18/8, WNRC; ORLL, 1st Sig Bde, 31 Oct 66, p. 27, file 228-07, 72A7128/5, WNRC; 1st Sig Bde, IWCS Weekly Status Rpt, Week Ending 24 Jan 67, file 139621, 72A25/7, WNRC.

[34]1st Sig Bde, IWCS Weekly Status Rpts, Weeks Ending 14 May 67, in file 139621, and 17 Jan 68 and 23 May 68, in file 139622. All in 72A25/7, WNRC.

after construction had already begun. In building a terminal near Chiang Mai Air Base in northwestern Thailand, the 1st Signal Brigade had to arrange with a Buddhist priest to propitiate the spirits believed to populate trees that would be cut down to build a road to the signal site. After the road and building foundations were constructed, the Thai government withdrew permission for use of the location because Thai communicators would be working there. Since the site overlooked the emperor's summer house, a Thai law prohibiting Thais from occupying positions elevated above the emperor would be violated. Moving equipment, reengineering another system, and building a new site and access road cost several million dollars and over a year's delay.[35]

Having obtained permission to use a location for a signal facility, the 1st Signal Brigade then had to coordinate with the U.S. Navy's Office in Charge of Construction (OICC), which supervised the contract with Raymond, Morrison, Knudson-Brown, Root, Jones Corporation, the American consortium that did most of the construction at large base areas. Coordinating construction and equipment installation was complicated. Before the Navy engineers would schedule work with the civilian contractors, Page had to provide them with a complete set of blueprints and the Army had to have a firm allocation of funds. Since the busy construction crews were booked months in advance and then frequently diverted to higher-priority construction projects, Page was reluctant to deliver equipment to a site or to schedule work by equipment installation crews based on the construction schedule. During monsoon season, when construction sites became muddy traps for heavy equipment and access roads up steep mountains were too treacherous for driving, schedules were particularly unreliable. At sandy coastal sites construction had to wait until after the planting of vegetation for erosion control. Difficulties in obtaining and transporting the ponderous forty-ton cranes to erect 120-foot billboard antennas frequently caused delays. With construction crews working against a deadline and shifting from one job to another, signalmen often had to fill the role of construction supervisor. They became adept at locating scarce items of construction gear and at convincing construction teams of the importance of precisely leveled foundations, well-grounded wiring, and reliable air-conditioning and power plants.[36]

As the Integrated Wideband Communications System extended beyond the well-developed secure enclaves, civilian contractors less frequently constructed sites. By Phase 3, Army engineers and Navy Seabees were performing all site construction under the supervision of Page and the 1st Signal Brigade. At the more isolated sites security measures increasingly influenced site configurations and the pace of construction. When the expansion of Camp Radcliffe put the signal site at An Khe in the line of base defensive fires, construction had to be halted. Since moving the terminal would require an expensive change from microwave to troposcatter propagation on the link to Qui Nhon, General Terry obtained permission to retain the terminal on the provision that personnel would not be

---

[35]USASCC History, FY–67, pp. 39–40; ibid., FY–68, p. 34.
[36]1st Sig Bde, IWCS Weekly Status Rpts, Weeks Ending 3 Sep 66 and 8 Apr 67, file 139621, 72A25/7, WNRC; Rienzi Debriefing Rpt, 4 Jun 70, pp. 60–61, CMH.

Barricade *of sand barrels is placed around an IWCS building.*

billeted at the site.

After a rocket attack destroyed the tape relay at Da Nang in February 1967, the Army contracted with Page to build dirt-filled aluminum and steel revetments around the electronic facilities on the sites. For a company accustomed to installing communications, building revetments presented some unique problems. Unless an escort went along with the convoys transporting the steel, which was in especially great demand as bunkering material at combat bases within the range of North Vietnamese heavy artillery in I Corps, U.S. combat units frequently diverted it. Since American and South Vietnamese base security officials did not trust the loyalty of the unskilled laborers hired to install the revetments, they sometimes did not allow them to work on sites within military installations. Page occasionally even had to use American and Filipino electronic technicians to install the revetments.[37]

Despite the revetments, Viet Cong attacks during the Tet offensive damaged ten sites. Since the fighting also affected the transport of cargo and personnel throughout South Vietnam, the offensive delayed the installation program by several months. A follow-up offensive in May 1968 caused damage to one site and delay in activating five links; a third offensive in August damaged three sites

[37]1st Sig Bde, IWCS Weekly Status Rpts, Weeks Ending 30 Sep 66, 7 Nov 66, 10 Feb 67, 2 Apr 67, 25 May 67, and 21 Jul 67, in file 139621, and 1 Jul 68, in file 139622. All in 72A25/7, WNRC.

and delayed two links.[38]

The Army's contract with Page did not extend to the provision of reserve sets of equipment, and the Army had to order most replacements for battle-damaged or defective equipment from factories in the United States. During the upgrading of BACKPORCH in Phase 1, technicians also found that five years of exposure to the harsh tropical climate had left the system's original MRC-85's in need of far more overhaul and replacement of parts than originally predicted.

Putting the Sites on the Air

E ven the installation of new terminals proved worrisome. Activation of a new system usually consisted of a two-week "burn-in" period to correct and adjust problems that inevitably appeared after the equipment was turned on. Then representatives of the Strategic Communications Command, members of the 1st Signal Brigade's Communications-Electronics Systems Management Agency, and technicians from Lockheed Aircraft Corporation tested and evaluated the quality of the systems prior to acceptance by the government. To be sure that a system was unaffected by periodic propagational or environmental influences, they monitored signal levels and noise disturbances for periods of thirty to forty-five days. Sometimes tests had to be discontinued while Page technicians returned to make adjustments. The testing program proceeded more smoothly after Page, at the Army's urging, assigned a new director to its own testing program in the spring of 1967 and teams from the Communications-Electronics Systems Management Agency began checking sites weekly.[39]

As with the installers, the testing teams found their schedule subject to frequent disruption. Believing that a tree in the propagation field of an antenna at Ban Me Thuot was causing the power level required to transmit a signal, called carrier intensity, on a system to Nha Trang to be marginal, they had to suspend testing for three weeks while the 1st Signal Brigade negotiated with the local province chief for permission to cut down the tree. On 2 June 1968, a team activating a microwave system between Vung Chua Mountain and Tuy Hoa in II Corps discovered that carrier intensity dropped during the afternoon hours. After two weeks of checking and tuning equipment and realigning antennas, the Page installers recommended to their headquarters in Washington that the power on the system be increased from ten watts to one kilowatt. While engineers in the Communications Systems Agency at Fort Monmouth reviewed the original specifications to determine if the additional cost of the recommended modifications was justified, Page experimented unsuccessfully with crystals of a lower frequency. Obtaining the Army's permission to raise the power, Page added a stronger amplifier. Then, during the burn-in period, minor frequency interference ap-

---

[38]USASCC History, FY–68, p. 36; Page Communications Engineers, Inc., Briefing, IWCS Area 1, 30 Aug 68, file U–193, 72A18/3, WNRC.

[39]1st Sig Bde, IWCS Weekly Status Rpts, Weeks Ending 3 Sep 66, 13 Jan 67, 5 May 67, 9 Oct 67, 13 Nov 67, file 139621, 72A25/7, WNRC.

peared, necessitating a wait of several weeks for new crystals. Between the time the Vung Chua–Tuy Hoa link was first tested in June and its acceptance by the military in September, the start of service had been delayed three months because of unanticipated technical problems.[40]

While a new link was undergoing testing, the staff of the Defense Communications Agency, Southeast Asia Mainland, and representatives of the different services comprising a MACV Integrated Wideband Communications System Cutover Committee prepared for the activation of circuits on the new link. The cutover committee recommended circuit priorities to the MACV signal staff who, in turn, validated circuit requests to the Allocations Branch of the Defense Communications Agency, Southeast Asia Mainland. Having determined the appropriate routing from subscriber to subscriber over the Integrated Wideband Communications System and over the extensions provided by transportable tactical equipment, the Allocations Branch forwarded a draft circuit engineering order (CEO) to the Engineering Branch of the Defense Communications Agency, Southeast Asia Mainland. The Engineering Branch prepared a master circuit plan indicating the wiring and equipment through which each circuit would pass and the level settings and quality standards for each piece of equipment. Specific circuits and the equipment through which they traveled were depicted by row and bay for each site on a circuit layout record in a computerized data bank maintained by the Regional Communications Group.[41]

The brigade's Networks Branch sent a copy of the circuit engineering order to the commander of each unit involved in activating the circuit and a copy of the circuit layout record to each technical control activity involved. As soon as the military's testing team accepted a system, technical controllers armed with copies of the circuit layout records moved into the new terminals to connect the circuits. Restricted by the narrow spaces between the stacks of electronic equipment, only six installers could work in a terminal at the same time. Each man connected ten circuits a day. Putting a terminal into operation, from the initial site survey to the activations of individual circuits, involved months of sequential operations, each fraught with the potential for human error or interference by nature or the enemy. Special attention to any one problem usually overcame delays at a particular site, but by late 1967 the volume and diversity of activities at the fifty-eight sites in South Vietnam and the thirty-five sites in Thailand that were in various stages of planning, construction, or operation overwhelmed most attempts to focus on a single problem.[42]

Nevertheless, the activation of new sites could be accelerated if need be. When priorities for activating sites in Phase 3 changed, the IWCS Management Office helped revise scheduling to complete an important link between Vung Chua

[40]Gardner Study, p. 29; CINCPAC History, 1968, vol. 4, pp. 4–6, CMH; Thomas H. Kilpatrick, "IWCS Communications System Really Works," *Microwaves*, November 1968; 1st Sig Bde, IWCS Weekly Status Rpts, for period 2 Jun 68–20 Oct 68, file 139622, 72A25/7, WNRC.

[41]1st Sig Bde, IWCS Weekly Status Rpts, Weeks Ending 21 Oct 66 and 20 Jan 67, file 139621, 72A25/7, WNRC; Maj. Robert H. Ammerman, Jr., "Circuit Activations on the IWCS," *Command Communications*, March 1968, pp. 48–53, CMH.

[42]Ammerman, "Circuit Activations on the IWCS"; 1st Sig Bde, IWCS Weekly Status Rpt, Week Ending 2 Apr 67, file 139621, 72A25/7, WNRC.

Circuit Conditioning Equipment in the Phu Lam Technical Control

Mountain and a new air base at Phu Cat. That first segment of Phase 3 was activated on 31 December 1967, nine months ahead of schedule. A month later, that system and others activated on an urgent basis during the following weeks were available to assist in the command and control of the successful counteroffensive to the Viet Cong's countrywide Tet offensive.[43]

Operating the IWCS Sites

As sites were completed, the Regional Communications Group assigned them to one of two Army signal battalions activated in 1966 to operate the Integrated Wideband Communications System. From the hub of the northern network at Pleiku, Long Lines North Battalion managed all systems in I and II Corps; from Vung Tau, Long Lines South Battalion operated the network in the two southern corps. In March 1968 the headquarters of Long Lines North moved to Cam Ranh Bay. In June 1969 the two battalions were redesignated: Long Lines

[43] 1st Sig Bde, IWCS Weekly Status Rpts, Weeks Ending 30 Oct 67, in file 139621, and 29 Dec 67, in file 139622. Both in 72A25/7, WNRC. A list of activation dates for all links is contained in MACV J-6, Briefing Notes, 12 Apr 69, sub: Integrated Communications System-Southeast Asia (ICS-SEA), tab D1, file 139865, 72A25/23, WNRC.

AN/TCC–66 Multiplexer Van at the Di An IWCS Site

North became the 361st Signal Battalion and Long Lines South the 369th Signal Battalion. The first battalion commander of the newly designated 369th Signal Battalion was Lt. Col. Emmett Paige, Jr., the former project officer for the network his unit was operating. Each battalion commander established area commands, assigning them to company commanders, to supervise the operations of terminals within each region.[44]

Commanding a unit or operating a site as part of the Integrated Wideband Communications System required managerial, technical, and leadership abilities. Most sites contained barracks, a dining hall, a clinic, and transportation and supply facilities. The operational heart of a typical site consisted of two single-story prefabricated buildings erected in the shadow of several large billboard or horn-shaped antennas. The electrical equipment building, often called the EE building, was split into three sections: a large operations bay containing radios, multiplexers, isolation relays, and amplifying equipment that packaged entire blocks of channels for relaying without demodulation; a support section containing offices as well as rooms for batteries and air-conditioning equipment; and a technical control section containing a central distribution frame, banks of circuit boards,

[44]Information concerning the long-lines battalions can be found in files 72A6973/2, 71A6880/21 and 22, and 72A403/14, WNRC. See also "Regional Communications Group," *Command Communications*, May 1969, pp. 2–25; Interv, Capt Hrair N. Badalian, CO, 23d MHD, with Col Milton M. Berry, CO, Regional Communications Group, 2 Apr 68, VNIT 120; 361st Sig Bn, AHS, Sep 69. Latter three in CMH.

The Vung Chua Mountain Site

and the pads, amplifiers, and other ancillary equipment used to connect with tactical systems. The second building housed a power plant usually consisting of four 200-kilowatt diesel generators for primary power and sixty 2-volt batteries providing direct current to operate switching and control gear for the generators. At sites where several systems terminated, the two buildings were usually expanded to include additional components. Because line-of-sight systems, which represented 53 percent of the links on the fixed network, required less power and equipment than troposcatter systems, the buildings and antennas for microwave terminals were more compact.[45]

Communicators working in cramped vans or carrying radios in the jungle envied men working in the clean, air-conditioned environment of a fixed site. Yet most signalmen on the sites felt that their comfortable working conditions barely compensated for the grueling regularity of working twelve-hour shifts day after day. Working in the windowless confines of a building that presented an inviting target to enemy gunners and mortarmen, and being unaware of what was happening outside, held its own dangers and terrors.

Nor were the signalmen assigned to nontactical sites immune to terrorism.

---

[45]For detailed descriptions of IWCS sites, see Introduction to the Integrated Communications System—Site 75 (Long Binh), and 1st Sig Bde, Reg Comm Gp, IWCS Orientation, Apr 68, chs. 4 and 7. Both in VNIT 458, CMH.

340

The first troposcatter operator to be killed, the chief of the BACKPORCH terminal at Qui Nhon, was shot in December 1964 while riding in a small boat just offshore from his site. Captured by the Viet Cong, his three team members were found dead three days later a few miles down the beach. In the ambush of the Page work party on the road to Pr' Line in November 1966, another man from a fixed site was killed. During the Tet offensive in Hue, the operations officer of the local company of the Long Lines North Battalion, Capt. John P. Onderke, was killed by a sniper. Many other signalmen at the fixed sites were wounded by fragments from the rockets and mortars that rained down on American bases during that offensive.[46]

In what could have been the most crippling attack on the network, shortly after midnight on 12 August 1968, a Viet Cong sapper unit staged a surprise assault on the Vung Chua Mountain relay. The guard at the gate was able to warn his comrades before being killed by the attackers. Having had a practice alert and defensive drill the previous afternoon, the signalmen reacted quickly. Although fighting raged until daylight, with several sappers killed as they tried to blow up communications equipment, only a single antenna was damaged by a satchel charge. The site's two courageous medics, who moved about the area throughout the harrowing night giving skillful medical care to wounded signalmen, saved the lives of all but two of the signalmen.[47]

Although enemy action delayed the construction of sites, it had little effect on the operation of the Integrated Wideband Communications System. *(Map 24)* Between November 1967 and February 1969 communications channels on the fixed network remained in operation 99.98 percent of the time. Hostile actions caused only about one-fifth of the outages. Nevertheless, the Army requested and obtained approval from the Department of Defense for the purchase of four TSC–82 microwave terminals, each mounted in three transportable vans, developed by Page for contingency use on the Integrated Wideband Communications System. In an emergency, the TSC–82's could be installed and operating in ninety-six hours. Although only one of the terminals was put into operation in South Vietnam, and the General Accounting Office subsequently criticized the Army for buying them, the Department of Defense defended its need for emergency backups by stating, "the sites were attacked and only the Viet Cong can say why they were not attacked more often for they were vulnerable."[48]

By December 1968 the fixed portion of the network was installed in South Vietnam. In April 1969 the 1st Signal Brigade installed a transportable TSC–82 microwave terminal at Dong Ha to extend a link from Quang Tri, marking the completion of the Integrated Wideband Communications System. Sixty-seven links in South Vietnam and thirty-three links in Thailand, costing approximately $315 million, provided 470,000 circuit miles throughout Southeast Asia. The net-

[46]USASCC History, FY–67, an. E; 361st Sig Bn, AHS, Sep 69, pp. 32–34.

[47]Ltr, USARV, AVHGG, to USARPAC, ACofS, C–E, 16 Aug 68, sub: Summary of Significant Activities, 10–16 Aug 68, file 139800, 72A25/20, WNRC; Sgt. Jim St. Clair, "The Defense of Vung Chua Mountain," *Signal*, March 1969, pp. 10–12.

[48]Quote from GAO Report B–168097, *Problems in Acquiring, Installing, and Operating A Communications System in A Theater of Operations*, 5 Jun 72, p. 31.

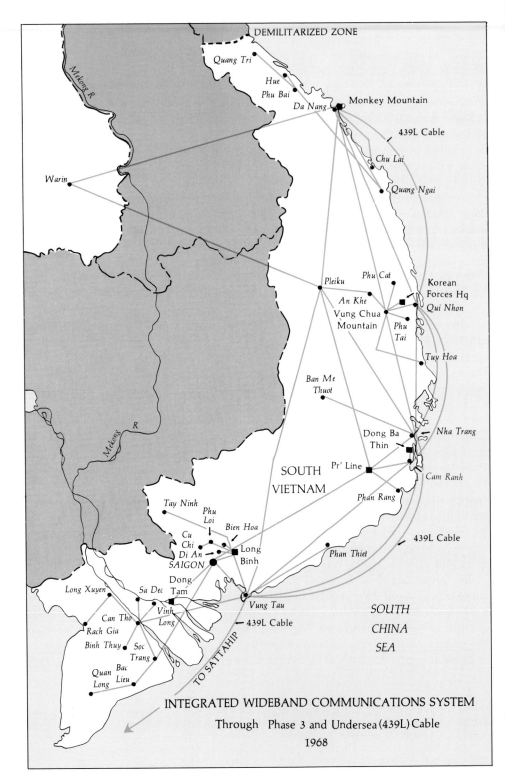

DEMILITARIZED ZONE

Quang Tri

Hue
Phu Bai
Da Nang   Monkey Mountain

439L Cable

Chu Lai

Quang Ngai

Warin

Mekong R.

Mekong R.

Pleiku   Phu Cat

An Khe   Korean
Vung Chua   Forces Hq
Mountain   Qui Nhon
         Phu
         Tai

Tuy Hoa

Ban Me
Thuot

Dong Ba   Nha Trang
Thin

SOUTH   Pr' Line

VIETNAM   Cam Ranh

Tay Ninh   Phan Rang
     Phu
     Loi
       Bien Hoa   439L Cable
Cu
Chi
Di An   Phan Thiet
SAIGON   Long
        Binh
Dong
Long Xuyen   Sa Dec   Tam
            Vinh   Vung Tau   SOUTH
Can Tho   Long   CHINA
Rach Gia   439L Cable
Binh Thuy   Soc   SEA
      Trang
Quan   Bac
Long   Lieu

 TO SATTAHIP

INTEGRATED WIDEBAND COMMUNICATIONS SYSTEM

Through   Phase 3 and Undersea (439L) Cable

1968

MAP 24

work combined the coastal cable and sophisticated automatic telephone, teletype, and data systems. They formed a regional communications system that enabled American commanders to control U.S. air power throughout Indochina, to manage widely dispersed logistical and administrative bases, and to link major commands throughout South Vietnam. Signalmen had overcome bureaucratic and technical difficulties, the ravages of nature and the enemy, and a seemingly unending series of logistical obstacles to produce an unprecedented technological feat of communications engineering.

While the entire network was not completed until the bulk of the fighting had ended, some of the earlier systems proved their worth. The links in the Saigon–Long Binh area, in Thailand, and at the air and logistical bases in the coastal enclaves of South Vietnam were particularly valuable. Tactical equipment could not have handled the volume of traffic required to sustain American ground and air forces in Southeast Asia. Nor could tactical transmission lines provide the quality required by the automatic telephone, teletype, and data networks installed between major bases.

For links to tactical bases, the fixed network proved less suitable. Conditions in the field were too primitive, transportation too unreliable, and the tactical situation too unpredictable to program fixed communications for combat units. The primary advantage to tactical communicators of the Integrated Wideband Communications System was that it released their mobile equipment from area missions and made it available for tactical uses. Thus the completion of the fixed network directly improved strategic communications and indirectly aided tactical communications.

15

American Communicators Withdraw From South Vietnam

The United States built the Integrated Wideband Communications System to meet its strategic and tactical communications needs. But there was another function that the communications network could fulfill, one that predated by a decade the deployment of American troops to South Vietnam. As a regional telecommunications system, it could unite the anti-Communist nations and permit them to coordinate their military, civil, and commercial enterprises. By the early 1960s plans for a regional system had been set aside as the South Vietnamese and their advisers turned to the more immediate needs of fighting the insurgency. Then American troops arrived and built their own nationwide system. In 1969 the impending withdrawal of American troops and a reduction of hostilities finally offered the South Vietnamese an opportunity to satisfy hopes for their own national telecommunications network.

They also appeared readier than ever before to grasp that opportunity. By 1969 the South Vietnamese Signal Corps had matured greatly. In fact, General Van Harlingen considered the average South Vietnamese radio-teletype operator to be more qualified than his American counterpart. He also found South Vietnamese signalmen to be meticulous in accounting for and maintaining their equipment. Because they had begun their careers in the 1950s with obsolete equipment, they had learned early the importance of preventive maintenance and improvisation. Even as their inventory steadily improved, they lagged behind American units by one generation of equipment and had to maintain signal gear for which spare parts were no longer manufactured. Although the average enlisted man in the Signal Corps had only a sixth-grade education, South Vietnamese soldiers proved to be good students in signal training. Most possessed inherent manual dexterity and an ability to learn by rote what they needed to know. American advisers and civilian technical representatives had nourished those talents well. Soldiers able to speak English had opportunities to attend signal schools in the United States or at the 1st Signal Brigade's headquarters, and they were adept at pass-

South Vietnamese Soldiers *learn microwave techniques at their signal school.*

ing on the knowledge they acquired from the Americans.[1]

Vietnamization

By the late 1960s almost every American unit had some mission in a "Vietnamization" campaign designed to prepare the South Vietnamese to assume more responsibility for their own defense. The 1st Signal Brigade's Vietnamization program was one of the oldest and most effective. Shortly after the brigade was formed, General Terry established a program called Buddies Together to match American with South Vietnamese signal units. The 39th Signal Battalion in Vung Tau sponsored the nearby South Vietnamese signal school; the 69th Signal Battalion was a sister unit to the South Vietnamese 600th Signal Battalion, which performed a role for the Joint General Staff similar to that the American battalion performed for the headquarters of the Military Assistance Command,

[1]Van Harlingen Debriefing Rpt, pp. 25–27, file 139772, 72A25/19; Ltr, MAAG, Vietnam, to CINC-PAC, 17 Oct 62, sub: Training Progress Reports of Contractor Technicians Furnished Under the Army Military Assistance Training Program, file 1007–07 (Training Assistance), 66A3142/2. Both in WNRC. Interv, Capt Hrair N. Badalian, CO, 23d MHD, with Col Un Duy Tao, commandant, ARVN Signal School, 21 Aug 69, VNIT 458, CMH.

Vietnam. Sister units often trained together, celebrated each other's holidays, and participated in joint civic action projects. The program gave the South Vietnamese units an opportunity to observe how Americans handled missions that would eventually be transferred to them and provided English instruction to soldiers planning to attend U.S. Army signal schools. When Brig. Gen. Thomas M. Rienzi took command of the signal brigade in early 1969, the gregarious officer became a popular visitor to South Vietnamese signal units. To encourage American participation in Buddies Together, General Rienzi told his battalion commanders that they would be judged not only on their battalion's performance but also on that of their sister unit. By 1970 the program had deve-

General Rienzi

loped so well that in some cases it obviated the requirement for signal advisers.[2]

Although the South Vietnamese Signal Corps was proficient in operating and maintaining tactical communications equipment, it remained dependent on the United States for long-distance communications. The Military Telecommunications Network, Vietnam, begun in late 1964, had never been completed. Relying on the sophisticated American fixed network, the South Vietnamese diverted their signal resources to tactical units. The 1st Signal Brigade provided the South Vietnamese with 244 long-haul circuits on the Integrated Wideband Communications System to forty-seven locations. From there, South Vietnamese signalmen extended the circuits using tactical equipment.

To enable South Vietnamese signal officers to understand how their communications were handled on the fixed system, in 1968 the Regional Communications Group established a three-day orientation course at the Vung Tau terminal. It led to an arrangement between the Regional Communications Group and the South Vietnamese signal school to train technical controllers to maintain South Vietnamese circuits in the terminals of the Integrated Wideband Communications System. Beginning in March 1969, thirty-two South Vietnamese enlisted men attended a course conducted by eight American technical controllers from the Long Lines South Battalion. After six weeks of theory and two weeks of practical instruction in the terminal at Vung Tau, twenty-two men were graduated. Fifteen continued on-the-job training at sites throughout South Vietnam; the rest re-

[2]1st Sig Bde, LOI 49–66, "Buddy System" for US/ARVN Signal Battalions, 11 Sep 66, file 2–09 (LOI) (66), 69A722/6; 1st Sig Bde, Command Progress Rpt, 4th Qtr, FY–67, pp. 2–22, 68A4975/2. Both in WNRC. Van Harlingen Debriefing Rpt, pp. 27–28; Interv, author with Lt Gen (ret.) Thomas M. Rienzi, former CG, 1st Signal Brigade, 28 Dec 79, Historians files, CMH.

mained at the South Vietnamese signal school to help American signalmen prepare a program of instruction for future classes. In November 1969 the Regional Communications Group added courses for microwave radio repairmen and multiplex equipment operators at the Vung Tau site. In each class several men were groomed as instructors to enable the South Vietnamese signal school eventually to take over the instruction.[3]

Pacification

Besides being pioneers in the Vietnamization program, signalmen also became involved early in pacification activities in the South Vietnamese countryside. In March 1962 the 39th Signal Battalion became the first American signal unit to embark on a pacification mission when teams from the battalion inaugurated the village and hamlet radio program for the U.S. Operations Mission, the operational arm in South Vietnam of the U.S. Agency for International Development. Even after the U.S. Operations Mission took complete responsibility a year later for American support to the village and hamlet radio system and most other nonmilitary communications, U.S. Army signal units continued to assist the local populace through a variety of civic action projects. During the course of the war signalmen built schools, dug wells, contributed clothes and money, and entertained orphaned children.[4]

In May 1967 General Westmoreland established a new staff, Civil Operations and Revolutionary Development Support (CORDS), to consolidate the civil and military aspects of pacification. American signalmen then became directly involved in communications support of the pacification program. Directed to provide communications to the senior advisers in all 44 province and 244 district capitals, General Van Harlingen used equipment and men not needed for the Defense Communications System. Within each corps the local battalions of the 1st Signal Brigade and the corps signal battalion, where available, established switchboards and teletype centers at each provincial headquarters and connected them to the corps headquarters and nearby South Vietnamese military installations by multichannel systems. For linking the provinces to districts they set up single-sideband or radio-wire integration nets.[5]

Equally important to the government's pacification effort were the nonmilitary communications systems operated by the Combined Telecommunications

---

[3]Intervs, Capt Hrair N. Badalian, CO, 23d MHD, with Capt James E. Horigan and Sgt Rodney T. Quinn, 369th Signal Battalion, Aug 69, VNIT 458; "Regional Communications Group," *Command Communications,* May 1969, p. 9. Both in CMH. Ltr, Rienzi to Brig Gen Harold R. Johnson, 23 Jan 70, file 228–06 (1st Sig Bde–70), ACC Historians files.

[4]Ltr, Brig Gen Wilburn C. Weaver to Col Pham Van Tien, Sep 71, file D9, CMH.

[5]Van Harlingen Debriefing Rpt, p. 16; "Communications in IV Corps for CORDS," *Command Communications,* May 1968, pp. 42–43; "CORDS Communications in III CTZ," *Command Communications,* January 1970, pp. 22–24; MFR, 1st Sig Bde, 31 Dec 68, sub: C-E Support for I CTZ CORDS/Adviser Detachments, file D9. Latter three in CMH. Ltr, MACV J-6 to MACCORDS et al., 21 Sep 67, sub: Plan for Integration of CORDS C-E Activities with the Military C-E System, file 139625, 72A25/7, WNRC.

Installing a Village Radio

Directorate of the Ministry of the Interior. A capable and energetic civilian advisory team from the U.S. Operations Mission's Public Safety Division helped the Combined Telecommunications Directorate expand a police communications network into a government-wide system. From national police headquarters in Saigon, the directorate used its own multichannel systems or borrowed channels on the Integrated Wideband Communications System to provide teletype and voice circuits to six regional police headquarters throughout the country. By using telegraph or voice radio, regional police headquarters extended communications to province and district police headquarters. By 1969 the Combined Telecommunications Directorate was also operating twenty-three dial exchanges, ranging in size from 100 to 2,000 lines, in major cities.[6]

The Combined Telecommunications Directorate also managed the older village and hamlet radio system with the assistance of military communicators. In 1967 General Westmoreland arranged for the military to provide $3.5 million to increase the village and hamlet system from 10,000 to 27,000 radios. The offer came at an opportune time because the U.S. Agency for International Development had become disenchanted with the program. An audit of the system during

---

[6]Ltr, MACV to Am Embassy et al., 14 Mar 69, sub: Minutes of 45th CESC Meeting, w/Incl, 334–75–250/2, WNRC. (Hereafter letters transmitting the minutes of meetings of the Communications-Electronics Staff Committee will be cited as Minutes of CESC.) MACV, Communications-Electronics Improvement and Modernization Plan, 1 Mar 72, an. M, CMH.

the summer of 1967 had shown that the radios were used primarily for military rather than for civil communications as the Agency for International Development had intended. Village radios were found in the command posts of the local Regional Forces units, while Popular Forces carried the hamlet radios on patrols. Military advisers had not discouraged this use since territorial security was a vital aspect of rural development and many hamlet and village chiefs operated from the command posts of the local security force. Still, the Agency for International Development was on the verge of abandoning the project until the newly established CORDS staff revived interest in the project and found ways to exploit both the civil and military potential of the village and hamlet radio program.[7]

General Westmoreland wanted to expand the network to additional hamlets and to issue radios to more military and paramilitary units. Besides extending governmental influence to isolated communities, an expanded radio network would provide the military a means of obtaining intelligence and swiftly clearing air and artillery strikes. With messages from villages and hamlets first transmitted to district or provincial headquarters for relay to South Vietnamese units on a military network, the effectiveness of South Vietnamese units had been impaired. Westmoreland wanted every South Vietnamese unit down to battalion size to have enough radios to monitor the local village and hamlet net.[8]

The Tet offensive occurred just as the expanded village and hamlet system was being established. Although twenty-three radio operators were killed and 214 radios were lost during the fighting, the system proved worthwhile. In a survey taken in 199 districts a few months later, the Public Safety Division found that 82 percent of the district chiefs had found their radios essential to both civil administration and military security during the Tet offensive. The importance of the radios during the offensive convinced the Agency for International Development to continue providing logistic support to the system after it was expanded. The Military Assistance Command, Vietnam, assigned a noncommissioned officer and a civilian technician to each province to help the province chiefs establish and maintain nets. To manage the comprehensive program, which eventually grew to over 30,000 radios, the signal staff of Civil Operations and Revolutionary Development Support, headed by Paul Katz, the electronics engineer who had designed the hamlet radios and launched the program in 1962, developed a computerized system to keep track of the location and maintenance status of each radio. Only the South Vietnamese military, which objected to having to rely on territorial radio nets, refused to support the village and hamlet radio system fully.[9]

---

[7]In 1965 the Joint Research and Testing Agency had declined to experiment with hamlet communications because it had "no clear-cut authority to evaluate it." JRATA, Second Semi-Annual Progress Report, 1 Jul–31 Dec 64, 15 Jan 65, p. 31, 68A3305/2, WNRC; CORDS, Public Safety Div, Telecommunications Projects Report, 1956–1968, 1 Jan 69, CMH.

[8]MAC J–6 Staff Study, sub: Military and Para-Military Units Interface Requirements for V/H Radios, Incl to DF, MAC J–6 to CORDS, 17 Jan 68, sub: Basis for Issue . . . Para-Military Units, CMH.

[9]Ltr, MACCORDS-PS to Sr Adv, ICTZ, et al., 9 Sep 68, sub: Village/Hamlet Radio System (VHRS) Technical and Logistical Support; Memo, John P. Robinson, Actg Dir, USOM, for Maj Gen George I. Forsythe, Asst Dep for CORDS, 23 May 68, sub: USAID Support of Expansion of Village/Hamlet Communications; Ltr, MACCORDS-PS to Sr Adv, ICTZ, et al., 21 Sep 68, sub: Village/Hamlet Radio System Survey Evaluation. All in CMH.

Preparing for the Transfer

To facilitate cooperation between South Vietnamese military and civilian communicators, in 1964 the Military Assistance Command convinced the South Vietnamese to establish a Communications-Electronics Staff Committee composed of representatives of the Joint General Staff, the Combined Telecommunications Directorate, and the Directorate of Posts and Telecommunications, the governmental agency that managed the remnants of the old French telecommunications system in Saigon and South Vietnam's commercial overseas radio communications. The committee was patterned after a similar American body composed of representatives of the U.S. military and various agencies of the U.S. Operations Mission in South Vietnam. Chairmen of the two committees were the respective signal officers. During the mid-1960s the two bodies accomplished little. Only with the prospect of the American withdrawal from South Vietnam, and the loss of the single reliable telecommunications network in the land, did the Communications-Electronics Staff Committees begin meeting in earnest. The South Vietnamese J–6, Col. Pham Van Tien, and the chief of the Directorate of Posts and Telecommunications, Bui Hu Lan, then worked together to plan a national network to meet military, civil administration, and commercial needs. They pressed the U.S. committee to tell them what communications facilities would remain after the Americans left. The Americans were unable to give the South Vietnamese precise information since various alternatives were still being considered in Washington. As a result, the frustrated South Vietnamese, unwilling to have scarce technicians train on U.S. equipment that might be withdrawn, temporarily stopped sending candidates to the technical controller courses conducted by the Regional Communications Group.[10]

Since 1962 the United States had considered a variety of plans for turning over base communications to the South Vietnamese. At that time the U.S. Army, Pacific, intended to help the South Vietnamese Army train a 1,000-man signal battalion to operate BACKPORCH and the troposcatter tails. Later, in justifying plans to build the fixed Integrated Wideband Communications System, the Military Assistance Command emphasized that the system would serve South Vietnam's civil needs while the country was rebuilding after the war. In Operation Plan 67–68, published in March 1967 to address a large-scale American withdrawal, the Pacific Command proposed that an American signal group, under the operational control of the signal officer of a reconstituted advisory group, remain to operate the network. As American withdrawal became more likely, the U.S. Communications-Electronics Staff Committee proposed a Basic Communications-Electronics Plan for Nation Building in the Republic of Vietnam, envisioning the transfer of the entire Integrated Wideband Communications System to the South Vietnamese to serve as a national telecommunications system. Recognizing that

---

[10]Interv, Capt Hrair Badalian, CO, 23d MHD, with Col Pham Van Tien, JGS J–6, 30 Aug 69, VNIT 464, CMH; Mins, Combined US/VN Communications-Electronics Staff Committee Meeting, 17 Jun 69, Incl to Ltr, 23d MHD to OCMH, 17 Sep 69, sub: Project ICS, VNIT 458, CMH; Mins, 43d Communications-Electronics Staff Committee Meeting (hereafter cited as Mins, CESC Meetings), 26 Sep 68, file 1101–05, 334–75–250/2, WNRC.

American Adviser *teaches South Vietnamese signalmen to use electronic testing equipment.*

the South Vietnamese lacked the technical and managerial expertise to take over the network, the U.S. Army, Pacific, proposed that a contractor operate it for the South Vietnamese or that an American consortium purchase it to operate commercially.[11]

Believing that the South Vietnamese Army should operate the system, General Van Harlingen in January 1968 proposed a three-year program of instruction to develop the needed technical and managerial skills within the South Vietnamese Army. At the Southeast Asia Signal School, candidates would spend one year learning English and the fundamentals of electronics. Those who completed that phase successfully would be sent to Fort Monmouth for six months of training at the IWCS facility there. One year of on-the-job training in South Vietnam would complete the course for all but the best students, who would return to Fort Monmouth to prepare to become instructors. Although the commandant of the U.S. Army Signal School, Brig. Gen. Thomas M. Rienzi, concurred in that initial

[11]Ltr, USARPAC to CINCPAC, 9 Oct 62, sub: Recommendations on Comprehensive Three Year Program for South Vietnam, Incl 4 to Summary Sheet, DA, 2 Nov 62, sub: Army Aviation in Vietnam, file 2214998, 65A3314/20; DF, USARPAC, CE, to Chief of Staff, USARPAC, 7 Mar 69, sub: Report of TDY Trip to Korea, Okinawa, Vietnam, and Taiwan, 12 Feb–1 Mar 69, tab D, file 139404, 72A4171/2; Rpt, USARPAC, Southern Cross, 27 Feb 69, file 139402, 72A4171/1. All in WNRC. CINCPAC History, 1968, vol. 4, pp. 14–15, CMH.

A Practical Exercise at the Vung Tau Signal School

plan, it was never carried out because the Tet offensive and the American counter-offensive overshadowed thoughts of a U.S. withdrawal.[12]

In late 1969 the Army finally did receive the mission to prepare the South Vietnamese to operate some fifty-five facilities—microwave and troposcatter terminals of the Integrated Wideband Communications System, dial exchanges, and tandem switches. *(Map 25)* By then General Rienzi had become the commander of the 1st Signal Brigade, and he proposed that the Regional Communications Group train the South Vietnamese at Vung Tau in conjunction with the South Vietnamese signal school.

Beginning on 1 July 1970, the troposcatter system from Phan Thiet to VC Hill and a microwave system from VC Hill to Vung Tau were used as training systems. After 20 to 40 weeks of English language training, students attending the jointly operated Signal Training Facility received 4 weeks of courses in technical language, 10 weeks of basic electronics schooling, and from 12 to 16 weeks of technical training, depending on their specialty. They then received 800 hours of on-the-job training over the next six months at an operational facility. The 1st Signal Brigade contracted with Page to help run the program. The goal of the

[12]Ltr, Van Harlingen to Rienzi, 19 Jan 68; Ltr, Rienzi to Van Harlingen, 26 Feb 68. Both in Van Harlingen Papers, CMH. Talking Paper, DA, CSAVCS-F-FAG, 13 Sep 69, sub: Training of Vietnamese to Augment U.S. Military Operations and Maintenance of Integrated Communications Systems (ICS)-SEA, CMH.

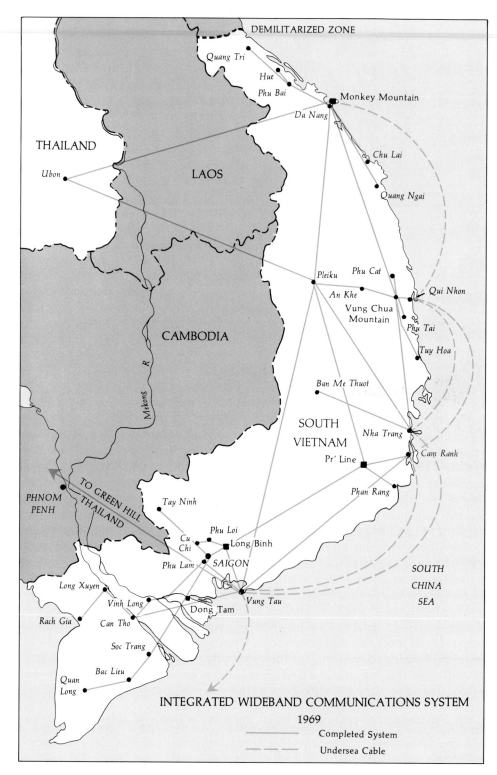

DEMILITARIZED ZONE

Quang Tri

Hue

Phu Bai

Da Nang

Monkey Mountain

THAILAND

LAOS

Chu Lai

Ubon

Quang Ngai

Pleiku *Phu Cat*

An Khe

Vung Chua
Mountain

Qui Nhon

CAMBODIA

Phu Tai

Tuy Hoa

Ban Me Thuot

SOUTH
VIETNAM

Nha Trang

Pr' Line

Cam Ranh

TO GREEN HILL
THAILAND

PHNOM
PENH

Tay Ninh

Phan Rang

Phu Loi

*Cu
Chi*

Long Binh

SOUTH

Phu Lam *SAIGON*

CHINA

Long Xuyen

SEA

Vinh Long

Rach Gia

Can Tho

Dong Tam

Vung Tau

Soc Trang

Bac Lieu

*Quan
Long*

INTEGRATED WIDEBAND COMMUNICATIONS SYSTEM

1969

Completed System

Undersea Cable

MAP 25

training program was to enable the South Vietnamese to operate the fixed network by July 1973 without American assistance.[13]

The Military Assistance Command proposed in late 1970 that the 1st Signal Brigade operate and maintain the facilities transferred to the South Vietnamese until they proved self-sufficient. But the new brigade commander, Maj. Gen. Hugh F. Foster, Jr., felt that he would be too busy operating American systems, dismantling equipment to be removed, training the South Vietnamese, and meeting his withdrawal quotas to retain responsibility for operating the South Vietnamese stations also. The Army then contracted with an American telecommunications firm, Federal Electric Corporation, to operate and maintain the sites being turned over to the South Vietnamese and to provide them with on-the-job training. Page, which had submitted an unsuccessful bid for the contract, challenged the award of the contract, claiming that Federal Electric was not qualified to maintain the equipment Page had installed. By the time a contract review board disallowed the challenge, the controversy had delayed the turnover to the civilians and the withdrawal of the 1st Signal Brigade.

General Foster deactivated the Regional Communications Group and formed the Contract Management Agency, Vietnam, to supervise the contract with Federal Electric Corporation. Trying to accelerate the withdrawal schedule, the 1st Signal Brigade hastily removed military operators from the sites, providing only a week of orientation for the civilian replacements. This brief overlap proved inadequate. The military had left behind incomplete cabling diagrams and blueprints, and the contractor's lack of familiarity with military procedures, especially with the military's logistical support system, soon caused a spate of unexpected difficulties. Many technicians, finding conditions too austere or dangerous, resigned soon after arriving, and the Federal Electric Corporation found itself short of technicians. The 1st Signal Brigade had to muster military operators to return to the sites for three months while the contractor recruited new operators to man the sites.[14]

Similar problems occurred when the 1st Signal Brigade transferred responsibility for advisory communications to South Vietnamese signal units. In September 1970 Go Cong Province in the delta became the first province in which the South Vietnamese took over all advisory communications. By the time that communications in five other provinces in the delta were transferred, advisers wanted the 1st Signal Brigade to return. The quality of circuits had deteriorated and restoral was slow. Language problems abounded. It took several months of working together, and many compromises by both sides, before the American advisers became accustomed to receiving their communications support from the South Vietnamese.

The drawdown brought new challenges for signal advisers. The J–6 of the Mili-

---

[13]Memo, JCS for CSA et al., 18 Nov 69, sub: Training of Local National Communications-Electronics Personnel in Southeast Asia; Maj Gen Hugh F. Foster, Jr., Debriefing Rpt, 20 Jul 71, tab H, pp. 29–31, file HRC 314.82. Both in CMH. Ltr, USARV, PVHGG-PT, to COMUSMACV et al., sub: USARV C-E LOI–10 RVNAF Communications-Electronics Training Plan, file 1501–09A, 334–75–249/2, WNRC.

[14]Msg, Foster ARV 0296 to Latta et al., 29 Jan 71, sub: Engineering Support for MTNV, Maj Gen Hugh F. Foster Backchannel file; USASCC AHS, FY–71, p. 37; "The Rise and Fall of CMAV," *Command Communications*, November 1971, pp. 5–6. All in CMH.

tary Assistance Command, Brig. Gen. Geoffrey Cheadle, U.S. Air Force, arranged for Army technical assistance teams to help the South Vietnamese maintain the large amounts of tactical equipment left behind by the Americans. Much of that equipment was worn out and needed repair before it could be put into full service. Despite these maintenance problems, the withdrawal continued. On 15 September 1971, the 73d Signal Battalion turned over the site on Lang Bian Mountain to the South Vietnamese 662d Signal Battalion. Since Lang Bian was the principal relay for tactical multichannel systems in II and III Corps, with that transfer the South Vietnamese essentially took control of the tactical area communications system.[15]

The U.S. Withdrawal

Throughout the withdrawal, the 1st Signal Brigade had to maintain local communications for American units until the last unit in each area departed. Although troop strength dropped from 544,000 when the 9th Infantry Division withdrew in July 1969 to 49,000 in July 1972 when the last Army combat unit departed, the number of circuits decreased by only 35 percent. The signal brigade had continuously to consolidate facilities and to reconfigure systems. By June 1971 the satellite terminal, high-frequency radio terminal, and automatic switching center at Nha Trang were shut down, and all circuits were routed through Phu Lam. When the Phu Lam switching center closed a year later, teletype and data centers in South Vietnam became subscribers of the automatic switching center in the Philippines. Meanwhile the signal brigade released people as fast as possible. Besides those returning to the United States, 230 men were transferred in August 1970 to Korea to fill a critical need for communicators there. When a cyclone devastated Pakistan in November 1972, the 1st Signal Brigade even sent teams of signalmen there to provide communications for relief forces.[16]

While drawing down, the 1st Signal Brigade had to remain strong enough to respond to a natural disaster or a military emergency in South Vietnam. In the winter of 1971, when South Vietnamese forces attacked Communist bases and infiltration routes in Laos, the 1st Signal Brigade had to rush extra tactical communications teams to the I Corps to operate relay sites at Khe Sanh and on hilltops along the main supply route from Quang Tri to the Laotian border. The commander of the 63d Signal Battalion, Lt. Col. Thomas C. Nelson, moved his headquarters to the command post of the 588th Signal Company at Quang Tri to be

---

[15]Msg, Maj Gen McCown, CG, Delta Military Assistance Command, CTO 0167 to Cheadle, 3 Feb 71, sub: Vietnamization of Communications in Military Region 4; Msg, Cheadle MAC 01273 to McCown, 7 Feb 71, same sub. Both in Foster Backchannel file. "Home from the Hill," *Command Communications*, November 1971, pp. 2–4. All in CMH.

[16]Ltr, MACCE to MACV, 13 Jun 72, sub: Award of the Meritorious Unit Commendation (Third Oak Leaf Cluster), DCA file, CMH; GAO Report B–159451, *Logistic Aspects of Vietnamization—1969–1972*, 31 Jan 73, p. 144; Foster Debriefing Rpt, tab A, pp. 5–6; "Communications Support to Pakistan," *Command Communications*, January 1971, pp. 31–36, CMH; Interv, author with Maj Gen (ret.) Hugh F. Foster, Jr., former CG, 1st Signal Brigade, 7 Feb 79, Historians files, CMH.

closer to the American base supporting the large helicopter task force ferrying South Vietnamese troops into Laos. His battalion also established a 24-channel troposcatter system from Khe Sanh to Phu Bai and a 48-channel microwave system from Khe Sanh to Quang Tri. In the midst of that operation, the coastal cable was cut accidentally between Vung Tau and Thailand. Before the cable ship *Neptun* was able to repair the break, a rocket struck the cablehead at Qui Nhon and put the cables to Da Nang, Nha Trang, and Cam Ranh Bay out of service. The Strategic Communications Command had to rush contingency equipment to South Vietnam to maintain communications until the cables could be restored.[17]

By the time Brig. Gen. Wilburn C. Weaver replaced General Foster as commander of the signal brigade in May 1971, it had become extremely difficult to maintain organizational integrity while at the same time dismantling the signal brigade. The normal procedures and documents for force structuring did not apply to such situations. While it took the Department of the Army at least a year to process changes to a unit's authorized manpower or equipment, General Weaver was modifying the brigade monthly. The brigade staff developed a computer program that produced printouts showing each commander his current authorizations. General Weaver ensured that a strong chain of command extended from his headquarters down to the smallest signal site and that each site had enough men to maintain security. His greatest problems occurred when inexperienced junior noncommissioned officers in charge of understaffed sites occasionally allowed command authority to disintegrate. To restore that authority, signal commanders had to transfer their best supervisors from site to site.[18]

As signal units departed, they took with them all transportable communications equipment not required by the South Vietnamese. To dismantle and ship fixed facilities that were no longer required or were needed at another location, the 1st Signal Brigade established the Communications Assets Recovery Agency. As its first mission in February 1970, it moved a terminal of the Integrated Wideband Communications System from Mukdahan, Thailand, to Bangkok. Later that year equipment was moved from several other sites to Vung Tau to build the training facility there. By 1971 the organization had expanded into three 42-man teams working under the operational control of the Communications Systems Engineering and Management Agency. They shipped some equipment to Korea for a wideband net being built there; the rest they sent back to the headquarters of the Strategic Communications Command in the United States for redistribution throughout the Defense Communications System. To protect equipment, the teams wrapped each component in heat-sealed paper filled with a dessicant, suctioned all air from the wrapped package, and placed it in a box into which foam was sprayed. By June 1972 the three teams had recovered 350 tons of elec-

---

[17]DCA-RVN Region, Historical Summary, 1 Jan 71–10 Mar 73, vol. 1, DCA files, CMH; Foster Debriefing Rpt, pp. 1–3 and tab A, pp. 6–7; Sp5c. Richard Wood, "Khe Sanh," *The Jagged Sword*, Fall 1971, pp. 4–6, published by 1st Sig Bde, Historians files, CMH. For detailed information concerning signal operations during the Laotian campaign, LAM SON 719, see files 8, 13, 18, and 19, 319–73–051/35, WNRC.
[18]Brig Gen Wilburn C. Weaver, Debriefing Rpt, 1 May 71–11 Jun 72, pp. 2–3, file HRC 314.82, CMH.

tronic equipment worth $55.9 million.[19]

Transferring Responsibility to the South Vietnamese

T he Communications-Electronics Improvement and Modernization Plan, a document issued in March 1970 by the Joint Chiefs of Staff, established the program for turning over fixed sites remaining in South Vietnam to the South Vietnamese Army. On 23 September 1971, the Military Assistance Command and the Joint General Staff signed a memorandum of understanding that the United States would transfer sites to the South Vietnamese as they were prepared to accept them; the South Vietnamese would provide whatever service American subscribers required. At that time the Integrated Wideband Communications System was renamed the Integrated Communications System. At each site the transfer occurred in three phases. During Phase 1 the Federal Electric Corporation provided on-the-job training to South Vietnamese soldiers assigned to the site and retained full responsibility for the site. In Phase 2 the South Vietnamese fully manned the site and had responsibility for operation and maintenance, with the contractor remaining to assist them and to operate elements of the system serving American subscribers. After some sixty days of successful operation in Phase 2, the contractors left. Before entering Phase 2 or 3, a combined American and South Vietnamese evaluation team ensured that the contractor had the equipment and records ready for transfer and that the South Vietnamese on the site were ready to accept the new responsibility. The original schedule specified that by June 1973 all sites would be at least in Phase 2 and twenty-five would be in Phase 3.[20]

Plans and schedules changed frequently. In early 1972 additional requirements for communications for the South Vietnamese armed forces caused the United States to increase the number of facilities to be left behind to thirty-four terminals of the Integrated Communications System and thirty-one dial telephone exchanges. One terminal was destroyed a few months later when the North Vietnamese overran the city of Quang Tri. On 26 June, the Dong Tam terminal became the first site in the Integrated Communications System to enter Phase 3 and be taken over completely by the South Vietnamese. In subsequent months the South Vietnamese progressed so well that the schedule was changed to have all sites at Phase 3 by April 1973. By 31 October 1972, enough South Vietnamese signalmen had been trained to enable the United States to terminate the contract with Page to operate the Signal Training Facility at Vung Tau. Thereafter South Vietnamese instructors ran the school and, because instruction no longer had to be presented in English, the number of qualified candidates for the school rose dramatically.[21]

---

[19]Ibid., pp. 5–6; USASCC AHS, FY–70, pp. 57–58, CMH; 1st Lt. James Eggensperger, "Taking Down and Packing," *The Jagged Sword*, Fall 1971, pp. 18–21, Historians files, CMH.

[20]Memo of Understanding Between MACV and JGS, RVNAF, for the Transfer of U.S. Communications-Electronics Facilities to RVNAF, 23 Sep 71, file 1501–09A, 334–75–249/2, WNRC; MACV History, Jan 72–Mar 73, an. E, pp. 38–39, CMH.

[21]MACV History, Jan 72–Mar 73, tab E, pp. 39–41, CMH.

To consolidate the management and operations of the Integrated Communications System and various South Vietnamese military, police, and civilian long-lines systems, the United States since the early 1960s had been urging the South Vietnamese government to establish an autonomous government telecommunications agency. Due to political disagreements between the South Vietnamese Ministry of Public Works, which was responsible for the Postes, Telegraphes, et Telephones, and the Ministry of Defense, discussions over a charter for the new organization, the Vietnam Telecommunications Organization, proceeded slowly. The South Vietnamese also worried that establishment of a quasi-commercial enterprise would mark the end of the generous financial support provided by the United States to military and civil communications projects. By 1972, frustrated by South Vietnamese indecision, the U.S. Agency for International Development, which had already spent $1 million for a civilian engineering firm to design a consolidated network, halted its efforts to convince the South Vietnamese to form the organization.[22]

Despairing of an overall national network, the Military Assistance Command ensured that the microwave and troposcatter terminals, the tandem switches, and the dial exchanges left behind by the 1st Signal Brigade were consolidated into one network that came to be called the Single Integrated Military System. To manage the network, in October 1971 the South Vietnamese Army established the Communications Management Agency, a unit similar to the U.S. Regional Communications Group. The 1st Signal Brigade contracted with Page to provide communications engineering and managerial advice to the new South Vietnamese organization. To operate tactical extensions from the system, the South Vietnamese Army expanded from five to seven the number of signal support battalions and upgraded the signal companies in every division to signal battalions.[23]

The Federal Electric Corporation gradually overcame its initial difficulties in operating and maintaining the facilities being turned over to the South Vietnamese. The company was working on a "cost plus award" contract, which permitted the government to adjust its payment each month from 2 percent below cost to 6 percent above cost depending on the quality of the contractor's performance. Federal Electric had lost money during the first six months of the contract when the 1st Signal Brigade had to send military technicians back to the sites. But with experience and with the help of South Vietnamese technicians graduating from the signal training facility, eventually the civilian contractor turned the network into an efficient system serving South Vietnamese military and civil authorities as well as the American advisory and support headquarters remaining in South Vietnam. Once the initial problems were overcome, service to American units on the Vietnamese-operated network was as good as it had ever been.[24]

[22]Ibid., tab E, p. 41; Mins, 59th, 60th, 64th, and 65th CESC Meetings, file 1101–05, 334–75–250/2, WNRC.

[23]MACV History, Jan 72–Mar 73, tab E, pp. 44–45; GAO Report B–159451, *Logistic Aspects of Vietnamization—1969–1972*, 31 Jan 73, pp. 140–42.

[24]1st Lt. Patrick Jones, "COMVETS Raises Unemployment," *The Jagged Sword*, Fall 1971, pp. 26–29, Historians files; Fact Sheet, USASCC, POA-SP, 27 Sep 72, sub: COMVETS. Both in CMH.

By the time the last U.S. combat forces departed in the summer of 1972, Brig. Gen. Charles R. Myer had replaced General Weaver as the commander of the 1st Signal Brigade, which consisted by then of only the Contract Management Agency, Vietnam, and the 39th and 69th Signal Battalions. In November 1972 the headquarters of the 1st Signal Brigade was transferred to Korea, and the newly established U.S. Army Strategic Communications Command, Southeast Asia, took responsibility for supporting the few remaining elements of the Military Assistance Command. Turning over command of the new organization to Col. Michael C. Fiorelli, General Myer departed South Vietnam with the 69th Signal Battalion, the unit he had commanded when it arrived in South Vietnam exactly seven years earlier. The 39th Signal Battalion, which was the first American battalion committed to South Vietnam, was the last remaining signal unit. Consolidating detachments scattered throughout the country, the battalion commander, Lt. Col. Terrence D. Sargent, established a signal company at each corps advisory headquarters. The South Vietnamese provided all other advisory communications.[25]

When in late January 1973 the United States, South Vietnam, North Vietnam, and the Viet Cong signed a cease-fire agreement that included a provision for the withdrawal of all foreign troops by 31 March 1973, the United States had to accelerate the turnover of all communications to the South Vietnamese. For the final signal mission of the war, the 39th Signal Battalion supported an international peacekeeping force monitoring the withdrawal and the exchange of prisoners. This force was composed of a Four Party Joint Military Commission with representatives from the United States, South Vietnam, North Vietnam, and the Viet Cong and an International Commission for Control and Supervision consisting of Canadian, Hungarian, Indonesian, and Polish representatives. The commission had seven regional headquarters throughout the country, and at each headquarters the 39th Signal Battalion provided telephone and teletype service for all delegations and secure telephone service for U.S. teams. Since American communications facilities had already been withdrawn from two of those locations—My Tho and Phan Thiet—the 39th Signal Battalion reestablished communications centers there, and the South Vietnamese deployed MRC–69 multichannel terminals to connect the headquarters with the Single Integrated Military System. The South Vietnamese also provided PRC–74 portable single-sideband radios to twenty-six field teams of the peacekeeping force, and American signalmen instructed team members in their use. When the 39th Signal Battalion withdrew in late February, the twelve-man American communications teams at each regional headquarters were reassigned to the peacekeeping force. Despite the hurried establishment of communications for the cease-fire preparations and the complications of providing communications for the North Vietnamese and Viet Cong, the operation went smoothly. By the end of March 1973 the regional signal centers had closed and the last American signalmen departed.[26]

---

[25]"First In, Last Out," *The Jagged Sword*, Final Edition, pp. 24–29, Historians files, CMH.
[26]MS, Maj David W. Gledhill, Communications-Electronics Support for the Vietnam Cease-Fire, 1973, CMH; Files entitled Four Party Joint Military Commission Signal Support, 319–74–051/11, WNRC; Mins, 68th CESC Meeting, 334–75–250/2, WNRC.

South Vietnamese Soldier *installs a new circuit as U.S. civilian technician observes.*

After the cease-fire, only a small Defense Attache's Office remained in South Vietnam to help the U.S. ambassador coordinate military matters with the Republic of Vietnam. A Director of Communications-Electronics, Col. Charles F. Lindberg, supervised communications support provided the office by U.S. government employees and contractors. Communications consisted of fourteen telephone trunks to the AUTOVON switch in the Philippines, data and teletype circuits to the AUTODIN centers in Korat and the Philippines, and an AUTOSEVOCOM switchboard in Saigon for secure telephone service. The American civilians also operated portions of the South Vietnamese Integrated Communications System linking Saigon with the cableheads at Vung Tau for the coastal cable to Thailand and to Nha Trang, where the system connected with the Wetwash cable to the Philippines. Civilian contractors from Page and Federal Electric Corporation also remained to assist the South Vietnamese with maintenance support to the Single Integrated Military System.[27]

---

[27]Mins, 68th CESC Meeting; Defense Attache's Office (hereafter cited as DAO) Qtrly Assessment, 3d Qtr, FY–74, ch. 10, pp. 5–7, CMH.

The South Vietnamese Alone

The number of American civilian technicians gradually decreased. By 1 September 1974, only twenty-eight contractors remained to assist the South Vietnamese with logistical support to the Single Integrated Military System, and twenty-seven engineers helped the Communications Management Agency. The South Vietnamese were doing well in operating the sites on their own. Their weaknesses were in managing the network—setting and maintaining priorities, evaluating quality control, and budgeting. In late 1973 when the South Vietnamese government finally established a quasi-autonomous governmental agency, the Vietnam Telecommunications Agency, to manage all long-haul and fixed communications as a single national network, the South Vietnamese armed forces transferred personnel from the Communications Management Agency to the new organization. But the new agency never became fully operational.[28]

A sharp reduction in American aid beginning in late 1973 forced the South Vietnamese Army to dismantle parts of the system it had worked so hard to consolidate. While requisitions for spare parts accumulated at inventory control points in the United States awaiting the release of funds, facilities in South Vietnam had to shut down. Since the South Vietnamese had to cannibalize or withdraw equipment from tactical units to maintain the area network, the army's combat signal capability declined drastically. By late 1974 the rate of inoperative communications equipment in South Vietnamese divisions rose to 40 percent, worse than it had been in the 1950s. As teletype became a luxury available only in major headquarters, all classified traffic had to be sent by courier. For communications below the level of division, signalmen relied on the old GRC–87 high-frequency radio, a relic of the 1950s, or on short-range FM radios. A 25 percent reduction in the allocation of batteries forced the South Vietnamese to consolidate radio nets. Once again, as in the early 1960s, requests for air support had to compete with operational traffic on busy command nets. Despite efforts to obtain additional materiel by Col. Elmer H. Graham, who replaced Colonel Lindberg in mid-1974 as the signal officer of the Defense Attache's Office, lack of repair parts and supplies caused a progressive deterioration of South Vietnamese communications.[29]

While South Vietnamese communications and combat capability progressively weakened, the North Vietnamese obtained modern multichannel equipment from their Communist allies to strengthen the base network in North Vietnam and to build a system along the Ho Chi Minh Trail to the Central Office for South Vietnam, located in the remote borderlands west 'of Loc Ninh. From nodal points located at way stations along the trail, the Communists extended the strategic communications system eastward into the heart of South Vietnam by wire lines run along main infiltration routes and by high-frequency radio nets. Unable to

---

[28]DAO Qtrly Assessments, 2d Qtr, FY–74, ch. 10, p. 2; 4th Qtr, FY–74, ch. 10, p. 1; and 1st Qtr, FY–75, ch. 10, pp. 1–2, all in CMH.
[29]DAO Qtrly Assessment, 1st Qtr, FY–74, ch. 3, p. 1, CMH; Mins, 73d CESC Meeting, file 1101–05, 334–75–250/2, WNRC; DAO Final Assessment, Jan–Apr 75, ch. 13, CMH.

obtain fuel and spare parts for the fleet of thirty-three direction-finding planes left behind by the Americans, South Vietnamese electronic warfare teams were unable to locate and counter their adversaries, who operated with impunity inside South Vietnam's borders.

When in late 1974 a large North Vietnamese force commanded by General Van Tien Dung embarked on an invasion of South Vietnam, it was supported by a fully motorized signal battalion equipped with the most modern communications gear. Wary of betraying the location of the invasion force's headquarters, Dung made his signal commanders establish radio stations far from the command post and move them frequently. Couriers on motorbikes carried messages back and forth between the radios and the command post. But General Dung found that communications security procedures sometimes restricted his flexibility excessively. When the South Vietnamese defenses crumbled faster than he had anticipated, he was unable to take decisive action in the heat of battle because his subordinates, rigidly adhering to original plans and schedules, maintained radio silence. While secure, wire lines often proved unreliable at critical times. South Vietnamese artillery sometimes cut cables or started fires that burned wire nets. When South Vietnamese forces attacked General Dung's command post, west of Ban Me Thuot, frightened pack elephants stampeded and tore up the command post wire net.[30]

As General Dung moved deeper into areas of South Vietnam where North Vietnamese troops had never operated, he relied increasingly on electronic warfare and on efficient communications to obtain intelligence. North Vietnamese intercept teams monitored local South Vietnamese nets to locate their defenses and determine their intentions; military intelligence units maintained constant contact with the Central Research Agency in Hanoi for up-to-date strategic intelligence. Dung even monitored international news broadcasts for information concerning the morale and intentions of the South Vietnamese. Before launching the final attack on Saigon, General Dung viewed a televised news broadcast showing the South Vietnamese defenses around the capital.

Before attacking Saigon, General Dung visited the Central Office for South Vietnam in War Zone D. Just as in earlier days, communications-liaison agents met the visitors from the North and guided them to the well-hidden headquarters complex. There General Dung could call Hanoi by telephone using the multichannel network extending along the Ho Chi Minh Trail. He also had access to the Viet Cong's territorial high-frequency radio and wire system covering the region around Saigon.

As the North Vietnamese pressed southward, they captured nodal points and tandem switches and disrupted the entire South Vietnamese Army's Single Integrated Military System. Because the South Vietnamese were unable to reroute circuits rapidly, surviving links became overburdened even though channels were available for new trunks. When routine technical problems occurred on systems in the southern region, technical controllers were too busy to take any action.

---

[30]Accounts of North Vietnamese communications during the last offensive are based on Foreign Broadcast Information Service transcripts of Van Tien Dung's "Great Spring Victory," published on 7 June 1976, in CMH files.

Although the cable ship *Neptun* repaired a break in the coastal cable between Vung Tau and Thailand in February 1975, channels on the critical system to Thailand were never restored. When Da Nang and Pleiku fell to the North Vietnamese Army in March 1975, South Vietnam lost the only other links to Thailand. On 1 April 1975, the Strategic Communications Command rushed a portable TSC–54 satellite terminal to South Vietnam to link the compound of the Defense Attache's Office at Tan Son Nhut with the outside world.[31]

By mid-April the fall of Saigon appeared inevitable, and the Defense Attache's Office made final plans for the evacuation of the thousands of American citizens remaining in the city. To avoid panicking the South Vietnamese, the evacuation had to be precisely timed and closely controlled. Colonel Graham's deputy, Lt. Col. Ronald W. Schuette, directed the preparation of communications for the evacuation. By 10 April mechanics in the motor pool at the Defense Attache's Office compound had installed VRC–46 FM radios in thirty-four buses and ten trucks and erected an antenna for a base station atop a water tower at the compound. A few days later, the vehicles picked up Americans throughout the city and transported them to Tan Son Nhut for evacuation on chartered aircraft. On several occasions when evacuation vehicles were held at South Vietnamese roadblocks, the drivers had to use the radios to call for assistance. The evacuation teams also had radio contact with fighters from an aircraft carrier in the South China Sea that were circling the city to give any necessary help.

When the runway at Tan Son Nhut was damaged by enemy fire, Americans had to use helicopters to move the evacuees to the aircraft carriers. At several locations on the compound of the Defense Attache's Office and on centrally located rooftops in Saigon, the Americans established helicopter landing zones equipped with communications kits. Each kit contained a PRC–77 portable voice radio, twenty flares, two cases of smoke grenades, four signal panels, and a mirror for signaling. Each rooftop landing pad was linked to a guardpost at the building's entrance by TA–312 field phones and field wire. Using only those rudimentary tactical instruments and visual signaling devices, the Americans continued the orderly evacuation by helicopter. By 21 April most of the civilian technicians assisting South Vietnamese signalmen in the depots had left; by 26 April the crews operating the communications center and satellite terminal at the Defense Attache's Office compound had been reduced to skeleton size.

When power to the compound was disrupted on the evening of 29 April, the satellite terminal went off the air, severing communications to the United States. Because the operators remaining in the compound were unable to bring the satellite system back on the air when power was restored, direct contact with the outside world was never reestablished. After destroying the satellite terminal and communications center to keep them from falling into enemy hands, the Americans fled the Defense Attache's Office compound in helicopters to the U.S. embassy, which had communications with U.S. Navy ships offshore. On the morning of 30 April 1975, helicopters from the ships evacuated the last Ameri-

---

[31]Accounts of the last days of the Defense Attache's Office are based on DAO Final Assessment, Jan–Apr 75, ch. 16.

cans from the embassy. Later that day, the South Vietnamese Army surrendered.

When American units departed in the spring of 1973, the South Vietnamese had been trained and equipped to defend their land. American communicators left behind an operating telecommunications network as good as any in the world. South Vietnamese signalmen were thoroughly trained to operate the network; in fact, many of them had more experience with the equipment than American soldiers who had worked on the system only during their one-year tour. To a lesser extent, the Americans had also left the South Vietnamese capable of maintaining their internal security. From hamlet radios to a national communications system, the communications were available to coordinate a civil-military pacification program. Those elements had been lacking a decade earlier when the South Vietnamese were trying to coordinate a counterinsurgency against the Viet Cong.

But by 1973 the insurgency was over, and the principal task was defeating a North Vietnamese invasion. The South Vietnamese were well capable of defending their country. They had a well-seasoned army supplied with modern weapons and equipment. It was true that their adversary had also grown much stronger, bolstered by an influx of modern equipment from North Vietnam's many Communist allies. But the South Vietnamese had the advantage of operating from strong bases strategically located for the best defense of their homeland. The ultimate difference, and the margin of victory for the North Vietnamese, was that their allies continued to sustain them while the United States failed to continue adequate support for the South Vietnamese. Modern equipment becomes a liability to a military force when it can no longer obtain the fuel, batteries, and spare parts necessary to keep its equipment operating. The collapse of signal networks during the final months before the surrender indicated that that was exactly what had happened to the South Vietnamese Army.

16

North Vietnamese and Viet Cong Communications

When the Geneva Agreements were signed in 1954, telecommunications in North and South Vietnam were in woeful shape. Military equipment, much of it dating from World War II, was worn out from years of hard use in the grueling climate and terrain of Indochina. Obsolete commercial communications networks built by the French before World War II lay in ruin from war damage and neglect. Although both nations faced formidable obstacles to the establishment of even rudimentary communications, prospects appeared much brighter for North Vietnam. Because the French had handled both military and civil communications in Indochina, their departure in 1956 left the new Republic of Vietnam with little serviceable equipment or native expertise to rebuild telecommunications facilities. The North Vietnamese, on the other hand, inherited the valuable communications resources of the victorious Viet Minh Army: experienced communicators and a battle-tested military signal organization.[1]

While the South Vietnamese laboriously rebuilt military signal units with the logistical and training support of American advisers during the late 1950s, the North Vietnamese interlaced their homeland with an austere, but comprehensive, communications network. By 1960 a powerful North Vietnamese governmental agency, the General Directorate of Posts, Telecommunications, and Broadcasting, had rehabilitated the old French wire network and installed radio-telegraph stations in every province. Encouraged by promises of aid from several Communist allies, North Vietnam then boldly embarked on an ambitious five-year modernization plan for telecommunications. The Communists intended to build a national microwave system, complete with automatic switchboards, to supplement the wire network. Automatic radio-teletype and voice radios would replace the existing radio-telegraph system, a slow, manual Morse net. They even

[1]Rpt, CAS 996, Am Embassy, 22 Jan 54, sub: Telecommunications in the Democratic Republic of Vietnam, Incl to Ltr, Army Attache, Saigon, to DA, ACofS, G-2, 17 Feb 54, sub: Information Received Through Local Special Assistant Liaison American Embassy, Saigon, Vietnam, file 102795, ACSI files, 66A3138/215, WNRC.

envisioned a television broadcasting system.[2]

Beginning the Insurgency in the South

A lthough few of those hopes for modernization were actually fulfilled by the end of the five-year term of the plan, the optimistic outlook for North Vietnamese communications probably influenced Communist strategists meeting in Hanoi in September 1960 to consider whether the time was ripe to step up the insurgency in South Vietnam. They knew what prodigious demands such a campaign would make on North Vietnam's communicators. Reliable domestic communications to every province in North Vietnam would be essential in coordinating mobilization of the nation's resources and movement of men and materiel to the southern front. Since the insurgency was to be orchestrated directly from Hanoi, communicators also would have to establish extensive long-distance networks to meet the needs of both the Communist Party's political administration of an underground government in the faraway provinces of South Vietnam and the military's strategic direction of campaigns against the South Vietnamese Army. To support tactical operations within South Vietnam, the military and political cadres actually conducting the insurgency would require lightweight, easily concealed radios. Undaunted by those requirements for domestic, strategic, and tactical communications, the North Vietnamese in December 1960 announced the establishment of the National Front for the Liberation of South Vietnam.

Communist leaders tried to insist that the National Liberation Front was a popular uprising of South Vietnamese nationalists displeased with Diem. Although the insurgents had a clandestine headquarters, called the Central Office for South Vietnam (COSVN), in a remote jungle area near the Cambodian border, doubtless Hanoi maintained direct communications with Communist bases throughout South Vietnam in addition to funneling strategic direction through the new field headquarters. Probably to relay communications from Hanoi to remote areas in the South, North Vietnamese communicators established a large communications complex at Dong Hoi about fifty miles north of the border with South Vietnam.[3]

The oldest and most reliable strategic communications system available to the North Vietnamese was the clandestine communications-liaison network in operation since the Franco–Viet Minh War along the Ho Chi Minh Trail. As infiltration increased in the early 1960s, communications-liaison took on increasing importance. By 1964 two communications-liaison battalions were handling strategic communications and infiltration along the trail.[4]

---

[2]CIA, *National Intelligence Survey: North Vietnam*, Jul 64 (hereafter cited as CIA, *North Vietnam*, Jul 64), pp. 14–15, CMH.

[3]Ibid., Jan 72 (hereafter cited as CIA, *North Vietnam*, Jan 72), p. 84, CMH.

[4]Rpt, MAC J–2, VC Infiltration, 31 Oct 64, GDRS Misc file, A76–332/9, D4, NSA; Col. Hoang Ngoc Lung, *Intelligence*, Indochina Monograph Series (Washington, D.C.: U.S. Army Center of Military History, Government Printing Office, 1982), p. 214. For a detailed discussion of the communications-liaison network, see ch. 3, pp. 65–67.

Broadcasting Over Radio Liberation

To communicate general information, policy, and propaganda to South Vietnam, the North Vietnamese employed voice and telegraph radio broadcasting. The Vietnam News Agency, an operating arm of North Vietnam's General Directorate of Information, managed the activities of both Radio Hanoi, the official North Vietnamese radio network, and Radio Liberation, a clandestine station located in South Vietnam near the headquarters of the Central Office for South Vietnam. Much of the broadcast equipment had been manufactured in the United States and captured from the French. Recognizing early the importance of undermining the South Vietnamese people's confidence in and allegiance to their government, North Vietnamese propagandists began beaming specially prepared programs to South Vietnam over Radio Hanoi soon after the division of the two countries. By 1962, when the South Vietnamese domestic broadcasting network comprised only fifteen small transmitters, all less than 25 kilowatts in strength, North Vietnam had ten 100-kilowatt transmitters and several relays in Cambodia beaming Radio Hanoi's signal throughout South Vietnam.[5]

To maintain the facade that the National Liberation Front was a legitimate revolutionary organization existing independently of North Vietnam, Radio Liberation operated an international broadcast station; that transmitter, however, was located not in South Vietnam, but at the Radio Hanoi communications complex

[5]Rpt, ASA, C-E Limited War Study, 20 Jan 65, CD-43-OJ, R-15/48/6, ASA.

in Me Tri, a suburb of Hanoi. As Communist propaganda assumed an increasingly important role after the beginning of the Paris peace negotiations in 1968, the Me Tri complex grew to house twenty-three transmitters beaming broadcasts throughout the world in ten languages.[6]

Of many special communications networks established as the insurgency accelerated during the early 1960s, one operated by the North Vietnamese strategic intelligence service, called the Research Agency, was the most comprehensive and active. To manage its covert operations in South Vietnam, the Research Agency used a combination of radio broadcast, courier, and radio-telegraph.[7]

Organized into small cells of three or four agents with cover identities and false documents, the members of the Research Agency lived a seemingly normal life in South Vietnam while covertly gathering intelligence on American and South Vietnamese military and governmental activities. Because the cell's communicator was the only one routinely to make contact with any member of the Communist movement outside the cell, he had to be especially careful to preserve his cover. The communicators required only a radio receiver, usually a common Japanese transistor radio, to receive missions and instructions broadcast directly from Hanoi. To avoid arousing any suspicion, a cell communicator normally left his radio in plain sight at his place of business or home and at a specified time, on an assigned frequency, listened for his instructions broadcast in Morse code and encrypted. Couriers handled outgoing communications to avoid exposing the cell communicators to radio intercept. If an agent had an urgent message to send to the Research Agency, such as news of an imminent bombing attack, the communicator brought the message to one of several clandestine transmitters hidden throughout South Vietnam for just such a use.

Communication of more routine intelligence was carefully compartmentalized to protect the identity of the cell communicators. After leaving encoded messages at an appointed pickup point, called a dead drop, a communicator summoned a courier by a prearranged signal. Signals might take a variety of forms: an unobtrusive chalk mark on a building, a particular arrangement of flower pots in a window, or even a specially worded notice in a newspaper. After passing through the hands of several couriers, messages reached one of two dozen contact bases located in Viet Cong–secured areas where the Research Agency operated field radio stations. There, cryptographers decoded messages from the cells, encrypted them in a different code, and passed them to radio operators for transmission to Hanoi. Radio operators transmitted messages during scheduled contacts with the Hanoi station. If they had urgent messages, they alerted Hanoi on a standby frequency, called a watch net, that was always monitored by the net control station at the Research Agency. The Hanoi station then met the contact base on the regular traffic net, and the message was passed. After processing information sent in from the field, the Research Agency broadcast intelligence

[6]CIA, *North Vietnam*, Jan 72, p. 83; CIA, Expansion of North Vietnam's International Broadcasting Effort, Jun 69, CMH; National Photographic Intelligence Center (NPIC), Selected Major Communications Facilities, NVN, May 69, DIL 123368, Defense Intelligence Agency (DIA).

[7]This discussion of communications for strategic intelligence is based on DIA, DRVN Strategic Intelligence Service, Jun 68 (Trampoline #2), CMH.

reports and warnings to agents and military units monitoring receivers in South Vietnam. Although military units had no contact with intelligence agents operating in their area, the units could pass requests for specific intelligence missions through the chain of command to the Research Agency, which then tasked the appropriate cell via the broadcast net.

The tedious procedures and circuitous routing of strategic intelligence communications were typical North Vietnamese practices. With control of the insurgency so centralized in Hanoi, the requirement for many strategic communications links to the South mandated strict scheduling of available radios and liberal use of courier and broadcast radio. Even more than communications economy, security dictated the character of Communist strategic communications. To reduce vulnerability to an enemy known to possess elaborate electronic surveillance equipment, the Viet Cong wherever possible employed broadcast radio and courier in place of two-way radio links.

Communications in North Vietnam

While the North Vietnamese were improving and increasing communications links with Communist cadres in South Vietnam during the early 1960s, domestic communications within North Vietnam changed little. North Vietnam's allies had failed to deliver promised equipment, and the anticipated modernization of telecommunications under the five-year plan of 1960 never materialized. The much vaunted program produced only a 3,000-line automatic switchboard in Hanoi and a few additional radio-telegraph nets for Communist Party, military, and police communications. In 1965 North Vietnamese communicators still depended on the old civil radio net and 7,000 miles of open wire lines.[8]

The expansion of the war to North Vietnamese territory in 1965—in the form of American bombing of strategic targets—ended all hopes of modernizing civil communications. Commercial microwave systems and television broadcasting were unaffordable luxuries in a nation at war, and automatic switchboards would be useless when wire lines were being cut by bomb shrapnel. North Vietnam's civilian communicators dedicated their limited facilities to support of air defense, military, and police forces defending the homeland.[9]

North Vietnam's armed forces had always depended on the civil networks for most administrative communications. The Signal and Liaison Bureau of the North Vietnamese general staff had focused on developing communications links to the South and on training and outfitting new signal units in the North Vietnamese Army. With the start of the bombing campaign, North Vietnamese signalmen began operating parts of the civil network and diverting tactical communications equipment from regular units to a civil defense network and to newly formed air defense regiments. When Communist allies sent the first multichannel radio

---

[8]Rpt, ASA, C-E Limited War Study, 20 Jan 65, pp. 83–84.

[9]CIA, *National Intelligence Survey: North Vietnam,* Dec 67 (hereafter cited as CIA, *North Vietnam,* Dec 67), pp. 25–26.

371

relay sets to North Vietnam, the equipment went to the air defense units to link radar sites, visual observation stations, and antiaircraft batteries. By the late 1960s the air defense organization possessed the most comprehensive and sophisticated network in North Vietnam.[10]

Military and civil authorities used the civil network to warn the populace of impending bombing attacks, to report bomb damage, and to coordinate reconstruction efforts. Because most wire lines were strung alongside strategic transportation arteries—highways, railroads, and bridges—the civil wire system itself was often a victim of the bombing attacks. During the laborious restoration of destroyed wire lines, the old single-channel radio-telegraph network was often the only means of communications for large sections of the country.[11]

Recognizing that some other means of national communications was needed, the North Vietnamese government decided to make better use of the facilities of Radio Hanoi for domestic broadcasting. Since Communist leaders, fearing that the populace might hear propaganda broadcasts from other countries, had limited the distribution of radio receivers, North Vietnamese communicators had to install a closed-circuit system. After wiring 180,000 loudspeakers to government-controlled receiving stations, the Voice of Vietnam (as Radio Hanoi called itself) added to the din in the markets and public places of the land. Providing a practical means of communicating civil defense information and of strengthening the North Vietnamese people's resolve to endure the sacrifices of the war, radio broadcasting soon became a major element of North Vietnam's domestic communications.[12]

Expanding the Insurgency in South Vietnam

By the time the American air campaign against North Vietnam began, the Communists in South Vietnam, capitalizing on political and religious dissension, were well established politically and had accumulated enough military strength through infiltration and recruitment in the South to challenge major units of the South Vietnamese Army. By late 1964 the Viet Cong had an army of 34,000 full-time guerrillas and about 100,000 part-time insurgents and sympathizers, and the North Vietnamese Army was moving several regiments into the northern provinces of South Vietnam. From its jungle headquarters northwest of Saigon, the National Liberation Front controlled a territorial governmental structure comprising five military regions. Forming a Communist shadow of the legitimate governmental hierarchy within each region, the Viet Cong established committees down to the provincial and sometimes even the hamlet level. By mid-1964 they controlled more than half of the territory in twenty-two of South Vietnam's

---

[10]Rpt, ASA, C-E Limited War Study, 20 Jan 65, pp. 88–89, 234; Intel Rpt, MACV, 8 Sep 69, 1516–1237–69, 334–74–010/74, WNRC.

[11]CIA, *North Vietnam*, Dec 67, p. 26.

[12]Rpt, ASA, C-E Limited War Study, 20 Jan 65, p. 88; CIA, *North Vietnam*, Jan 72. For photos of North Vietnamese communications installations, see NPIC, Communications Facilities, NVN, Feb 68, DIL 112592, and NPIC, Selected Major Communications Facilities, NVN, May 69, DIL 123368, both in DIA.

forty-three provinces.[13]

Even after the size of the Viet Cong organization grew unwieldy, leaders in Hanoi were reluctant to relinquish control of the insurgency to the National Liberation Front. They continued to attempt to disguise their direct involvement in Viet Cong operations and to perpetrate the myth that the National Liberation Front was conducting a popular rebellion. To control and coordinate the activities of Viet Cong and North Vietnamese Army units operating in critical areas of the northernmost region of South Vietnam, Military Region 5, the high command established National Liberation Front headquarters there.[14]

Although at each level of the Viet Cong hierarchy down to province and regiment a signal section chief had supervisory responsibility for general communications matters, signal responsibility was more diffuse than in the U.S. or South Vietnamese armies. Nevertheless, Viet Cong signal staff chiefs wielded considerable influence during the planning and conduct of combat operations. They always accompanied combat commanders on reconnaissance and during battles. As in the U.S. Army, they wrote and distributed all Signal Operating Instructions, the documents that assigned frequencies, call signs , and procedures. When enforcing communications policies and procedures, they demanded an almost slavish obedience from the commanders of subordinate communications units. In some cases, especially at the provincial and regimental levels, the signal staff chief also served as the commander of the organic communications unit.[15]

Because of the protean evolution of the insurgency, there was little standardization of Viet Cong signal organizations or equipment. Most signal units traced their origins to a single communicator serving as both radioman and messenger to a small Viet Minh cell during the 1950s. As the movement grew, so too did the communications organizations. In 1965 some uniformity in the organizational structure for communications began to appear: the Central Office for South Vietnam and Military Region 5 were each supported by a signal battalion, the other military regions and the infantry regiments all had organic signal companies, and provinces and battalions had signal platoons. Divisions of the North Vietnamese Army fighting in South Vietnam were supported by organic signal battalions. By late 1966 the Viet Cong and the North Vietnamese had approximately 150 combat battalions in the field under the command and control of thirty-two regimental headquarters and seven divisional headquarters. Besides the organic signal units assigned at each level, that entire force was supported by three area support signal battalions.[16]

When the U.S. 1st Infantry Division entered War Zone C during early 1967 to attempt to overrun the headquarters of the Central Office for South Vietnam,

[13]*U.S.-Vietnam Relations*, vol. 3, pt. IV.C.1, pp. 57–90.

[14]NSA, The South Vietnam Liberation Army: A Review of Vietnamese Communist Forces Committed Against the Government of South Vietnam, 26 Apr 72, pt. 2, ch. 2, pp. 1–3, CMH.

[15]CICV Rpt, VC/NVA Signal Order of Battle Update (ST 67–067), 16 Sep 67, pp. 1–8 (hereafter cited as CICV Rpt, ST 67–067), and CICV Rpt, VC C-E Capability in RVN-Part 2 (ST 67–006), 3 Dec 65 (hereafter cited as CICV Rpt, ST 67–006), both in 319–74–053/3, WNRC.

[16]CICV Rpt, ST 67–067, pp. 1–8; CIA Rpt, Guide to a Viet Cong Province, May 71, p. 28; CICV Rpt, VC Signal Organization in RVN (ST 67–001), 3 Dec 65, pp. 1–5 (hereafter cited as CICV Rpt, ST 67–001); MACV J–2, Briefing for Staff Members of Preparedness Investigative Subcommittee, Senate Committee on Armed Services, 18 Oct 66, Viewgraph 8. Latter three in CMH.

a single large signal battalion supported the Communist headquarters. Commanded by Lt. Col. Tam Sai, who also was the chief of the COSVN Signal Bureau, the signal battalion provided internal headquarters communications and operated radios on nets to Hanoi, to the military regions, and to combat units providing security in the area around the headquarters. The combat unit protecting the Viet Cong headquarters, the *9th Viet Cong Division*, had a 400-man signal battalion. Within the division each regiment also had some 225 communicators: 100 men in the regimental signal company, 35 in each combat battalion, and small sections in the antiaircraft, mortar, and reconnaissance companies. The number of signalmen in Viet Cong tactical units was roughly equivalent to the strength of American units.[17]

Support to the territorial communications network was more austere, except in the vast Military Region 5. There the signal section chief, Lt. Col. Low, commanded a 150-man company that operated internal headquarters communications, a school, and a maintenance facility. He also exercised staff supervision over two battalions: one maintained contact with Hanoi and the Central Office for South Vietnam and provided communications from the headquarters to provinces, cities, and major combat units in the region; the other maintained communications with units during combat operations.[18]

Dictated by the needs of the war and by available resources, command relationships, signal configurations, and organic equipment changed throughout the course of the conflict. Most communications units conformed to some type of tripartite organization—a battalion would have a radio company, a wire or telephone company, and a messenger company. Whatever the organization, the quality and availability of Chinese, Soviet, and captured American equipment usually dictated the actual capability of the unit. As the magnitude of the Communist military effort increased, new units assumed some missions of overburdened units. By 1972, for example, several signal battalions were supporting COSVN headquarters.

Training

U sing veteran Viet Minh signalmen as instructors, the North Vietnamese had begun formal military signal training in 1957 to prepare a cadre for the large field army that confronted the Americans and South Vietnamese a decade later. The *330th North Vietnamese Infantry Division* operated the first military signal school. The division's signal unit, the *17th Signal Battalion*, was staffed by a cadre of officers and noncommissioned officers who served as both battalion leaders and signal instructors. The ranks of the battalion were filled with students. As signalmen graduated from the various training courses, they were reassigned to the division's combat and support battalions where they gained practical experience. New

---

[17]II FFV, PERINTREP 23, 12 Jun 67, p. H–1, and II FFV, PERINTREP 13, 4 Apr 67, p. 7, both in file 501–04, 69A6621/4, WNRC.
[18]II FFV, PERINTREP 23, 12 Jun 67, pp. H–2 through H–4.

Viet Cong Radio Operators in Training

recruits filled the battalion's student positions.[19]

Recruits competed to gain acceptance to signal school. Because the North Vietnamese high command emphasized technical fields, communications offered high pay and promise of rapid advancement. Literacy and youth were the basic prerequisites for signal candidates. The literacy requirement reflected the obvious need for communicators who could read technical manuals and message texts. The desire for young signal trainees presaged the North Vietnamese intention to employ the communicators trained during the late 1950s as leaders and cadres for a signal organization that would be communicating throughout a prolonged war.[20]

The veteran instructors in the *17th Signal Battalion* school took great care to ensure that their students were well prepared for future leadership positions. Those who failed to show such promise were simply taught Morse radio operation and, after acquiring a minimum proficiency of twelve words per minute, were sent to a unit to become radio operators. Most students, however, were groomed to move ahead to noncommissioned officer signal courses and prepare to become communications chiefs. Six days a week for two years, the students studied ad-

---

[19]Intel Rpt, 9 Nov 71, TIR VN 2-207-6078-71, file 520-04 (68) TIR VN #4 (71), A73-42/5; Intel Rpt, 17 Feb 67, TTIR RVN 11-67, file 516-02(77) TIR VN 67, A69-21/2; Intel Rpt, 16 Mar 71, TTIR RVN 09-71, 520-04(98) TTIR VN (71), A73-42/5. All in ASA.
[20]Ibid.

vanced electronics theory, field signal procedures, politics, and military tactics. They became experts in operating and maintaining the Chinese Communist model 102 and 103 radios and an equivalent radio used by the South Vietnamese, the American GRC–9. The students were made communications chiefs only when their instructors were convinced that they could independently operate and maintain every item of equipment likely to be found in South Vietnam.[21]

By the time noncommissioned officers graduated they could send and receive Morse code at a rate of twenty to twenty-two words per minute. To keep radio operators and communications chiefs proficient with Morse code while assigned to units in North Vietnam, where most communications were handled by land line, Hanoi beamed Morse code exercise messages throughout the country over a practice net.[22]

In 1961 the North Vietnamese released the *17th Signal Battalion* from its training mission and dispersed instructors and communications chiefs throughout North Vietnam to establish signal schools at the military regions. The most highly qualified communications chiefs moved south to install and operate the communications complex for the Central Office for South Vietnam. After installing the headquarters communications, twenty of those communicators then established a signal school. Presenting courses in radio, messenger, and telephone operations, they were soon teaching over 700 students from throughout South Vietnam. Determined to maintain the high standards of the North Vietnamese schools, the instructors worked their trainees ten hours a day, seven days a week. Radiomen had to attain a proficiency of twenty words per minute in Morse code, a criterion even higher than that maintained for radio operators in the schools of North Vietnam.[23]

To meet demands for additional communicators to staff the Viet Cong's expanding army, the Central Office for South Vietnam directed military region and unit staffs in South Vietnam to set up signal schools to train Viet Cong communicators in basic skills. The instructors at the COSVN school then emphasized more specialized instruction: a one-year signal equipment repair course and a six-month officer-training course for noncommissioned officers. Taught by graduates of schools in North Vietnam, the Viet Cong schools in the South presented the basic signal doctrines to which the North Vietnamese Army adhered. Tactics and techniques appropriate to the insurgency in South Vietnam were added to curricula based on personal experience and trial and error.[24]

In 1965 the Central Office for South Vietnam held a conference of signal officers for the express purpose of evaluating doctrine and tactics practiced during the early 1960s. They decided that more communicators would have to be recruited from South Vietnam and more training conducted by Viet Cong units; but those decisions proved difficult to implement. Diffusion of the training responsibility

---

[21]Ibid.

[22]Ibid.

[23]Ibid.; Intel Rpt, 31 Mar 71, TTIR RVN 15–17 (hereafter cited as Intel Rpt, 31 Mar 71, TTIR RVN 15–71), file 520–04(98) TTIR VN (71), A73–42/5, ASA.

[24]Intel Rpt, 27 Mar 71, TTIR RVN 13–71, file 520–04(98) TTIR VN (71), A73–42/5, ASA; CICV Rpt, ST 67–067, p. 14; CICV Rpt, ST 67–006, p. 4; Cap Doc, Ltr, HQ, Armed Liberation Forces, Region 2, to Signal Section, 1st Dong Thap Rgt, 21 Jan 65, ARPA files, roll 40, CMH.

to units and military regions within South Vietnam imposed a taxing burden on the field headquarters and caused a noticeable decline in the quality of Viet Cong communications. The poor academic background of many instructors left them unprepared to develop and teach a formal course of instruction. Without standardized equipment and with recruits arriving sporadically, the Central Office for South Vietnam was unable to develop a packaged, uniform course that could be taught throughout the schools and units in the field. Because the recruits usually were uneducated and slow to grasp basic concepts, they had to be kept at the school for long periods and given particularly intensive training. When the schools came under attack or changed locations, training was further prolonged and disrupted. During the late 1960s, casualties caused a further erosion in Viet Cong training. Instructors were reassigned to units operating in the field, and students were graduated before their courses ended. By 1971 many communications chiefs working in the field had received no formal schooling; most had worked their way up from operator of a hand-cranked power generator to radio operator and then to radio chief.[25]

Tactical Signal Operations

S ignal commanders in the field compensated for inadequate training by demanding of their subordinates rigorous obedience to their directions and to Viet Cong doctrine and communications procedures. Although most procedures were based on common sense and fundamental technical principles followed by communicators throughout the world, Viet Cong doctrine was unique in its meticulous attention to detail. Most communicators carried with them a small notebook containing a comprehensive list of every action they had to perform for each different type of situation they might encounter. The "recipe book" approach was ideally suited to training and directing poorly educated men who could not be expected to extrapolate from more general instructions or to develop sound conclusions based on previous experience. Tight discipline within the Viet Cong ranks and close scrutiny by signal staff officers ensured that the prescribed procedures were followed religiously. Deviations, especially when they might compromise security, were dealt with harshly. Although separate lists of prescribed procedures existed for every combat situation, all Viet Cong doctrine was marked by a pervasive concern for communications security and a corresponding reluctance to use radio communications because of their ease of interception.[26]

In preparing for operations, the Viet Cong anticipated and laboriously practiced every action that might have to be taken. Certain basic guidelines applied

---

[25]CICV Rpt, ST 67–006, pp. 3–6; CICV Rpt, ST 67–067, pp. 14–18; CICV Rpt, NVA/VC Signal Order of Battle (ST 67–021), 18 Jan 67, p. 9 (hereafter cited as CICV Rpt, ST 67–021), CMH; Intel Rpt, 31 Mar 71, TTIR RVN 15–71.

[26]CICV Rpt, ST 67–006, pp. 2–3, 6–8; CICV Rpt, ST 67–067, pp. 10–14; Intel Rpt, 26 Jul 66, TIR 79–66, file 516–02 (77) TIR VN 66, A68–7/2, ASA. CICV Rpt, ST 67–021, an. B, and CICV Rpt, ST 67–067, an. A, contain good summaries with diagrams of various communications procedures applicable to each type of operation.

to every situation. When an attacking force left its staging area, it was to use only couriers, turning on radios only if an enemy attacked during the move. Once in attack positions, wiremen were to install a telephone net between commanders at each echelon and to supporting mortar and rocket units. If the attack was to be an ambush, wire teams were to install a switchboard and a complete telephone net between ambush positions, observation posts, and reinforcing units. The Viet Cong followed established communications procedures so rigorously that ambush forces were known to allow their targets to pass unscathed because wiremen had not yet completed linking every ambush position.[27]

Only after an attack or ambush started were Viet Cong communicators permitted to use radios. Commanders controlled their forces by unencrypted voice transmissions using captured American PRC–10 FM portable radios or Chinese Communist 71 or K–63 radios, low-powered, portable AM sets commonly used at lower echelons. Coordination with higher headquarters and rear support units was usually handled by Morse code using the model 71's or K–63's or, if the distances were great, the Chinese Communist model 102 fifteen-watt AM radio. Couriers operated throughout the attack. If the attackers were to hold the objective, wiremen followed on their heels to set up a telephone net on the objective.[28]

Withdrawal from an attack, especially under close pursuit, was a particularly demanding period for Viet Cong communicators. Because Viet Cong wiremen always had to retrieve or destroy all wire, they were often separated from their unit and had to regroup at prearranged rallying points. To avoid compromising locations during withdrawals, the use of radios was strictly forbidden; couriers handled all communications until the unit safely reached its base area.[29]

When courier, radio, or wire communications were impossible, the Viet Cong had procedures and codes for employing audiovisual signals. Surrounded by an enemy, for example, Viet Cong radio operators might tap on a radio microphone to summon assistance. Sappers commonly used the blink of a flashlight to notify a force waiting to attack an objective that they had cut the perimeter wire. Bugles sometimes announced the beginning of an attack or withdrawal.[30]

Prior to most important operations, the Military Intelligence Agency at the Central Office for South Vietnam dispatched small, elite teams, called military intelligence sections, to the battle area to conduct reconnaissance, to act as guides for combat units, and to assist as couriers during the attack. The radioman assigned to each three-man team was usually handpicked and specially trained at a school operated by the Military Intelligence Agency's own communications battalion. While the team moved about the objective area for weeks, and sometimes months,

---

[27]CICV Rpt, ST 67–021, an. B; Cap Doc, 19 Nov 68, TIR RVN 281–68 (hereafter cited as Cap Doc, 19 Nov 68, TIR RVN 281–68), file 516–02(77) TIR VN #6, A70–7/3, ASA; Cap Doc, 2 Oct 67, TIR RVN 131–67, file 516–02(77) TIR VN (2), A69–21/2, ASA; MACV, Handbook for U.S. Forces in Vietnam, Dec 68, pp. 17–18, AD 838949, DDC.

[28]CICV Rpt, ST 67–067, an. A, pp. 1–12; Intel Rpt, 5 Oct 67, TTIR RVN 26–67, file 516–02(77) TIR VN 67, A69–21/2, ASA.

[29]Cap Doc, 25 Mar 67, TIR RVN 54–67, file 516–02(77) TIR VN 67, A69–21/2, ASA.

[30]Cap Doc, 19 Nov 68, TIR RVN 281–68; Cap Doc, MACV J–2, 28 Jul 66, file 516–02(77), TIR VN 66, A68–7/2, ASA.

Chinese Communist K–63 Radio
captured in Hau Nghia Province.

before the planned action to study terrain and enemy defenses and to coordinate with local Viet Cong, the radioman contacted the Central Office for South Vietnam twice each day to relay information that was used to construct the detailed plans for the future operation. Besides controlling the radiomen in the field, the intelligence agency's communications battalion operated the base station for the teams and an express messenger company outfitted with motorcycles to carry intelligence received from the field to staff sections spread throughout the huge COSVN complex in War Zone C.[31]

The radiomen on the field teams had the most demanding and dangerous job in the military intelligence battalion. Usually working behind or close to enemy lines, they had to worry about concealing their equipment as well as their radio transmissions. Far from support facilities, they had to be able to repair any malfunctioning equipment. And they had to know the fine art of reconnaissance as practiced by the Viet Cong, a skill requiring a thorough understanding of American and South Vietnamese doctrine and organization and patient observation of every detail of terrain and fortifications.

Understandably, proximity to an enemy known to have sophisticated monitoring equipment dictated elaborate security precautions and precise procedures for tactical operational and intelligence communications. But the Viet Cong were just as strict in controlling administrative communications. Signal staff chiefs at the regional and provincial headquarters closely monitored the reliability and security of communications carried out within their domain. In monthly status reports they freely distributed encouragement, praise, or blunt criticism. Usually their exhortations were delivered in ideological, rather than technical, terms; a typical report ended with the assurance that "determination, emulation, and training will result in the killing of many Americans." Those communicators who failed to perform their mission adequately were told that they had allowed themselves to be tainted by bourgeois laziness or were not sufficiently dedicated to revolutionary ideals. Recurring complaints and criticisms found in captured signal staff reports during the course of the war indicates, however, that the rigorous directives and precise procedures for Viet Cong communications were not always

---

[31]Lung, *Intelligence*, p. 214.

Captured Chinese Communist Field Radio

followed in practice.[32]

Because radio and power resources were critically short and radio was the communications mode most vulnerable to American intercept, Viet Cong signal officers closely supervised the conduct of radio communications. They precisely scheduled every available radio for use on different nets throughout the day. To conserve batteries and reduce the opportunity for intercept, Viet Cong radios were turned on only for brief periods and at the lowest possible power output. Messages were concise, and operators used abbreviated communications jargon instead of normal conversation to coordinate their communications. They were far more disciplined than American operators, who tended to converse on the radio as they would on the telephone. To ensure that radio emanations did not betray the location of the headquarters a company was supporting, the Communists set up radio transmitters as much as five kilometers away from the headquarters and moved them frequently.[33]

The most stringent requirement imposed upon a radio operator, and a means

[32]Cap Doc, 23 May 67, TIR RVN 81–67, Incl 4, file 516–02 (77), TIR VN 67, A69–21/2; Cap Doc, 19 Aug 67, TIR RVN 111–67, file 516–02(77) TIR VN 67 (2), A69–21/3; Cap Doc, 11 Jan 71, TIR RVN 2–207–6012–71, file 520–04(98), TIR RVN (2) (71). All in ASA. The tone and format of signal officer reports changed little between 1967 and 1971.

[33]II FFV, PERINTREP 23, 12 Jun 67, pp. H–1 through H–7; CICV Rpt, ST 67–001, an. F; HQ, John F. Kennedy Center for Special Warfare, The Viet Cong, 22 Nov 65, ch. 7, pp. 7–9, CMH.

by which his superiors could monitor him, was a precise schedule, called a sked, that he had to follow in making his routine communications contacts. At specific times he had to enter each net on which he worked and pass any messages. To confuse intercept monitorers trying to reconstruct the organization of a net, the times and frequencies of transmission changed daily according to a complicated pattern. Staff officers carefully planned the patterns of skeds to avoid frequency interference and to ensure each station had enough operators and radios to meet each sked. Recognizing that the complex scheduling system could easily break down if skeds were not adhered to, signal officers dealt harshly with operators for "breaking a sked," the phrase used to describe missing a scheduled contact. To ensure that operators understood and remembered their skeds and frequencies, radio chiefs made each operator copy his schedule by hand into his own note-book. Except when enemy intercept was suspected, skeds were rarely missed.[34]

The Viet Cong used three types of radio nets in consonance: a traffic net, a CQ net, and a watch net. For the CQ and traffic nets operators had planned skeds; the watch net was used in emergencies only. Most communicating was done se-quentially. Rather than communicating with several stations on a single common frequency as in American radio nets, the Viet Cong normally communicated with each subordinate station at different times and on separate frequencies. After pass-ing traffic, the two stations then broke contact until the next sked.[35]

At a scheduled time and frequency, all stations monitored the net for a com-munications check by the net control station. If it had traffic addressed to several stations, it normally sent a blanket message to avoid having to retransmit the same messages to each station over the scheduled net. The radio company in the *44th Viet Cong Signal Battalion* operated four alert nets for the Central Office for South Vietnam: one with the military regions, two with divisions and regi-ments, and one as a warning net.[36]

Because the Viet Cong's communications were far more complicated than those of the Americans or the South Vietnamese, their nets had to be more closely regu-lated to avoid confusion. Viet Cong signal officers felt, however, that it was the only way their radio communications could survive a vigorous American elec-tronic warfare program. Encryption of traffic would not by itself thwart an enemy possessing sophisticated monitoring and direction-finding equipment. The short-age of radios and batteries also prohibited the relatively unrestricted use of radios enjoyed by the Americans and South Vietnamese.[37]

Besides enhancing communications security and economizing on the use of communications equipment, the strict regimen of Viet Cong radio communica-tions improved the technical expertise of Viet Cong radiomen. Required to use low power settings on their radios to save batteries and lessen the opportunity for intercept, Viet Cong operators usually had to use Morse code for reliable com-

---

[34]Intel Rpt, 24 May 66, National Intelligence Center (NIC) no. 207/66, CMH; Intel Rpt, 13 Feb 67, TTIR RVN 02–67 (hereafter cited as Intel Rpt, 13 Feb 67, TTIR RVN 02–67), file 516–02 (77) TIR VN 67, A69–21/2, ASA.

[35]Intel Rpt, 13 Feb 67, TTIR RVN 02–67.

[36]Intel Rpt, 24 May 66, NIC no. 207/66; II FFV, PERINTREP 23, 12 Jun 67, pp. H–1 through H–7; Intel Rpt, 11 Jun 71, TIR VN 2–207–6078–71, file 520–04 (68) TIR RVN (2) (71), A73–42/5, ASA.

[37]Intel Rpt, 16 Feb 67, TTIR RVN 11–67, file 516–02(77) TIR VN 67, A69–21/2, ASA.

Couriers Move Supplies Down the Ho Chi Minh Trail

munications. Permitted to operate their equipment on high power, American operators normally communicated by voice and lost their facility with Morse code, the most reliable mode of communications in times of atmospheric interference or equipment limitations. The Viet Cong were also more proficient in using antennas than were American radiomen. With long wire antennas installed between tree branches, Viet Cong radiomen extended the range of the Chinese Communist model 71 portable radio from eight to seventy kilometers. The requirement for Viet Cong operators constantly to change frequencies and to retune their sets to meet skeds precluded the boredom and atrophy of technical skills that plagued American radio operators working continuously on one frequency. Keeping radiomen more intensely involved in communications duties also eliminated opportunities for unnecessary conversations, called operator chatter, that often caused security breaches on American nets.[38]

Because of security worries Viet Cong signal officers preferred wire or courier communications to radios. Lacking any multichannel or cable equipment, however, their telephone system was restricted until the final year of the war to local communications within secure base areas. Although some American signal officers, seeking to explain why the Viet Cong rarely attacked American multichannel facilities, thought that the Viet Cong might be entering the Ameri-

[38]Intel Rpt, CMIC, 16 Apr 67, sub: VC/NVA Signal Methods and Equipment, US 323–67, CMH.

382

can long-lines network on circuits allocated to the South Vietnamese, no proof of such surreptitious use was ever detected. For long-distance communications the Viet Cong apparently relied completely on fifteen-kilowatt high-frequency radios, the Chinese Communist 102, or captured American GRC–9's, and the communications-liaison network.[39]

Managed by the Military Post Office Division of the Central Office for South Vietnam, and operated by communications-liaison units in each province, throughout the war the communications-liaison network filled the bulk of the communications needs of the political and military apparatus of the Viet Cong and of the North Vietnamese military units operating in South Vietnam. At several points along the western borders of South Vietnam, the network linked with the courier system operated by the *559th Transportation Group* along the Ho Chi Minh Trail.[40] The network also served in overland and seaborne infiltration. In an isolated coastal area of Military Region 5, for example, a special communications team maintained coordination between local communications-liaison units and ships transporting supplies and personnel from North Vietnam. Picking up infiltrated supplies and personnel at night on a deserted beach, couriers started them on their journey over the communications-liaison network. In the mountains on the western borders of South Vietnam similar transfers from the Ho Chi Minh Trail infiltration route took place.[41]

Logistics

A lthough the North Vietnamese tried continually to move supplies and equipment into South Vietnam by land and sea, the flow of signal supplies was often irregular and undependable. Communicators had an especially difficult time in finding reliable sources of equipment, repair parts, and batteries. Because communications equipment was easily damaged by rough handling on the long journey from the North, it was frequently in need of repair. A staggering variety of parts was required to maintain an inventory of equipment from more than a dozen countries, and some communications gear, especially batteries, required a controlled environment to remain usable. Obtaining support for communicators challenged the ingenuity of enemy logisticians throughout the entire war.[42]

The first radios brought to South Vietnam arrived during the 1950s with groups of Communists infiltrating from the North. Each group was assigned four or five radiomen to report its progress to Hanoi. When the Soviet Union and the People's

---

[39]CICV Rpt, ST 67–067, p. 10.

[40]Discussion of the communications-liaison network within South Vietnam is based on MACV History, 1968, vol. 1, pp. 122–23, CMH; Rand Corporation, *Insurgent Organization and Operations: A Case Study of the Viet Cong in the Delta, 1964–1966,* Rand Memorandum, RM–5239–ISA/ARPA, Aug 67, pp. 151–54; and CIA Rpt, Guide to a Viet Cong Province, May 71, pp. 15, 42–44, CMH.

[41]Intel Rpt, 10 Nov 69, TTIR RVN 37–69, file 516–02(77) TTIR VN 69, A71–14/3; Intel Rpt, 13 Feb 67, TTIR RVN 05–67, file 516–02(77) TTIR VN 67, A69–21/2. Both in ASA.

[42]Good summaries of signal logistics support are contained in CICV Rpt, ST 67–067, pp. 18–24, and CICV Rpt, ST 67–021, pp. 11–16.

Republic of China gave North Vietnam large stocks of communications equipment during the mid-1960s, the North Vietnamese first outfitted their regular divisions and then sent the rest to Viet Cong signalmen through porters traveling the communications-liaison network. Much of the equipment provided by North Vietnam's allies during those early years was primitive and ill suited for the harsh use it received in combat in South Vietnam.[43]

Captured communications equipment was the highest-quality gear in the Communist inventory. Units often entered battle with special squads whose only assignment was to capture radios. Some agents specialized in stealing equipment directly from warehouses. By mid-1966 the village and hamlet radio program had lost 1,324 radios to the Viet Cong. When American units began arriving in the mid-1960s, their new PRC–25 voice radios became prime targets for the Viet Cong and for warehouse thieves. First priority for issue of those valuable radios went to the Viet Cong units monitoring American communications, but by the early 1970s so many PRC–25's had been captured that the radio was standard in most enemy line units.[44]

The Viet Cong also used communications equipment and supplies purchased at or stolen from the commercial markets of South Vietnam and Cambodia. Electronic warfare units even used common transistor radios stolen from American post exchanges or sold by Americans on the black market to monitor transmissions on American military nets. The Viet Cong also used the commercial receivers to monitor their own watch and warning nets or dismantled them to build homemade transceivers in ammunition cans. Because telephone wire was too heavy to transport in large amounts from North Vietnam and too bulky to store, the Viet Cong retrieved field wire from abandoned allied positions or purchased common electrical wire in local markets. Other items that would not survive the long trip over infiltration routes, such as fragile tubes and perishable batteries, they stole from American or South Vietnamese units.[45]

Once the Viet Cong had acquired materiel in South Vietnam, they had an especially difficult time storing and distributing it. To avoid weighing down mobile guerrilla forces and territorial units working in the midst of the enemy, they had to centralize the storage of communications equipment at depots established near the Cambodian border. Because conditions in the jungle depots were usually quite primitive, much of the communications equipment stored there was damaged by weather. Loss of batteries, which deteriorated rapidly in the heat, was especially high.[46]

The Viet Cong did not maintain their communications equipment well. In addition to a totally inadequate supply of spare parts, maintenance suffered from the inattention of operators. Although the Viet Cong were experts at fabricating

---

[43]Msg, COMUSMACV MACJ3 7076 to AIG 924, 30 Aug 63, sub: Headway Reports, CMH; I FFV, PERINTREP 43–67, 22–28 Oct 67, an. C, 70A499/8, WNRC.

[44]Memo, MACJ222 for ACofS, J–2, 27 Oct 66, sub: Availability of Commercial and Military Radio Equipment to the Enemy, CMH.

[45]Ibid.; Msg, MACV to USARV et al., 15 Nov 66, sub: Availability of Commercial and Military Radio Equipment to the Enemy, CMH.

[46]II FFV, PERINTREP 17, 2 May 67, pp. 10–11, file 501–04, 69A6621/4, WNRC.

a workable piece of equipment from odd parts and used gear that Americans would discard as being unrepairable, they were not equally competent at keeping operational equipment in good repair by performing preventive maintenance. Higher-echelon maintenance was little better. A shortage of trained repairmen and insufficient maintenance training programs restricted the Viet Cong to manning centralized maintenance shops at the regional and regimental headquarters only.[47]

In the late 1960s the entire logistical support system improved considerably with development of large support bases, or *binh tram,* along the Ho Chi Minh Trail. Troops from the North Vietnamese Army's *559th Transportation Group* had moved into eastern Laos and Cambodia and converted the communications-liaison way stations on the old strategic messenger route into headquarters for the *binh tram.* Complete with depots, repair shops, and hospitals, the support bases were concealed from aerial observation by heavy canopied jungle and, in many cases, were built partially underground.[48]

Manned by two North Vietnamese Army signal battalions, the communications complexes that evolved around the *binh tram* functioned much as army area signal centers in the U.S. Army. From a switchboard at each *binh tram,* wire lines emanated to all supporting and security forces. Radio nets linked each *binh tram* with the regional headquarters and units in South Vietnam that it supported. From north to south along the trail, a Morse code net linked the way stations. In the early 1970s the group's signalmen began installing cable and modern Soviet and Eastern European radio relay equipment between *binh tram.* With the completion of that system along the entire chain in 1974, the North Vietnamese had a sophisticated multichannel system to handle direct telephone and teletype communications between Hanoi and the Central Office for South Vietnam. In twenty years the old messenger trail had grown from an unsophisticated communications-liaison network to a major logistical corridor supported by a modern strategic communications system.[49]

In 1971 Communist communicators from throughout South Vietnam met as they had six years earlier to determine whether new developments in the war dictated any adjustments in signal tactics or doctrine. By then, North Vietnamese units with modern equipment had almost entirely replaced depleted Viet Cong forces. The Americans were withdrawing from direct participation in the conflict and transferring responsibility for national communications to the South Vietnamese Army. Since the South Vietnamese used the same tactics and equipment as the Americans, the conferees decided that the communications methods of their adversary would change little. Similarly, since the common source of both Viet Cong and North Vietnamese Army communications doctrine traced back to signal schools operated by the *17th Signal Battalion* during the late 1950s, shifts

[47]CICV Rpt, ST 67–067, pp. 23–24.
[48]CIA, Growth and Current Development of the Laotian-Based 559th Transportation Group (ER IM 71-25), Feb 71, GDRS Misc file, A76–332/9, NSA; DIA, TAC Intel Digest 8, 24 Feb 71, p. 4, A76–332/8, NSA.
[49]Intel Rpt, 12 Oct 71, TIR VN 2-207-6064-71, file 520-04 (98) TIR RVN #4 (71), A73-42/5, ASA; CIA Rpt, Guide to a Viet Cong Province, May 71, pp. 15–16.

of communications responsibilities in the Communist ranks demanded little change. An increase in the number of voice radios available in the South, both captured PRC–25's and newly issued Soviet FM radios, caused some deemphasis in the use of wire and Morse code for short-distance communications; but the standard fifteen-watt AM radios were still the mainstay of long-distance communications. Even the modern multichannel system to connect the *binh tram* followed the route of the old messenger trail. The Communist signal officers decided to continue to build upon the foundations begun two decades earlier. They adhered to that decision up to the final offensive.

17

The Electronic Battlefield

Throughout the war, communicators from both sides were engaged in a conflict on an electronic battlefield that ultimately affected the outcome of battles fought by ground combat troops. Monitoring an adversary's plans, tracking his movements, deceiving and manipulating him, and disrupting his communications— all were elements of a deadly contest of electronic warfare.[1]

The principal contenders on the electronic battlefield were, on the one side, the men of the U.S. Army Security Agency (ASA) and the South Vietnamese Special Security Technical Branch and, on the other, teams of Communist intercept operators, called technical reconnaissance agents. Handpicked for loyalty and intelligence, the men of both sides were deadly proficient, continuously perfecting the art of electronic warfare. To counter that effectiveness, communicators of the opposing armies developed elaborate procedures and sophisticated equipment in a defense against electronic warfare called communications security.

Traditionally, offensive electronic warfare ranged from disrupting an enemy's communications to covertly monitoring them for intelligence. During the conflict in South Vietnam both sides restricted more overt forms of electronic warfare so as not to interfere with or compromise their collection of intelligence. Electronic warfare in South Vietnam thus was waged largely in its most covert form. Motivating, training, and equipping communicators to defend against that hidden threat tasked the ingenuity of cryptographers and the leadership of signal officers on both sides throughout the course of the war.

---

[1]Although U.S. intelligence agencies restrict the definition of electronic warfare to activities involving electronic countermeasures, electronic countercountermeasures, and electronic support measures, in this volume the term is used more broadly to embrace operations involved in maintaining communications security and conducting electronic surveillance.

Foundations of the U.S. Electronic Warfare Program

A lthough the South Vietnamese had some American radio intercept equipment left behind by the French Army, they had little success with it. Thus, in 1958 President Diem requested electronic warfare assistance from the United States to locate clandestine Communist radio stations in South Vietnam. The U.S. Intelligence Board resisted hazarding the loss of highly classified electronic warfare equipment to the Communists until President Kennedy, responding to an increasingly urgent need to penetrate a burgeoning Viet Cong insurgency, directed the Army Security Agency on 29 April 1961 to send men to assist and train the South Vietnamese in conducting radio direction finding. On 13 May the first contingent of American electronic warfare specialists arrived in South Vietnam.[2]

During General Maxwell D. Taylor's visit to South Vietnam in the fall of 1961, he noted problems with the collection and reporting of signal intelligence. Responding to Taylor's troubling news, Assistant Secretary of Defense (International Security Affairs) John H. Rubel directed the secretary of the Army and the director of the National Security Agency to improve American electronic warfare operations in South Vietnam. Before tackling that job, the Army re-equipped the teams in South Vietnam with more reliable radios and established a separate Operations and Intelligence Net for disseminating intelligence to advisers. The paucity of signal intelligence was less easily remedied. Signal Corps engineers dispatched from the U.S. Army Electronics Command at Fort Monmouth found that equipment assigned to the teams, although the best available, was designed for operations in Europe and was ill suited for the peculiar propagational characteristics of Southeast Asia.[3]

Since it was impossible reliably to track the extremely high angle sky waves produced by Viet Cong high-frequency radios in the tropic atmosphere over South Vietnam, monitoring teams were limited to intercepting transmissions located in the range of a ground wave—about five miles, or some 5 percent of the available targets. After modifying the antennas of the intercept equipment, the engineers returned to the Electronics Command laboratories at Fort Monmouth to develop better equipment. Working with engineers from the Army Security Agency, they experimented with completely new approaches to radio intercept. They discovered that by taking direction-finding equipment aloft in an aircraft, they not only eliminated terrain and vegetation barriers, but they also raised their receiving antennas into the path of the radio waves from enemy transmitters and gained additional mobility. In March 1962 three specially modified L–20 airplanes flew the first operational missions against Viet Cong transmitters in the III Corps sector,

---

[2]See Chapter 1 for a discussion of early efforts to obtain electronic warfare assistance for South Vietnam. Msg, CINCUSARPAC, DAIN 137177, to DA, ACSI, 23 Jul 58, CMH; USARPAC, 82d USASA Special Operations Unit in SVN, 26 Nov 63, p. 3, 73A3330/40; Memo, Asst Secy of Defense (SO) for Asst Secy of Defense (ISA), 12 May 61, sub: Intelligence Assistance for South Vietnam, file I–1855–61, ISA 091.3 VN, 64A2382/54. Both in WNRC.

[3]Memos, JCS for Asst Secy of Defense (ISA), 5 Dec 61 and 12 Dec 61, sub: Beef-up Status Report, file I–17639/61, 413.44 VN, 64A2382/43, WNRC; USARPAC, 82d USASA Special Operations Unit in SVN, 26 Nov 63, pp. 7–8; Trip Rpt, Army Chief of Staff, 10–17 Jun 62, p. 7, file 154189, 66A3138/82, WNRC.

and within a month airborne direction-finding teams had located the transmitters of six major Viet Cong headquarters.[4]

The several coups, attempted coups, and countercoups during the first half of the 1960s interfered with the development of South Vietnamese intelligence organizations and the conduct of clandestine activities against the Viet Cong. The party in power always suspected that those operations might be turned against it rather than against the Viet Cong. Because of that suspicion, it was not until 1964 that the position of communications intelligence officer (J–7) was established on the Joint General Staff to supervise clandestine operations carried out by the military. Even then, assignment of electronic warfare teams and equipment to field units where their use could be most effective came slowly. Not until 1968 were the first three South Vietnamese divisions provided with small electronic warfare units, called technical detachments. Another year passed before the rest of the divisions received detachments and each corps was assigned a fixed radio direction-finding station.[5]

The dramatic evolution and success of the U.S. Army's electronic warfare program stunted the development of South Vietnam's program during the 1960s. Within a short time after arriving in South Vietnam, the U.S. Army Security Agency took control of all electronic warfare activities. The Army's efforts were supplemented in January 1962 by the arrival of forty-three marines from the 1st Composite Radio Company (USMC).

Conducting both offensive and defensive electronic warfare programs, and tasked with a training and advisory mission as well, the Army Security Agency's 3d Radio Research Unit was stretched thin. In early 1963 the Army Security Agency assigned the 7th Radio Research Unit the defensive communications security mission for U.S. units in South Vietnam. Thereafter, the 3d Radio Research Unit concentrated on offensive electronic warfare, while providing direction and staff supervision to the 7th Radio Research Unit. Assigned to the U.S. Army Security Agency, Pacific, the two radio research units operated under the staff supervision of the MACV deputy chief of staff for intelligence and received logistical support from the U.S. Army Support Command, Vietnam, and the U.S. Army Security Agency Materiel Support Command in Virginia.

With the American troop buildup of 1965 came a requirement to improve the organization for electronic warfare. As each division and separate brigade arrived with its own direct-support unit of the Army Security Agency, it became more difficult to control the American electronic warfare effort from the agency's Pacific headquarters in Hawaii. In mid-1966 the Army Security Agency deactivated the 3d Radio Research Unit and formed a new headquarters, the 509th Radio Research Group, to manage all Army electronic warfare operations in South Vietnam. Under the operational tasking of the Military Assistance Command, the 509th Group received command direction and technical support from headquarters of the Army

---

[4]USARPAC, 82d USASA Special Operations Unit in SVN, 26 Nov 63, pp. 7–8; MACV, Briefing for Maj Gen Joseph A. McChristian, Airborne Radio Direction Finding, J2/D004167/67, 319–75–054/20, WNRC; MS, Lt Col Robert M. Burch, Tactical Electronic Warfare Operations in SEA, 1962–1968, Project CHECO, 10 Feb 69, K717.0413–93, OAFH.

[5]Lung, *Intelligence*, pp. 61–62, 125–26.

Security Agency, Pacific, in Hawaii and logistical support from the U.S. Army, Vietnam.[6]

Designed to give cryptologic support to a field army, the 509th Group had four major radio research components: the 303d Battalion, the 313th Battalion, the 8th Field Station, and the 224th Aviation Battalion. It also had responsibility for the 101st Radio Research Company (formerly the 7th Radio Research Unit) which had a countrywide communications security mission and provided direct support to the two major U.S. headquarters in South Vietnam, the Military Assistance Command and the U.S. Army, Vietnam. The 303d Battalion provided similar support to the II Field Force headquarters at Long Binh and controlled the Army Security Agency's companies and detachments supporting the combat divisions and separate brigades assigned to the II Field Force; and the 313th Battalion, located at Nha Trang, performed a corresponding role in support of the I Field Force.

Allied Offensive Electronic Warfare

To the envy of many—especially communicators in the 1st Signal Brigade—and to the aggravation of a few, the Army Security Agency's units in South Vietnam enjoyed an unrivaled independence. ASA battalion commanders were serving and reporting to so many different headquarters that they never had to submit entirely to one authority. Avoiding domination by field combat commanders and retaining strong ties with their parent organization, the Army Security Agency in Washington, the agency's field commanders could speak out more freely concerning their own areas of expertise and could experiment with new techniques without fear of interference.

Through continued trial and error, field technicians improved airborne direction-finding techniques. By the spring of 1966 the Joint Chiefs of Staff had approved a fleet of fifty-seven Army and forty-seven Air Force aircraft to support the program begun by the 3d Radio Research Unit. The old L–20's, redesignated U–6's, were supplemented by Army U–8's and Air Force C–47's, all carrying direction-finding equipment. To coordinate the tasking and scheduling of missions between Army and Air Force airborne radio direction-finding units located throughout South Vietnam, in June 1966 the MACV intelligence staff established a coordination center, jointly manned by representatives of the 509th Radio Research Group and the 6994th Security Squadron, the Air Force unit responsible for electronic warfare in South Vietnam.[7]

---

[6]3d Radio Research Unit, Annual Historical Rpt, Jan–Mar 64, 73A3330/11, WNRC. For its accomplishments during the period 13 May 1961 to 31 December 1962, the 3d Radio Research Unit won the first Meritorious Unit Commendation awarded to an Army unit since the Korean War.

[7]Memo, Asst Secy of Air Force (R&D) for Vice Chief of Staff, USAF, 10 Jul 62, sub: Direction Finding in Counterinsurgency Operations, 66A3138/86; Memo, DA, ACSI-CI, for Col Thomas W. Riley, Jr., USA, JCS Project Officer, 19 Sep 62, sub: Improvement of High Frequency Radio Direction Finding Capabilities, South Vietnam, 66A3138/89; Ltr, ASA to ACSI, DA, 10 Nov 64, sub: Formal Programming for Airborne Platform, file 373.1, 66A3201/64. All in WNRC.

Although South Vietnamese Army pilots had begun flying direction-finding missions with American instructors in 1963, the South Vietnamese program was ineffective until the early 1970s, when the Vietnamization program afforded them more sophisticated aircraft and more opportunity. The rapid growth of the South Vietnamese program, matched by the equally rapid decline of the American role, enabled the South Vietnamese eventually to provide 95 percent of the intelligence gained from airborne electronic warfare. After the 1973 cease-fire, with aircraft losses increasing from improved enemy air defenses and deteriorating logistical support within the South Vietnamese armed forces, South Vietnam's airborne program took a precipitous decline.[8]

Direction-Finding Equipment *in support of the 11th Infantry Brigade, 1968.*

Although American airborne direction-finding efforts overshadowed the ground program, the Army Security Agency's direct-support units were essential to American electronic warfare. Operating against a variety of enemy units, they identified targets for further exploitation by airborne teams. Since they worked against the same Communist targets every day, they acquired the best understanding of local Communist communications. Building an informal enemy communications order of battle, the commander of every detachment knew which enemy units provided the most important information and which had the worst security discipline.

Analysts familiar with local communications patterns could garner important information. Realignment of radio nets and relocation of terminals often indicated changes in the enemy order of battle or forecast an impending operation. Disappearance of an enemy station after an allied attack obviously suggested success. American intelligence officers attempted to confirm the observations of astute electronic warfare analysts with information from collateral intelligence—captured documents or prisoners of war.[9]

The commander of the direct-support electronic warfare units on the ground had the responsibility of maintaining the vital link between the entire electronic warfare community and the tactical commander and his staff. He had to bridge the chasm between the esoteric science of cryptology and the practical concerns of the battlefield command post. Detachment chiefs of direct-support units ad-

---

[8]Lung, *Intelligence*, pp. 126–27, 141–42.
[9]Lewy, *America in Vietnam*, p. 35; Memo, Gen W. C. Westmoreland for Chief of Staff, U.S. Army, 30 Mar 65, sub: Evaluation of the Memorandum Prepared by DA Concerning the Situation in the Northern Provinces of RVN, CS091VN (30 Mar 65), 68A3305/1, WNRC.

vised tactical commanders of the enemy order of battle and of the electronic warfare resources, both ground and airborne, that were available to support particular operations.

Even after equipment and techniques improved, American electronic warfare efforts remained limited against short-range enemy communications, both telephones and low-powered radios. Teams were unable to move close enough to wiretap enemy lines or monitor short-range radio without jeopardizing the security of men and equipment.[10]

The Americans increasingly turned to unattended equipment to fill that role. In 1966 the United States began to build an electronic barrier of acoustic, seismic, and radio sensors across the northern border of South Vietnam, the panhandle of Laos, and the eastern regions of Thailand to detect North Vietnamese infiltration. A group of American scientists, who had assembled secretly in the summer of 1966 to consider means for harnessing American technology for the war, had conceived of the ambitious approach. To implement it, Secretary of Defense McNamara formed the Defense Communications Planning Group on 15 September 1966 under Lt. Gen. Alfred D. Starbird, the director of the Defense Communications Agency.[11]

Using the technical resources of the Electronics Command and several other governmental laboratories and commercial manufacturers, the Defense Communications Planning Group spent $670 million to develop and produce large stocks of sensors camouflaged as pieces of vegetation to use in the barrier, which had come to be called the McNamara Line. Seeded from the air throughout the Laotian panhandle in the fall of 1967, the sensors transmitted the sounds of enemy activity to aircraft orbiting the region. At an Infiltration Surveillance Center at Nakhon Phanom in northeastern Thailand, the Seventh Air Force plotted the recorded detections and launched air strikes against the most promising targets.[12]

In South Vietnam the sensors were being installed in conjunction with fortifications and barriers along the Demilitarized Zone when Khe Sanh came under siege in early 1968. General Westmoreland diverted the sensors to ring the Marine base. They were so successful in warning of enemy movements and identifying targets for artillery and air support that General Westmoreland obtained permission to postpone the completion of the McNamara Line to use the sensors in tactical operations. By 1969 the Military Assistance Command had installed sensors on perimeters of military installations, along main convoy routes, and across principal enemy avenues of approach in the border areas of South Vietnam. Tactical units and Special Forces teams monitored the sensors. To aid in the communication of readings from remote areas, a radio relay aircraft orbited the tri-border area west of Pleiku and a ground relay operated from the top of Nui Ba Den.

---

[10]MFR, Special Activities Section, Thailand, Operations Branch, 8 May 62, sub: Thailand Operations, ACSI file 6–2412, 66A3201/155, WNRC; MACV Directive 381–45, 5 Apr 69, sub: Exploitation of Enemy Landline Communications Systems, CMH.

[11]For an account of the work of the Defense Communications Planning Group and the use of sensors in Southeast Asia, see Paul Dickson, *The Electronic Battlefield* (Bloomington, Ind.: Indiana University Press, 1976).

[12]MACV History, 1968, pp. 911–34, CMH.

The Nui Ba Den Relay Site

Although the McNamara Line had only limited success in halting infiltration or in strategic interdiction, the sensors were used effectively by tactical units. While it was impossible to know whether the source of a sensing in a remote area was enemy activity, the sensors pinpointed the area of a sensing. Local units could then investigate the cause.[13]

Although offensive American electronic warfare activities in South Vietnam were devoted primarily to finding the enemy and collecting intelligence, occasionally other approaches were tried. A few attempts were made at manipulative communications deception, a technique in which false transmissions were deliberately made on one's own communications nets to mislead an eavesdropping enemy. For example, the Americans would transmit false strength reports to indicate the weakening of a base's defenses, thereby enticing the enemy into a trap. On several occasions following manipulative communications deception, the enemy did attack and suffered heavy casualties. Imitative deception, involving a more difficult procedure of entering the enemy's communications network to transmit false or misleading information, was never attempted by Americans in South Vietnam.

Jamming or interfering with enemy communications was infrequently used. Secretary McNamara in mid-1966 suggested that the military jam enemy com-

[13]Ibid., 1969, ch. 7, pp. 1–15, CMH.

munications to disrupt operations. Pointing out that the enemy used his radios seldom and that combat operations were brief, General Westmoreland responded that except for the Ia Drang battle there had been little opportunity for jamming enemy communications. The Army attempted ground-based jamming only twice, once at Pleiku and Nha Trang to override the broadcast of Viet Cong propaganda intended to incite a Montagnard revolt. The only formal jamming program was that employed by the Navy against enemy communications and radar signals in North Vietnam to suppress antiaircraft defenses.[14]

It was not easy to overcome the enemy's communications defenses. American electronic warfare operators were always looking for intelligence on enemy communications procedures and equipment. A special detachment from the 509th Radio Research Group reviewed every captured document and report of interrogation of prisoners and defectors for clues to the operation of enemy communications. If an interrogation report indicated that a prisoner or defector might be a source of additional communications information, specially trained interrogators from the Radio Research Unit continued questioning him. Often those special interrogation reports elicited requests for additional questioning on particular points. Another special unit, the 18th Signal Detachment, which was assigned to an operating branch of the MACV intelligence staff called the Combined Materiel Exploitation Center, studied captured communications equipment and provided intercept operators with a valuable guide to the operational range and characteristics of Viet Cong communications.[15]

The Communist Defenses

The enemy's security did not crack easily. A wary people by nature, the North Vietnamese had cloaked the insurgency in South Vietnam in a pervasive secrecy. Captured communications security directives indicated that as early as 1962 the Communists were taking a serious and sophisticated approach to protecting their communications. For example, they permitted unencrypted transmissions only on news broadcasts.[16]

Besides the Communists' natural prediliction for secrecy, an unswerving adherence to directives and plans within the ranks enhanced the security of Communist communications. Communist radio operators were more likely to follow rigid security directives than their more highly educated American contemporaries, who tended to interpret rather than follow directions and to look for shortcuts which sometimes compromised communications security. Because the Communists maintained tight discipline over their troops, they also could

---

[14]Rpts, JCS 222/994, 6 Sep 66, through JCS 222/994–6, 22 Nov 66, sub: Jamming VC/PAVN Field Communications, JACO (1966), DA/6,NARS; Alfred Price, *Instruments of Darkness: The History of Electronic Warfare* (New York: Charles Scribner's Sons, 1978), pp. 265–68.

[15]"C-E Technical Intelligence," *Command Communications*, September 1967, pp. 72–76, CMH.

[16]CICV Rpt, ST 67–006, pp. 6–8; Cap Doc, 24 Aug 67, TIR RVN 114–67, file 516–02(77) TIR VN 2, A69–21/2, ASA.

plan and rehearse operations in precise detail with the confidence that each step would be carried out exactly as directed, a factor that lessened the need for communications for command and control during those operations. Less communications, in turn, meant fewer opportunities for Americans or South Vietnamese to use electronic warfare against Communist communications.

In addition to strictly regulating communicators, the Communists educated other staff officers to maintain communications security. They enjoined them to avoid using electrical transmission whenever courier service was available. Any information transmitted by radio had to be protected even after it was no longer classified, lest an enemy discover it in an unencrypted form and break signal codes by comparing the text of encrypted and unencrypted communications. Perhaps the greatest impetus to enemy communications security was the universal belief throughout the ranks that the Army Security Agency was practicing electronic warfare against Communist communications.[17]

The Central Office for South Vietnam distributed codes, call signs, and frequency assignments to the signal staffs at each military region headquarters, where signal representatives from units and provinces picked up extracts of the information pertaining to their own operations. From those extracts each radio operator copied into a notebook only that information that applied to him. Although much less efficient than the American practice of mimeographing an entire package of communications information, called Signal Operating Instructions, and giving it wide distribution, the enemy methods were far safer. By strictly controlling distribution, signal officers not only limited the amount of signal information vulnerable to capture but also made it impossible for radio operators to enter any nets in which they did not belong, a practice that could cause breakdowns in net discipline and security.

The Viet Cong assigned professional cryptographers to every regiment and every province. Since radio operators were kept physically separated from the cryptographers and were even forbidden to associate with them during off-duty time, radio operators had little opportunity to handle or have knowledge of any unencoded classified information. Besides restricting access to important cryptographic material, the compartmentalization of communicators and cryptographers precluded the inadvertent transmission of classified information in the clear by a careless radio operator. Because of the sensitive nature of cryptographers' work, they were usually handpicked Communist Party members who had received intensive training at a special school in Hanoi.[18]

Even in low-level units without cryptographers, radio operators followed precise operational procedures that made communications more secure. The Communist practice of communicating with each station on a net only at a scheduled time and on a prescribed frequency—and of varying those times and frequencies periodically—made it difficult for an enemy to intercept a particular station by continually monitoring a single frequency. The enemy made mandatory the use of international procedural words, called prosigns, to communicate signal infor-

[17]Cap Doc, 28 Jun 67, TIR RVN 98–67, file 516–02(77) TIR VN 67, A69–21/2, ASA.
[18]Intel Rpt, 25 Dec 67, TTIR 31–67, file 516–02(77) TTIR VN 67, A69–21/2, ASA; I FFV, PERINTREP 43–67, 22–28 Oct 67, an. C, 70A499/8, WNRC.

mation. Using these shortcuts meant that transmitters were on the air a shorter time and were thus less exposed to enemy intercept. How diligently the various procedures were followed depended to a great extent on the quality of the supervision rendered by local signal staff officers. Most were quite harsh in enforcing communications discipline. In their reprimands of violators they even equated laxity with disloyalty to the Communist cause.

When voice radio came into wide use on enemy nets during the late 1960s, it became more difficult to control those speaking directly, usually extemporaneously, on communications channels. Signal officers issued voice codes, but operators frequently neglected to use them or developed their own unsecure brevity codes. Because voice radio operators usually received less training than Morse code radiomen, quality of communications and net discipline were also lower on voice nets.

As the Americans improved their airborne direction-finding techniques, net discipline and operational procedures became as important as cryptography to the Communists. They knew that even if the Americans could not read the text of a station's traffic, they could still home in on the signal emitter of the transmitter. Suspecting that American radio direction finders guided B–52 bombers that were dropping their large bombs with deadly accuracy on the transmitters serving major Communist headquarters, in 1965 commanders began ordering their signal officers to set up transmitters as far away from supporting headquarters as possible. In addition enemy radiomen learned to recognize by sight and sound the types of aircraft used for airborne radio direction finding and to shut off their transmitters when they were in the area.[19]

U.S. Communications Defense

Americans had greater difficulty enforcing communications security. In South Vietnam some Americans were lulled into a false sense of security by believing that encoding was unnecessary because the enemy was unable to understand English. While the Viet Cong planned operations in great detail to minimize communications during actual execution, Americans, valuing flexibility and spontaneity, relied heavily on radio and telephone communications to make last-minute adjustments to plans and to control fast-moving airmobile operations. Perhaps from a sense of isolation in a strange land, American radio operators chattered incessantly on their nets. Most felt it their job to make frequent communications checks and to notify higher headquarters concerning even the most unimportant happenings in the field. Coupled with American disdain for secrecy, the heavy use of communications made Americans lucrative targets for electronic warfare unless cryptographers found means to protect their communications.[20]

---

[19]Cap Doc, 28 Sep 68, TIR RVN 245–68, file 516–02(77) TIR VN 5 (68), A70–7/3; Cap Doc, 22 Aug 67, TIR RVN 112–67, file 516–02(77) TIR VN 2, A69–21/2. Both in ASA.

[20]Memo, DA, Asst Secy of Army (R&D) for Chief of Staff, 14 Apr 61, sub: Communications Effectiveness in Future Combat; Ltr, 3d Bde to 4th Div, 18 Apr 69, sub: Combat Operations AAR-Operation GREENE THUNDER II, VNI 181. Both in CMH.

During the 1950s American advisers made virtually no attempt to protect their communications. Only cumbersome manual coding procedures were available to them. Nor was there any check to determine whether South Vietnamese or American communications were being compromised. Not until late 1960, after a disturbing report by an Army Security Agency inspection team from Hawaii illuminated communications security deficiencies in South Vietnam, were the first steps taken to assign responsibility for improving communications security in Southeast Asia. The Military Assistance Advisory Group assigned to the chief signal adviser staff supervision for communications security matters, and the Joint Chiefs of Staff directed the Army Security Agency to provide cryptologic support to the advisory group. In the spring of 1961 the Army Security Agency sent a team to monitor telephone circuits on the combined South Vietnamese–American switchboard in Saigon. In November of the same year, a mobile team set up monitoring operations in support of the advisory detachment at the I Corps headquarters in Da Nang. By March 1963, when the 7th Radio Research Unit became responsible for communications security in South Vietnam, ten teams were monitoring wire and radio circuits throughout the country.[21]

The monitoring program revealed compromises of classified information. Alerted to the vulnerability of communications, General Paul D. Harkins directed the MACV Assistant Chief of Staff for Communications-Electronics, Lt. Col. Philip S. Pomeroy, to establish a position on his staff for an assistant for communications security. Colonel Pomeroy made the newly arrived 39th Signal Battalion the cryptographic distribution authority for all American cryptographic equipment, a formidable mission involving distributing, repairing, and accounting for all cryptographic machines and documents in South Vietnam. During the next two years the battalion handled three generations of communications security equipment. Off-line cipher machines, installed with the Operations and Intelligence Net in 1962, were replaced the following year by on-line machines.[22] They, in turn, were replaced in 1964 by a more rugged and reliable on-line machine. Although many American units in South Vietnam continued to use older sets on low-level nets for several years, the on-line system eventually became standard for U.S. tactical teletype communications. As the off-line system was replaced, it was turned over to the South Vietnamese.[23]

From a concern to help South Vietnamese communicators as well as from a desire to protect American communications over South Vietnamese channels, signal advisers of the Military Assistance Advisory Group pressed for American cryptographic support for the South Vietnamese. In addition to the compromise of classified information, nonsecure South Vietnamese communications offered the enemy an excellent start in breaking codes that protected secure American systems transmitting

---

[21]USARPAC, 82d USASA Special Operations Unit in SVN, 26 Nov 63, pp. 12–13.

[22]Off-line encryption and decryption take place independent of the communications process; on-line encryption and decryption occur while a message is being transmitted and received. The off-line system uses a typewriter that produces an encrypted tape for transmission over a teletype or Morse code circuit, while an on-line system automatically encodes and decodes regular teletype pulses as they are being processed by transmitting and receiving equipment.

[23]USARPAC, 82d USASA Special Operations Unit in SVN, 26 Nov 63, pp. 5–14; MACV J–6 History, FY 1962–63, pp. 2–3, file GF–3, 338–75–1009/63, WNRC.

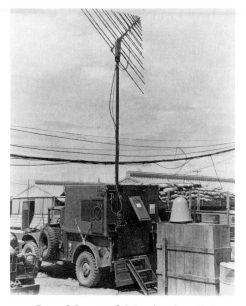

Jeep-Mounted Monitoring Set

identical information.

With the assistance of the 39th Signal Battalion, the signal staff of the Military Assistance Command conducted classes for the South Vietnamese in the use of cryptographic equipment. Officers from the 3d Radio Research Unit inspected the facilities in which the devices were to be installed and assisted the South Vietnamese in meeting stringent physical security requirements. In September 1962 the first secure South Vietnamese nets came on the air. By the spring of 1964 all high-level communications of the Joint General Staff and the corps headquarters were secured by an on-line teletype system, and every division and regiment had received off-line devices for use on tactical Morse code nets.[24]

As voice radio and telephone replaced teletype and Morse code as the primary modes of American communications, officers of the Army Security Agency could take little consolation in improvements to the cryptographic equipment for teletype or Morse code nets. Although devices existed for on-line protection of telephone conversations, they were not widely available in South Vietnam because they were still being tested and were extremely expensive. Only a constant awareness of the vulnerability of voice communications and careful use of operations codes could defend against breaches of telephone security. In the absence of proof that the Viet Cong were intercepting American transmissions, advisers were unconvinced of a real threat and rarely used operations codes. While the security experts of the 7th Radio Research Unit could provide communications security training for operators of teletype and Morse code nets, who were professional communicators, they were unable to reach everyone with access to a telephone or voice radio.

The problem was destined to get worse. As American combat units began deploying to South Vietnam during 1965, every combat leader from squad to division would have the battlefield replacement for the ubiquitous American telephone: an FM voice radio. Simple to operate, the radios were conveniently at hand to maintain constant command and control, to request air and artillery fire support, and to seek logistical support. With the high power setting habitually used by Americans, the FM voice radio had tremendous range and transmitted its signal in all directions. Those qualities—reliability, convenience, and range—made the FM voice radio a lucrative target for Viet Cong electronic warfare tech-

---

[24]MS, HQ, USARPAC, History of the U.S. Army Buildup and Operations in the Republic of Vietnam (RVN), 1 Jan 61–31 Jan 63, pp. 166–67, and ibid., 1 Feb 63–31 Dec 63, pp. 231–35, both in CMH; MACV J-6 History, FY 1962–63, p. 5; Msg, MAAG, Saigon, DAIN 136493, to CINCPAC, 2 Aug 61, sub: Communications Security Assistance to Vietnam, CMH.

nicians. The proliferation of these radios throughout South Vietnam, moreover, made it simple for the Viet Cong to capture or steal them to use in electronic warfare operations.

As new U.S. units arrived in South Vietnam during the mid-1960s, the 7th Radio Research Unit warned them of the dangers of relaxing communications security. They played recordings of security breaches detected in the monitoring program and taught classes to radio operators on security precautions to be taken to protect American communications. But continued monitoring of American radios and telephones demonstrated the futility of those efforts.

Since the 7th Radio Research Unit could monitor only about 6 percent of all American communications in South Vietnam, the Army Security Agency studied the security of tactical communications in one unit, the 1st Cavalry Division, to assess the seriousness of the situation. For the last three months of 1965, soon after the division arrived in South Vietnam, the 7th Radio Research Unit provided a contingent of monitoring teams to augment the division's own 371st Radio Research Company. Selection of the 1st Cavalry Division for the study was fateful, for the teams were soon to find themselves monitoring the communications of units engaged in the most savage fighting yet experienced in the war—the first American engagement with North Vietnamese troops in the Ia Drang valley.

Monitoring 10,902 voice, teletype, and Morse code transmissions during the three weeks before the battle, the team noted little concern for fundamental communications security precautions. The air cavalrymen rarely used available authentication systems to protect against imitative deception.[25] Even though many net frequencies and call signs had been compromised by transmission in the clear, signal officers seldom changed Signal Operating Instructions, which assigned frequencies and call signs to divisional units.

Although the commander of the 371st Radio Research Company reported the findings and made remedial suggestions, the division's signal officers had no time to tighten communications security before the division became hotly engaged in battle. Then the monitoring team found that American communications security in areas near the enemy not only failed to improve, but sometimes worsened. Restricting the program to voice communications, the teams monitored 28,023 voice transmissions during the month-long fight. They found that once the battle was joined, communications security was completely ignored. Sensitive information was broadcast in the clear and critical messages accepted without any authentication challenge. The only attempt to protect information was the occasional use of an unauthorized, homemade code and easily compromised point-of-origin systems.[26] Neither approved operations codes nor off-line security devices were ever used during the battle. Officials in the Army Security Agency and the National Security Agency were most alarmed that communicators in front-line combat units had failed to use the security measures available to them: off-line coding machines and authorized authentication and operations codes. Commu-

---

[25]Authentication codes, the radio operator's password system, were used to challenge the legitimacy of stations passing traffic in a net.

[26]Point-of-origin systems were based on the use of encoded reference points from which locations could be identified. For example, "CP located 600 meters northeast of point *Alpha.*"

nicators and commanders throughout South Vietnam were less surprised by the findings; they saw in them a reflection of practices prevalent throughout tactical units. Off-line encryption methods took time, and on the battlefield American commanders felt that time was more crucial than security.

The Ia Drang findings provided new impetus to a prior request by the commander in chief, Pacific, for the National Security Agency to develop speech security equipment for tactical units in South Vietnam. Initially reluctant to produce a cryptographic device for the combat infantryman that would undoubtedly be captured, the National Security Agency in January 1966 nevertheless agreed to develop a security device for portable radios. The National Security Agency and the U.S. Army Electronics Command designed the PRC-77, a modified PRC-25 that could be connected to the speech security gear. The findings from the Ia Drang also influenced a decision by the Defense Communications Agency to expand the Automatic Secure Voice Communications System (AUTOSEVOCOM) to include narrowband terminals for tactical units.[27]

While awaiting the development of new equipment, officers of the Army Security Agency in Southeast Asia turned their attention to ways of supplementing conventional monitoring for security violations with more preventive approaches. They advised units about techniques to protect communications. Through selective monitoring they next tested, and reported to the commanders, how well specific recommended security practices worked. The results of monitoring were then applied in future plans.

When the United States began installing the infiltration detection system, the McNamara Line, the U.S. Army, Pacific, sent a five-man team to the Infiltration Surveillance Center in Thailand to determine how to keep the highly classified project secret. After two months of monitoring telephone circuits and voice radio nets, the team obtained names, locations, organizations, and security and communications plans for the entire operation. To avoid further compromises, they recommended that communications concerning the project be restricted to secure teletype as much as possible. They even advised discontinuing the use of the code names for the project. Improvements were gradual and subtle. Although the new preventive approach did not offer any dramatic solution to communications security problems, it did give electronic warfare specialists the opportunity to influence operational planning.

Even though the 1st Cavalry Division's experience in the Ia Drang made commanders aware of the deplorable state of communications security, they still felt that most communications security measures were unnecessary and restrictive. They were not convinced that the enemy was monitoring their communications. They felt that practicing communications security meant sacrificing the tactical flexibility and control provided by extensive open communications. While more sympathetic to the importance of communications security, division signal officers

---

[27]Chief of Staff of the Army Memorandum 94-66, Chief of Staff of the Army to JCS, 28 Feb 66, sub: Tactical Voice Security, Incl to JCS 222/934; Memo, Dir, NSA, for Dep Secy of Defense, 19 May 66, sub: Secure Tactical Voice Communications, Incl to JCS 222/953-1; Memo, DA for Dep Secy of Defense, 29 Jun 66, sub: Secure Tactical Voice Communications, JCS 222/953-2. All in JACO (1966), DA/4, NARS.

agreed with their commanders that the conflict between operational efficiency and fundamental signal security measures appeared irreconcilable. Cross-attachment of units and daily interaction with support aircraft based hundreds of miles away made it virtually impossible to issue compatible codes to all forces participating in an action or to change frequencies and call signs often. After changing the call signs on all the radio nets in the 1st Cavalry Division during the Ia Drang battle, the division signal officer, Lt. Col. Tom M. Nicholson, discovered that he had caused so much confusion that he had to return to former call signs to reestablish basic command and control. The revision of a division's Signal Operating Instructions and their distribution to every unit—a task usually handled by the division radio officer—was so prodigious that it usually demanded the full attention of the division signal officer's staff for an entire week. Those Signal Operating Instructions were sometimes compromised by loss or capture even before they could be fully distributed.

Rather than limiting access to communications to improve security, signal officers were under pressure to keep open as many channels as possible to ensure that warnings and emergency requests were quickly received and disseminated. Since the Americans passed information about planned air and artillery bombardments to South Vietnamese troops and civilian authorities to preclude accidents and civilian casualties, any attempt to encode those warnings by using unfamiliar call signs might cause confusion that could lead to casualties. Similarly, the American medical evacuation system relied on rapid clear communications. Even such vital battle information as unit location and numbers of casualties was transmitted in the clear on medical evacuation nets. No signal officer dared change the standard frequency or call sign—DUSTOFF—used to summon medical evacuation helicopters throughout South Vietnam.[28]

Powerless to change many of the routine procedures and practices that contributed to a lack of communications security, the men of the 7th Radio Research Unit concentrated on warning commanders of violations which, if monitored by the enemy, would jeopardize lives or give advance warning of an operation. Although some warnings were heeded and compromised plans changed, many were ignored. Even when enemy ambushes followed unheeded warnings, few commanders would admit that the Communists were reacting to intercepted American communications.

Enemy Offensive Electronic Warfare

Aside from isolated intelligence reports, usually based on the claims of enemy prisoners, there was little conclusive evidence that the Viet Cong and North Vietnamese were exploiting American communications. Credit for finally producing confirmation of the effectiveness of the enemy's communications intelligence

---

[28]Capt. Dennis K. Whitmer, "Aviation Communications Security," *Aviation Digest*, May 1968, pp. 10–13.

efforts rested with a platoon of infantrymen from the 1st Brigade, 1st Infantry Division, and an investigation team from the 509th Radio Research Group. On 20 December 1969 the infantrymen overran the camp of a technical reconnaissance unit, known as *A3*, assigned to the Viet Cong's Subregion 1 on the outskirts of Saigon and captured twelve members of the team with their equipment and logs. Four days later the target exploitation team briefed the MACV commander, General Creighton W. Abrams, Jr., on the startling results of the interrogations of the enemy radio interceptors.[29]

Captured during the last days of 1969, the *A3* technical reconnaissance unit was living proof of the spectacular evolution of the Viet Cong's technical reconnaissance during the preceding decade. Although relatively low in the organizational hierarchy, the little unit was manned by a well-equipped team of experienced professionals guided in their work by doctrinal publications and procedural manuals evincing a keen insight into the weaknesses of American and South Vietnamese communicators and into the means of exploiting those weaknesses. Working with the attention to detail and ingenuity that had become trademarks of the Viet Cong's technical reconnaissance operation, the *A3* team was found with over 1,400 handwritten copies of voice transmissions.

The team had been monitoring voice and Morse code traffic of American and South Vietnamese units operating in Subregion 1 for several years. Their equipment was simple and well maintained: two captured PRC–25's and one captured PRC–77 for monitoring FM voice traffic, and one Chinese Communist R–139 receiver and seven small commercial transistor radios for monitoring AM Morse traffic. With precisely engineered antennas the intercept operators were employing the equipment at far beyond its normal range limitations.

Study of the logs kept by the *A3* team chief indicated that members of the team knew more about the communications of local American and South Vietnamese units than did most allied communicators. They even knew the voice characteristics and communications habits of many of the radio operators working in the area. After following the American nets for several years—a continuity no U.S. signal officer on a one-year tour enjoyed—the Viet Cong intercept operators had discerned various exploitable patterns. Having heard the confusion on American and South Vietnamese nets when frequencies and call signs were changed, they learned to adjust to new Signal Operating Instructions more quickly than the communicators in the nets. Knowing that each unit had a limited block of frequencies for switching among its nets, when Signal Operating Instructions were changed the intercept operators would simply monitor each frequency in a division's assignment block for recognizable voices and then begin reconstructing the nets. Sometimes their American adversaries, in attempting to reorganize the nets quickly, would make the intercept team's adjustments even easier by giving the frequencies and call signs in the clear to confused radio operators.

---

[29]Ltr, 509th Radio Research Gp to ASA, 26 Mar 70, sub: Historical Monograph on Project Touchdown, w/1 Incl and 16 Tabs, CMH, contains the complete study of Project Touchdown on which this account is based. The tabs contain transcripts of the interrogations and translations of the documents. A short, but thorough, discussion of Project Touchdown is contained in MACV, Lessons Learned No. 79: Enemy Exploitation of Allied Tactical Communications, 8 Mar 70, AD 508351, DDC.

Since radios were used extensively to coordinate the planning and conduct of joint ground and air operations, the *A3* unit focused on air nets both as lucrative sources of operational intelligence and as keys to reconstructing other nets. Working against the 1st Cavalry Division, for example, the Viet Cong listened each evening to transmissions of the 11th Aviation Group, the division's helicopter support unit, to learn which units would be airlifted into battle the following day and what their destinations would be. During those nightly warning orders to the pilots, even the command frequencies of the supported ground units were passed by a simple frequency designation code which the Viet Cong broke in the first week of its use. Undoubtedly many air assault landings were ambushed using intelligence gathered from the nightly reports.

When the distribution of secure-voice equipment to the 11th Aviation Group put an end to that source of intelligence in the summer of 1969, the Viet Cong merely turned their attention to other divisional nets. The Air Liaison Net, on which medical and special aviation support was arranged, still operated in the clear to give stations without security equipment an opportunity to request assistance. The most fertile source of all was the Air Warning Net; it broadcast information concerning air strikes, artillery barrages, and impending enemy attacks to every fire base and to all aircraft flying through the area. Besides receiving prior warning of maneuver and fire support plans, the Viet Cong also learned from the Air Warning Net whether their own attack plans had been compromised and whether American and South Vietnamese units were being alerted. Even more important was advance warning of pending strikes by B–52's. After monitoring a B–52 warning, the Viet Cong knew that they had between ten and twenty minutes in which to dispatch a courier to a nearby radio station and send warnings to other Viet Cong units in the area before huge, 750-pound bombs rained from the sky.

Although the phenomenal success of the *A3* team came as a great surprise to most American tactical commanders, the very preoccupation of the Viet Cong with the defense of their own communications had long before convinced the men of the 509th Radio Research Group of the value that the Viet Cong placed on electronic warfare and led them to conclude that they needed to develop a strong offensive capability. Apparently recognizing the increased effectiveness of electronic warfare when applied covertly, the Viet Cong went to great lengths to conceal the fact that they had any capability at all. Carefully shielded by security forces, technical reconnaissance soldiers were segregated from other Viet Cong troops and forbidden to acknowledge the nature of their work. Technical reconnaissance information was transmitted only by courier or else encrypted in a high-level code for radio transmission.[30]

The capture of the *A3* unit finally gave substance to a threat that officials of the Army Security Agency had previously been able to define only vaguely. More than simply exposing the activities of one unit, the revelations illuminated the whole obscure history of Viet Cong electronic warfare and corroborated previ-

---

[30]Ltr, USARV to 1st Sig Bde et al., 20 Nov 69, sub: Operations Security, w/Incl, 72A6443/26, WNRC.

ously unsubstantiated evidence. Logs containing entire texts of American messages copied by the A3 unit made credible the capabilities and successes that commanders had once dismissed as unfounded pessimism by advocates of communications security. The cool professionalism of the intercept operators on the A3 team, if universal throughout the technical reconnaissance forces, would explain both the success and secrecy of Viet Cong electronic warfare. The documents captured with the team contained doctrinal principles and instructions reflecting a refinement in the art of electronic warfare that could have developed only over many years.

The French had suspected as early as 1952 that a Viet Minh radio intercept unit was listening to their communications from a site just east of Hanoi. By the early 1960s the Viet Cong had organized small strategic intelligence cells to conduct radio interception against high-level South Vietnamese communications. In 1963 those cells were organized into the *47th Technical Reconnaissance Battalion,* which operated under the direction of the Intelligence Section of the Military Staff of the Central Office for South Vietnam. Meanwhile, in local Viet Cong units communicators using captured radios were experimenting with various forms of electronic warfare on their own. Monitoring of South Vietnamese logistical communications nets became an important source of information for Viet Cong units planning to ambush convoys. During attacks they monitored South Vietnamese communicators to determine where the defenses were weakening and if reinforcements were being summoned. Some Viet Cong provincial units kept captured GRC–9's on the command frequency of local South Vietnamese units to learn of proposed attacks and bombing missions. After learning the operating procedures of the South Vietnamese nets, emboldened Viet Cong communicators even practiced jamming and imitative deception against the South Vietnamese. News of electronic warfare successes spread throughout the Viet Cong's ranks, and by 1964 some province committees were even conducting informal training programs in electronic warfare for their communicators.[31]

Encouraged by that success, but also worried lest the activities in the field units alert the South Vietnamese and disrupt the flow of high-level communications intelligence being collected by the technical reconnaissance battalion, the Central Office for South Vietnam decided in 1965 that the entire electronic warfare effort needed direction and organization and convened a special intelligence conference to discuss the topic. The conferees called for a combined tactical and strategic technical reconnaissance organization reaching down to provincial and regimental levels. In addition to giving direct tactical support to local units, technical reconnaissance squads with the regiments and provinces were to send intelligence to a technical reconnaissance platoon stationed at the military region headquarters. There, it would be analyzed for strategic intelligence to be sent to the Central Office for South Vietnam. The technical reconnaissance battalion was to manage the entire operation and to provide communications for the clandes-

---

[31]MACV J–2, Log entry 8–99–65, 30 Aug 65, Cap Doc dtd 7 Jul 64, p. 8, A76–332/15, NSA; CICV Rpt, ST 67–006, pp. 8–9.

tine network.[32]

By mid-1966 most of the technical reconnaissance organizations planned during the conference were in operation, and the original plan was being broadened to include cells at district level. Viet Cong communications officials scoured the ranks for the most intelligent and reliable soldiers to be sent to technical reconnaissance schools established at the Central Office for South Vietnam and the regional headquarters. Numerous informal training programs took place at the unit level, and many Viet Cong radio operators became part-time intercept operators. In response to a dramatic increase in targets resulting from the arrival of American units, the entire Viet Cong electronic warfare program continued to expand.[33]

Technical reconnaissance grew so quickly—from 179 men in 1964 to over 1,500 men in early 1967—that Viet Cong leaders worried that the high performance and secrecy of the program might be decreasing. The battalion at the Central Office for South Vietnam, which had been the nucleus of the whole effort, had been drained of its most experienced men to serve as cadres in the field and instructors at the school. Since the quality of the battalion's management of the entire technical reconnaissance operation seemed to be suffering, the chief of the Military Intelligence Bureau at the Central Office for South Vietnam in February 1967 ordered the unit deactivated and its mission and personnel transferred to a newly formed staff section of the Central Office for South Vietnam, the Technical Reconnaissance and Intelligence Department. Thereafter technical reconnaissance developed an organizational structure involving over 4,000 elite troops enjoying the highest priority of support and protection.[34]

With the additional authority implicit in that arrangement, the new technical reconnaissance organization was able to get more English linguists to use against the Americans. Rather than simply adding to the total body of communications intelligence, the intercept of American communications dramatically improved the quality of the effort against the South Vietnamese. Information monitored on American nets supplemented and confirmed information obtained from South Vietnamese nets. To pit American and South Vietnamese communicators against each other, Viet Cong cryptologists also caused suspicions between the two allied forces. Exploiting parallel nets of U.S. advisers and their South Vietnamese counterparts, where one net might be encrypted and the other insecure, technical reconnaissance agents reconstructed entire coding systems by comparing encrypted and plain text traffic. Although high-level operations codes were never broken, the two-front attack on communications aided the Viet Cong in breaking the low-level codes used by the South Vietnamese prior to 1969 and in more easily understanding the simplistic, unauthorized codes often used by ingenious, but

[32]Ltr, USARV to 1st Sig Bde et al., 20 Nov 69, sub: Operations Security, an. A, pp. 1–5; CICV Rpt, VC/NVA Electronic Warfare Capability (ST 67–061), 1 Jul 67 (hereafter cited as CICV Rpt, ST 67–061), pp. 10–11, 71A4237/12, WNRC.

[33]Ltr, USARV to 1st Sig Bde et al., 20 Nov 69, sub: Operations Security, p. 2; CICV Rpt, ST 67–061, pp. 12–14.

[34]Ltr, USARV to 1st Sig Bde et al., 20 Nov 69, sub: Operations Security, an. A, p. 2; MACV, Counterinsurgency Lessons Learned No. 64: Imitative Communications Deception (hereafter cited as Lessons Learned No. 64), 15 Sep 67, p. 2, AD 505525, DDC.

naive, Americans who thought that they could fool their adversary by cloaking sensitive information in uniquely American references.[35]

Although the Communists had decided to forsake more overt electronic warfare techniques, such as jamming, so as not to interfere with the monitoring program or to put targeted communicators on guard, Viet Cong communicators sometimes employed jamming and communications deception. The jamming usually consisted of whistling, humming, or playing music while an American station was attempting to communicate. More common than jamming were attempts at communications deception, a variation of which was commonly practiced during unit movements to cover the displacement of headquarters, a period of extreme vulnerability to attack, and to make it more difficult to find units in their new positions. While a headquarters moved, its radio station would remain behind and continue passing traffic as if nothing had changed. When the relocation was completed, a new station would come on the air at the new location, but to confuse any intercept, the old station would continue transmitting for several weeks. There were no documented cases of the Viet Cong's attempting more direct manipulative deception by deliberately passing information on their own nets with the intention that it be intercepted. There were, however, numerous examples of imitative deception, where the Viet Cong entered an American or South Vietnamese radio net posing as an authentic station. Success or failure in the deception usually depended on whether the receiver of the message used authentication codes to challenge the validity of the person transmitting the message.[36]

Viet Cong deceptions were most successful when rapid response by the receiving station was required. Entering fire control or air support nets, they would request a halt to fire that was hitting their positions or even call in fire on American or South Vietnamese positions. Helicopter pilots, who rarely employed authentication codes, sometimes found themselves drawn into traps by false radio messages or smoke grenades, the latter a means by which ground troops marked their location for helicopters. The Viet Cong used smoke grenades both to ambush helicopters and to divert American and South Vietnamese fire. For the Viet Cong, visual signals had the additional virtue that using them required no fluency in English.[37]

The Viet Cong also tapped telephone lines stretched between guard bunkers on the perimeters of American and South Vietnamese camps and fire support bases to garner intelligence and conduct deception operations. In several cases they successfully learned the nature of perimeter defenses by calling outposts for strength reports. In the most successful imitative deception operation, a Viet Cong killed an American perimeter guard at the Da Nang Air Base and used his telephone to direct the base defense unit to the north side of the base just as a large Viet Cong force was about to attack from the south. Meeting little resistance,

---

[35]The number thirty-nine, for example, was routinely expressed as Jack Benny's age and became a much-used numerical reference point. NSA, Deadly Transmissions, Dec 70, pp. 12–13, K370.04–6, OAFH.

[36]CICV Rpt, ST 67–061, pp. 2–6; MACV, Lessons Learned No. 64.

[37]CICV Rpt, ST 67–061, p. 6; MACV, Lessons Learned No. 64, p. 5.

the force caused $15 million in damage to the base and its planes.[38]

Convinced of the success of Viet Cong electronic warfare by the revelations made in the wake of the capture of the technical reconnaissance team, American commanders began to take communications security more seriously. Rejecting former misconceptions concerning the adverse effects of communications security measures on operations, Maj. Gen. Elvy B. Roberts, the commander of the 1st Cavalry Division, admitted, "The fear has always been that airmobile operations would get so tied up it would not be worth the sacrifice one would have to make in effectiveness of airmobile operations. . . . I find the fear of it to be like many other fears—more imagined than real."[39]

With the support of commanders, signal officers were able to enforce previously disregarded communications directives. Once signal officers were given the authority to instruct net control stations to prohibit stations from entering nets unless they used authorized operations codes and authentication tables, the use of point-of-origin systems and informal codes ended. A pocket-size wheel device made of laminated plastic containing operations and authentication codes developed in 1969 by the National Security Agency specifically for use in South Vietnam also gained wide acceptance once radio operators and staff officers were forced to use it.[40]

Speech security equipment, developed as a cooperative venture of the National Security Agency and the Army and introduced in mid-1968, was less readily accepted. Fragile connecting cords and insufficient spare parts caused some initial logistical problems. The Electronics Command sent teams to South Vietnam to train radiomen to operate the new sets, but commanders found that operators experienced problems in communicating between secure and nonsecure stations. Those using nonsecure radios, unable to monitor communications between secure radios, sometimes unknowingly interfered with secure communications. When signal officers established separate secure and nonsecure nets, operators, incorrectly believing that the secure devices significantly reduced range, would use only the nonsecure net. Until the introduction of secure retransmission devices in 1970, secure nets were unable to take advantage of the added range provided by airborne retransmission. Perhaps the greatest disadvantage of the secure devices was the twenty-four pounds they added to the burden of the radio-telephone operator. Only the heightened awareness of the enemy's threat to communications instilled by the capture of the technical reconnaissance team and pressures by signal officers overcame those objections. Within six months of the team's capture, the percentage of radios using portable security devices increased from 53 to 83 percent, and those using vehicular security devices increased from 52 to 90 percent. Use of voice and teletype security equipment and the new operations codes effectively ended the Viet Cong threat to American communications. Even though the Communists captured some devices, they were unable to use

---

[38]MACV, Lessons Learned No. 64, pp. 3–4; NSA, Deadly Transmissions, p. 10.
[39]Quote from MS, Lt Col Norman E. Archibald, Tactical Communications, 1st Cavalry Division (Airmobile), Vietnam, October 1969–July 1970, 14 Mar 75, pp. 8–9, CMH.
[40]Maj Gen Thomas M. Rienzi, Debriefing Rpt, 4 Jun 70, pp. 46–48, file HRC 314.82, CMH; I FFV Daily Staff Journal, 24 Oct 67, item 5, 70A478/33, WNRC.

them due to the daily rekeying of devices on American nets.[41]

In retrospect it is difficult to determine which side was most successful in waging the electronic war. During the early 1960s the enemy clearly monitored South Vietnamese communications with impunity, and from the arrival of U.S. combat units until the introduction of voice security equipment, Viet Cong technical reconnaissance agents enjoyed similar success against American voice radio nets. Because the Communists' principal electronic warfare weapons were small commercial transistor receivers and stolen or captured radios rather than special electronic intercept equipment, their success appeared in some measure more noteworthy than that achieved by the Americans with their sophisticated eavesdropping devices.

American largesse was one source of American weakness. An abundance of easily operated voice radios in the hands of operators indifferent to proper security precautions gave the Viet Cong's technical reconnaissance agents more and easier targets. Undoubtedly many American operations were compromised and lives lost due to Communist exploitation of loose radio procedures. American operators, on the other hand, not only had the handicap of fewer targets but also faced an enemy whose habit of making detailed plans and executing them without deviation reduced his reliance on electronic communications. When the Communists did communicate, they did so with an appreciation for their adversary's electronic warfare capability and a corresponding adherence to stringent communications procedures and safeguards.

In the final balance, technological superiority gave the Americans the edge in both the offensive and defensive aspects of the electronic warfare struggle. Airborne direction finding, for example, provided American operators an ability to locate and track enemy units and afforded a means of determining enemy order of battle and locating targets to be attacked. Rather than automatically homing on radio emissions to pinpoint a unit's radio, as the Americans could do with their direction-finding equipment, the Communists had to look for clues to an American unit's location in the text of the message traffic. From the defensive standpoint, once the Americans finally improved the security of their voice communications, Viet Cong technical reconnaissance agents lost their targets. By then, however, Viet Cong technical reconnaissance teams had done their damage during the years of the most critical fighting. And American plans to withdraw from South Vietnam denied the opportunity for the United States to exploit fully its technological superiority in the electronic war.

---

[41]Memo, JCS for Asst Secy of Defense (I&L), 25 Nov 67, sub: Secure Tactical Voice Communications, JCS 222/953–4, JACO (1965), DA/2, NARS; ORLL, 1st Sig Bde, 31 Jul 70, p. 9, 72A7128/5, WNRC; Rienzi Debriefing Rpt, p. 45.

18

Signalmen

The enemy found it far easier to keep signalmen qualified than did the Americans. While North Vietnamese and Viet Cong communicators remained in South Vietnam gaining valuable experience in battle, American communicators stayed only for one-year tours. The Army's signal schools at Fort Monmouth and Fort Gordon had to train a constant stream of replacements, many of whom needed highly technical skills that required long periods to acquire. With a booming American electronics industry competing for the same skills and offering high salaries, the Army lost most of its trained signalmen after they had completed their two- or three-year enlistments and before they could return to South Vietnam. To keep communicators available as long as possible for operational duties, signal educators had to find ways to shorten training time. The expedients adopted to accomplish this pressing and critical objective sometimes adversely affected operations.

Following the crisis in the Gulf of Tonkin in the summer of 1964, the commander in chief, Pacific, warned the Joint Chiefs of Staff of difficulties he expected in opposing an invasion of Indochina by conventional Communist forces due to the "austere personnel manning . . . and low skill level" of the signalmen assigned to operate the communications base in Southeast Asia. The Army's ability to operate and maintain the sophisticated communications installed by civilian contractors throughout the region had deteriorated in the two years that the 39th Signal Battalion had been in South Vietnam. Contractors' attempts to give military operators practical training on the sophisticated equipment at the operational sites had failed.[1]

[1] Msg, CINCPAC to JCS, 6 Sep 64, sub: Communications Support for CINCPAC OPLAN 32-64, file 139441, 72A25/1, WNRC.

Early Staffing and Training

Most of the Army's troposcatter operators in the first contingent sent to South Vietnam in 1962 had attended the microwave radio repairman course at Fort Monmouth and then received some practical experience at the factories where the consoles were being assembled. Since all the equipment produced had been rushed to Southeast Asia in the summer of 1962, replacements arriving in 1963 and 1964 had to wait until they reached the field to receive on-the-job training. Operation of the sensitive troposcatter equipment by unqualified soldiers had begun to damage delicate electronic components and to degrade communications service. During one six-week period in the spring of 1964, parts of the long-lines system were off the air for three days due to operator errors.[2]

The Army's entire signal manpower and training base had been slow to respond to events in South Vietnam. Prior to 1964, official pronouncements of an impending withdrawal of American troops had discouraged consideration of instituting special courses for soldiers going to South Vietnam or of buying expensive troposcatter equipment for training. Courses in advisory and counterinsurgency techniques given at Fort Bragg were reserved for advisers of combat arms units. The exclusion of signal officers from those courses made them even less prepared than signal technicians for service in South Vietnam. The signal schools exposed students to counterinsurgency techniques using only a two-hour televised presentation unsupported by any class discussion. Veterans of duty in South Vietnam, enjoined from discussing their activities there for security reasons, could convey very little of their practical experience to students at the signal schools. Not until 1965, when eight hours' instruction in counterinsurgency signal operations was added to the curriculum of the signal officers basic course, the eight-week school for newly commissioned signal officers, did the signal schools begin to deal seriously with the issue of guerrilla warfare.[3]

Before 1965 signal units in South Vietnam also suffered from a low priority in obtaining personnel replacements. The commander of the 39th Signal Battalion in 1963, Lt. Col. Edwin Paulmann, wondered "if anyone in the United States knew there was a war going on." Although his battalion was at full strength, it had four times its authorized number of men in the lower three enlisted grades and offsetting shortages of the higher-ranking supervisors and skilled technicians so vital to the management of isolated sites and the operation of sophisticated equipment. Two-thirds of the eighty officers in the 39th Signal Battalion were second lieutenants. Since the chief signal officer had a long-standing policy that newly assigned Regular Army officers serve their first assignment in divisional signal battalions, and there were then no U.S. divisions in Vietnam, few of the lieutenants in the 39th were career signal officers. The prevailing view in the Sig-

---

[2]Ltr, 39th Sig Bn to USASCV, 24 Jun 64, sub: Technical Assistance for AN/TRC-90, file 19, 338-75-1009/65; USARPAC Sig Ofcr, Quarterly Rev Rpt, 1st Qtr, FY-65, p. 16A, 338-75-1009/53. Both in WNRC. USASCV AHS, 1964, pt. 2, an. K, CMH.

[3]MS, Joseph T. Jordan, Jr., Training, 1975, p. 4. A department chief at the U.S. Army Southeastern Signal School, Mr. Jordan had taught at Fort Gordon throughout the war. USCONARC Agenda, School Commandants' Conference, 1965, tab F. Both in CMH. General Donn A. Starry, *Mounted Combat in Vietnam*, Vietnam Studies (Washington, D.C.: Government Printing Office, 1978), p. 19.

nal Branch of the Office of Personnel Operations in Washington was that the best assignments were in the United States and Europe with signal units involved in conventional training and operations. Before American combat units deployed to South Vietnam in 1965, only a few prescient signal officers challenged the view that South Vietnam was a career backwater.[4]

Once the buildup began, this earlier neglect of South Vietnam took an especially heavy toll on the Signal Corps. Technicians required far more training than infantrymen. Even though the Army had finally purchased some TRC–90's for Fort Monmouth in mid-1964 and established a complete troposcatter operator's course, it had been too late. By the time the United States began expanding BACK-PORCH to support the buildup, only 120 operators, barely enough to operate the troposcatter tails off the BACKPORCH net, had graduated from the new 26-week course.[5]

The causes of the Signal Corps' lack of preparedness to mobilize manpower rapidly for the buildup went far deeper than a failure to recognize and respond to the deepening commitment in South Vietnam. In 1955 President Eisenhower's Science Advisory Committee had predicted a "continuous sapping of the strength of the Armed Forces in the selective loss of the more highly trained and educated personnel."[6] As technological breakthroughs in the post–World War II years produced increasingly sophisticated military electronic equipment, the signal schools developed lengthy courses to prepare soldiers to operate and maintain that equipment. Not only did that excellent training keep men from their units longer, it also made the Signal Corps a prime source of manpower for a rapidly expanding civilian electronics industry that was also exploiting the fruits of the new technology. Civilian firms could lure away soldiers completing their enlistments with salaries 50 percent higher than military pay. While the Army-wide reenlistment rate in the summer of 1954 was 23.2 percent, microwave radio repairmen and electronic repairmen reenlisted at the rate of 3.7 percent, the lowest in the Army. The constant turnover forced the Signal Corps to train almost half its entire complement of 60,000 communicators yearly and caused a perennial shortage in the most highly technical specialties.[7]

The Signal Corps' share of the total enlisted strength of the Army had risen from 2.5 percent during World War II to 7.3 percent in 1958 in response to a proliferation of electronic equipment in the military. Nevertheless, the Signal Corps rarely received a large enough share of the recruits with a good academic background and high scores on aptitude tests to operate all the complex communications gear in the Army. While the Signal Corps consistently had an excess of men qualified for the few signal courses requiring a minimum of aptitude for

[4]Interv, author with Col (ret.) Edwin Paulmann, former CO, 39th Signal Battalion, 21 Jun 78, Historians files, CMH; Rpt, Signal Officers' Conference, Nov 61, sec. IX, p. 6, file 201–45, 67A4845/1; USARPAC Briefing, Command Supervision of Readiness, 4 Mar 65, pp. 18–21, 338–75–1009/55. Both in WNRC. Interv, author with Col (ret.) William A. Van Sandt, former chief, Signal Branch, Office of Personnel Operations, 10 Feb 78, Historians files, CMH.

[5]DA, DCSOPS, AHS, FY–65, an. F, sec. III, pp. 4–5, CMH; USASCV Quarterly Rev Rpt, 1st Qtr, FY–65, p. 16A.

[6]Executive Office of the President, Technological Capabilities Panel of the Science Advisory Committee, Meeting the Threat of Surprise Attack, 14 Feb 55, p. 178, 66A3210/3, WNRC.

[7]Ibid., pp. 169–84; Rpt, Signal Officers' Conference, 1961, sec. IX, p. 4.

electronics, the signal schools were unable to obtain enough qualified candidates for more technical training. Although other branches had fewer technical specialties than the Signal Corps, they sought the increased stability and reliability usually found in the more intelligent and better educated recruits.[8]

Competition with civilian industry and other branches was even more fierce for technically qualified officers. In 1961 the chief signal officer had to retain temporarily in the Army 128 officers who had requested retirement. An attempt to encourage officers from other branches to transfer to the Signal Corps produced only twenty-nine new officers. Since the combat arms received a greater share of promotions, quotas for senior service schools, and general officer positions than the technical services, the Signal Corps was unattractive to ambitious officers desiring to progress to the highest levels of the Army. By the spring of 1962, when the 39th Signal Battalion was sent to South Vietnam, the Signal Corps was short 23 percent of its authorized lieutenant colonels and 20 percent of its majors.[9]

The crises of the early 1960s—Berlin, Laos, Cuba, and South Vietnam—confirmed the dire predictions of the President's Science Advisory Committee that shortages of critical, highly technical skills would cause serious problems for the Army. The commander of the Strike Command, General Paul D. Adams, warned that the dispatch of his most qualified signal technicians to trouble spots had left his strategic contingency force dangerously short of communications. Even the Supreme Allied Commander, Europe, General Lyman L. Lemnitzer, warned the Army chief of staff that the signal battalion supporting his headquarters was 18 percent understrength. In requesting relief, those senior commanders recommended a variety of solutions to the Signal Corps' problem of keeping signal technicians in the Army: proficiency pay and reenlistment bonuses to those possessing critical skills, branch transfers, and crash training programs. But as the Army's appetite for signalmen increased with the expansion of the war in South Vietnam, each of those expedients proved inadequate to overcome the lure of civilian industry and keep a stable technical manpower base in the Signal Corps. Throughout the war reenlistment rates for signal technicians remained low, and fewer than 30 percent of other than Regular Army Signal Corps officers stayed in the Army beyond their obligated tours. The long period of initial training required for signal recruits meant that signalmen returning from a one-year tour in South Vietnam had barely enough time to become productive in a job in a stateside unit before the termination of their service. Signal schools had to begin training a replacement for a communicator within a few months of his graduation from the school.[10]

---

[8]Rpt, U.S. Army Signal Board, Signal Training in the Army, Case 673 (hereafter cited as Signal Board Rpt, Case 673), 1 Sep 58, pp. 3–4, 54, CMH. This report chronicles the Signal Corps' attempt to deal with the training implications of the increasing complexity of communications technology.

[9]OCSO, Signal Corps Summary of Major Events and Problems, FY-60, p. 142; ibid., FY-62, pp. 70-71. Both in CMH. Rpt, Signal Officers' Conference, Nov 61, sec. X, p. 2; Memo, Maj Gen Earle F. Cook for CSA, 21 Jun 63, sub: Final Report of the Chief Signal Officer, file CS 319.1, 43027457–166, 66A3140/19, WNRC.

[10]Ltr, Adams to Lt Gen Russell L. Vittrup, 1 Aug 62, file 2210860, 65A3314/5; Ltr, Lemnitzer to Gen Earle G. Wheeler, 10 Jun 63, file 2309235, 66A3140/14. Both in WNRC. Joint Logistics Review Board, *Logistic Support*, 2: 167, and *Monograph 14: Military Personnel in Operational Logistics*, pp. 52–53, both in 71A2351/6, WNRC.

Rapid technological progress in military electronics further complicated the task of the schools. Equipment was changing so quickly that several generations of equipment were being used in the field at the same time. Unsure of what an operator would encounter on his assignment, the school had to train him to operate every model in his specialty. Courses had to be lengthened and great varieties of expensive equipment purchased and maintained for training.[11]

At the same time, signal schools were under pressure to reduce training time and expenses. With the exhortation that "student time is ineffective time," in February 1957 Under Secretary of the Army Charles C. Finucane directed the Army schools to shorten their courses and move students more quickly to their units. There, they could complete their education with on-the-job training while contributing to the accomplishment of operational missions. Facing budget and personnel reductions, the signal schools experimented with a multilevel training concept for certain specialties. For the microwave radio repairman specialty, draftees with only a two-year enlistment attended fifteen weeks of schooling, while enlistees with three-year enlistments were eligible for the standard 26-week course. The multilevel concept caused confusion in personnel management once the numbers of trainees increased with the buildup in South Vietnam. The schools eventually abandoned the short course and allowed only men on three-year tours to take the long courses. By the time the buildup started, the harm of reducing schooling time had been done: unqualified operators had adversely affected troposcatter operations on BACKPORCH, and an inadequate nucleus of qualified instructors was available to teach expanded courses in the schools.[12]

During the five years before the buildup in South Vietnam, the organization of the Signal Corps' training establishment changed several times. In July 1960 the chief signal officer established a training command at Fort Monmouth to take responsibility for all signal training activities at Forts Monmouth and Gordon. Although relinquishing operational control over signal training to the new command, the Personnel and Training Division in the Office of the Chief Signal Officer at the Pentagon retained staff supervision. Two years later, as part of Secretary McNamara's reorganization of the Army, all responsibility for training was transferred from the chief signal officer to the Continental Army Command, the training command was abolished, and all command ties between the chief signal officer and the two signal schools were cut. The subordination to a headquarters that had formerly been responsible only for nontechnical training heralded an era of diminished independence for signal educators and a new round of pressures to

[11]Memo, CSO for DCSOPS, 21 Feb 63, sub: Signal Enlisted Shortages, file 4300737, 66A3140/14, WNRC; USCONARC Agenda, School Commandants' Conference, 1965, tab R; DF, Col Edward Moran to USCONARC, 16 Sep 66, sub: USCONARC Training Liaison Team Visit–Viet Nam, p. 2, file U–461, 72A18/8, WNRC.

[12]The military did develop a multilevel skill classification system. In 1965 the military occupational specialty (MOS) classification became a five-digit alphanumerical code. For example, all microwave radio repairmen graduated with the designation of 26L20 and progressed with experience to 26L50. Rpt, Under Secy of Army, Analysis of the Training, Distribution, and Utilization of Military Personnel, 15 Feb 57, excerpts contained in Signal Board Rpt, Case 673, p. 41, CMH; Ltr, OCSO to USCONARC, 17 Sep 57, sub: Reevaluation Army School Program, copy in Signal Board Rpt, Case 673, pp. 51–58; Ltr, DA to USCONARC et al., 31 Dec 62, sub: Revision of MOS Training System, file 3201612, 65A3314/16, WNRC; Memo, Cook for CSA, 21 Jun 63, sub: Final Report of the Chief Signal Officer.

make the time allowed for signal training comparable to that for combat arms training.[13]

Preparing for the Buildup

President Johnson's televised announcement on the evening of 28 July 1965 that he was authorizing a 50,000-man increase in troop strength in South Vietnam, with further augmentations possible, took few members of the staff at the Southeastern Signal School at Fort Gordon by surprise. Aware of the planning that had been taking place in the Pentagon throughout the spring, they were anticipating a modest increase in students to fill out reserve and National Guard units expected to be called up as part of any mobilization. They planned to handle the student increase by augmenting the teaching staff from the ranks of reservists possessing experience in the civilian electronics industry. But they were shocked when President Johnson declared that he did not intend to call the reserves to active duty. The signal school's staff and faculty called an emergency meeting that very night to decide how to confront the seemingly insurmountable task of training communicators in time to deploy with combat troops who required far less training.[14]

Since Fort Monmouth trained men for nontactical units, the crisis was felt more sharply at Fort Gordon, the site of one of the Army's eleven training centers as well as a signal school. There went the soldiers who would carry the radios, lay the wire, and operate the switchboards in field units sent to Southeast Asia. Most of them were recent draftees. Before coming to Fort Gordon they had been sworn in at an induction center near their homes and given testing and counseling at a military post to determine the type of work they would do in the Army. If their test scores were high enough, they were given the option of volunteering for a third year of service to obtain advanced schooling after their basic training. After eight weeks of tough conditioning and drilling in a basic training unit, most of those chosen to become communicators took eight weeks of advanced individual training at one of several training centers teaching basic communications skills: radio-telephone operator (Military Occupational Specialty [MOS] 05B), field radio mechanic (MOS 31B), or field wireman (MOS 36K). Some of those trainees were transferred, sometimes before completing their eight weeks of advanced individual training, to the signal school for more advanced schooling as radio-teletype operators (05C), field radio repairmen (31E), or linemen (36C). Those trainees who had enlisted for three years to obtain signal training often went directly from basic training to one of the signal schools. Because the Army was unable to train enough

---

[13]The training command was first proposed in Signal Board Rpt, Case 673, pp. 13–15. OCSO, Signal Corps Summary of Major Events and Problems, FY–61, p. 146, CMH; Interv, Joseph T. Jordan, Jr., with Col Emmett R. Arnold, former commandant, U.S. Army Southeastern Signal School (USASESS), Fort Gordon, 7 May 65, CMH.

[14]Interv, author with John T. Holleran, former assistant chief of plans and operations, USASESS, 29 Nov 77, Historians files, CMH; Joint Logistics Review Board, *Monograph 14*, pp. 24–25.

men to fill units deploying to South Vietnam during 1966, some signal units had to conduct their own basic training and advanced individual training program.[15]

Besides training the new recruits destined to join the signal units being deployed to South Vietnam, the signal schools also had to continue training signalmen for the rest of the Army, for foreign allies, including South Vietnam, and for the reserves and National Guard. Reservists comprised some 15 percent of the student population. Since many World War II–era barracks had just been demolished, Fort Gordon erected several hundred large tents to house as many as 5,100 soldiers until the completion of permanent barracks in the spring of 1967. Most soldiers preferred to live in the tents, which were cooler and easier to keep clean than the old wooden barracks. Academic facilities were also inadequate, and the signal school operated on double and triple shifts. The shifts were first employed in 1964 as a temporary expedient to fill sudden requirements for avionic repairmen and radio relay operators. By late 1965 most courses at Fort Gordon were conducting around-the-clock training, with shifts from 0700 to 1450, 1500 to 2250, and 2300 to 0650 hours. Dining halls, recreation facilities, and post exchanges operated night and day to serve the trainees. Most students preferred to attend classes at night, when classrooms were cooler and classes more relaxed. Since failing students were sent back to the day shift where supervision was greater, the quality of students and the level of instruction were generally higher in the night courses.[16]

Although the triple-shift arrangement had little effect on academic work at the school, it contributed to a breakdown of unit cohesion. With men coming and going at all hours, the cadres of the training companies were unable to assemble or inspect their entire units. Men could be missing for several days without their absence being noted, and in the summer of 1966 the rate of soldiers absent without leave at Fort Gordon rose to a high 18.8 per 1,000. Visiting Fort Gordon that summer, the deputy commanding general of the Continental Army Command discovered inexperienced captains commanding training battalions and second lieutenants commanding companies of over 1,000 men. Most company commanders had only a first sergeant and one platoon sergeant to assist them. Thereafter the Continental Army Command sent to Fort Gordon sufficient cadres, many of them returning veterans from South Vietnam, to create more manageable 250-man companies. By 1969 the cadre-to-student ratio had increased to one platoon sergeant for every fifty students.[17]

Because of a constant movement of skilled military technicians between South Vietnam, Europe, and the United States and levies for newly activated units, the signal schools were unable to retain a stable base of instructors. Since typically instructors stayed at the school only eight months, they barely had time to be-

---

[15]MS, Hermes, The Buildup, ch. 8, pp. 2–13, CMH; Memo, USASESS, DCTE, for Adv/Ed Monograph Task Force, 16 Apr 75, sub: Monograph Inputs on Proponency Training, CMH.

[16]MS, Jordan, Training, 1975, pp. 65–67; Rpt, USASESS, COMSEA Study Group Request for School Information, Feb 69, pp. 6–7 and Incls 42–43, file U–354, 72A18/6, WNRC; USCONARC Agenda, School Commandants' Conference, 1965, tab X; Interv, Joseph T. Jordan, Jr., with John T. Holleran, former assistant chief of plans and operations, 7 Feb 75, CMH.

[17]Intervs, Jordan with Holleran, 7 Feb 75, and with Arnold, 7 May 65.

come proficient. To supplement military instructors, Fort Gordon increased the number of civilian instructors from 398 to 1,057. Fort Monmouth even hired high school teachers to teach mathematics and electronics in the evenings and during the summer.[18]

Seeking additional noncommissioned officers for units and the schools, the Army offered promotions to discharged soldiers if they would return to active duty; but time and technology had left the Army too changed for many to adjust. Most of them required refresher training, and few were successful in their new jobs. Army units in the field had more success with training promising enlisted men in locally run noncommissioned officer schools of five to six weeks' duration. At the signal school at Fort Gordon the most qualified students could volunteer for a skills development program, in which they received three weeks of leadership training after graduating from their regular course and then ten additional weeks in a more advanced technical course. Upon completion of the thirteen-week program they were promoted to sergeant and assigned either as a supervisor in a field unit or as an instructor at the signal school. Although commanders had the authority to take the stripes from the novice leaders if they proved unable to fulfill their supervisory responsibilities, most performed well after a few months' experience.[19]

Training at the Signal Schools

On 20 September 1965, the Southeastern Signal School activated the 1st Officer Candidate Battalion, commanded by Maj. John J. McManus and staffed by tactical officers from the Officer Candidate School at Fort Benning. The new school gave outstanding enlisted men an opportunity to earn commissions to fill the growing need for junior officers in an expanding Signal Corps. The first class of sixty-seven students entered in November 1965 and graduated the following April. Normally a new recruit expressing interest in attending the Signal Officer Candidate School was given leadership opportunities during basic and advanced individual training. If he showed leadership potential and met physical and mental standards, he was accepted to the 23-week officers training course. For the first thirteen weeks drill instructors and tactical officers honed the candidates' leadership abilities; during the next five weeks they received more specialized signal training; and during the last five weeks the students practiced their newly acquired leadership and technical skills during intensive field exercises. The course was so difficult and standards so high that the attrition rate averaged 45 percent

---

[18]Interv, Jordan with Holleran, 7 Feb 75.

[19]Joseph T. Jordan, Jr., Resume of Interviews, 27 Feb 75, sub: USASIGS Skills Development Base Program 1968–1970, CMH; Trip Rpt, Col Moran, 16 Sep 66, p. 3, U–461, 72A18/8, WNRC; USASESS, Trip Rpt of Lt Col Dean B. Dickinson to South Vietnam from 9 Sep 69 to 3 Oct 69, 10 Oct 69, pt. 2, p. 48, CMH.

and sometimes rose to 70 percent.[20]

By the time the final class graduated in February 1968, the Officer Candidate School at Fort Gordon had grown to encompass a brigade of two battalions and six companies and had graduated 2,210 signal officers. Although enrollment in the Reserve Officers Training Corps in American colleges dropped during the war, graduates of the Officer Candidate School and college graduates receiving direct commissions more than made up the difference. In fact, between 1965 and 1967 the number of officers in the Signal Corps increased 46 percent, from 7,167 to 10,431. In late 1966 the Army also alleviated a shortage of captains by reducing the required time in service for promotion from first lieutenant to captain from three years to thirty months.[21]

The Officer Candidate School and the signal officer basic course for newly commissioned officers were held at Fort Gordon.[22] Most other officer training was done at Fort Monmouth. There, captains attended a 39-week advanced course to prepare them for company command and higher-level assignments. Fort Monmouth also trained officers, usually lieutenants and warrant officers, in specialties such as radio techniques, frequency management, wire and switchboard operations, and communications center operations. Senior captains and field grade officers attended courses at Fort Monmouth to learn to manage automatic data processing systems and to engineer commercial communications.

Fort Monmouth also provided highly technical instruction for the enlisted men who would operate the sophisticated dial exchanges, technical controls, automatic tape relays, troposcatter and microwave radios, and satellite terminals in South Vietnam. Much of that equipment was so expensive and so scarce in the Army inventory that Fort Monmouth had difficulty obtaining enough equipment for its specialty courses. Because the Department of Defense had deferred for over a year the Army's request for funds to build a training facility at Fort Monmouth for the Integrated Wideband Communications System, it was not until after Phases 1 and 2 of the network were already on the air that the signal school was able to graduate soldiers with adequate practical training. In November 1967 Page finally built a replica of an IWCS terminal at Fort Monmouth. Two months later the signal school opened a facility to train operators to work on the AUTODIN network. The school was able to obtain a tandem switch training facility in 1968, before a direct-dial system was put in service in Southeast Asia.[23]

To ensure that instructors were prepared to train soldiers to operate and maintain new equipment as soon as it was fielded, the signal schools maintained close

---

[20]Rpt, USASESS, COMSEA Study Group Request for School Information, Feb 69, Incl 45; US-CONARC Agenda, School Commandants' Conference, 1965, tab M; MS, Jordan, Training, 1975, p. 68.

[21]DF, Maj Bernard L. Stewart to USCONARC, 6 Jul 67, sub: Report of USCONARC Training Visit to RVN, 8–21 Jan 67, p. 1, file U–461, 72A18/8, WNRC; Joint Logistics Review Board, *Logistic Support*, 2: 42.

[22]In 1964 and 1965, the Army sent all newly commissioned Regular Army officers to Ranger School instead of to the basic course.

[23]Interv, author with Harold Silverstein, former civilian staff officer, OCSO, 26 May 77, Historians files, CMH; Ltr, USCONARC to DA, DCSOPS, 11 Jan 63, sub: Initial Supply of Equipment to U.S. Army Schools and Training Centers, in Tab L of USCONARC Agenda, School Commandants' Conference, 1965; USASCC AHS, FY–68, pp. 38–39; USASCC AHS, FY–69, pp. 67–68. Both in CMH.

coordination with the electronics command staffs developing new items of equipment. As soon as the VRC–12 series radio became a standard item of equipment in June 1960, the Southeastern Signal School began establishing training requirements for the new FM radios. Although preparations for courses were delayed when 103 sets ordered for the school arrived without connecting cables, test equipment, or technical manuals, in March 1963 a New Equipment Introductory Team from the Electronics Command presented training on the new radios to twenty-six instructors from the school. In November 1963, after they passed that instruction on to their contemporaries, the school included one week's instruction in maintaining the new radios in the radio repair course. Operator training had to wait until July 1964 when the Continental Army Command finally approved the school's proposed program of instruction for the new FM radio equipment. By that time the signal school was also preparing courses for the new family of single-sideband radios, the GRC–106's. Instructors from Fort Gordon familiarized themselves with the new set at the manufacturer's plants and returned to Fort Gordon in the fall of 1964 to train other instructors and to help prepare training literature and classroom aids. Formal training began in the fall of 1965, soon after the first models of the radios arrived at the school. While recruits were learning about the new FM and single-sideband radios in the signal school, New Equipment Training Teams formed by the Electronics Command traveled to South Vietnam to teach communicators to use and maintain the new equipment.[24]

The schools rarely had enough equipment to conduct adequate hands-on training. Simply maintaining the classroom sets, which received continual hard use as three shifts of trainees tinkered with them every day, required constant care by already overworked instructors. Investigating whether an abnormally high rate of failure of components of the GRC–106 single-sideband radio in South Vietnam was due to insufficient practical training, investigators found that half of the school's twenty-two sets were inoperable. Although the Southeastern Signal School was authorized seventy-five PRC–25 radio sets for training, it began instruction in early 1964 with only six sets and two years later still had only forty-two sets. The need for large quantities of equipment for training was never satisfied, and four or five students usually had to work together on each piece of equipment, a practice called piggybacking. Piggybacking made it so hard for instructors to be sure that all students were performing all the classwork that poor students inevitably slipped though courses and graduated.[25]

The complaint most often heard from commanders in South Vietnam was that students left the signal schools with a lack of practical experience. Facing continuous operational requirements, they wanted journeymen communicators ready to work with a minimum of supervision. With insufficient equipment and training time, the school could only graduate apprentices who still required a few months of good supervision and on-the-job training. The need to prepare each

[24]USCONARC Agenda, School Commandants' Conference, 1965, tab L; Interv, Jordan with Holleran, 7 Feb 75; USARV, Agenda for BG Terry's Briefing, 15 Mar 68, tab I, file 139870, 72A25/24.

[25]Rpt, USASESS, COMSEA Study Group Request for School Information, Feb 69, Incls 26 and 38; Ltr, Brig Gen William M. Van Harlingen to Maj Gen Walter B. Richardson, 13 Oct 67, Van Harlingen Papers.

class of signalmen for the wide variety of equipment and situations they might encounter worldwide precluded the signal school from tailoring instruction to the equipment or the situation in South Vietnam.[26]

Since each course provided only a few days of field training, men were especially lacking in the ancillary skills—equipment grounding, antenna erection, generator operations, and driving and vehicle maintenance—so indispensable to signal operations in the field. Even during outdoor exercises, the trainees connected their vans to permanently erected antennas and grounding rods and used commercial power. Under such ideal conditions students could concentrate on learning to establish and maintain communications; but they rarely encountered the great variety of problems and annoyances that were common in the field. Nor did they learn to troubleshoot, the indispensable ability to locate the source of a technical malfunction. Experiencing problems in the field, graduates of the signal schools usually replaced major components until their set was functioning again. That practice was wasteful in the use of equipment for spares. It was likewise wasteful of vehicles used to carry replaced components to repair shops and of the time repairmen spent examining good equipment. Haphazard troubleshooting delayed the resolution of outages and degraded the performance of sets containing components precisely tuned to operate together. After a jolting ride to a repair shop in the bed of a truck, good equipment removed unnecessarily by an unskilled operator also frequently became damaged.[27]

Operating in Vietnam

Insufficient opportunity in signal courses to set up entire signal centers— switchboards, teletype centers, radios, multichannel terminals, patch panels, and interconnecting cables—produced graduates with little understanding of their role in a cohesive communications system. As one battalion commander in South Vietnam stated, ''People seem to be trained in a vacuum. . . . They don't seem to know what happens to circuits after they leave their vans.''[28] Switchboard and teletype operators had difficulty finding alternate routes for messages when primary circuits were out; multichannel operators were unable to coordinate with distant terminals to restore circuits traveling over their systems. Officers and noncommissioned officers, who usually did have more comprehensive understanding of entire communications systems, had to leave their supervisory tasks and become involved in technical troubleshooting and circuit restoration.[29]

[26]Interv, Jordan with Holleran, 7 Feb 75.

[27]Trip Rpt, Maj Stewart, 6 Jul 67, p. 78; DF, Col T. F. Schweitzer to USCONARC, 8 May 68, sub: RVN Liaison Training Visit, 17–30 Apr 68, pp. 17–20. Both in file U–461, 72A18/8, WNRC. Ltr, Maj Gen Walter B. Richardson to Brig Gen William M. Van Harlingen, 26 Oct 67; Ltr, Van Harlingen to Richardson, 15 May 68; Ltr, Richardson to Van Harlingen, 5 Jun 68. Latter three in Van Harlingen Papers.

[28]Rpt, 121st Sig Bn, 20 Apr 68, sub: Status of Signal MOS Trainees in 121st Sig Bn, p. 30, file U–461, 72A18/8, WNRC.

[29]Memo, CO, 53d Sig Bn, for Col Schweitzer, 25 Apr 68, sub: Comments Regarding MOS Training, pp. 26–29; Trip Rpt, Col Schweitzer, 10 Oct 69, p. 4. Both in file U–461, 72A18/8, WNRC.

Signalman Checks Circuits in MSQ–73 Technical Control Van

After the signal schools in 1965 established formal courses of instruction for fixed station controllers (MOS 32D) and for tactical patch panel operators (MOS 31N), a few enlisted men with enough understanding to coordinate total communications systems began to filter out to field units. Prior to that time, only a few fixed station controllers could be found in South Vietnam at the large technical controls at Phu Lam or Nha Trang. Those men had graduated from the signal school as fixed station radio operators and had become technical controllers after on-the-job training at the communications center at Fort Ritchie, Maryland. Even after the formal courses were started, there never seemed to be enough men with a comprehension of the entire communications system in South Vietnam. Commanders supplemented trained technical controllers and patch panel operators with their more intelligent signalmen, especially multichannel operators. Those communicators could be found testing circuit quality in the large technical control facilities of the Integrated Wideband Communications System, monitoring and troubleshooting an entire unit's communications operation from a battalion systems control, or interconnecting in patch panels the multitude of circuits passing through an area signal center.[30]

When the concept of area communications support for the so-called theater

---

[30]USARPAC Sig Ofcr, Quarterly Rev Rpt, 1st Qtr, FY–65, p. 18, 338–75–1009/53, WNRC; Interv, author with James L. McIntosh, chief, Technical Controller Course, USASESS, 9 Jan 78, Historians files, CMH.

An SB–675 Patch Panel

army replaced the traditional doctrine of communications support paralleling the chain of command in the late 1950s, the task of the communicator became more complicated. The new concept provided more comprehensive coverage and greater redundancy to a dispersed force than the simple axial approach of the past, but it confronted communicators in a signal center with a constantly changing array of subscribers moving in and out of the area that they serviced and a confusing multiplicity of operators from a variety of other signal centers to work with.

In addition to technical controllers and patch panel operators who had to coordinate and interconnect circuits at each signal center, the area system depended on the radio relay and multichannel operators (MOS 31M) who manned the systems connecting the area signal centers. Each multichannel terminal at the signal center had enough equipment to operate two twelve-channel systems, and usually one of those equipment banks was kept in reserve. Each of the twelve channels comprising a system presented the operators with a unique communications challenge. Since most circuits transited several systems, installing or resolving trouble on a channel required several different multichannel operators to coordinate with each other as well as with patch panel, teletype, and switchboard operators and even subscribers on sole-user circuits. Few multichannel operators had the broad understanding of communications systems or the technical background required to handle such coordination. Because noncommissioned

Testing a Field Wire Circuit

officers in the multichannel specialty were too scarce to assign one to every terminal, many multichannel teams operating from remote fire bases in South Vietnam consisted of three young soldiers, all recent graduates of the twelve-week radio relay and multichannel course at Fort Gordon. Although the course operated on a triple shift to handle a student population that had jumped in a short time from 25 to 255 a week, a practice of taking the top 20 percent of the graduates to receive additional schooling as radio relay repairmen (MOS 31L) reduced the quality and quantity of multichannel operators in the field. In 1968 the signal school obtained permission to add two weeks to the course for multichannel operators to improve their ability to handle the installation and troubleshooting of circuits; but then the curriculum had to be diluted to include instruction in the use of the new generation of pulse code–modulated multichannel equipment being issued to some units in South Vietnam.[31]

The signal schools traditionally had far less difficulty in preparing men to operate tactical switchboards and to install field wire and cable. Since wire equipment was less complex and less subject to technical modernization, the students at the courses for switchboard operators (MOS 72C) and wiremen (MOS 36C) were usually soldiers with the lowest scores in electronic aptitude tests and the least amount of civilian schooling. When the Army instituted Project 100,000, a program to induct men who were unable to meet the regular physical or mental qualifications but who showed promise that their deficiencies could be corrected, the signal school puts its quota of those trainees in the switchboard operators course. Experience in South Vietnam soon demonstrated that the Signal Corps had underestimated the aptitude required of switchboard operators and wiremen. Although their work was nontechnical, men in these two signal specialty fields came in contact most often with those outside the signal community. To many, a signalman was the wireman installing batteries in field phones in the command post or a member of the crew hanging cables alongside the road. The switchboard operator was the voice of the Signal Corps.[32]

Wiremen generally made a good impression. Although a rough and tumble

---

[31]MS, Jordan, Training, 1975, pp. 39–40; Rienzi Debriefing Rpt, 4 Jun 70, pp. 36–37; Interv, Jordan with Holleran, 7 Feb 75; Ltr, Maj Gen William B. Latta to Col Edward E. Moran, 28 Feb 69, Van Harlingen Papers.

[32]MS, Jordan, Training, 1975, pp. 41, 70; USASESS, Trip Rpt, Lt Col Dean B. Dickinson to South Vietnam from 9 Sep 69 to 3 Oct 69, 10 Oct 69, pt. 2, pp. 2, 5, 9, 16.

Cablemen Restore Telephone Communications After a Battle

lot, they took great pride in their work, their equipment, and their units. Because they usually worked together in teams, often under enemy fire, their unit cohesion and respect for supervisors were strong. The physical nature of their work alleviated frustrations. The work of switchboard operators, on the other hand, was filled with tension. Impatient subscribers, noisy circuits, and harried operators at the far end of circuits took their toll of switchboard operators. Even the most stable operators became emotionally fatigued, losing the tact and courtesy so essential to the job. Those with low intelligence or a poor command of English were befuddled by an ever-expanding long-distance network. Alternate routes of communications, which to a telephone traffic engineer meant more efficiency and reliability, to the switchboard operator were only additional sources of confusion. Maintaining control and cohesion in a unit that was working around the clock tested the imagination and energy of supervisory switchboard noncommissioned officers.

Soldiers had to have high electronic aptitude scores to qualify for training as radio-teletype operators (MOS 05C), yet few radio-teletype operators were fully challenged in South Vietnam. The best trainees in the radio-telephone operators courses (MOS 05B) at the Advanced Individual Training Centers went to Fort Gordon to receive ten additional weeks of training as radio-teletype operators. There they learned Morse code, cryptographic operations, typing, and advanced radio techniques. Since only about 2 percent of the graduates ever used Morse

Operators Man a Brigade Switchboard

code after leaving the school, the Continental Army Command and the signal school tried to replace it with additional training in antenna propagation and radio procedures. Arguing that code was essential in transmitting over long distances and during propagational or jamming interference, the Department of the Army persistently refused to release the school from the requirement to teach Morse code. Although signal commanders in South Vietnam tried to enforce practice exercises for radio-teletype operators to keep their skills current, infrequent use of Morse code or teletype on operational missions made those psychomotor skills difficult to maintain.[33]

Applying the Lessons of Vietnam

The signal schools periodically assessed the performance of graduates to determine how training could better meet the peculiar needs of operations in South Vietnam. Returning Vietnam veterans assigned as instructors at the signal schools provided the best source of feedback; questionnaires sent to graduates were rarely returned and were the worst means of obtaining information from

[33]MS, Jordan, Training, 1975, pp. 43–44; Trip Rpt, Maj Stewart, 6 Jul 67, p. 58.

the field. Liaison teams sent from the signal schools to South Vietnam annually beginning in the summer of 1965 observed operations and interviewed commanders to determine training deficiencies. Although the reports of those teams sparked a number of changes in curricula, repeated observations in follow-on reports concerning troubleshooting problems and lack of a comprehensive understanding of communications systems indicated the school's inability to resolve those deficiencies. Beginning in September 1966 the signal staff of the U.S. Army, Vietnam, every few months published *Command Communications*, a digest of communications-related articles. It provided the signal school and the Electronics Command a source of information from the field as well as a means of giving pointers and advice to communicators in units. A small staff at the signal school at Fort Monmouth that was responsible for evaluating signal doctrine and training analyzed *Command Communications* and the quarterly Operational Reports–Lessons Learned submitted by signal units in South Vietnam and passed pertinent information to instructors. The most productive means of sharing information between the field and the signal schools was the correspondence between the commanders of the 1st Signal Brigade and the school commandants, begun by General Van Harlingen and continued by his successors.[34]

Members of a field office of the Electronics Command and engineers and scientists participating in research and development programs in South Vietnam brought back to the schools useful observations and information. One team studying the use and maintenance of field radios in late 1967 discovered that only 50 percent of radio-telephone operators had received any formal training and that the average experience of the radiomen was only eight months. Many were infantrymen and wiremen drafted to replace wounded radio operators. The Electronics Command used such information to justify the added expense of designing easy-to-operate equipment; the signal schools used the data to argue for instruction in the operation of the PRC–25 for all trainees in the Army.[35]

Meeting Specialized Requirements

After the Army reorganization of 1962 the influence of Signal Corps officers over training they deemed essential to signal operations was severely curtailed. The Continental Army Command, which reserved authority to approve changes amounting to over 10 percent of a course's content, was sometimes slow and dictatorial in responding to the needs of signal training. Trying to apply to technical training the same standards that governed combat training, the command pressured the signal schools to shorten signal courses and to make more use of soldiers with lower academic qualifications. The Southeastern Signal School

[34]U.S. Army Signal Training Command, "A CONARC Program and a Poor Response," *Tec Tac,* no. 98 (27 April 1962):15–17, CMH; Trip Rpt, Col Moran, 16 Sep 66, p. 1; Ltr, Brig Gen William M. Van Harlingen to Maj Gen Walter B. Richardson, 22 Aug 67, Van Harlingen Papers.
[35]R&D Technical Rpt ECOM–3058, John S. Rakowski, Portable Radio Operation in Viet Nam, 8 Dec 68, ECOM Historians files.

did cut a course for teletypewriter repairmen (MOS 31J) from twenty-six to twenty-two weeks. But since students enrolled in courses of less than twenty-four weeks could not be promoted upon graduation, that restriction created a morale problem among the students of the vital course. A request for a waiver languished in the staff channels of the Continental Army Command and Pentagon until the school secretary, Col. Joe W. Finley, personally went to the Pentagon to obtain the waiver.[36]

For greater economy the Department of Defense designated a single service, command, or school as the proponent for development of a particular type of equipment or training in a certain skill. While the signal schools retained proponency for most Army communications training, they lost authority over training in related fields, such as generator operation and signal supply, that were vital to successful communications. Although instructors on the faculty of the signal schools were well acquainted with problems with generators in signal units in South Vietnam, their colleagues at the Engineer School at Fort Belvoir, Virginia, were less aware of the peculiar difficulties facing generator mechanics in maintaining equipment to power signal sets that required precise, steady levels of power. Because the Engineer School was not as quickly made aware of the frequent changes in types of equipment and manpower authorizations in field signal units, shortages of trained generator mechanics (MOS 52B) consistently plagued most signal units. As late as September 1968 the 1st Signal Brigade had only 62 percent of its authorized generator mechanics. Not until 1970 did the Engineer School have a facility for training mechanics for the large generators powering the Integrated Wideband Communications System. In coordinating the training and assignment of signal supply specialists, who were trained at the Quartermaster School at Fort Lee, Virginia, signal officers encountered similar difficulties.[37]

The worst shortages in Army signal units in South Vietnam occurred in the cable-splicer field (MOS 36E), for which the Army had relinquished training responsibility to the Air Force. During the early 1960s when polyethylene cable replaced lead-covered cable, the Department of Defense decided it would be more economical to consolidate all cable-splicing training in one service school rather than to have all service schools teach splicing techniques for the new type of cable. Since the Army had become dependent on multichannel radio relay to link its field signal centers under the area communications concept, the Department of Defense gave the training mission to the Air Force, which still needed cable to serve facilities on air bases. Sending only a few Army communicators to a course at Sheppard Air Force Base, Texas, the Army depended on civilian contractors for most of its cable splicing on posts in the United States and Europe. When the installation of fixed dial exchanges and teletype centers at major bases in South

[36]MFR, ATSN-MTF, SESS, sub: Monograph, Training Chapter, Administrative Problems Resulting from Advances in Training Practices, CMH; MS, Jordan, Training, 1975, pp. 36–38.
[37]Interv, Jordan with Holleran, 7 Feb 75; USASESS, Trip Rpt of Lt Col Dickinson to South Vietnam from 9 Sep 69 to 3 Oct 69, 10 Oct 69, pt. 2, p. 28; 1st Sig Bde, Briefing for Maj Gen Walter E. Lotz, Jr., on Personnel and Training, 9 Sep 68, file 228-03, ACC Historians files; GAO Report B–168097, *Problems in Acquiring, Installing, and Operating A Communications System in A Theater of Operations,* 5 Jun 72, p. 46.

Vietnam created a need for extensive cable plants, the Army had too few military cable splicers to accompany cable installation teams. Even as late as 1968, after the Army had increased its enrollment in the Air Force's school, the 1st Signal Brigade still had only 37 percent of its authorized cable splicers. Miles of cable damaged by shrapnel and soaked by moisture awaited repair by overworked cable-splicing teams.[38]

Even in those specialties for which the Signal Corps had proponency, the introduction of new equipment during the war restricted the ability of the signal schools to train operators and repairmen adequately. The Electronics Command sent training teams to the field with new equipment and signal schools added instruction in its use, but signal units in the field still had to train men transferring to South Vietnam from units having older equipment. As late as December 1966, 30 percent of the operators of troposcatter equipment in South Vietnam lacked any formal training on that equipment. Even those who had graduated from the signal school after troposcatter equipment had been installed at Fort Monmouth needed from two to six weeks' on-the-job instruction to understand the complexities of troposcatter systems in South Vietnam. Even less prepared by schooling were the fixed communications center operators (MOS 72F) working in the AUTODIN station at Phu Lam, who required an entire year of on-the-job training to become proficient in all the aspects of their highly technical duties. That meant that just as they were becoming fully competent, they were completing their year's tour.[39]

Training in Vietnam

Although commanders in the field recognized the need for a short period of on-the-job training to introduce new graduates to the realities of field operations and to familiarize veteran communicators with new equipment, they balked at having to divert resources from an operational mission to perform training they felt should have been done in the signal schools. The precedent of shifting some of the training burden from schools to operational units was set by the Signal Training Command in the late 1950s on the assumption that "no graduate fresh out of school is supposed to be a finished product." The Signal Training Command expected the signal schools to bring the trainee only "to the requisite state of readiness for on-the-job training." Thus, when the BACKPORCH system was fielded in the late summer of 1962, the Chief Signal Officer, Maj. Gen. Earle F. Cook, confidently predicted that on-the-job training of military specialists in the 39th Signal Battalion would obviate the need to renew the contract of the Page

---

[38]Rienzi Debriefing Rpt, 4 Jun 70, p. 37; USASESS, Trip Rpt of Lt Col Dickinson to South Vietnam from 9 Sep 69 to 3 Oct 69, 10 Oct 69, pt. 2, pp. 70–72.

[39]DF, USARV Sig Ofcr to ACofS, G–3, 14 Dec 66, sub: Signal Survey (hereafter cited as USARV Signal Survey), Incl 2 to Ltr, CONARC to Ofc of the Dir, COMSEA, 12 Mar 69, sub: Special Study: Communications Evaluation in Southeast Asia (COMSEA), CMH; USASESS, Trip Rpt of Lt Col Dickinson to South Vietnam from 9 Sep 69 to 3 Oct 69, 10 Oct 69, pt. 2, pp. 7, 98.

employees operating the network.[40]

No allowance was made in that contract for the contractor to train soldier attendants nor was any program set up for structured on-the-job training by the military. In 1969, after Page had operated the backbone network in South Vietnam for seven years, a liaison team from the signal school found that on-the-job signal training still was ineffective on the Integrated Wideband Communications System. Rarely were military supervisors held responsible for training their inexperienced subordinates nor were trainees tested to determine their progress. With every piece of equipment committed to an operational task, most signal facilities were too busy to allow for the tinkering and experimentation so essential to developing a complete understanding of equipment and techniques. Overworked supervisors were more concerned with keeping equipment on the air and quickly restoring outages than with methodically explaining every procedure to new men. Few units could spare an officer or noncommissioned officer to manage a unit training program and to keep progress and evaluation records. If a man wanted worthwhile on-the-job training, he had to take the initiative to look over the shoulders of more experienced men.[41]

The consequences of having unqualified men work unassisted on sophisticated signal equipment were serious. Besides inadvertently causing inferior communications, they often damaged expensive components. Improperly tuned troposcatter radios routinely destroyed klystron tubes costing hundreds of dollars. Technical assistants working in the Electronics Command field office reported that training deficiencies were the most prevalent cause of maintenance problems.[42]

As the pressure to install new tactical communications systems abated, the 1st Signal Brigade began improving training programs in tactical units. The staff of the brigade Training Division distributed lesson plans to signal units and monitored the use of technical qualification records to document each man's on-the-job training. By the spring of 1968 the signal brigade had 5,810 men enrolled in formal on-the-job training. The Training Division also was responsible for providing orientation for new men arriving in South Vietnam, leadership training for officers and noncommissioned officers, and functional training in such ancillary duties as driving trucks and operating generators. When General Van Harlingen transferred the Training Division from the busy Operations Directorate to the Personnel Directorate, the emphasis on training increased and the matching of personnel positions and training qualifications within the brigade improved considerably.[43]

The activation in September 1968 of the U.S. Army Signal Training Facility, 1st Signal Brigade, later renamed the Southeast Asia Signal School, provided a

---

[40]U.S. Army Sig Trng Cmd, "A CONARC Program and a Poor Response," *Tec Tac*, no. 98 (27 April 1962):15–16; Signal Board Rpt, Case 673, pp. 24–25.

[41]Interv, author with Thomas M. Shimabukuro, former engineer with Page Communications Engineers, Inc., 21 Feb 78, Historians files, CMH; USASESS, Trip Rpt of Lt Col Dickinson to South Vietnam from 9 Sep 69 to 3 Oct 69, 10 Oct 69, pt. 2, pp. 99, 119.

[42]USARV Signal Survey; Ltr, Van Harlingen to Richardson, 22 Aug 67, Van Harlingen Papers.

[43]Briefing for Lotz, on Personnel and Training, 9 Sep 68; Interv, Maj Fremont E. Binder, CO, 23d MHD, with Col John B. McKinney, Dep Cmdr, 1st Signal Brigade, 22 Jan 68, VNIT 112, CMH.

General Van Harlingen

structured environment for signal training and relieved the pressure on operational units trying to manage and conduct on-the-job training. The school trained signalmen to operate and maintain equipment newly introduced to South Vietnam, such as pulse code–modulated multichannel sets and the small, four-channel GRC–163 radio relay set. It also presented courses to alleviate the perennial shortage of cable splicers and technical controllers.[44]

By the time the signal training facility was established at Long Binh under the supervision of the brigade's 160th Signal Group, the 1st Signal Brigade had already trained 3,302 American and 224 South Vietnamese communicators in an unofficial signal school operated for over two years by the Regional Communications Group in Saigon. To compensate for the lack of a thorough understanding of communications systems and to prepare Army technicians to adhere to the Defense Communications Agency's standards of technical control and reporting procedures, in the summer of 1966 General Terry had directed the Regional Communications Group to teach a technical controllers course. When the first models of the new transportable MSQ–73 technical control vans arrived a few months later, two were installed at the school and the New Equipment Training Team accompanying the equipment conducted training there for operators assigned to units throughout South Vietnam. After the addition of a second course, cryptographic maintenance, in January 1967, the small school became the site for instruction in a wide variety of subjects taught by experienced technicians levied from the units of the brigade.[45]

It took a year and a half to convince headquarters in the United States of the necessity for a more formal school. Unwilling to allocate men for a mission that the Continental Army Command was supposed to perform, the Strategic Communications Command disapproved General Terry's first request for a 167-man faculty and reemphasized the need for on-the-job training. Recognizing the difficulty of providing substantive on-the-job training in units where men were

[44]The original twelve courses taught in the school were technical control, teletype circuit restoral, pulse-code modulation, telephone key systems, cable splicing, GRC–50 maintenance, GRC–106 maintenance, switchboard operation, KL-7 maintenance, GRC–163 operation, TRC–24 operation, and GRC–106 operation. Ltr, 160th Sig Gp to 1st Sig Bde, 10 Apr 70, sub: Recommendation for Award of the Meritorious Unit Commendation, CMH. "US Army Training Facility, 1st Signal Brigade (STRATCOM)," *Command Communications*, October 1968, pp. 23–29, CMH.

[45]"1st Signal Brigade School," *Command Communications*, April 1967, pp. 50–51, CMH. The U.S. Army Signal Training Facility, 1st Signal Brigade (USASTRATCOM), Catalog in file U–519, 72A18/9, WNRC, contains a complete listing of courses presented in the early signal school and training facility.

working at their communications stations twelve hours a day in addition to performing guard and garrison duties, General Van Harlingen in late 1967 resubmitted the request with an offer to provide spaces drawn from brigade units. The Department of the Army also balked at duplicating the training mission of the Continental Army Command, but, after long delays, in the summer of 1968 it approved a school to teach courses on only the equipment and tactics unique to Southeast Asia. The decision acknowledged that the signal schools, with the responsibility to ready soldiers for service in ninety-four countries and to present instruction on equipment changing rapidly with the technological state of the art, were unable to prepare signalmen completely for operations in South Vietnam. Headed by Lt. Col. Joseph F. Rankin, who had been the commandant of the unofficial brigade school, the U.S. Army Signal Training Facility, 1st Signal Brigade, had a permanent faculty of three officers and forty-eight enlisted men.[46]

The signal school gained universal acceptance from field commanders. Rather than begrudging the loss of men from operational units to attend the signal courses, which varied in length from two days to four weeks, most commanders anxiously sought quotas to the school. In fact, some argued that high prerequisites for admission excluded some of those who most needed the training. By spring of 1970, when the focus of the school had shifted to the training of South Vietnamese signalmen to replace withdrawing American communicators, the school had graduated 4,877 students from practically every U.S. and allied signal unit in Southeast Asia and was teaching twenty-three courses.[47]

Improvements to Stateside Training

While the 1st Signal Brigade was improving the capability of its signalmen to communicate in the unique environment of South Vietnam, the signal schools were developing better facilities and techniques. At Fort Gordon, the assignment of the 385th Signal Company (Support) from Fort Campbell provided a means for instructors to present realistic field training. Watching the experienced signalmen of the company demonstrate the installation of a signal center, trainees gained an appreciation of the cooperation and team effort involved in establishing a successful communications system. Actually operating the company's equipment under the supervision of the men of the signal support company gave the trainees a measure of hands-on experience and an exposure to troubleshooting techniques that they were unable to acquire in more controlled practical exercises in the classrooms.[48]

[46]Memo, 1st Sig Bde, SCCPV-PL-FD, for Chief, Force Development Division, 10 Jul 68, sub: Final Report of Captain Ronald J. Schwartz, Organization Officer, Force Development Division, Plans Directorate, file 14A, 69A5363/11, WNRC; Ltr, SEASS to 160th Sig Gp, 6 Aug 68, sub: Additional Justification for the Southeast Asia Signal School, VNIT 458, CMH.

[47]Ltr, 160th Sig Gp to 1st Sig Bde, 10 Apr 70, sub: Recommendation for Award of the Meritorious Unit Commendation; Interv, Capt Hrair N. Badalian, CO, 23d MHD, with Capt Lynn C. Vandeberg, CO, Company C, 43d Signal Battalion, 13 Nov 69, VNIT 580 (2). Both in CMH.

[48]USCONARC Agenda, School Commandants' Conference, 1965, tab Y.

To keep pace with the demands of training soldiers to handle ever more sophisticated products of modern technology, the signal schools employed the most advanced instructional techniques. In a pioneering effort that was acclaimed by both civilian and military educators, the Southeastern Signal School in 1960 developed a self-paced instructional package to teach students basic principles of mathematics and electronics that they had to understand before embarking on more specialized courses. Called programmed instruction, the approach employed texts and evaluation exercises written in such a way that each student could progress through an instructional block at a pace suited to his own comprehension. Instructors concentrated their attention on those having difficulty, while fast learners finished rapidly and moved on to more advanced work. The Army had first experimented with televised instruction in 1952 at Fort Gordon, and by 1965 the signal school had an extensive television facility which produced entire blocks of instruction in basic electronics. In 1968 the signal school at Fort Monmouth exploited the advantages of television and programmed learning to develop an eleven-hour block of electronics instruction using an innovative technique called computer-assisted instruction. Working at a cathode-ray-tube screen and a typewriter keyboard connected to a computer, each student reviewed instructional material that appeared on his screen when he pressed a button on his keyboard. To test the student's retention of the material at various stages of instruction, questions appeared on the screen. The student could answer by writing with an electronic pen on the screen or by typing on the keyboard. Correct answers were then flashed on the screen along with an evaluation of the student's responses. Depending on that evaluation, the computer would continue with the instructional block, repeat the sections dealing with concepts involved in the questions that the student answered incorrectly, or even present another subcourse with more detailed instruction in problem areas. Instructors monitoring the students' progress on a central console in each classroom were available to help students having problems or to answer specific questions.[49]

Because Fort Monmouth taught some of the most highly technical courses of any Army school, the imagination and ingenuity of the faculty were constantly challenged to find better and faster methods of training skilled communicators. During the course of the war the U.S. Army Signal School at Fort Monmouth developed forty-nine new or revised programs of instruction in direct response to requirements from South Vietnam. With the assistance of the American Telephone and Telegraph Company, the signal school revised its one-year commercial communications course for officers destined for assignments involved with fixed communications. Instruction took place in the classrooms at Fort Monmouth and in the nearby facilities of the telecommunications company. Many of the graduates of that course went directly to the Southeast Asia Telephone Management Agency. In addition to providing general instruction in automatic data processing in several officer and enlisted courses, the signal school also offered a nine-week computer management course in which students performed systems analyses for local civilian and governmental agencies. Graduates of that course

[49]Ibid., tab E; Interv, Jordan with Holleran, 7 Feb 75.

were instrumental in connecting facilities in South Vietnam to the new AUTODIN network. While technically qualified, many signal officers lacked the fiscal and management skills to budget and plan for the expensive systems in South Vietnam. In 1970 the commander of the 1st Signal Brigade, Maj. Gen. Thomas M. Rienzi, who had spent two and a half years as commandant of the U.S. Army Signal School before coming to South Vietnam in September 1968, convinced his successor at Fort Monmouth, Brig. Gen. Richard C. Horne, to include instruction in planning, programming, and budgeting in the officer advanced course.[50]

During 1968 the signal school at Fort Monmouth increased the number of specialties taught from forty to fifty-nine. As automatic telephone, teletype, and data networks went into operation, Army training had to become more specialized to keep pace with increasingly sophisticated and diverse military equipment and to prevent signalmen from spending most of their enlistments obtaining required technical training. When the length of the cryptographic equipment repair course reached sixty-nine weeks, the Army had to split the specialty to create a separate field for tactical cryptographic equipment repairmen (MOS 31S) and for fixed cryptographic equipment repairmen (MOS 31T). In the thirty years since the eve of World War II, the number of specialties taught at the Army's signal schools had increased from two to ninety to keep pace with technological developments.[51]

Personnel Management

For those who managed the assignment and replacement of signal personnel in South Vietnam, technology rather than the enemy provided the greatest difficulties. Compared to combat branches, the number of signal casualties that had to be replaced was insignificant. But the many occupational specialties and skill identifiers in the Signal Corps complicated the distribution of replacements for positions requiring precise qualifications. Because the skill required in a unit depended on the equipment being used there, the schools and the Office of Personnel Operations in Washington worked closely with the 1st Signal Brigade to get accurate projections for the completion of new signal sites. After the installation of dial exchanges fell behind schedule, highly trained soldiers sent to maintain the exchanges had to be used as field wiremen. When the signal schools assigned some graduates trained for the Integrated Wideband Communications System to microwave facilities in other parts of the world rather than send them to South Vietnam where they would have to wait for the completion of delayed terminals, the General Accounting Office criticized the Army for improperly assigning specially trained soldiers. In other cases, unanticipated accelerations

[50]Ltr, USASCS to COMSEA Study Group, 25 Feb 69; Ltr, Rienzi to Horne, 19 May 70. Both in CMH.
[51]Col. Gerd S. Grombacher, "CE Training Crisis Ahead," *Signal*, September 1970, pp. 32–34; Interv, Capt Hrair N. Badalian, CO, 23d MHD, with Lt Col Emmett Paige, CO, 361st Signal Battalion, 16 Aug 69, VNIT 469, CMH.

of projects left the schools and personnel managers unable to fill requisitions from the field. After the Army tripled the amount of communications security equipment in South Vietnam to support the AUTOSEVOCOM and AUTODIN systems and the newly developed PRC–77 portable radio, it took two years to fill requests from the 1st Signal Brigade for cryptographic equipment repairmen.[52]

Complicating the assignment of personnel to signal units in South Vietnam was the existence of two personnel pipelines: through the Strategic Communications Command to the 1st Signal Brigade and through the U.S. Army, Pacific, to tactical units assigned to the U.S. Army, Vietnam. The 1st Signal Brigade was the only unit in the Strategic Communications Command manned at full strength. Even so, because the 1st Signal Brigade was the only major Army unit in South Vietnam not assigned to the U.S. Army, Vietnam, it was unable to share in a general relaxation of personnel restrictions and manpower limitations that the Department of the Army permitted in the U.S. Army, Vietnam. To maintain a balance between the signal brigade and tactical units in the most critical skills, General Van Harlingen had his staffs at the 1st Signal Brigade and the Office of the Assistant Chief of Staff for Communications-Electronics at the U.S. Army, Vietnam, coordinate the redistribution of personnel weekly.[53]

After the buildup in 1965, signal commanders found the Signal Branch chiefs at the Office of Personnel Operations to be cooperative and sympathetic to their needs. General Terry later called the branch chief during the formation of the signal brigade, Col. William A. Van Sandt, an "unsung hero." Because Colonel Van Sandt had been responsible for signal operations in Southeast Asia during his previous tour as signal officer of the U.S. Army, Ryukyu Islands, Van Sandt knew that he had to compensate for the low priority formerly given to assignments to South Vietnam. His successor, Col. Edward D. Meares, had a particularly difficult time providing enough qualified lieutenant colonels to command the battalions of the 1st Signal Brigade. General Van Harlingen felt that by rotating battalion commanders every six months he could improve the quality and professionalism of the Signal Corps, populate his signal staff with former commanders better able to understand the needs of subordinate units, and prevent the physical fatigue for which several signal battalion commanders had been hospitalized. While the combat arms had been able to assign their officers for six-month command tours, Colonel Meares had a far smaller pool of candidates for command. Although the Signal Corps was only 0.3 percent below its authorized level of 6.7 percent of the officer corps, it was drastically short of majors and lieutenant colonels. Because only a small percentage of Signal Corps officers had been selected during the previous decade to attend the Command and General Staff College at Fort Leavenworth, the Signal Corps in mid-1967 had only 517 graduates to fill 726 signal jobs requiring graduates of the Army's mid-career officer school. Every battalion commander was supposed to be a graduate. While

---

[52]GAO Report B–168097, *Problems in Acquiring, Installing, and Operating A Communications System in A Theater of Operations,* 5 Jun 72, app. V; Msg, USARV ARV 279D to DA, 10 Oct 68, sub: Availability of Trained COMSEC Maintenance Personnel, CMH.

[53]Rienzi, *Communications-Electronics,* pp. 137–38; Memo, Col Edward D. Meares for Maj Gen Walter E. Lotz, 19 Jan 68, sub: Summary of OPD Briefing, 22 Jan 68, Van Harlingen Papers.

the Infantry Branch had three times more battalions than the Signal Corps, it had six times more graduates of the Command and General Staff College than the Signal Corps. Considering the difficulties in finding qualified battalion commanders and the problem of command turbulence—which meant that a soldier had three different battalion commanders during a one-year tour—General Van Harlingen later retracted his advocacy of the six-month command tour.[54]

The war in South Vietnam had imposed difficult burdens on the signal training schools. Electronic equipment was constantly being changed to keep up with the state of the art, schools were not augmented with reservists, and one-year combat tours imposed constant personnel turnovers in the schools. Because it proved impossible to train military operators sufficiently to operate and maintain the equipment on the Integrated Wideband Communications System without help, civilian technicians had to remain in South Vietnam throughout the war.

By the early 1970s a reduction in the strength of the signal brigade, which peaked at 23,000 in late 1968, made it easier to replenish signalmen in South Vietnam. The hard work of signal trainers at Fort Monmouth and Fort Gordon and in South Vietnam had successfully overcome the difficulties involved in rapidly preparing soldiers to function in a technologically advanced combat environment. To students living in new air-conditioned barracks at the signal schools, the tent complexes where their predecessors had lived were part of the forgotten past. Although improved facilities and instructional innovations had not completely obviated the need for on-the-job training and for a signal school in South Vietnam, the presence of supervisors in signal units who were veterans of previous tours in South Vietnam made the training of new soldiers much easier and more beneficial. As American units began withdrawing from South Vietnam, signal units and schools were well prepared to train South Vietnamese soldiers to take over communications.

---

[54]Interv, author with Maj Gen (ret.) Robert D. Terry, 5 Oct 78, Historians files, CMH; Memo, Meares for Lotz, 19 Jan 68, sub: Summary of OPD Briefing, 22 Jan 68; Ltr, Van Harlingen to Meares, 16 May 68; Ltr, Meares to Van Harlingen, 4 Jan 68. Latter three in Van Harlingen Papers.

19

Materiel

Stating that it was "difficult, if not impossible, to put a Ford engine into a Vietnamese oxcart," U.S. Ambassador to South Vietnam Frederick E. Nolting, Jr., used an apt technological metaphor in 1963 to caution the secretary of defense against using American technology to solve South Vietnam's military problems. Secretary McNamara's quick response, "We can do it," revealed a faith in technology shared by most Americans of the day.[1] Confident that "the tools of modern technology" could repair the war-torn foundations of South Vietnamese society, President Kennedy had already convinced President Diem to join with the American military in establishing a joint scientific research facility to develop "new techniques to help us in our joint campaign against the Communists."[2]

The American faith in technology also was rooted in an awareness that the United States was inextricably committed to a continuation of technological progress. The American war machine was too big and complex, too dependent on computers and fast-moving aircraft, to gear down to the speed of a society still marching to the cadence of the nineteenth century. A revolution in the electronics industry in the late 1950s, sparked by the development of the transistor, had accelerated the surge in American technology. Signal Corps soldiers and technicians quickly became caught up in the technological momentum of the war.[3]

Changing Signal Logistics

The chief signal officer, responsible for research, development, and support of all electronic materiel in the Army, was very much in control of the application of electronic technology to the Army before the Vietnam War. Through the Signal Board at Fort Monmouth he approved all requirements for

[1]Michael Charlton and Anthony Moncrieff, *Many Reasons Why: The American Involvement in Vietnam* (New York: Hill and Wang, 1978), p. 82.
[2]Ltr, Kennedy to Diem, 8 May 61, *U.S.-Vietnam Relations*, 11:132-33.
[3]Draft MS, ECOM, ECOM in Southeast Asia, ch. 7, ECOM Historians files.

communications-electronics equipment and formulated the doctrine for its employment. His staff supervised the signal schools where that doctrine was taught and planned and managed the operation of much of the electronic equipment in the field. His office directly supervised the operating signal logistical agencies: the Army Signal Research and Development Laboratories, the Army Signal Materiel Support Agency, and the Army Signal Supply Agency.

With the creation of Department of Defense–wide organizations during the early 1960s he began to relinquish some of those responsibilities. The Defense Electronics Supply Center, an arm of the new Defense Supply Agency, assumed the mission of procuring and supplying electronic items common to all services. After the reorganization of the Army and consolidation of the Army's materiel management under the new Army Materiel Command on 1 August 1962, the chief signal officer lost all responsibility for signal logistics. The Electronics Command, one of five commodity commands (weapons, munitions, missile, mobility, and electronics) established under the Army Materiel Command, took over the field support agencies, depots, and laboratories of the Signal Corps. The commander of the new organization, Maj. Gen. Stuart S. Hoff, became so hampered by the institutional turbulence and staff rivalries unleashed by the Army reorganization that he was unable to make the changes in signal logistics that he felt were necessary. Retiring after only a year in command, he was succeeded by Maj. Gen. Frank W. Moorman who, by mid-1964, had reorganized the Electronics Command into four operating agencies to handle the separate missions of research and development, procurement and production, supply and maintenance, and personnel and training. He also established commodity management offices to monitor the development and support, from initial research to disposal, of seven categories of electronic equipment. To manage the development and use of complex communications systems or families of equipment, the Army Materiel Command assigned to the Electronics Command three major projects: Universal Integrated Communications/Strategic Army Communications (UNICOM/STARCOM), Selected Tactical Radios, and Army Area Communications Systems. The UNICOM/STARCOM program manager directed the installation of the Integrated Wideband Communications System and other Army projects in the Defense Communications System until the project office was transferred in February 1967 to the new Communications Systems Agency.[4]

The turmoil within the Electronics Command was typical of that experienced throughout the logistical core of the Army in the wake of the reorganization. Supply and procurement transactions of the commodity commands and supply centers, called National Inventory Control Points, were handled by 166 different computer systems operating with little technical coordination or centralized control. As the American buildup in South Vietnam began in 1965, the Army was still converting to the radically different organization needed to apply the concept of functional logistical support in the field. While units in Europe and Korea had completed conversion, those from the U.S.-based strategic force, which had

---

[4]ECOM AHS, FY–64, pt. 1, pp. 1–45, chronicles the development of the Electronics Command during its first two years. Army Materiel Command (AMC), *Arsenal for the Brave*, 1969, pp. 165–82, CMH. ECOM AHS, FY–67, CMH, provides a history of project management in the Electronics Command.

been slow to reorganize, were moving to South Vietnam organized as they had been under the old concept of logistical support through separate technical service channels. Even after the logistical structure in South Vietnam changed in mid-1966, a dearth of doctrine and of experienced personnel, especially in highly technical electronic fields, hampered supply and maintenance operations.[5]

From the very first months of the reorganization, difficulties with signal logistics had interfered with operations.[6] Signalmen in Southeast Asia, at the end of the worldwide logistical pipeline, suffered most from the confusion left in the wake of the reorganization. The chief signal adviser of the Military Assistance Advisory Group in South Vietnam, Col. Howard E. Porter, despaired of trying to work through the labyrinth of unsettled logistical support channels in the Pacific. He wrote to friends stationed at Fort Monmouth to obtain supplies, technical literature, and information directly from the Electronics Command. By March 1965 he was able to arrange for General Moorman to visit South Vietnam to determine how the Electronics Command could better suppport an endeavor that appeared about to change from an advisory program to a full-scale American ground combat effort.[7]

When General Moorman went to South Vietnam, the U.S. Army, Ryukyu Islands, in Okinawa, which had been providing general support to the 39th Signal Battalion and the STARCOM station, was transferring responsibility for Army units in South Vietnam to the 1st Logistical Command being established in Saigon. A 147-man signal forward maintenance company was en route to operate a central signal depot in Saigon and five field support detachments. Recognizing that the company was barely large enough to support the signal units already in South Vietnam handling communications for the advisory program, General Moorman argued for additional signal logistical support for the anticipated American combat forces. The Department of the Army denied his request in accordance with the Defense Department's policy of disapproving requests for support units based on anticipated requirements.[8]

Returning from his visit to South Vietnam convinced that a signal support crisis was imminent, General Moorman alerted his staff to be prepared for an urgent call for support. The staff drafted four operations plans that formed the basis for the Electronics Command's preparations for the war. The National Inventory Control Point at Philadelphia, which handled electronic supply support, expeditiously filled requisitions from Southeast Asia and from units most likely to be the first to deploy. The avionics commodity manager and the Avionics Laboratory planned for the provision of navigational equipment to the 11th Air Assault Division (later renamed the 1st Cavalry Division [Airmobile]) in anticipation of its move to South Vietnam. The staff agency responsible for support of troposcatter equipment, the Office of the Program Manager, Universal Integrated Communications/Strategic

---

[5]Joint Logistics Review Board, *Monograph 14*, p. 13; MS, Hermes, The Buildup, ch. 11.
[6]See Chapter 8 for a discussion of problems during the Cuban missile crisis.
[7]OCMH, The Signal Corps Role in the Cuban Crisis-1962, p. 10, file 201–45 MH, 67A4846/1, WNRC; Interv, author with Col (ret.) Howard E. Porter, former chief signal adviser, MAAG, Vietnam, 18 Jan 78, Historians files, CMH.
[8]Ltr, ECOM to AMC, 29 Apr 65, ECOM Historians files.

Army Communications (UNICOM/STARCOM), coordinated with Collins Radio Company to rush spares to South Vietnam to rehabilitate the TRC–90's and to develop improved versions of the mobile radio. Commodity and project managers prepared lists of equipment to be developed and procured when the Army finally received additional funds to support the increasingly inevitable American buildup.[9]

Despite the Electronics Command's preparations, signal units were sent to Vietnam short of logistical support. Within weeks of President Johnson's announcement of the buildup, combat and signal units were on their way to Southeast Asia, while logisticians were still engaged in contract negotiations to obligate newly released funds needed to start production lines. Since General Westmoreland felt he needed a rapid infusion of combat forces to stem a Communist tide that threatened to engulf South Vietnam, even some logistical units needed to support deploying combat units found it difficult to get space on the planes and ships rushing infantrymen to Southeast Asia. When Maj. Gen. Oren E. Hurlbut, the Army's new special assistant for supply and maintenance, Southeast Asia, went to South Vietnam in December 1965, he found that the quick injection of combat power had stopped the Communists but that the delay in establishing a logistical base had limited American exploitation of those initial successes. To work with General Hurlbut's staff in restoring a proper balance of logistical support in South Vietnam, Maj. Gen. William B. Latta, who replaced General Moorman in October 1965, gathered twenty-seven handpicked men to form a special staff office, the Operational Readiness Office. Until it disbanded in 1971 after planning for the withdrawal of American units from South Vietnam, the office monitored the progress of every program and activity of the Electronics Command dealing with Southeast Asia.[10]

By mid-1966 the turbulence caused by the reorganization and the delay in building a logistical base had abated. The 9th Logistical Command had moved from Okinawa to Thailand to support Army units there and was replaced in Okinawa by the 2d Logistical Command. The 1st Logistical Command, having grown to a healthy 22,000-man strength, operated the fully automated 14th Inventory Control Center to manage supply support throughout South Vietnam. It also built three area commands at Saigon, Da Nang, and Cam Ranh Bay to handle direct and general support on a regional basis. The 34th General Support Group, a subordinate agency of the 2d Logistical Command in Okinawa, handled all aircraft and avionics support. Perhaps because the 34th General Support Group had a specialized mission, it gained a reputation as the most efficient logistical unit in South Vietnam.

When the 1st Signal Brigade was formed, General Latta sent one of his staff, Lt. Col. Blaine Buckingham, to be the brigade's director of logistics. The signal

---

[9]Ltrs, ECOM to AMC, 7 Jul 65 and 17 Sep 65, ECOM Historians files; Maj. Gen. Frank W. Moorman, "ECOM in the Pacific," *Signal*, September 1965, pp. 27–30.

[10]MS, Hermes, The Buildup, ch. 11, pp. 1–10; Joint Logistics Review Board, *Monograph 12: Logistics Planning*, 1969, pp. 22–23, 71A2351/6, WNRC; Draft MS, ECOM, ECOM in Southeast Asia, ch. 2; DF, AMSEL-PT-O to ECOM Historian, 17 Jun 71, sub: Historical Summary and Feeder Material for Monograph, ECOM Historians files.

staff of the U.S. Army, Vietnam, coordinated logistical support to all other communications units in South Vietnam. To assist signal logisticians, the Electronics Command opened a field office in Saigon. Growing from an office of one civil service employee and thirty-three manufacturers' representatives in mid-1965 to a 141-man staff three years later, the field office provided civilian technical assistance to all research, supply, and maintenance activities in support of communications equipment in South Vietnam. Concerned that the one-year tour left units with too few experienced military logisticians, General Latta took every opportunity to expand the civilian staff in Vietnam.[11]

Having representatives in South Vietnam also enabled General Latta to obtain advance warning of upcoming

General Latta

requirements and problems. Although the Army had prescribed procedures for reporting equipment difficulties and recommending improvements, General Latta had been frustrated by the failure of such information to filter through the many layers of headquarters isolating the Electronics Command from the units using electronic equipment in South Vietnam. Particularly incensed when he learned of problems with communications equipment in South Vietnam in a commercial magazine, General Latta began a personal monthly correspondence with the deputy commanding general of the U.S. Army, Vietnam, and with the 1st Signal Brigade commander.[12]

Many problems with signal equipment resulted because personnel at the 1st Logistical Command lacked the experience and technical expertise to repair complex electronic gear and did not adequately appreciate the special handling required for signal supplies. With the deactivation in 1966 of the signal supply and maintenance companies—the last remnants of the old technical services organization—and the inclusion of electronic support in maintenance units and supply depots responsible for all commodities, signalmen lost the ability to solve their own logistical problems. When the signal staff at the U.S. Army, Vietnam, tried to manage the support of certain especially critical electronic items, it was rebuffed by the 1st Logistical Command, which felt that the headquarters signal staff was too small to coordinate with the inventory control center, the area support commands, and the seventy direct and general support units handling com-

---

[11]Ltrs, Van Harlingen to Latta, 6 Oct 67, and Latta to Van Harlingen, 18 Oct 67, Van Harlingen Papers; USARV, The Logistics Review, 1965–1969, vol. 1, ch. 9, p. 4, CMH. For a comprehensive account of the activities of the Electronics Command, Vietnam, office, see "The U.S. Army Electronics Command-Vietnam," *Command Communications*, October 1968, pp. 56–63, CMH.

[12]Ltr, Latta to Terry, 11 Oct 66, ECOM Historians files.

munications gear in South Vietnam. The 1st Signal Brigade itself maintained logistical responsibility only for the nonstandard equipment associated with the Integrated Communications System and for communications security equipment.[13]

While logisticians argued that the signal staffs were not equipped to manage items handled within the vast functional logistical system, they themselves were having a particularly difficult time keeping track of a multitude of small, but essential and expensive, electronic components. Accustomed to dealing in gross tonnages, they had difficulty adapting to situations where the spare parts for a communications assembly for an entire year were contained in a small box. Thrown in a bin with truck parts, small packages of electronic items were easily damaged or lost. If wrappings were torn or markings obliterated, the identity of the circuit boards or the modules within was often impossible to determine.[14]

The Army's Role in the Electronic Revolution

A rmy research and development conducted during the 1950s at the Fort Monmouth laboratories had led to the miniaturization that bedeviled supply handlers in South Vietnam fifteen years later. When Bell Telephone in 1948 produced the first transistor as a replacement for bulky, power-hungry electron tubes, civilian industry showed little inclination to invest the vast sums of money necessary to switch to a radically different and untested technology. Anxious to reduce weight, size, and power specifications for electronic gear for aircraft and man-pack radios, the military decided to underwrite the costs of developing facilities and methods to mass-produce transistorized equipment. In 1957 the laboratories at Fort Monmouth began producing transistors for scientists at Huntsville, Alabama, who were building America's first space satellite. By the early 1960s, after the military services had invested $20 million in the new technology, the price of producing a transistor had dropped from $200 to $2, the frequency range of transistors had increased from ten megahertz to three gigahertz, and the entire electronic and data processing industry had begun exploiting the vast potential of what had come to be called solid-state electronics.[15]

During the 1950s the laboratories at Fort Monmouth shifted from the development of particular types of equipment to a greater concern for pure scientific research. Technicians obtained advanced degrees and returned to embark on esoteric theoretical studies. Then in 1962, as the laboratories were adjusting to the difficult birth of the Electronics Command, President Kennedy's concern with finding a means to harness modern technology for use in unconventional warfare

[13]USARV, The Logistics Review, 1965–1969, vol. 1, ch. 9, p. 6 and vol. 8, an. W, p. 7.

[14]Intervs, author with Maj Gen (ret.) William B. Latta, former CG, Electronics Command, 13 Sep 78; and with Charles Foster, former chief, Electronics Command, Vietnam, 15 Sep 78. Both in Historians files, CMH.

[15]For a good discussion of the influence of transistors on the military, see Frederick W. Griggey, "The Impact of Microminiaturization on Logistics," *Signal*, May 1965, pp. 83–88.

wrenched the orientation of the laboratories back to a concern for the practical.[16]

The United States viewed Southeast Asia as a field laboratory. When President Kennedy proposed a joint research endeavor to President Diem in 1961, the South Vietnamese leader readily agreed. His first military adviser, Lt. Gen. John W. O'Daniel, had predicted in 1954 that South Vietnam would become a testing ground where the United States would determine how it would fight the Communists throughout the world. The Army contracted with civilian technical consultants to perform research in Indochina to determine the appropriate equipment for combat and for internal security communications in developing countries. Soon after the establishment of the Military Assistance Command, Vietnam, in 1962, the Joint Chiefs of Staff formed the Joint Operational Evaluation Group, Vietnam, to act as General Harkins' research and development staff. The chief of the group also directed a field unit of the Department of Defense's Advanced Research Projects Agency (ARPA). The Department of the Army sent its own field research staff, the Army Concept Team in Vietnam (ACTIV), headed by Brig. Gen. Edward L. Rowny, to "test doctrine, organization, and materiel in a counterinsurgency environment." Coordinating with the Electronics Command, the Army team studied a wide range of improvised antennas for use in the jungles, searched for an effective early-warning device for villages, and tested numerous models of a proposed lightweight patrol radio capable of transmitting over long distances in jungles and mountains. The team coordinated a 39th Signal Battalion test of several standard items of new equipment, an endeavor that was halted when it began detracting from the battalion's primary support missions.[17]

The Advanced Research Projects Agency conducted basic research on geographical, seasonal, and diurnal influences on radio propagation in the tropics. The Electronics Command's highly theoretical laboratory, the Institute for Exploratory Research, sponsored similar tests in Thailand while also conducting more practical studies on such esoteric topics as tunnel detection, intrusion devices, and the corrosive effects of the soil of Southeast Asia. Although these studies revealed much concerning a region of the world about which scientists had little information, they were sometimes criticized as being too academic and impractical. For example, to determine the source of difficulties of Thai militiamen in communicating with FM radios, a linguistics expert was hired to ascertain whether the tonal qualities of the Oriental voice were not capable of transmission over FM radio frequencies. After a year of analysis scientists concluded that only an unfamiliarity with radios, which appeared to uneducated militiamen as strange, unintelligible combinations of dials and buttons, caused the problem. To curb the natural inclination of scientists to examine every possibility, the military staff

[16]Hans K. Ziegler, Presentation at Siemens A.G., Munich, Germany, "Thirty Years of Electronics Research and Development in USA: Methods, Results, Lessons Learned," 4 Oct 76, transcript in ECOM Historians files. (Hereafter cited as Ziegler Presentation, "Thirty Years of Electronics Research and Development in USA.") USASS, "Millions of Micro-modules for Signal Corps Equipments," *Tec Tac* (28 June 1962):3–8, CMH; Interv, author with Marvin W. Curtis, former staff member of Electronics Command, 1 Mar 79, Historians files, CMH.

[17]Msg, MAAG to DEPTAR, 27 Jul 54, file 7616.00/7–2754, records of Dept of State; DF, DA, DCSOPS, to CRD, 13 Aug 62, sub: Review and Evaluation of RAC (ORO)–T–408, file 320178, 65A3314/15; 232d Sig Co History, 1963, p. 16, 338–75–1000/145. Latter two in WNRC.

of the Electronics Command encouraged the laboratories to find fast and practical solutions while at the same time ensuring that a portion of the laboratory staff considered the future beyond the Vietnam War.[18]

Conducting research during the 1960s was particularly frustrating for scientists at Fort Monmouth who had to contend with vague and ever-changing requirements from the field. Before the laboratories could complete the design for a piece of equipment meeting particular specifications, the requirements would often change. Sometimes the differing doctrinal attitudes of military officers assigned successively to the Combat Developments Command, the agency responsible for defining requirements, caused them to favor different solutions to the same problem. In other cases new developments by industry permitted better means of satisfying requirements. By the mid-1960s the commercial electronics industry, capitalizing on advances in solid-state technology, was creating innovations that made military gear obsolete even before it was tested. Nor were the laboratories able to retain enough scientists familiar with the newest developments. In the fierce competition for qualified electronic engineers, wages had soared far higher than government pay. Seeking replacements for the civilian scientists lost to industry, General Latta interviewed every officer and enlisted man with an advanced degree in electronics at the signal school at Fort Monmouth. Invariably, they had already received bids from civilian companies offering them more than they could ever hope to receive from the government.[19]

Despite such inducements, older scientists who had been with the laboratories since the end of World War II and had risen to higher grades remained with the laboratories. Some, like the chief scientist, Hans K. Ziegler, had immigrated to the United States from Germany after the war. They worked in a huge green building called the Hexagon, whose hundreds of cavernous rooms were filled with meters, test sets, and electrical gadgets accumulated during two decades of experimentation. The roof of the Hexagon bristled with antennas—some used in testing new radios, others left behind from some long-forgotten experiment. When General Moorman reorganized the Electronics Command he formed a Directorate of Research and Development on his staff to oversee the work being done in the Hexagon. He split the Electronics Laboratories into six separate laboratories (Communications and Automatic Data Processing; Electronic Components; Electronic Warfare; Combat Surveillance and Target Acquisition; Avionics; and Atmospheric Sciences) and the Institute for Exploratory Research.[20]

As new equipment made its way to the field, the scientists at Fort Monmouth hungered for word of its performance. Because the men in South Vietnam had too many duties and too little time during a one-year tour to develop well-founded opinions, their reports usually consisted only of general praise or undocumented complaints. Only after General Latta formed Research and Development Tech-

---

[18]For a summary of the findings of the radio studies in Indochina, see L. G. Sturgill, "Tactical Radio Communications Research in Jungle Environments," *Signal*, May/June 1969, pp. 81–87. DF, ECOM, COMM/ADP Lab, to Hist, 3 Jul 68, sub: USAECOM Historical Feeder Reports, file C–157; DF, ECOM, Institute for Exploratory Research, to Admin Ofc, 28 Jun 68, sub: Historical Coverage of the Army Role in Southeast Asia, file C–158. Both in 72A25/6, WNRC.

[19]Interv, author with Latta, 13 Sep 78.

[20]AMC, *Arsenal for the Brave*, pp. 165–82.

nical Liaison Teams, groups of five to seven representatives from the laboratories who went to South Vietnam for three-month tours, did the realities of communicating in Southeast Asia begin to reach the Hexagon. The teams also helped the men in the field to understand the complexities of equipment development. As one laboratory scientist wrote of his eye-opening experiences with the troops using Army communications equipment in South Vietnam, "Every one of their complaints about equipment was legitimate. Trying to explain and justify the slow response of Fort Monmouth's R&D men to their needs was difficult. I persuaded them that the time from laboratory concept and proof to factory production and issue was unavoidably long. Yet I felt very inadequate . . . , it seems almost like a 'con job' perpetrated on men who deserve better."[21]

Technicians at the laboratories, accustomed to responding to an impersonal military bureaucracy, suddenly were impelled by a desire to help the soldiers with whom they or their associates had recently shared the dangers of war. In answers to letters from friends in South Vietnam technicians sent packages of much needed spare parts; technical papers that could be condensed were included in the bimonthly periodical, *Command Communications*, published and distributed by the signal staff of the U.S. Army, Vietnam. Returning team members spent long extra hours at their workbenches in the Hexagon resolving baffling problems encountered in the field.[22]

While in South Vietnam, the technicians tried to determine which critical parts were most likely to fail, notified the laboratories of design deficiencies, and helped soldiers make interim repairs and corrections. When a large number of radios in the tanks and armored personnel carriers of the 11th Armored Cavalry became inoperative during Operation JUNCTION CITY, the technicians discovered that surges of voltage from the vehicles' powerful ignition systems were damaging electronic equipment. Because technicians in the laboratories had recognized the possibility of that problem, they had directed that the radios be issued with instructions that they be turned off before starting vehicles. In South Vietnam the scientists saw that such a precaution was unrealistic in the heat of battle. The liaison team returned to the laboratories to fabricate a voltage suppressor that could be added to the vehicular-mounted radios to block voltage surges.[23]

Sometimes liaison officers were surprised to discover problems in equipment that had been thoroughly tested. Representatives from the Avionics Laboratory found that the engine transmissions in helicopters were causing radio interference during operation in South Vietnam and designed special filters for microphones used in helicopters that alleviated the problems. Because the mechanical engineers at the laboratories subjected equipment to the most exhaustive impact and immersion testing, they were perplexed by reports that radio handsets and antennas were not withstanding the rigors of combat in South Vietnam. Then a liaison engineer from the laboratory, Ross E. Stauffer, joined a patrol of the

[21]Quote from Ltr, Malvin L. Shar to Marvin Klayton, 2 Feb 69, Malvin L. Shar Papers, CMH.
[22]Ltr, Latta to Terry, 5 Jun 67; Ltr, Latta to Lt Gen Bruce Palmer, Jr., 20 Nov 67. Both in ECOM Historians files. Draft MS, ECOM, ECOM in Southeast Asia, ch. 3.
[23]Rpt, Steven J. Bartosh, Electronic Components Laboratory, Voltage Transient Suppressors, in Historical Coverage of the Army Role in Southeast Asia file, ECOM Historians files.

173d Airborne Brigade, the unit with the worst record for damaging its communications equipment. Carrying a radio he had personally checked beforehand, he joined the patrol in a jungle he described as a "wall made up of dense growth with no openings nor other areas for ease of entering." In a two-kilometer march, he fell repeatedly, had to jerk his gear free of vines and thorns, and had his radio antenna bent back towards the ground by overhanging branches. Then, examining his radio, he found several loose connections, a clip torn from his microphone, and an antenna broken at three rivets. Having discovered the unanticipated stresses on the equipment borne by the radio-telephone operators in infantry units, the technicians in the mechanical laboratories were better able to understand the standards that had to be met by the gear they designed.[24]

Radio-Telephone Operator on Patrol. *For protection, radio antenna is folded down, microphone covered with plastic.*

Technicians on the liaison teams also sought to overcome climatic influences. They devised ways to repaint vans with solar heat–reflecting paint and to replace fans in signal shelters with air conditioners. When swollen data cards clogged automatic data processing equipment, they arranged for cards to be packaged in moisture-proof plastic during shipment. That relatively simple solution saved $720,000 each year.[25]

Although half of the sixty recommendations submitted by the liaison technicians, including one to develop a stronger radio handset, were implemented during the first year of the liaison program, some remedies had to wait for the fielding of new equipment. Information concerning the propagational effects of climate and geography was considered in the design of equipment still under development. Since the cost of designing unique equipment to withstand the peculiar conditions of South Vietnam was prohibitive, the laboratories were unable to solve every problem. For example, because there were not enough air conditioners for all tactical sets, repairmen in the field had to learn to cope with equipment failures induced by the climatic extremes of the tropics. Unable to work in the stifling heat of communications shelters, operators left van doors open, allowing dust to blow freely through signal components. Moving parts on

[24]Ltr, Latta to Brig Gen Richard J. Seitz, 18 Jun 66; Memo, Stauffer for Ch, Mechanical Engineering Branch, 15 Dec 67, sub: R&D Technical Liaison Team in Vietnam. Both in ECOM Historians files.
[25]Rpt, John N. Warren, COMM/ADP Lab, Efficiency of Data Card Handling at USASTRATCOM's SVN Facilities Is Increased by 300%, in Historical Coverage of the Army Role in Southeast Asia file, ECOM Historians files.

teletypewriters gummed up; clogged filters restricted the flow of air through components, causing them to overheat. When operators removed covers on circuit panels and teletypewriters to allow air to circulate, their sweat dripped onto the equipment and corroded unprotected internal components.[26]

In developing equipment, the Signal Corps had allowed for environmental extremes such as those found in South Vietnam. But because much of the gear used there initially was worn out, it no longer performed to design specifications. Where clearly defined requirements and well-managed research and testing guided the development of new equipment, it usually proved successful in the field. Hasty development inevitably caused problems. When the Army tried to replace the tactical high-frequency radios in use since the Korean War by accelerating the development of the GRC–106 single-sideband radios, it later had to recall them from units in South Vietnam to make major modifications. Since the development of new VHF multichannel and FM voice radios had progressed further by the time American combat units arrived in Vietnam, those radios proved more reliable.[27]

The Army's old twelve-channel VHF terminals, consisting of the TRC–24 radio and the TCC–7 carrier, had served the Army well in South Vietnam ever since the 39th Signal Battalion arrived in the spring of 1962 with its MRC–69 terminals. To modernize those workhorses, which had been built in the mid-1950s, the Army had developed a series of multichannel terminals consisting of transistorized radios and carrier equipment that employed new signal concepts such as pulse-code modulation. Called the Army Area Communications System (AACOMS) family, the new multichannel equipment consisted of four separate sets: low-capacity (6 or 12 channels), medium-capacity (12 or 24 channels), high-capacity (48 or 96 channels), and troposcatter (24 channels) sets. The equipment had been designed and developed specifically to fulfill the Army's new doctrine of area-oriented communications. The Electronics Command had planned to send the first sets from the production line to South Vietnam, even assigning to the 1st Signal Brigade a full-time liaison officer to help units install and activate the new equipment. But demands for multichannel equipment for the Army's strategic reserve and for units in Europe, whose inventory of signal gear had been depleted to support the buildup, slowed the issue of those new sets to South Vietnam. Not until December 1967 did the first medium-capacity sets arrive. In late 1969 high-capacity sets replaced tactical TRC–29 microwave terminals. Low-capacity equipment was not manufactured until the early 1970s, and division signal battalions continued to use the old TRC–24 radio relay equipment until the end of the war.[28]

---

[26]Ltr, Latta to Lt Gen Bruce Palmer, Jr., 27 Sep 67; Ltr, Latta to Van Harlingen, 22 Sep 67; Memo, Stauffer for Ch, Mechanical Engineering Branch, 15 Dec 67, sub: R&D Technical Liaison Team in Vietnam. All in ECOM Historians files. Charles P. Lascaro, "Electronic Maintenance in Vietnam," *Command Communications*, January 1968, pp. 26–29, CMH.

[27]USARV, Agenda for BG Terry's Briefing, 15 Mar 68, tab L, file 139870, 72A25/24, WNRC; Ltr, Latta to Lt Gen Frank T. Mildren, 11 Mar 69, ECOM Historians files.

[28]Ltr, Latta to Palmer, 22 Dec 67; Ltr, Latta to Van Harlingen, 26 Jul 68. Both in ECOM Historians files. DF, PM AACOMS to USAECOM, AMSEL-AD-H, 16 Apr 68, sub: Historical Record, Project AACOMS in Support of SEA Activities, Oct 65–Dec 66, file 139613, 72A25/6, WNRC; Fact Sheet, USARV, AVHGG-MM, 16 Aug 69, sub: Status of AACOMS Equipment for RVN, VNIT 458, CMH. See also AACOMS files in 71A6880/19, WNRC.

Developing FM Combat and Squad Radios

The new VRC–12 family of FM radios did have a significant effect on communications in South Vietnam. By 1967, less than two years after the first models were sent, MACV deputy commander General Creighton W. Abrams, Jr., was calling the PRC–25 "the single most important tactical item in Viet Nam today." The flow of new FM radios had started in the summer of 1965 when General Westmoreland, frustrated by the short distance and restricted frequency range of the PRC–10 voice FM radios, requested an immediate issue of 1,500 PRC–25's for his advisers and for the Special Forces. In less than a month the Electronics Command had transferred a shipment of the new radios, destined for Europe, to South Vietnam. Thereafter the Army issued the new series of radios to American units preparing for deployment to South Vietnam, and the Avionics Commodity Management Office at Fort Monmouth converted radios in the Army's growing fleet of aircraft to the new series of FM radio. Subsequently the laboratories, using data and recommendations sent back from South Vietnam, refined the various designs of FM radios to adapt them to the propagational and environmental conditions in South Vietnam. The Electronics Command's representatives in South Vietnam in turn evaluated those modifications under actual field conditions.[29]

Development of the PRC–25 and associated radios in the VRC–12 series began in 1948 when scientists at Fort Monmouth decided to exploit frequency modulation, which the Signal Corps laboratories had pioneered during World War II, in designing new vehicular-mounted radios. With frequency modulation, information was passed by varying the frequency of a signal, while with the older mode of amplitude modulation, the amplitude of the signal varied. The AM radios then being used were bulky and susceptible to interference from vehicular engines. In 1949 research began on a portable FM radio, and in 1955 the Signal Corps decided to make the vehicular and portable radios compatible and to exploit solid-state technology in their design. In 1958 the original developmental model of the PRC–25, a twenty-pound set with a limited frequency range called the XC–1, was replaced by the XC–2, an engineering model, which in turn was replaced a year later by the XC–3, a testing model. After two years of testing and refinements, in May 1961 the chief signal officer designated the final prototype, the PRC–25, as Standard A, making the radio a basic item of equipment in the Army's inventory. A year earlier, he had made the FM vehicular sets, the VRC–12 series radios, Standard A. To manage the production and fielding of the radios and the development of ancillary equipment and improvements to the basic radio, the Electronics Command established a project manager for FM radios. That responsibility later was expanded to include a new series of single-sideband radios. The

---

[29]Msg, CINCUSARPAC to DA, 30 Jun 65, sub: Urgent Requirement for AN/PRC–25 Series Radio Sets for Vietnam; Msg, COMUSMACV to U.S. Army ATCO, Travis Air Force Base, Calif., 16 Jul 65, sub: Urgent Requirement for AN/PRC–25 Series Radio Sets. Both in CMH. The complete file of documents describing the development and use of the new series of FM radios is contained in Ltr, PM, Selected Tactical Radios, to CG, ECOM, 29 May 68, sub: Historical Coverage of the Army Role in Southeast Asia, Period Feb 65–Dec 67, file 139614, 72A25/6, WNRC.

decision to introduce the radios in South Vietnam rather than in Europe as originally intended had profound consequences for communications tactics in the war and for the technical refinement of the radio by its testing in combat.[30]

Within weeks of the issue of the first radios to units and advisers in South Vietnam, the Electronics Command was receiving reports of needed improvements. The first concerned the handsets, which looked and functioned like telephone receivers. Handsets on the portable radios were cracking and becoming waterlogged. Discovering that many operators failed to use the bulky backpack issued to carry the radio, which had a pocket for the handset, and were cramming the handsets into shirt pockets from which they easily slipped, laboratory technicians quickly fabricated and dispatched to South Vietnam clips to attach the handsets to clothing. The laboratories also sent plastic moisture barriers for the handsets to keep water from seeping into the microphone. When those expedients proved insufficient to protect the handsets from the hard use they received in the jungles and mountains and from frequent immersion in the waters of the delta, the laboratories developed a handset to withstand frequent dropping and immersion for two hours in three feet of water.[31]

Development of a more rugged antenna for the PRC–25 was less successful. After troops of the 1st Infantry Division and the 173d Airborne Brigade tested models of a telescopic antenna and a trailing wire antenna, the Army Concept Team in Vietnam concluded that the standard antenna was still the most sturdy available. The laboratories did fabricate 15,000 bushings to adapt old PRC–10 antennas to the PRC–25 after heavy combat losses during the battles of 1967 had depleted the Army's entire inventory of PRC–25 antennas. Because units in South Vietnam used their FM radios to maintain continuous contact between command posts and fire bases, the Electronics Command developed more efficient AC power packs to preclude the need for continual running of vehicle engines or heavy use of batteries.[32]

The laboratories had to develop batteries to withstand the heat and moisture of operation and storage in the tropics. The standard zinc battery developed for the PRC–25 had to be refrigerated during transit. When it proved to have only a twenty-hour life in South Vietnam, the Electronics Command developed a magnesium battery with a fifty-hour life even after thirty days' storage at 160 degrees Fahrenheit. The Electronics Command issued each battery with a red tape stating that it had twice the usage life of the old model to ensure that the expensive new battery was kept for its full life. Because radio-telephone operators habitually changed batteries when experiencing the slightest difficulty with communications, waste of batteries for the PRC–25, which lacked a device to test battery strength, was an expensive loss in South Vietnam.[33]

[30]Information concerning the development of the PRC–25, PRC–77, and VRC–12 series of radios is contained in Synopsis-History of Major Items 1962–1968, PM, Selected Tactical Radios, Incl 10 to Ltr, ECOM to USARPAC, 17 Mar 69, sub: Data on USAECOM Logistical Support of SEA, file 139839, 72A25/23, WNRC.

[31]Ltr, Latta to Palmer, 2 Dec 67; Ltr, ECOM to AMC, 5 Dec 68. Both in ECOM Historians files.

[32]Ibid.

[33]Ltr, Latta to Maj Gen Richard J. Seitz, 17 May 66; Ltr, Latta to Palmer, 22 Dec 67. Both in ECOM Historians files.

In late 1967, after 15,000 PRC–25's and 7,000 models of the VRC–12 series radios were in the hands of American troops, and 9,000 PRC–25 models were being issued to the South Vietnamese Army, the Electronics Command produced an improved version of the PRC–25. Even before the first PRC–25's had been sent to South Vietnam, the laboratories at Fort Monmouth were working to replace the power amplifier tube, the only vacuum tube in the set, with solid-state circuitry to lessen power requirements. They also added filters to reduce spurious signal emissions and to decrease the susceptibility to mutual interference that later plagued communicators on crowded retransmission sites such as Nui Ba Den.

In December 1965 a means for connection with a security device, called an X-mode capability, was added to the specifications, and the new radio was designated the PRC–77. Although the Army had tested and produced the new radios by the fall of 1967, it delayed shipping the sets to South Vietnam until May 1968 to give the National Security Agency time to correct deficiencies in the companion security devices. Having had difficulties linking components of major assemblies in South Vietnam even when they were transported together, the Army wanted to issue the radios and the security devices, the KY–38's (KY–28's for aircraft use), at the same time. The most serious problem encountered when the radios were finally fielded was the breaking of the cables connecting the radio to the security device. Then 500 replacement cables which had been quickly fabricated in a depot in the United States were lost in the crash of a cargo plane. The National Security Agency resolved another problem by developing a pressure-relief valve to preclude the buildup of hydrogen gas from the KY–38 batteries that had caused several KY–38's to explode after prolonged operations. By December 1968 modifications were completed, and over 9,000 new radios were in the hands of American combat radiomen.[34]

While the development of the PRC–25 and VRC–12 series radios progressed steadily, the quest for a smaller radio for use at the squad level floundered for lack of definitive requirements. Initial requirements in the late 1940s were for a radio weighing less than nine pounds with a range of one mile to link the "foot troops of the most forward elements . . . and close support armored elements." The laboratories at Fort Monmouth used newly perfected subminiature tubes to develop the hand-held PRC–6, often called the walkie-talkie. Even before production of the PRC–6 began, the Infantry School asked the signal laboratories to develop another radio weighing less than one pound with a range of 500 yards for communications within the squad. Because the state of the art in 1949 offered little hope of building a radio that small, the laboratories developed a model weighing 3 1/4 pounds that met most of the other specifications of the infantrymen. After the Infantry School in 1954 rejected it as too heavy, the laboratories designed a lighter model using transistors. It was rejected in 1958 when the Army decided the squad radio had to be compatible with the PRC–25 and to have a range of one mile so that it could replace the PRC–6, which had proved too awkward for

---

[34]Ltrs, Latta to Van Harlingen, 27 Nov 67; to Palmer, 20 May 68; and to Mildren, 26 Jun 68; Ltr, Brig Gen Thomas M. Rienzi to Maj Gen Walter E. Lotz, 20 Mar 70. All in ECOM Historians files.

Squad Leader, *wearing the squad radio on his helmet, uses his radioman's PRC–25.*

a rifleman to carry.[35]

Portability as well as size then became an issue in meeting the Infantry School's requirement for a miniature radio. The laboratories considered and rejected strapping the radio to the arm, putting it in a holster, and embedding it in the stock of a rifle. The Army then tested 1,000 belt-mounted radios and 1,600 radio receivers embedded in fiberglass helmets. The infantrymen in the 101st Airborne Division who tested the equipment found that cords on the belt radio became entangled too easily, but that the helmet receiver worked well for squad members when the squad leader had both a transmitter and a receiver. The search for a squad radio appeared over. In preparing a formal request, called a qualitative materiel requirement, for development of a production model for a squad radio, the Infantry and Armor Schools both decided to minimize cost and weight by having the radio consist of two sections: a transmitter and separate receiver. Squad leaders would carry small, hand-held transmitters, and all squad members would have receivers clipped onto their helmets. Within a year after the chief signal officer had given the laboratories the mission to build the squad radio, engineers had

[35]R&D Technical Rpt ECOM–4451, Marvin W. Curtis, History of the Squad Radio, Nov 76, CMH, contains a detailed account and copies of related documents concerning the development and fielding of a squad radio.

designed a transmitter weighing only eighteen ounces and a receiver weighing 8.6 ounces and the Electronics Command had issued a contract for sixty-six receivers and forty-one transmitters. As final testing of those prototype radios was about to begin in 1964, the Combat Developments Command declared that it was unhappy with the concept of a two-section radio. After extensive discussion and delays, the Army, recognizing that rejection of the concept would set the program back at least three years, decided to proceed with final testing and production of the two-part squad radio.

Designated Standard A in January 1966, the PRT–4 transmitter and the PRR–9 receiver were hailed as the answer to the infantrymen's need to talk to each other in the dense vegetation that blocked visibility and personal communication in the jungles of South Vietnam. Within months after the first 400 models arrived in South Vietnam in March 1967, the Army discovered that those expectations were not to be met. To reduce weight, the batteries were strapped unprotected to the radio, but heat and humidity were turning them into masses of dripping cardboard. Not realizing that the helmet served as part of the antenna, soldiers tried to use the receivers apart from the helmets and were disappointed with poor reception. Despite test findings that squad members needed only receivers, soldiers in South Vietnam were unhappy without a means to respond to directions.

Following a period of heavy use in the first year after its introduction, the squad radio gradually disappeared from the battlefield. Unwilling to take the time to adjust to using the sets, soldiers left them behind at fire bases when going out on patrols. To protect the small radios from being misplaced or inadvertently stepped on, many commanders consigned them to footlockers in supply rooms where they remained for the rest of the war. An attempt to save money had led to the development of a rarely used two-section radio costing $1,044 each.[36]

Procuring Signal Gear

Both fiscal pressures and doctrinal changes influenced the development of communications equipment used during the Vietnam War. In the decade ending in 1958 the communications capability, measured in total miles of communications, planned for a typical field army had more than quadrupled. Besides the increased demands for a means of control over more mobile and dispersed army forces, the tactics and consequences of nuclear-age warfare imposed a need for reliable communications from the battlefield to the president. American commanders and staffs expected communications during crises and combat to be at least as good as those to which they were accustomed in everyday life. What com-

[36]DFs, COMM/ADP Commodity Management Ofc, to ECOM, AMSEL-AD-H, 2 Jul 68 and 31 Jul 69, sub: Historical Coverage of the Army Role in Southeast Asia, file 139612, 72A25/7, WNRC; Ltr, Latta to Terry, 4 May 67; Ltr, Van Harlingen to Latta, 10 Mar 68; Ltr, Latta to Van Harlingen, 26 Mar 68. All in ECOM Historians files. Interv, author with Malvin Shar, ECOM electronics engineer, 14 Sep 78, Historians files, CMH.

mercial telecommunications companies had taken years to install, military signalmen had to be prepared to set up, dismantle, and move in a matter of days. By the early 1960s the costs of meeting the Army's voracious demand for commercial-quality communications had become so great that signalmen were marked as the culprits for the Army's financial woes in a time of increasingly limited budgets. Calling on the Army staff in 1962 to reduce sharply its requirements for communications, the Assistant Secretary of the Army (Installations and Logistics), Paul R. Ignatius, pointed out that the projected increase in channel miles for the field army for the next eight years would cost more than the entire current Army budget. Army Chief of Staff General Earle G. Wheeler agreed that "overrefinement" and "overdurability" of communications equipment were straining the Army's budget and in early 1963 charged the chief signal officer to reduce by 10 percent the costs of signal materiel authorized in the Army and by 5 percent the authorizations for communications personnel.[37]

While the Signal Corps was being told to cut back on plans to develop expensive, sophisticated equipment to meet the burgeoning requirements of the Army, the actual inventory of signal equipment in the Army was critically low. By mid-1964 communications-electronics had the worst ratio of assets to requirements of any commodity except aviation. Of $3.9 billion worth of validated requirements for communications-electronics materiel, only $1.9 billion worth of equipment was actually on hand. After the decision to commit American forces to South Vietnam, restrictive procurement procedures, indefinite planning guidance, and an industrial base that could not react quickly made it difficult for the Electronics Command's Procurement and Production Directorate to close that gap.[38]

To reduce costs, the Department of Defense required competitive bidding in the award of contracts for materiel. Even when the commanding general of the Strike Command, General Paul D. Adams, pressured the Army in 1963 to hasten the purchase of the long-range radio sets he needed to meet impending contingencies, the Army had been unable to waive those restrictions. Besides lessening the time required to place an order, noncompetitive, sole-source procurement permitted the Army to choose a producer, often the same firm that had developed an item, who could deliver better-quality equipment from already established production lines. Only when the rapid buildup in South Vietnam started did the Department of Defense relax the restrictions on sole-source procurement and permit the Army to issue letter contracts, which enabled firms to begin production even before a final contract was signed with the assurance that the U.S. government would pay costs if the order was canceled. The secretary of defense also raised from $100,000 to $500,000 the minimum cost of projects requiring time-consuming review and approval by the Department of Defense. The

[37]Raymond E. Lacy, "Progress and Problems in U.S. Army Communications," *Proceedings of the Institute of Radio Engineers (IRE)*, May 1959, pp. 651–60; DA, Memorandum for Record of Conversation with General Wheeler on Saturday, 17 November, 20 Nov 62, file 3201698, 65A3314/24, WNRC; Memo, Asst Secy of Army for General Hamlett, 21 Nov 62, sub: Requirements for Communications Support, and DF, DCSOPS to CSO, 25 Jan 63, sub: Reduction of Materiel Requirements, both in file 2301207, 66A3140/19, WNRC.

[38]Joint Logistics Review Board, *Logistic Support*, 2:43; DF, CSO to DCSLOG, 12 Dec 62, sub: Expedited Production of HF Transportable Radio Equipment, AN/TSC–18, file 2217465, 65A3314/20, WNRC; DA, Army Buildup Progress Rpt, 17 Nov 65, p. 42, CMH.

Department of Defense also gave the Military Assistance Command, Vietnam, authority to make contract amendments on short notice, enabling signalmen in South Vietnam to direct contractors to dismantle and install fixed communications facilities as troop dispositions changed.[39]

Although procurement officers found it easier to obtain money for communications materiel, the number of firms willing and qualified to produce for the military was decreasing. The work force and the dollar volume in the electronics industry were doubling each year, but the space program and civilian demand for computers and color television sets, rather than military purchases, were driving the surge. The administration's emphasis on maintaining a prosperous, consumer-oriented economy and downplaying the extent of the military commitment in Southeast Asia made electronics manufacturers hesitant to make expensive changeovers to production of war materiel. For example, the Army was restricted to budgeting for communications support only for forces approved for deployment to South Vietnam during the 1965 buildup. Even while the Army was planning to deploy additional forces, it had to limit its resource planning by assumptions, imposed by Secretary McNamara, that the war would be over by the end of the fiscal year. This constraint limited budget requests for fiscal years 1966 and 1967 and prohibited the Army from giving civilian manufacturers the extended multiyear contracts that would assure steady employment for the large work force they would need to start up production lines.[40]

Piecemeal purchasing forced the Army either to buy off-the-shelf equipment—commercial substitutes for gear normally built to military specifications—or to pay high prices to manufacturers willing to produce for the unpredictable military market. Off-the-shelf gear, often built with unnecessary gadgets and accessories, lacked the ruggedness and compactness desired by the military. Being nonstandard equipment, it also complicated maintenance and resupply operations.

Rather than pay high prices to reluctant manufacturers, the Electronics Command dealt with the many small companies hastily formed to harvest the fruits of solid-state technology. Usually established with little capital by a group of engineers previously in the employ of a larger firm, most small companies operated from rented loft space with an unskilled work force. Each company produced a few simple circuit boards or modules, or assembled components from other manufacturers into complete sets. These companies usually submitted lower bids than the more established firms, and the Small Business Administration encouraged the military to give them preference. Nevertheless, General Latta was reluctant to order an essential piece of equipment urgently needed in South Vietnam from an inexperienced company whose only virtue was its low price and optimistic delivery date and which might go bankrupt before delivering the order.

---

[39]Ltr, Adams to Lt Gen Ben Harrell, 13 Dec 66; Ltr, Harrell to Adams, 30 Dec 63. Both in file 1401–01 (AN/TSC–38 Communication Centrals for STRICOM), 66A3140/19, WNRC. MS, Hermes, The Buildup, ch. 10; Rienzi, *Communications-Electronics*, p. 171.

[40]Joint Logistics Review Board, *Logistic Support*, 2:169; AMC, *Arsenal for the Brave*, pp. 95–96, CMH. A collection of documents pertaining to the procurement activities of the Electronics Command during the buildup in Southeast Asia is contained in file 139617 (Historical Coverage of Procurement and Production Directorate Role in Southeast Asia), 72A25/7, WNRC.

Even after a product was delivered, General Latta was concerned about its future support. To enable companies facing backruptcy to continue producing spare parts for equipment or to complete partially filled orders, General Latta sometimes had to help them stay in business. He occasionally was able to arrange for a troubled firm to consolidate with one of the large electronics conglomerates whose capital and marketing support enabled a faltering production line to continue operating.[41]

With larger manufacturers often subcontracting with small firms to build various components of communications sets, instability in the industry affected orders for equipment with even the most reputable and well-established firms. A sudden spate of orders for the PRC–25 after General Westmoreland's emergency request in the summer of 1965 created turbulence in that portion of the industry making modules for FM radios. Unable to produce the radios quickly enough, prime contractors increasingly turned to less reliable subcontractors. The assembly of an entire shipment of radios might be delayed awaiting the delivery of a single module from a subcontractor who, unable to meet his payroll or pay his rent, had stopped production. For example, the first production run of the PRC–77 was halted for lack of a single capacitor whose manufacturer had gone bankrupt. A search of depots and canvas of other manufacturers by the Product Surveillance Division of the Electronics Command failed to find any capacitors. General Latta finally obtained the permission of a U.S. District Court judge to open the bankrupt company's warehouse and remove the capacitors. Accomplished in a single weekend, the fast response averted a six-month delay in producing the essential radios.[42]

In 1967 the United States began outfitting the South Vietnamese Army with the VRC–12 series of FM radios. At the same time, it was converting from PRC–25's to the new PRC–77. The industrial base suddenly became saturated. Manufacturers had to stop producing new radios to fill emergency requests for repair parts for radios already in the field. General Latta had to pressure the large electronics companies to divert more of their capital and engineering support from the booming consumer market to their divisions making military gear.

Many companies were not eager to do business with the military. The manufacturing of military products, with its emphasis on standardization, tied up production lines over long periods of time, while civilian products for the commercial market changed yearly to exploit rapid advances in the state of the art and shifts in consumer tastes. Ambitious engineers and production managers shunned corporate divisions filling military contracts where they would be doomed to work on obsolete equipment. To obtain the full support of a firm, General Latta often had to appeal to the patriotism of the older company presidents and vice presidents who had started their careers working on military contracts during World War II, when the entire electronics industry was mobilized to support the military. Nor did he shun political pressure. The president of a company producing

---

[41]Interv, author with Brig Gen Emmett Paige, Jr., CG, Communications Systems Agency, 2 Sep 77, Historians files, CMH; Interv, author with Latta, 13 Sep 78; Draft MS, ECOM, ECOM in Southeast Asia, ch. 7.

[42]Interv, author with Latta, 13 Sep 78; ECOM, Historical Coverage of Procurement and Production Directorate Role in Southeast Asia, Jan 67–Dec 67 (hereafter cited as Historical Coverage of Procurement and Production Directorate), p. 17, file 139615, 72A25/7, WNRC.

inferior radios complained to his congressman, who happened to be the Speaker of the House of Representatives, that the Electronics Command was rejecting and returning too many of his radios. General Latta simply told the congressman that he refused to equip soldiers with bad radios. Within days the company's board of directors fired the president and the troubles with that firms's products halted.[43]

In 1965 the services transferred the responsibility for monitoring the fulfillment of contracts by manufacturers in the United States to the Defense Contract Administration Service; the Electronics Command then lost much of its formal authority to hold producers to their contract obligations. Learning of defective new equipment arriving in South Vietnam, but unable to put inspectors from the Electronics Command in the factories, General Latta decided to ship the first models of new items from manufacturers to a signal depot. There they were uncrated and checked before being released for shipment to South Vietnam. Continuing the procedure with random groups of later production models and returning defective items to factories, General Latta eventually convinced the electronics industry that despite industrial turbulence and bureaucratic obstacles the Army's standards would remain high.[44]

Maintaining Equipment

Defects in manufacturing and problems in developing new equipment ultimately affected maintenance in South Vietnam, where overworked repairmen struggled to keep communications on the air. In some busy field communications centers, repairmen remained with operators around the clock to repair gear as it broke down; but shortages of skilled repairmen forced most signal organizations to evacuate equipment to centralized shops where civilian technical assistance was available. There, repairmen often found that inexperienced operators had sent them incorrectly diagnosed equipment. Repairmen on a one-year tour in South Vietnam were also ill prepared to deal with problems unique to South Vietnam, since they could observe only once the effects of seasonal changes on signal equipment. During peak times of temperature inversion, microwave and troposcatter equipment that in fact needed no repair clogged maintenance shops. Repair shops often lacked appropriate tools and testing equipment to fix all the new components sent to South Vietnam. Since the new gear usually was sent directly to the field in answer to an urgent request, even repairmen newly graduated from signal schools encountered it for the first time in South Vietnam.[45]

For nineteen of the most critical electronic items, the Electronics Command instituted a direct exchange program, called closed-loop support, to replace items

---

[43]Interv, author with Latta, 13 Sep 78; Ltr, Latta to Palmer, 22 Dec 67, ECOM Historians files; Ziegler Presentation, "Thirty Years of Electronics Research and Development in USA."

[44]ECOM, Historical Coverage of Procurement and Production Directorate, pp. 28–33; Interv, author with Latta, 13 Sep 78.

[45]USARV, The Logistics Review, 1965–1969, vol. 8, an. W, p. 4; USASCS, *Communications Electronics Trends*, October 1968, pp. 22–23, 26, CMH; Interv, author with Latta, 13 Sep 78.

Technician Repairs Field Teletypewriter

with spares at centrally located points in South Vietnam. Damaged equipment was returned to depots in the United States for overhaul and eventual return to South Vietnam as replacement stocks. For some items such as teletypewriters, the system worked; for radios, which were in too great demand, logisticians found the maintenance float constantly depleted for operational commitments. A repair and return system, applied to a more extensive inventory of equipment, permitted repairmen to remove certain designated modules from equipment and ship them directly to the Sacramento Army Depot in California for repair. That program gained impetus when General Latta, noticing that many modules were being damaged in shipment or lost before reaching the depot, had his laboratories design and issue to maintenance shops throughout South Vietnam special packages, called jiffy bags, preprinted with the depot address. Then the system worked too well. The depot eventually became so overwhelmed with modules which, by 1969, were arriving at the rate of 5,000 a month, that the Electronics Command had to reduce the list of items supported by the program.[46]

With modular equipment being used more frequently, the maintenance of electronic gear eventually became more a problem of supply and distribution than

[46]USARV, The Logistics Review, 1965–1969, vol. 8, an. W, app. 6 and 7; Draft MS, ECOM, ECOM in Southeast Asia, pp. 243–49.

of repair. The transition from vacuum tube to solid-state technology had, in fact, caused a crisis in the military supply system. Spurred by the introduction of transistorized components, by 1961 the number of electronic items in the Defense Supply Agency catalog was increasing at the rate of 15,500 a month. Since it cost the government some $1,000 a year to manage each item, the Department of Defense encouraged the services to eliminate obsolete items and to avoid duplication by standardizing similar items. Although the Signal Corps tried to determine which items were interchangeable with those used by the other services, logisticians in the other services procrastinated. In 1964 the General Accounting Office found that the Department of Defense was losing $17 million annually in unnecessary procurement of electronic items common to all services. In trying to manage a burgeoning inventory of parts, the Army supply center in Okinawa was unable to keep up with changes in equipment lists and technical manuals and had a mounting backlog of orders for repair parts for new equipment.[47]

When American combat units began deploying to Southeast Asia in 1965, the Electronics Command calculated how many batteries and repair parts each unit would have to carry with it to have a thirty-day supply on hand. Based on projected failure rates provided by the Maintenance Engineering Directorate and on planning factors for combat losses listed in the most recent supply bulletin, experts allocated materiel in accordance with the number of major items in each unit. The combat loss estimates proved overly pessimistic. Actual losses of radios to hostile action were less than one-half, and of other communications gear less than one-third, of the projections.[48]

The Electronics Command applied those calculations in assembling "push packages," resupply packages automatically sent to South Vietnam every fifteen days for six months after the arrival of a unit. But lack of transportation and storage facilities complicated resupply. As units moved about the countryside on operations, push packages were left exposed to the elements on fire bases or in open depots near the ports. Sensitive electronic gear and batteries were damaged by the elements or misplaced in storage. The depots in South Vietnam became so clogged that inventory management broke down, and units had to requisition from the United States items already sent to South Vietnam. Thousands of batteries sent to power the first shipment of PRC–25 radios were lost; entire communications sets remained idle during the search for a box containing a few essential parts. While signalmen tried to locate parts for fixed dial exchanges, crews of highly paid civilian installers remained idle and the completion of the vital telephone project was delayed over six months. In June 1966 the Army finally

---

[47]GAO, Lack of Progress Under the Defense Standardization Program Resulting in Unnecessary Procurement and Supply Management Costs for Electronic Items, Sep 64, pp. 8–16, Incl to Ltr, Comptroller General of the United States to the Speaker of the House of Representatives and the President Pro Tempore of the Senate, 17 Sep 64, file 201–45, 67A4846/1, WNRC; Draft MS, ECOM, ECOM in Southeast Asia, p. 30.

[48]Interv, author with Franklin Weiss, former member of Materiel Management Directorate, Electronics Command, 9 Jan 79, Historians files, CMH; USARV, Combat Operations Loss and Expenditure Data, FY–68, vol. 2, file 139813, 72A25/21, WNRC.

stopped sending the indigestible stream of push packages to South Vietnam.[49]

To respond to the desperate supply situation, the Army transferred equipment to South Vietnam from units worldwide and developed special programs to alleviate the most critical shortages. In filling demands for the highest-priority equipment, called FLAGPOLE items, the Army had authority to make noncompetitive procurement or to divert stocks from war reserves or active Army units. The 11th Signal Group, the strategic signal reserve at Fort Lewis, eventually turned over all its troposcatter assets to the 1st Signal Brigade. In December 1965 the Army instituted Operation RED BALL, the air delivery of repair parts to South Vietnam, to return to service essential equipment that was inoperative. RED BALL requests were typed on data cards and sent daily to the United States with returning service members who turned them in at a special office near Travis Air Force Base, California. From there they were transmitted to the National Inventory Control Point operated by the Electronics Command in Philadelphia. The Electronics Command took whatever means necessary to have the required materiel air-shipped to Saigon within a week. Of the 7,109 RED BALL requests received by the Electronics Command in the first six months of the program, 86 percent arrived in South Vietnam within five days and 95 percent within twenty days. By the end of 1967 the Electronics Command, having handled over 27,000 RED BALL requisitions during the previous year, had the best record of all the commodity commands in the Army Materiel Command in filling the emergency requests. While the entire Army Materiel Command filled an average of 97.8 percent of orders from South Vietnam within thirty days of requisition, the Electronics Command filled an average of 99.2 percent of orders in the same period.[50]

Even RED BALL parts were occasionally lost in the clogged depots in South Vietnam. The 14th Inventory Control Center was established in South Vietnam in 1966 to maintain records of all supplies handled by the 1st Logistical Command. It was unable to keep up with a continually changing inventory. During the early years of its operation it also had too few high-quality communications circuits for transceiving data. Stock clerks in the depots had difficulty sorting unfamiliar electronic gear. In the restructured logistical system, signal supply had lost its independence and visibility. Although electronic parts represented almost one-half the total number of items in the 1st Logistical Command's inventory in South Vietnam, they amounted to only 3 percent of the total tonnage. In a system geared to handling shipments in terms of gross tonnages to be stored or transported, signal logistics was at a disadvantage. An entire division's supply of repair parts could be lost with the misplacing of a few crates.[51]

[49]USARV, The Logistics Review, 1965–1969, vol. 1, ch. 9; Joint Logistics Review Board, *Logistic Support*, 2:94; Draft MS, ECOM, ECOM in Southeast Asia, ch. 7; Msg, COMUSMACV to CINCPAC, 3 Sep 65, sub: Urgent Requirements for Dry Battery, BA–386; Msg, CINCUSARPAC to CGUSARV, 29 Oct 65, sub: Combat Replacement Levels for AN/PRC–25 Radio Set. Latter two in file 13, 70A2328/6, WNRC. Interv, Maj John F. Hummer, CO, 16th MHD, with 1st Lt Joseph C. Avent, 369th Signal Detachment, 25 May 66, VNIT 6, CMH.

[50]Ltr, Latta to Palmer, 22 Dec 67; Ltr, Latta to Maj Gen Richard J. Seitz, 18 Jun 66; Joint Logistics Review Board, *Logistic Support*, 2:171 and app. A, p. 53.

[51]Ltr, Van Harlingen to Latta, 27 Sep 67; Ltr, Latta to Van Harlingen, 4 Jun 68. Both in Van Harlingen Papers. USARV, The Logistics Review, 1965–1969, vol. 1, ch. 9, p. 7.

Resupply Tasks *included providing water to isolated signal sites.*

Although the commander of the 1st Logistical Command, Maj. Gen. Joseph M. Heiser, Jr., admitted that a lack of technical knowledge in the signal sections of his depots contributed to supply problems, he was unwilling to accede to requests that the support of signal equipment be consolidated in a signal depot, as was support to Army aviation units. He did permit signal units to send representatives directly to the depots to find supplies. General Terry himself visited depots weekly to locate critical signal equipment. He eventually directed signal units to assign a noncommissioned officer to remain full time at the depots to pinpoint arriving electronic supplies before they could be lost in a cavernous warehouse. Called expediters or scroungers, some of those soldiers built legendary reputations for being able to find anything a unit required. Since the fifteen aircraft of the 1st Signal Brigade were insufficient to move even a fraction of the supplies from depots to the over 250 sites operated by the 1st Signal Brigade, the best expediters also maintained good relationships with Air Force and Army aviators to ensure that their supplies moved quickly and safely to their destinations.[52]

The traditional method of maintaining a steady resupply of repair parts was for units to maintain stocks based on prior usage rates, called prescribed load lists. Analyzing why that approach did not seem to work with solid-state electronic equipment, civilian consultants to the Electronics Command discovered that "the failure of electronics equipment, unlike mechanical equipment, appears to be unrelated to age or use and cannot be predicted by past needs."[53]

The random failure of electronic parts obviated the prediction of repair parts usage based on historical records of demand. While the pipeline was filled with a wide range of unnecessary parts, it was unable to respond to sudden spurts of requisitions. At the same time the Electronics Command had difficulty obtaining additional stock funds to buy the needed parts. Troops in the field often found it impossible to comply with requirements to turn in inoperable modules along with new requisitions. But that inability made it difficult for the Electronics Command to justify replenishment of its stock fund.[54]

---

[52]Interv, author with Maj Gen Robert D. Terry, former CG, 1st Signal Brigade, 4 Oct 78, Historians files; Interv, Capt Hrair N. Badalian, CO, 23d MHD, with Maj James C. Davis, XO, 43d Signal Battalion, 13 Nov 69, VNIT 580 (1); Ltr, Col Lennart N. Nelson to Col Joe Finley, 12 May 75. All in CMH.

[53]ECOM Briefing, Improvement of Logistics Support for Communications-Electronics Equipment in South Vietnam, 29 Jan 69, file U–654, 72A18/53, WNRC.

[54]Ltr, Latta to Palmer, 25 Mar 68, ECOM Historians files.

To alleviate some of the problems with signal supply, the Electronics Command had been sending men on temporary duty from the National Inventory Control Point to work with the 1st Logistical Command and the 14th Inventory Control Center in South Vietnam. In January 1968 the National Inventory Control Point established a permanent office in South Vietnam, and civilian supply technicians from the Electronics Command replaced the military expediters checking shelves and records to locate equipment in the depots.[55]

Refining the Logistical System

General Latta's visit to South Vietnam during the early spring of 1968 sparked a reevaluation of signal logistical support. On his advice, the U.S. Army, Vietnam, began to regulate more stringently the accountability for electronic equipment. To halt the practice of dismantling components from vans and to reconstitute sets that had been dismounted and installed in bunkers years before, new directives prohibited the dismantling of communications assemblies without the direct approval of a general officer and without a provision for reconstituting sets within six hours. In October 1968 General Latta sent a six-man team to monitor the distribution of repair parts in response to continued complaints of erratic resupply. Reviewing 1,557 open requisitions for 177 of the most critical electronic repair parts, the team discovered that only half of the requisitions had been recorded at the Electronics Command; another 30 percent had been shipped and should have been received in South Vietnam.[56]

The team concluded that the most essential and most frequently required items failed to receive enough attention within the mass of 40,000 electronic items supplied to units in South Vietnam. The team recommended that 2,500 items, representing over 80 percent of the total demand for electronic repair parts, be given intensive management. They also discovered that repair shops in South Vietnam were repairing 80 percent of the electronic equipment in less than two hours with 15 percent of the parts in the supply system, but were spending excessive man-hours and stocking thousands of little-used items in trying to fix the rest. They recommended that equipment requiring more specialized repairs be immediately evacuated to stateside depots even though repairs might be authorized at the direct-support or general-support level. To supervise the intensive management of electronic equipment recommended by the team, General Latta convinced Lt. Gen. Frank T. Mildren, the deputy commanding general of the U.S. Army, Vietnam, to allow him to train seventeen signal officers to work in the 1st Logistical Command and to establish provisional direct-support shops in the signal brigade with authority to deal directly with 1st Logistical Command's

---

[55]Ibid., 19 Oct 67, ECOM Historians files. Reports of supply technicians are contained in file U–653, 72A18/50, WNRC.

[56]Ltr, ACofS, CE, USARV, to ACofS, CE, USARPAC, 23 Apr 68, sub: Summary of Significant Activities, 13–19 Apr 68; ibid., 28 Jun 68, sub: Summary of Significant Activities, 22–28 Jun 68. Both in file C–292, 72A25/20, WNRC. Findings and recommendations of General Latta's six-man team are contained in file U–464, 72A18/8, WNRC. Ltr, Latta to Van Harlingen, 4 Jun 68.

depots. The special management for electronic equipment was a departure from the doctrine of functional logistical support instituted after the abolishment of the technical services; but the expedient worked so well that General Mildren encouraged General Latta's successor at the Electronics Command, Maj. Gen. Walter E. Lotz, Jr., to train replacements for the Signal Corps officers at the end of their year's tour as logisticians.[57]

Besides making special arrangements for supply and maintenance support for communications equipment in South Vietnam, the Army found it had to deviate from traditional methods of equipment development and procurement. Because the costs of producing and supporting nonstandard equipment were high, the Army initially resisted diverting scarce technical and financial resources from the development of standard equipment, such as the FM voice radios, to fill requirements for specialized equipment for unconventional warfare. In 1960, when President Diem had requested long-range radios for South Vietnam's newly organized commando forces, the U.S. Army provided him with only a few prototype models of the TRC–77, an experimental high-frequency set. The first U.S. Special Forces teams deploying to South Vietnam had to use models of an agent radio used by the Central Intelligence Agency since World War II. In December 1962 the Joint Department of Defense and Central Intelligence Agency Committee for Counterinsurgency Research and Development Programs stated an urgent need for a more modern portable radio for long-range communications.[58]

The Army sought a radio capable of using FM, AM, and single-sideband modes of transmission, weighing less than thirty-five pounds, and having a range of 25 miles with voice and 1,500 miles with Morse code. Determining that such a light radio was infeasible, especially if it was to be rugged and capable of dissipating heat, the Army Materiel Command deferred that ambitious requirement until further advances in miniaturization made the technology available. The Combat Developments Command then assembled a group of representatives of the Military Assistance Command, Vietnam; the U.S. Army, Pacific; and various staffs, laboratories, and testing agencies in the United States to determine alternate methods for improving communications in South Vietnam. The group's findings provided the basis for the Army's approach to counterinsurgency communications. Besides directing the Electronics Command to continue research to design a suitable lightweight long-range radio, the Army staff allocated funds for the purchase of 220 sets, comprising eleven different models of civilian and military experimental radios that the study group had found to approach most closely the Army's needs. In addition to reporting on the performance of the radios in actual field operations, the Military Assistance Command tested various antennas, including a balloon-borne antenna for the PRC–10. Based on tests by the Special Forces, the Electronics Command converted one of the radios, the commercial HC–162, into a portable single-sideband set, the PRC–74, that was used

---

[57]USARV, The Logistics Review, 1965–1969, vol. 8, an. W, app. 4, pp. 2–3; Ltr, Latta to Lt Gen Frank T. Mildren, 16 Jul 69; Ltr, Mildren to Lotz, 20 Dec 69. Both in ECOM Historians files.

[58]Interv, author with Col (ret.) Rodney P. Harrington, former member of the Signal Board, 10 Aug 78, Historians files, CMH; DF, CSO to DCSOPS, 28 Jan 63, sub: DA Position on Joint DOD/CIA Committee (CI) Recommendation, file 201–45, 65A3314/4, WNRC.

by isolated subsector advisory teams and patrols operating beyond the range of PRC–25 radios.[59]

By 1965 the Electronics Command was involved in several other special projects called Quick Reaction or ENSURE (Expedited Nonstandard Urgent Request for Equipment) to develop or fabricate special signal equipment, usually in a lightweight airmobile assembly, for South Vietnam. Hastily prepared and with portions of the development and testing cycle omitted, most of those projects suffered from technical problems and shortages of spare parts. When the Army in less than a year developed and fielded the MSQ–73, a mobile facility in which tactical and fixed communications lines could be connected and monitored, the technical controls required numerous modifications and rewiring by the contractor's representatives in the field. Full use of the VSC–2, a hastily fabricated jeep-mounted radio-teletype terminal, was restricted by difficulties in mounting communications security equipment. Although in isolated regions of III Corps the 53d Signal Battalion had successfully employed the MRC–112, a lightweight multichannel terminal developed for an airmobile multichannel capacity, signalmen discovered that where many FM radios were concentrated in one area, frequency interference rendered the terminal useless.[60]

To avoid frequency conflicts and to ensure compatibility between air and ground radios, the Electronics Command had to give special attention to avionics development, a field that included aircraft communications, control, and navigation. Although every service required efficient avionics, the Army's need was the most difficult to satisfy. Because helicopters were subjected to severe environmental conditions and performed missions requiring greater ruggedness and precision than fixed-wing aircraft, avionics technology was not easily adaptable to the fleet of rotary-wing aircraft the Army was producing for use in South Vietnam. Setting down in the most primitive of landing zones, where dust, vegetation, or the muddy water of rice paddies was blown about by the blast from rotors, a helicopter offered far less protection to internal equipment than tightly shuttered fixed-wing aircraft using paved runways. Besides having to be resistant to dust and moisture swirling about the exposed interior of helicopters, avionics gear also had to withstand the constant vibration of rotary-wing craft. Because military helicopter pilots flew close to the ground, following the contours of the earth to limit the enemy's observation and the effectiveness of suppressive antiaircraft fire, navigation gear had to be capable of adjusting to sudden changes in altitude and direction and communications equipment had to be able to cope with terrain barriers.[61]

[59]DA, FOR/MR/RE, Proposed QMDO for an Extended Frequency Man-Pack Special Warfare Radio, 8 May 63, file 1401–01, 66A3140/19, WNRC, contains the various proposals and responses of technical feasibility. USACDC, A Review of the Problems of Man-Pack Jungle Radios, 10 Jun 63, file 3300760; DF, ACSFOR to CRD and DCSLOG, 20 Aug 63, sub: Jungle Radios South Vietnam, file 1401–01. Both in 66A3140/19, WNRC.

[60]Ltr, SCV Sig Ofcr to MACV J–6, 13 Nov 64, sub: Procurement of FRC–93 (KWM–2A), Incl to QHS, SCV Sig Ofcr, 1 Oct 64–31 Dec 64, pt. 2, 338–75–1009/92; Info Brief, DA, OCC-E, 9 Feb 66, sub: Technical Control Vans for SE Asia: (Center Communications Technical Control, AN/MSQ–73), file 139773, 72A25/19. Both in WNRC. Ltr, Latta to Maj Gen Richard J. Seitz, 22 Nov 66, ECOM Historians files.

[61]A comprehensive study of Army avionics is contained in Research Analysis Corporation, Avionics Development and Technology (RAC–R–22), Oct 67, AD 386337, DDC.

AN/MRC–112 Radio *mounted in a trailer and cooled by a fan.*

Although the Air Force, Navy, and Marine Corps also had helicopters, the Army's fleet was much larger and more exposed to the wear and tear of daily combat. The design of electronic components and external antennas for Army aircraft, which were generally lighter than those of the other services, was restricted by weight and air resistance. While requiring air control and navigational equipment compatible with that used in large commercial aircraft, Army airplanes and helicopters also needed radios to communicate with ground troops. Since Army voice radios were constantly being modernized throughout the war, Army avionics also was in constant flux. While the transition from one model of vehicular radio to another only involved installing new mounting brackets, the modification, or retrofit, of avionics components affected the aerodynamic stability and electrical power distribution of the aircraft.[62]

Aware of the complexities of avionics, early signal officers at the Military Assistance Command, Vietnam, and the Army Support Command, Vietnam, established positions for avionics officers on their staffs. With the establishment of the U.S. Army, Vietnam, Army avionics was jointly supervised by Signal Corps

---

[62]DA, DCSOPS, AHS, FY–65, an. H, pt. 3, p. 1, CMH; Lt. Col. R. N. Gempeter, "Avionics," *Signal*, October 1964, pp. 52–56; Maj. Gen. George E. Pickett, "Avionics-Military and Civil," *Signal*, January 1971, pp. 13–15.

AN/VSC–2 Radio-Teletype Terminal

officers on the signal, aviation, and logistics staffs. Signal detachments with each aviation unit handled avionics supply and maintenance until the Army transferred the mission to the 34th General Support Group (Aircraft Maintenance and Supply), the general support unit for Army aviation in South Vietnam. Maintenance units of each division continued to handle direct support for divisional aviation units.

Signal Corps logisticians at the Electronics Command managed a large inventory of expensive and complex avionics components—over 81,000 items costing $230 million—in South Vietnam. In January 1966 the Avionics Laboratory at Fort Monmouth established the Avionics Configuration Control Facility to monitor the continually changing design of the avionics components on Army aircraft to ensure their compatibility with other ground and air electronic gear and to overcome environmental and aerodynamic problems. At the Aviation Command headquarters in St. Louis, Missouri, the Electronics Command maintained the Aviation Electronics Agency to monitor the installation of electronic equipment in newly built aircraft and the retrofit of avionics gear in older craft. In South Vietnam the Electronics Command had more civilian technical assistants working with the 34th General Support Group than with the 1st Logistical Command and the 1st Signal Brigade combined. Besides helping the group maintain all Army avionics equipment, those technicians monitored the retrofit of aircraft radios in

South Vietnam by civilian contractors. By 1968 the technicians had installed the VRC–12 series radio in all Army aircraft in South Vietnam and security devices in over half the Army fleet of aircraft. They also modernized the navigational and radio instruments in Army aircraft to keep pace with the increasing sophistication of the equipment used to guide and regulate air traffic over South Vietnam.[63]

Supporting New Equipment

S upport arrangements for newly developed equipment were as important to its success as the equipment's technical design. Before the MRC–112 was sent to South Vietnam in June 1966, the Electronics Command's Maintenance Engineering Directorate had prepared an introductory letter, a preliminary operation and maintenance manual, and a spare parts list for the first year's operation to accompany every set. Signalmen in the field experienced no significant maintenance problems with the new set. On the other hand, in responding to an ENSURE request for a lightweight multichannel terminal that used the VRC–12 series of FM radios, the Army developed a good set but failed to provide for its maintenance and supply support. Taking only twelve months to develop the four-channel GRC–163, the Army negotiated for production of the terminals even as it was still testing models fabricated in the depot. The first sets, delivered to hard-pressed units in I Corps during the Tet offensive of 1968, performed well, but after a few months of continuous operations they began to break down for lack of maintenance. In the haste of putting the equipment in the field, the Electronics Command had been unable to prepare and distribute technical manuals and parts lists to guide operators and repairmen in maintaining and obtaining spare parts for the sets.[64]

For multichannel communications beyond the line-of-sight range of VHF and microwave radio, the Army continued to use updated versions of the TRC–90 troposcatter radio, the first piece of communications equipment specially developed for use in South Vietnam. For several years support problems were resolved only with the help of the contractor's representatives and special deliveries of parts directly from the factory. An attempt to replace it with an adaptation of an Air Force troposcatter radio, the TRC–97, demonstrated that support was just as difficult to obtain for equipment belonging to another service. The only available troposcatter terminal mounted in a 3/4-ton truck, the TRC–97 seemed the

[63]"Aviation Communications-Electronics," *Command Communications*, September 1967, pp. 61–64; "The U.S. Army Electronics Command-Vietnam," *Command Communications*, October 1968, p. 61; ECOM, Annual Program Review, FY–66, Avionics Configuration Control Facility, Jul 67; Msg, Norton MAC 3408 to Seneff, 5 Jul 65. All in CMH. USARV, Agenda for BG Terry's Briefing, 15 Mar 68, tab A.

[64]Msg, USARV to CINCUSARPAC, 14 Sep 65, sub: Lightweight Multiplex Terminal Equipment, file 12, 70A2378/6, WNRC; Ltr, Latta to Palmer, 27 Sep 67, ECOM Historians files; DFs, COMM/ADP Commodity Management Ofc to ECOM, AMSEL-AD-H, 2 Jul 68 and 31 Jul 69, sub: Historical Coverage of the Army Role in Southeast Asia; DF, ECOM, Directorate of Maint Engineering, to AMSEL-AD-H, 10 May 68, sub: Historical Coverage of the Army Role in Southeast Asia, file 139615, 72A25/7, WNRC.

ideal response to an ENSURE requirement for an airmobile troposcatter radio for use in the mountains of II Corps. Although the required twenty-six sets were available by late 1967, having been produced earlier for the Air Force, delays in the manufacture of generators and portable antennas specially ordered for the Army's models held up the deployment of the sets to Southeast Asia until mid-1968. By that time the Pacific Air Force had decided that it would be unable to honor an agreement to provide on-site maintenance support that had been negotiated over a year earlier between the Departments of the Army and Air Force. Finding that an Air Force compromise proposal to use on-call repair teams from the Philippines was insufficient, the U.S. Army, Vietnam, in late 1968 sent eight Army technicians to Clark Air Base for a four-week course in the maintenance of the terminals. The Electronics Command negotiated a contract for the manufacturer to send two technicians to assist the newly trained soldiers and to ship repair parts, which were unavailable through Army channels, directly to South Vietnam. Thus, for almost two years during which tactical units desperately needed light multichannel sets, the TRC–97's were unavailable for lack of maintenance.[65]

Since even the Air Force lacked the ability to maintain the MRC–85's it gave to the Army for BACKPORCH systems, the Army had to contract with Page to provide all logistical support to the strategic network. As other nonstandard communications and data processing equipment was sent later to South Vietnam, the using commands contracted with manufacturers to provide repair services. In many cases maintenance could be obtained only on an on-call basis from the Philippines or Okinawa. Visiting South Vietnam in the spring of 1966 and finding hundreds of items of automatic data processing equipment being supported by a variety of contractual arrangements, General Latta directed the Communications and Automatic Data Processing Commodity Management Office at Fort Monmouth to determine how the Electronics Command could better manage its logistical support of such commercial equipment.[66]

The Army could not afford to stock parts for nonstandard equipment or to train men to repair it. The manufacturers were in a better position to supply parts directly from the factory and to provide qualified technicians. But providing transportation for direct delivery from factory to field units and paying for special supply support were expensive. Normal replacement of the klystron and traveling wave tubes in the Integrated Wideband Communications System alone cost $1 million each year. That network contained 1,100 different end items, modules, and major components not in the military inventory. Other fixed facilities and automatic telecommunications systems had thousands of other commercial components. The Army had to have some means of managing logistical support for its extensive fixed systems in South Vietnam.[67]

[65]Ltrs, Latta to Van Harlingen, 5 Apr 68 and 13 Nov 68; Msg, CG, ECOM, to CofS, USAF, 26 Feb 69, sub: Maintenance Support for Radio Set AN/TRC–97B; Ltr, Latta to Lt Gen Frank T. Mildren, 26 Jul 68. All in ECOM Historians files. Ltr, ACofS, CE, USARV, to ACofS, CE, USARPAC, 4 Dec 68, sub: Summary of Significant Activities, file 139800, 72A25/20, WNRC.

[66]Ltr, ECOM to AMC, 11 May 66, sub: Logistics Management of Commercial ADP, ECOM Historians files.

[67]Msg, SCC-PAC to SCC, 10 Feb 66, sub: Lessons Learned, pt. 2, file 2–05, 69A722/5, WNRC; Msg, Latta to Lt Gen Frank T. Mildren, 15 Apr 69, ECOM Historians files.

In December 1966 the Army Materiel Command dispatched a three-man team to South Vietnam to assist Page in establishing a depot in Saigon to stock repair parts for the Integrated Wideband Communications System. When the Army asked for $21 million to build consolidated facilities in which it could store non-standard parts and supervise contractor maintenance of components for all fixed facilities in South Vietnam, the Department of Defense disapproved the request on the grounds that the work should be performed within existing military channels. After a request for reconsideration was again rejected in April 1968, the Department of the Army dispatched the commanding general of the Communications Systems Agency, Brig. Gen. Hugh F. Foster, Jr., to South Vietnam to analyze the requirements for logistical support for fixed equipment. Evaluating support for every type of nonstandard equipment used in Southeast Asia, from dial telephones to troposcatter radios, he concluded that the Army should build and operate three depots in Southeast Asia for logistical support of all fixed and nonstandard communications equipment in that area. Finally obtaining Defense Department approval in mid-1969, the Army opened two depots, called Area Maintenance and Supply Facilities, at Long Binh and at Bangkok. A third depot planned for Cam Ranh Bay never became fully operational. Staffed by civilian contractors and military technicians, the Area Maintenance and Supply Facilities performed the same role as general-support and direct-support maintenance shops. Troubleshooting teams of military technicians were stationed at the system's nodal points, such as the AUTODIN and tandem switches, from which they were dispatched to provide on-site maintenance for subscribers and tributary facilities. Later this concept of area logistical support was extended to the maintenance of fixed-station equipment in other theaters around the world.[68]

The Area Maintenance and Supply Facilities handled only commercial equipment; military shops had to support the remainder of the electronic equipment in the war. New equipment introduced during the war inevitably strained the logistical system. Even when the Electronics Command dispatched adequate technical literature and support packages with the equipment, men in the field still lacked the expertise to operate and maintain it until the signal schools could include it in courses for recruits and refresher training for supervisors. To compensate, the Electronics Command sent instructors to the field with the new equipment. For nonstandard equipment manufacturers' representatives usually accompanied the first models to the field and trained a cadre of military instructors who then traveled throughout the country giving courses. To perform such training, the Special Forces, which tested many items of new communications equipment during the early 1960s, used a four-man "think team" that also provided troubleshooting service and liaison with the Army Concept Team in Vietnam. When the Electronics Command introduced new items of standard mili-

---

[68]USARV, The Logistics Review, 1965–1969, vol. 8, an. X; U.S. Army Communications Systems Agency, Logistical Support of Fixed Communications-Electronics Systems in Southeast Asia, 10 Sep 68, vols. 1–5, 72A18/9, WNRC; USASCC AHS, FY–68, pp. 39–41; ibid., FY–69, pp. 44–45. Latter two in CMH.

tary equipment, such as the FM or single-sideband radios, it sent along teams of military technicians and civilian government employees, the New Equipment Training Teams, to instruct operators and maintenance men. During 1967 the Electronics Command sent thirty-nine New Equipment Training Teams to units about to deploy to South Vietnam or already there. Until the expansion of the 1st Signal Brigade's own signal school most training was presented in the field, where instructors were exposed to the dangers of combat. One member of a team deployed in 1967 was killed in action.[69]

Despite these training programs, technical representatives of the Electronics Command stationed in South Vietnam believed most new equipment problems stemmed from inadequate training and the inexperience of operators and repairmen. Men schooled in the techniques of operating old equipment were inadvertently damaging new gear or sending it to maintenance shops for nonexistent problems. There, mechanics unfamiliar with new sets might put the equipment out of calibration or unnecessarily replace parts. The one-year tour also left soldiers in South Vietnam unaware that problems they were encountering with new equipment had already been confronted and resolved by their predecessors. When the new tactical multichannel sets, which operated in a higher frequency range than the old VHF terminals, were introduced, they were affected by a mysterious diurnal and seasonal fading of signals and fluctuation in range. Only after much readjustment of equipment and unnecessary repairs did signalmen recognize that the problem was caused by temperature inversion, the same phenomenon that had bedeviled scientists when the troposcatter radios were introduced in South Vietnam seven years earlier.[70]

Because the Army recognized that the introduction of new equipment sometimes caused more aggravation than benefit to troops in the field, it was reluctant to respond to requirements from the field by developing special equipment requiring elaborate support and training arrangements or by rushing into production developmental equipment that might later require extensive modifications. Nor did it want to develop equipment suitable for only one theater or type of operation. The added cost of deviating from long-range development plans also dissuaded the Army from expediting equipment for South Vietnam. Despite repeated requests from signal commanders for replacement of World War II–vintage teletypewriters and switchboards with modern solid-state electronic equipment that would be less susceptible to dust and overheating, the Army did not accelerate its development of the new teletype and switching gear. The mechanical equipment built in the 1940s remained in South Vietnam throughout the

---

[69]DF, ECOM, Dir of Maint Engr, to AMSEL-AD-H, 10 May 68, sub: Historical Coverage of the Army Role in Southeast Asia; USARV, The Logistics Review, 1965–1969, vol. 8, an. W, p. 3; Interv, author with Col (ret.) James V. Bailey, former signal officer, 5th Special Forces Group, Vietnam (Provisional), 16 Jan 78, Historians files, CMH; Ltr, Latta to Palmer, 19 Oct 67.

[70]Ltr, ACTIV to ECOM, 1 Dec 69, sub: Vietnam Laboratory Assistance Program, Army Request for Development, ECOM Historians files; Memo, Coordinator, USAECOM Tactical Equipment, for Ch, USAECOM Area Ofc, Vietnam, 14 Dec 68, sub: Summary Report for Nov 68; Rpt, ECOM, Vietnam, 15 Jan 69, sub: USAECOM Representative Summary of Tour of Duty in South Vietnam. Latter two in file U–653, 72A18/50, WNRC.

course of the war.[71]

Like teletypewriters, power generators and air conditioners were susceptible to rapid deterioration in the tropical climate. Because the Mobility Command, rather than the Electronics Command, was the commodity manager for power and environmental equipment, signal officers had little control over its development or support. While electronic engineers strove to design lightweight signal assemblies, the overall configuration of a truck-mounted set depended on the power generator provided by the Mobility Command. As with the TRC–97, the slow production of generators or air conditioners sometimes delayed the fielding of new electronic equipment.[72]

The wide variety of generators ranging in power from 1 to 400 kilowatts found in Southeast Asia made it difficult to keep generator mechanics qualified and to maintain stocks of repair parts. When the 39th Signal Battalion tried to install a tactical troposcatter system in Thailand in 1963, a four-month delay in the resupply of repair parts left 75 percent of the generators for the TRC–90's inoperative. The diversity in generator models made cannibalization impossible.[73]

Improvements to public utilities later made commercial power available to signal sites near populated areas. As American forces prepared to go on the offensive in II Corps in 1967, the commander of the 21st Signal Group, which had 58 percent of its generators out of service, warned that he was so dependent on commercial power that "an enemy strike aimed at those commercial sources would eventually effect near total outages of mission equipment at some of our sites." Vulnerability was worst at the more isolated sites where a single young generator mechanic might be maintaining the power source for a major signal relay. Loss of power at the relay could disrupt the countrywide network. Because neighboring compounds often drew power for equipment and security lights from a signal site's generators, during generator breakdowns many signal officers found themselves under more pressure from power customers than from communications subscribers. Although signal officers regretted the added aggravation, they welcomed control over power sources since voltage irregularities and surges could damage their electronic equipment.[74]

Another type of equipment vital to signalmen for which the Electronics Command lacked any logistical responsibility was communications security (COMSEC) equipment. Because of the sensitive nature of cryptographic materiel, it had to be given greater protection than that offered in normal logistical channels. In 1964 the Army gave responsibility for supply and maintenance of that specialized equipment to the Strategic Communications Command. Research and development

---

[71]USARV, The Logistics Review, 1965–1969, vol. 8, an. W, app. 1, p. 2; Interv, Maj Fremont E. Binder, CO, 23d MHD, with Brig Gen William M. Van Harlingen, CO, 1st Signal Brigade, 26 Jan 68, pp. 40–44, VNIT 72, CMH; Msg, Latta MTH 297 to Van Harlingen, 12 Jul 68; Msg, Van Harlingen ARV 1910 to Latta, 20 Jul 68; Msg, Latta MTH 327 to Van Harlingen, 24 Jul 68. All in Brig Gen William M. Van Harlingen Backchannel file, CMH.

[72]Ltr, Latta to Terry, 12 Jan 67; Ltr, Latta to Van Harlingen, 23 Jan 68. Both in ECOM Historians files.

[73]Cannibalizing equipment involves the taking of working parts from unrepairable equipment to keep other gear in operation. USARPAC Sig Ofcr, Trip Report to STARCOM Det 1, UDORN, 22 Jan 63; COMUSMACTHAI to CINCPAC, 23 Jan 64, sub: Support for C-E Base Thailand. Both in file 139364, 72A4171, WNRC.

[74]ORLL, 21st Sig Gp, 31 Jan 67, p. 6, 69A722/5, WNRC.

of equipment and preparation of key lists and operations codes were the responsibility of the National Security Agency; the Armed Forces Courier Service handled their distribution.[75]

To replace small detachments assigned to the signal brigade to handle the supply and maintenance of communications security equipment, the Strategic Communications Command in mid-1967 formed a unique unit, the 57th Signal Company. It consisted of a 98-man COMSEC Logistics Support Center, Vietnam, to manage the overall logistical support of Army communications security equipment and six 31-man COMSEC Logistics Support Units to provide general and direct support by region. Assigned to the 160th Signal Group, the 57th Signal Company established an extensive maintenance float system enabling repairmen to replace nonoperational equipment during repairs. While maintenance shops had little difficulty in obtaining replacements for the 3,000 repair parts handled in cryptographic channels of the National Security Agency, they did have problems with resupply of some of the 17,000 standard parts associated with cryptographic assemblies, such as interconnecting cables. After the issue of voice security equipment, which caused the quantity of cryptographic equipment to increase by over 500 percent, logistical burdens were magnified: 33,000 items of communications security equipment were dispersed to 239 locations throughout South Vietnam. The U.S. Army, Vietnam, then supplemented the 57th Signal Company with a fifteen-man COMSEC Division Contact Detachment assigned to each American division in South Vietnam.[76]

Withdrawing Equipment

A s the Army made the transition from the PRC–25 to the new PRC–77 backpack radios and their security devices, there were disagreements over what to do with the replaced PRC–25's. As new equipment was sent to South Vietnam, the U.S. Army, Vietnam, was supposed to return the replaced equipment to the United States through logistical evacuation channels. Although the Army's policy was that such equipment should not be retained for operational needs without specific approval, hard-pressed signal officers, reluctant to become completely dependent on untested new gear, usually found a way to keep their old equipment. They also objected to diverting men from operational commitments to assemble and process equipment for shipment to the United States. When General Van Harlingen sent out a Base Development Study Group in late 1967 to visit every signal site to identify excess equipment, the team retrieved only an insignificant amount of equipment. He had to cancel a second, more stringent effort when the Tet offensive created a surge of demands for equipment to replace destroyed communications and to support the American counteroffensive. Most

---

[75]A comprehensive discussion of logistical support to communications security equipment is contained in USARV, The Logistics Review, 1965–1969, vol. 8, an. Y.

[76]USARV Communications Operations Division, COMSEC Briefing, 6 Jan 69, file U–322, 72A18/6, WNRC.

transportable equipment ultimately remained in South Vietnam with the unit to which it was originally assigned and was not returned to the United States until the unit withdrew. That practice increased supply and maintenance burdens in units.[77]

Withdrawal of fixed equipment, because it had to be dismantled and packaged, was a major project for signalmen during the final years of the war. Shortly after the American withdrawal was announced, the signal brigade commander, Maj. Gen. Thomas M. Rienzi, established a Communications Assets Recovery Agency to inventory and prepare the fixed gear for shipment. But lack of firm guidance concerning which facilities would be turned over to the South Vietnamese government delayed until late 1970 the dismantling of most fixed facilities that were to be removed from South Vietnam. By that time, General Rienzi's replacement, Maj. Gen. Hugh F. Foster, was caught in a dilemma. Having to maintain communications to an area until the last supported unit had departed, he then had to dismantle equipment quickly before his own men had to leave. Army policy was that only complete assemblies would be returned, which forced signal units to retain all three vans of each MRC–85 terminal while using only the multiplexer van. But General Foster moved every nonoperational piece of equipment off the sites as quickly as possible.[78]

Besides wanting to reduce the amount of equipment that had to be maintained and protected by the diminishing signal command, or later by the South Vietnamese, General Foster felt that the Army was in danger of losing valuable equipment to commercial salvage companies if it was left to be picked up by property disposal teams. Rather than wait for the Army Materiel Command to issue disposition instructions and provide transportation for the equipment, General Foster arranged with General Latta, who in 1969 had become the commanding general of the Strategic Communications Command, and with General Lotz, who had replaced Latta at the Electronics Command, to move the dismantled equipment to Fort Huachuca, Arizona. From there it was reassigned to other worldwide projects of the Strategic Communications Command or to Korea for a backbone system being built there. Despite increasing pressure to halt the informal shipment, General Foster continued to collect and ship dismantled communications equipment and engineer construction material from fixed signal sites. The procedures adopted by General Foster, in a strict sense a violation of Army policy, did improve the readiness of the strategic reserve in the United States and of overseas units whose signal resources had been depleted to support the buildup in South Vietnam during the previous decade.[79]

The interest of Generals Foster, Lotz, and Latta in assuring the proper disposition of equipment from South Vietnam was personal as well as professional. As MACV assistant chief of staff for communications-electronics during the

---

[77] USARV, Agenda for BG Terry's Briefing, 15 Mar 68, tabs M and N.
[78] Rienzi Debriefing Rpt, 4 Jun 70, pp. 63–64; Maj Gen Hugh F. Foster, Jr., Debriefing Rpt, 20 Jul 71, tab F, HRC 314.82, CMH. Msg, Foster ARV 2223 to Latta, 12 Aug 70; Msg, Foster ARV 2572 to Latta, 13 Aug 70. Both in Foster Backchannel file.
[79] Msg, Foster ARV 0921 to Latta, 15 Mar 71, Foster Backchannel file; Interv, author with Lt Gen Walter E. Lotz, Jr., 20 Sep 78, Historians files, CMH.

buildup in 1965, General Lotz had been the architect of the communications system for the war; General Foster, a former UNICOM/STARCOM program manager, had overseen the acquisition and fielding of much of the equipment used in the system; and General Latta, commander of the Electronics Command for most of the war, had kept that equipment operating. Having harnessed a balky electronics technology and made it work despite difficult bureaucratic and environmental obstacles, the three were unwilling to see the results of the toil of thousands of signalmen like themselves be lost.

20

Conclusion

For communicators, the Vietnam War was twenty-five years of hard, unforgiving conflict against determined adversaries and numerous obstacles. American signalmen fought the Viet Cong and North Vietnamese regulars on two fronts—in battle and in an electronic war. They contended with terrain and climate that punished both men and equipment and that made "getting the message through" a never-ending challenge. American communicators also had to respond to a demand for communications that grew so insatiable that the MACV commander termed it a "bottomless pit."

The most vexing challenges that signalmen faced were those posed by technology, for technology was both solution and problem, opportunity and obstacle. Advanced electronics provided Americans the means to master the terrain and to overcome the enemy; yet sophisticated equipment also imposed inherent vulnerabilities that, had the enemy exploited them, could have led to certain defeat. Because American signalmen were the first to face the challenges of advanced electronic technology on the battlefield, their experience will profoundly influence future military tactics and strategy.

The vagaries of the Vietnam War make it extremely difficult to trace events from concept to decision to implementation to result. Few concepts were translated intact into reality. Decisions were revised, tactics changed, programs took on new directions. The causes of that impermanence were many: ill-defined foreign policy goals and strategies, traditional American frustration and impatience with problems not amenable to quick solutions, the rapid pace of technological change, and one-year tours for military personnel. The results were devastating to signalmen—costly false starts, requirements for ever more telecommunications service, and constant demands to build new systems before existing ones could be made to work properly. No task ever seemed to be completed before a new one was begun.

A case in point was the unfulfilled need for a regional telecommunications network to bind more closely the free peoples of Southeast Asia. A regional system extending to the provinces and major cities could have improved commerce and economic development, strengthened political control of the central govern-

473

ments, and enabled military units to work more closely with local police and security forces. American advisers first considered building such a system in the mid-1950s when the French withdrew from Indochina, taking their communications facilities with them. If a network had been built then, the new South Vietnamese government might have been able to use it to coordinate its civil nation-building efforts and to direct its security forces in defeating the fledgling Communist insurgency. But for a variety of technical, political, and bureaucratic reasons, the United States missed the opportunity that emerging communications technology offered to help its ally.

By the time the United States began to establish a regional telecommunications network in the early 1960s, military necessity had overshadowed nation-building goals. The Communists had launched a full-scale insurgency, and the South Vietnamese government was on the defensive. Communications installed in the region were needed primarily for U.S. forces rushed to South Vietnam. It was not until the early 1970s that the U.S. Army could turn over to South Vietnam and Thailand an operational system. By then the South Vietnamese were concerned not with the Viet Cong, but with an invasion of conventional forces from the North. The effectiveness of a modern telecommunications network in helping to defeat an insurgency was never tested.

Although the system installed by the United States in the mid-1960s, the Integrated Wideband Communications System, never fulfilled the plans for a regional civil-military network, it did demonstrate that a high-capacity area telecommunications system was both effective and necessary to support U.S. military operations in remote and less developed regions. The Vietnam conflict marked a permanent shift to an area-oriented communications doctrine, and technology was directly responsible for the shift. The long range and heavy logistical requirements of modern weapons, coupled with increased reliance on coordinated air-ground operations, dictated more flexible and extensive communications support than that offered by the traditional chain-of-command approach. Technological breakthroughs in communications also made it possible to satisfy the complex requirements of interconnecting an area network.

The evolution of signal doctrine to include an area orientation challenged the ingenuity of signalmen. Signal tactics, organizations, and missions all had to change. A fading of the basic dichotomy between strategic and tactical communications epitomized those changes. That bifurcation, which had dictated everything from organizational structure to budgets, had become meaningless in a world of instantaneous communications. With Americans viewing combat actions on the evening news, tactical decisions often had national consequences. It is not surprising, then, that leaders in Washington used those same communications to monitor, and even to control, events on the battlefield in South Vietnam. As early as 1965 President Johnson spoke from the White House directly to a regimental commander under fire in the hills outside Da Nang. Three years later Johnson had a huge mock-up of Khe Sanh built in the White House so that he could follow the daily battles around the besieged fire base. While tactical commanders found little advantage in such added scrutiny, they still appreciated the improved communications provided by modern technology. Responsible for directing operations employing complex weapons and aircraft, they had to have communications with range and capacities formerly provided only by strategic systems.

Within Southeast Asia the merger of tactical and strategic communications was implemented institutionally in 1966 by forming the 1st Signal Brigade in South Vietnam as a part of the U.S.-based Strategic Communications Command. Tactical leaders, fearing a loss of their means of command and control, initially resisted the prospect of having their communications provided by a unit assigned to a worldwide, rather than a theater, command. But they eventually discovered that the organizational arrangement benefited them greatly. From the area network in Southeast Asia, which was an integral part of the sophisticated worldwide (formerly considered strategic) system, they obtained high-quality communications that extended to their brigades and battalions. Brigade commanders could even use area communications systems to control combat operations undertaken far from their base camps and to coordinate air support launched from distant air bases. Area networks also linked them to intelligence, personnel, and logistical centers in the United States. Meanwhile, combat commanders also retained their organic tactical communications, giving them autonomous means of responding quickly to military requirements.

While area and command signal units might be similar in hardware, mobility, and personnel structure, they differed in the way they supported the tactical commander. The area unit had a responsibility to stay linked into the worldwide network while the command signal unit could be used in any way the tactical commander wanted. Throughout the conflict the dual approach worked well to support both combat and support forces.

Despite the doctrinal changes caused by the development of an area communications system, communications tactics during combat actions differed little from those in previous conflicts. Field telephones connected by single-strand lines formed the nerve system for every artillery battery, linking guns, fire direction centers, and commanders. Most infantry platoon command posts used a small field switchboard to tie together the wire lines leading out to squads, sentries, and listening posts. Communications between platoons and companies were usually handled by FM radio or messenger.

Once the fighting began, the radio-telephone operator carrying a PRC–25 became the unit leader's primary means of exercising command. Using that single radio, a tactical leader directed his subordinates, informed and received direction from his own commander, coordinated air support, and requested resupply and evacuation. Even when combat units moved back from the field, they used PRC–25's to supplement base camp communications. The PRC–25, or its vehicle- and aircraft-mounted counterparts, were the primary means of combat command communications for squads, platoons, companies, battalions, brigades, and divisions—every unit from 10 men to 10,000. Although that widespread use created a tremendous frequency management problem, attempts to design different equipment suited for particular units—such as the squad radio—all failed. The PRC–25 was too good: no one wanted to give it up. And because it was so ubiquitous, every commander knew that he could reach whomever he needed in an emergency.

Tactical units also used mobile multichannel radios, switchboards, and tele-type centers to interconnect headquarters throughout the chain of command and to link combat and combat support units. Because that equipment was common to Army units throughout the world and produced through the regular Army research, development, and procurement process, it was relatively easy to support. Military schools could train appropriate numbers of qualified operators for standard equipment, and the regular logistical system was adequate to keep it in operation.

Such was not the case with all the equipment in the area network. Although the extensions to subscribers on the fringes of the area system usually used the same standard military equipment as that found in the chain-of-command system, most of the area network was composed of a variety of commercial-type sets. Standard military equipment was insufficient for the high volume of information, the long distances, and the many subscribers handled on the area system. Using different configurations of commercial equipment, signalmen designed each link to handle a particular communications load. Depending on the needs of the subscribers at each location in the systems, different types of terminal equipment provided voice, teletype, and data service.

The most important parts of the area system were the major nodal points where several links interconnected and the information from the diverse equipment at the various terminals was transferred. The technical controllers who installed and monitored those interconnections at the nodes became the crucial operators in the loop. Yet neither they, nor the planners and engineers who designed the systems, had any area-oriented training to guide them or any doctrinal manuals for reference. They were training on the job, formulating doctrine as they went. They did amazingly well, and they passed on a wealth of knowledge that helped the Signal Corps adapt to the changes in doctrine and technology in the years after Vietnam.

Of all the factors affecting communications in the Vietnam War, none had greater influence than the decision to employ advanced technology in South Vietnam. It proved to have tremendous ramifications and to be irrevocable. Technology offered new opportunities, but it imposed new vulnerabilities. For example, near-instantaneous communications at every command headquarters, from the platoon leader's command post to the Pentagon, expanded the command and control of military commanders. At the same time, their flexibility and autonomy were restricted by a lack of direct control over their communications systems and a dependence on civilians, rather than their own soldiers, to operate those communications. And by enabling tactical decisions to be made and implemented at much higher levels, efficient communications sometimes undermined the authority of the commander on the ground.

Civilian specialists in South Vietnam did an outstanding job. Since they were more highly trained and usually served longer tours than the military, they provided a continuity and expertise that became indispensable. But as the military effort became increasingly dependent on them, commanders worried that they might refuse to continue to work during intense hostilities when they would be most needed. Signal commanders realized the diminution of their own authority as they helplessly watched a civilian repairing a component whose malfunction had interrupted a critical communications circuit to Washington or shut down the main computer for an infantry division's logistical system. Meanwhile, an entire operation might be stalled, waiting for the system to "come back up."

The ingenuity that had been the hallmark of earlier "fix anything" signal soldiers did not work with complex modern equipment. It simply took too long to teach a soldier about the myriad of sophisticated gear he might encounter in the military communications networks. Rapid changes in the state of the art, constantly confronting the communicator with new equipment, made it difficult to build an experience base. Because the close tolerances and precise calibration of sophisticated equipment usually made the improvisation of field expedients impossible, military communicators learned quickly not to tinker with the system and to call the civilian experts when there were problems.

Technology also imposed an interdependency among systems that became a subtle, but dangerous, source of vulnerability to forces in South Vietnam. The supply system depended on computers that required data communications facilities; they in turn were computer controlled and needed the support of an extensive and efficient supply system. And all needed power. When any one variable in that technological equation was lost, all the systems failed. Flexibility decreased as technical refinement increased.

To maintain their flexibility, the Special Forces took the radical approach of scrapping high-performance technical equipment for its less efficient predecessor. Throughout the Vietnam War, the Green Berets were issued a succession of sophisticated long-range portable radios to meet the special needs of their far-flung teams. But by the mid-1970s many Special Forces units throughout the world had adopted as their primary long-range radio the 1950s-vintage Morse code set they originally took to Vietnam in the early 1960s. The radio was sturdy and simple to repair. Most important, it worked with a variety of power sources, including a hand-cranked generator. For the Special Forces, flexibility was security; when technical sophistication limited their flexibility, they discarded technology.

Contributing to the difficulties with introducing high-technology solutions was the uncertainty of finding reliable power sources. In fact, the military in South Vietnam had a foretaste of the energy crisis that was to grip American society in the 1970s; they quickly learned not to take power for granted in energy-poor Vietnam. Batteries were hoarded and generators given the sturdiest bunkers. Because sophisticated equipment required precise levels of power, soldiers watched their power gauges and meters as closely as they watched their radar screens for an approaching enemy.

Strangely, the enemy did not exploit the vulnerabilities of technology. The Viet Cong rarely attacked exposed power plants or tried to overrun the lightly defended fixed communications sites whose noisy generators and large billboard antennas advertised their presence. The reason for that welcome reprieve has never been determined. Possibly the Viet Cong were enjoying the fruits of a technology they could never afford, tapping into the phone system and draining off electrical power. Or perhaps, anticipating victory, they wanted to preserve the large fixed signal installations for their own future use.

Just as the enemy did not exploit the vulnerabilities of America's technology, the United States did not take full advantage of its technological strengths. For example, President Johnson's decision against a major call-up of the reserves denied the Defense Department access to the experienced and skilled technical talent working in civilian industry. That single decision imposed a triple burden on military technical training programs, particularly at the Army signal schools: it increased the number of recruits who had to be inducted and trained; created a student population with little or no technical background; and denied the schools access to reservists with prior experience who could serve as instructors.

The plight of the signal schools was worsened by the combination of one-year combat tours, two-year service enlistments, and constantly changing, sophisticated equipment. Courses had to be long enough to teach a soldier the complexities of the various models of equipment he might encounter, but short enough to allow him to serve a full tour in Vietnam before his enlistment ended. To reduce the recruit training requirements, the Army offered bonuses to induce experienced, technically trained soldiers to remain in the service beyond their enlistments. But the military found it impossible to compete with civilian firms offering far higher salaries. Some former military communicators even returned to Vietnam as contractor employees to work on the same sites where they had served in the military.

Technological changes since the Vietnam War offer some promise that the many difficulties encountered during the war can be overcome in the future. For example, the electronic equipment used in the Vietnam War was built primarily with early generation solid-state technology. Although smaller and more efficient than earlier vacuum tubes, those solid-state components were still the product of the electronics industry's trial and error with a new technology. The further development of the semiconductor in the 1970s permitted a dramatic decrease in size and power requirements. In turn, the microprocessor revolution has led the electronics industry to build modules rather than discrete systems. Miniaturization, greater standardization, and the use of modules have made commercial equipment less expensive, more adaptable to military requirements, more mobile, and easier to protect during conflict. Since standard modules can be replaced, civilian maintenance specialists are no longer required on site to repair equipment. Although standardization has placed greater demands on the supply and transportation systems, those difficulties are more easily overcome than the daunting problems faced by signlamen in meeting the challenges of technology in the Vietnam War.

Improved technology cannot eliminate, and could even exacerbate, an explosion of information like the one which overwhelmed both communicators and tactical commanders in South Vietnam. Every time the capacity and speed of communications channels increased, the volume of information carried by those channels also increased. That parallel expansion not only offset the technical improvements in communications but also increased the amount of data that had to be absorbed by commanders and their staffs. The Vietnam experience demonstrated that command and control do not necessarily improve as communications improve.

The overload of information in South Vietnam was caused by a number of factors that will have to be dealt with in future conflicts. Most important, the growing complexity of missions and equipment in modern military operations has continued to increase the requirement for specialization—both in units with narrowly defined missions and in individuals with technical specialties. As the number of those units and specialties has grown, the amount of information needed to coordinate their activities has grown in geometric proportions.

The disruptive effects of specialization on the flow of information can be overcome by strengthening unit stability and simplifying command arrangements. In Vietnam, just the opposite situation occurred. The one-year tour and the practice of rotating commanders every six months disrupted the organizational cohesion and mutual trust necessary to maintain cooperation and coordination with minimal formal communications. Frequent personnel changes made internal unit communications difficult; the proliferation of military commands and governmental agencies involved with operations in Southeast Asia blurred the lines of authority and complicated the passage of information between headquarters. Even straightforward orders and requests for support had to be approved by a myriad of headquarters. Consequently, thousands of memorandums and messages for comment and action clogged the communications channels.

What was needed, but never adequately addressed, during the Vietnam War was a coherent and comprehensive approach to information processing that defined the relationship between computers, communications, and command and control. While computers enabled military organizations to analyze data in making decisions and managing resources, communications provided the means of transmitting the raw data and ensuring that decisions and instructions reached those who had to implement them. But both computer and communications systems were, and must be, only tools to enable military leaders to command their units and control the many functions supporting military operations.

As signalmen learned from their labors in Vietnam, the act of communicating is now an inseparable part of both the decision-making and command processes. In making and implementing decisions in a world where technology has compressed time and space, commanders are thoroughly reliant on their communications. Failure to recognize or accept that emerging reality in the Vietnam War at times forced communicators to take extreme measures to accomplish their mission. With the onrush of technology and the increasing complexity of command, military leaders will no longer have that luxury. Upon the skill of the communicator will rest the success of the commander.

Bibliographical Note

Most source documents and indexes to files used in research for this volume are located in the Washington, D.C., area. The National Archives and Records Service (NARS) maintains Army files of actions conducted by the Joint Chiefs of Staff in the retired records of the Office of the Deputy Chief of Staff for Operations, Record Group 319; the Washington National Records Center (WNRC) in Suitland, Maryland, holds additional Army staff files and most records retired from Army units in South Vietnam and from the Headquarters, U.S. Army, Pacific. Since the Washington National Records Center is a temporary repository, those files will eventually be transferred to the National Archives. The Office of Air Force History (OAFH) at Bolling Air Force Base, D.C., has a comprehensive microfilm file of Vietnam War–related documents. The archives of the former Army Security Agency (ASA) at Arlington Hall Station, Virginia, and of the National Security Agency at Fort Meade, Maryland, contain records pertaining to electronic warfare during the war. The Defense Technical Information Center, formerly the Defense Documentation Center (DDC), at Cameron Station, Virginia, maintains copies of many operational and technical reports prepared by or in support of communicators in South Vietnam.

To aid in locating sources within those repositories, the numerical designations of document files or interview tape indexes are listed in footnotes immediately following the identification of a document. Then follow the accession and box numbers identifying the location of the source within a group of retired records. Where such information has changed due to subsequent transfer of records, researchers should be able to locate sources through indexes maintained by the Records Management Division of the Adjutant General Center in Washington, D.C. Because archivists of the Adjutant General Center processed and catalogued many of the files retired by Army units in South Vietnam and maintain indexes of all Army files in the Washington National Records Center, the Adjutant General Center is the central point for information concerning Army files pertaining to the Vietnam War.

The U.S. Army Center of Military History in Washington is also a good repository of information concerning sources and background pertaining to the Vietnam War. The center holds the annual historical reports of major Army commands and of Department of the Army staff agencies, as well as an extensive collection of taped interviews conducted by military history detachments in South Vietnam. Drafts of published and forthcoming volumes produced by the Center of Military History—particularly Ronald H. Spector's story of the period before 1960, Vincent H. Demma's work on the 1960–1964 era, Richard A. Hunt's manuscript on pacification, and George L. MacGarrigle's accounts of combat actions in

1965–1967—were invaluable sources of background information for the signal story. An element of the Center of Military History, the Military History Institute (MHI) at Carlisle Barracks, Pennsylvania, also provided worthwhile information from its collection of unit histories and its holdings of the personal papers of retired Army senior officers. At the Army War College at Carlisle Barracks, as well as at the senior service colleges of the National Defense University in Washington, D.C., can be found studies and papers written by students who held signal positions in South Vietnam.

The signal schools at Fort Monmouth, New Jersey, and Fort Gordon, Georgia, collected documents throughout the war to use in developing course curricula and in preparing texts. That material was used by Lt. Gen. Thomas M. Rienzi and Lt. Gen. Charles R. Myer, both former signal school commandants and senior commanders in South Vietnam, in preparing Vietnam Studies monographs, and later transferred to the Center of Military History. General Rienzi's *Communications-Electronics, 1962–1970* and General Myer's *Division-Level Communications*, both well-written, authoritative works done under the sponsorship of the Department of the Army, are the only published secondary sources addressing communications in the war.

Because the U.S. Army Communications Command (formerly the Strategic Communications Command) and the Communications-Electronics Readiness Command (formerly the Electronics Command) have full-time historical staffs writing histories of the role of their commands during the Vietnam War, documents from the Vietnam era are still kept at those headquarters. The records of the Electronics Command (ECOM) at Fort Monmouth provide an annual chronicle of the activities of the laboratories, procurement agencies, commodity offices, and the National Inventory Control Point in providing logistical support to signal equipment being used in South Vietnam. Records of the Strategic Communications Command at Fort Huachuca, Arizona, document the staffing and engineering performed in support of the command's largest unit, the 1st Signal Brigade.

Material developed and accumulated in the preparation of this volume can be found in the files of the Center of Military History. It includes copies of documents from personal or unofficial collections, notes from the fifty-eight interviews conducted by the author, unpublished manuscripts and information papers, and correspondence concerning issues addressed in the volume. The background papers for this volume will eventually be retired as an entity to the Washington National Records Center.

Source material used to write about communications during the pre-1960 period consists primarily of semiannual reports of the Military Assistance Advisory Group and the Temporary Equipment Recovery Mission, which can be found in the retired records of the Military Assistance Advisory Group, Vietnam, in Record Group 334 in the Washington National Records Center, and of the personal papers of Lt. Gen. Samuel T. Williams, the chief of the Military Assistance Advisory Group during the late 1950s. General Williams' papers, which have been retained at the Center of Military History, are well indexed and represent a comprehensive record of military advisory support and participation on the country team during that early period. In addition to the important correspondence of the Military Assistance Advisory Group, that collection contains transcripts of meetings between General Williams and President Diem. Files retired by the Office of the Assistant Chief of Staff, Intelligence, in Record Group 319 in the Washington National Records Center contain correspondence from the military attache in Saigon that provides illuminating appraisals of the abilities of the South Vietnamese and Communist forces during that early period. While the information in the periodic reports of the advisory group and in General Williams' papers reflects the perceptions of those intimately involved in executing the military aid program in South Vietnam, the reports of the military attache offer a more objective, while less personal, description.

As the United States became increasingly involved strategically with Southeast Asia during the early 1960s, information concerning communications in the region began to appear in high-level documents. The minutes of conferences held by Secretary of Defense Robert S. McNamara in Honolulu during 1961–1962 detail the rationale behind the critical decisions to provide increased advisory and combat support to the South Vietnamese. Transcripts of those conferences and copies of the theater contingency plans prepared during the early 1960s are held at the Center of Military History. Information concerning those early strategic decisions can also be found in published editions of the Pentagon Papers. The edition used in this work is that published by the U.S. Government Printing Office—*United States–Vietnam Relations, 1945–1967: A Study Prepared by the Department of Defense,* 12 vols. (Washington, D.C., 1971). Deliberations and decisions of the Joint Chiefs of Staff to improve communications support to the region are contained in the JCS papers in Army files in the National Archives. Army efforts to shift forces to balance the competing demands for resources in Europe and Southeast Asia are described in documents of the Office of the Deputy Chief of Staff for Operations in Record Group 319 in the National Archives.

Because the records associated with the 39th Signal Battalion's preparations to deploy to Southeast Asia could not be located, information concerning the battalion's mustering, deployment, and first months in South Vietnam is derived from interviews with members of the battalion. Beginning in December 1962, the battalion and each of its subordinate companies submitted annual historical reports. Together with staff office reports of the signal officer of the U.S. Army Support Group, Vietnam, those records provide comprehensive documentation of the American signal program at the lowest levels during the early 1960s. Periodic historical reports prepared by the U.S. Army, Pacific, describe signal activities from a theater perspective. Those documents, as well as files of letters and messages between Army signal staffs in Hawaii, Okinawa, South Vietnam, and Thailand, were retired by the Historical Office of the U.S. Army, Pacific, to the Washington National Records Center as part of Record Group 338.

Information concerning joint signal projects and advisory communications support throughout the 1960s can be found in the annual MACV command histories held at the Center of Military History. Air Force communications support is well documented in monographs of the Office of Air Force History. Good summaries of Special Forces communications are contained in the debriefing reports of the commanders of the U.S. Special Forces Group in South Vietnam that are held at the Center of Military History.

An excellent file of correspondence relating to advisory support during the early 1960s is contained in the papers of a former senior adviser of II and III Corps, Col. Wilbur Wilson, at the Military History Institute. Interviews with former signal advisers provided further insights into the problems that they encountered in helping the South Vietnamese Signal Corps absorb and use the large quantities of American equipment it received during the period. The personal papers retained by an employee of the U.S. Operations Mission, Paul Katz, described the evolution of the village and hamlet radio system. His papers and the files of the Civil Operations and Revolutionary Development Support staff held at the Center of Military History and the Washington National Records Center provide information about the communications supporting the pacification program.

Planning for the deployment of U.S. combat troops and for installation of communications to support the buildup is described in messages and correspondence of the U.S. Army, Pacific. Once units arrived in South Vietnam, their activities were chronicled in different types of quarterly reports. By late 1965 the format of the quarterly report was standardized into a two-part Operational Report–Lessons Learned (ORLL), containing a narrative historical report and an analysis of lessons learned. Every battalion, brigade, and division submitted the Operational Report–Lessons Learned through channels to the Department of the Army. For the remainder of the war the Operational Report–Lessons Learned was the primary historical record of activities of U.S. units. Combat experiences, on the other hand, were documented in after-action reports submitted to higher headquarters after every major operation or enemy encounter. Most after-action reports for major operations contained a section addressing communications. The Operational Reports–Lessons Learned and combat after-action reports are catalogued at the Center of Military History and stored at the Washington National Records Center.

With the establishment of the 1st Signal Brigade in early 1966, documentation of signal activities became more extensive. In addition to the Operational Reports–Lessons Learned, the signal brigade prepared command progress reports, mission and functions manuals, and site reports. Together with the signal staff of the U.S. Army, Vietnam, the signal brigade published the bimonthly *Command Communications*, a journal containing articles about signal units, operations, tactics, and logistics. The brigade's 23d Military History Detachment wrote lengthy special reports on several brigade units, conducted taped interviews of brigade personnel, and selectively accumulated for retention important documents that might otherwise have been destroyed. Most signal brigade records were retired to the Washington National Records Center.

The largest single accession of Vietnam War signal records in the Washington National Records Center was collected by a team that visited signal headquarters throughout South Vietnam in early 1969 to gather data for a study entitled Communications Evaluation in Southeast Asia (COMSEA). The team amassed some eighty-four boxes of documents and computer disks—a wealth of narrative and quantitative information concerning U.S. signal operations in the Vietnam War. Because the study team was particularly interested in signal command and control, the files of correspondence addressing signal command arrangements and the activation of the signal brigade are extensive. The technical description and evaluation of fixed communications facilities, especially the Integrated Wideband Communications System, are also thoroughly documented in the COMSEA papers. Communications requirements and usage data are stored on magnetic disks and listed on computer printout sheets that are part of the collection. The COMSEA data base also contains detailed listings of signal equipment used in South Vietnam.

The U.S. Army, Vietnam, prepared a comprehensive study entitled The Logistics Review, 1965–1969, that contained annexes addressing signal logistics, and the Joint Logistics Review Board prepared a monograph on communications as part of its large-scale study of U.S. logistical support during the conflict. Both studies were retired to the Washington National Records Center. The most detailed and valuable information concerning signal logistics is contained in the papers assembled by the historian of the Electronics Command. They include letters and reports of technicians and scientists who traveled from the laboratories at Fort Monmouth to South Vietnam to check on the usage and maintenance of electronic equipment there. The firsthand accounts of those highly educated observers provide a uniquely objective and articulate account of the adaptation of modern technology to the rigors of combat and an inhospitable environment.

The story of Viet Cong and North Vietnamese communications and electronic warfare tactics was reconstructed from special reports prepared by the Combined Intelligence Center, Vietnam, and from intelligence and interrogation reports. The best source of enemy signal data is the files of a special detachment from the Army Security Agency that focused solely on intelligence concerning Communist communications. The detachment conducted special interrogations of captured enemy communicators and analyzed captured documents for signal information. A major study of Communist tactical electronic warfare doctrine, called Project Touchdown, was prepared from interrogations of members of an entire technical reconnaissance team captured in late 1969. The team's records provided valuable insights into enemy intercept operations and demonstrated the degree of success enjoyed against American and South Vietnamese communications.

The volume of available documentation for the final years of the war dwindled as the American withdrawal progressed. Besides the MACV Command History and the Operational Reports–Lessons Learned of the few remaining American units, a file of personal cables, called backchannel messages, from the signal brigade commander to senior signal officers in the United States is the primary source of information concerning the signal situation during the final years of the brigade's existence. For information concerning South Vietnamese communications during the period in which the United States was relinquishing responsibility to its ally, the best source is the minutes of the Communications-Electronics Staff Committee, which was composed of U.S. military signal staff officers and civilian communicators of the various agencies comprising the U.S. Operations Mission. Those minutes and messages are filed in the Center of Military History.

For events after the cease-fire and withdrawal of all U.S. forces in the spring of 1973, the quarterly assessments of the Defense Attache's Office in Saigon are the primary sources of information concerning both American and South Vietnamese communications. The story of North Vietnamese communications during the final offensive was based on the personal account of the North Vietnamese commander of the invasion forces, General Van Tien Dung. A translation of that account and the reports of the Defense Attache's Office are filed in the Center of Military History.

Glossary

ACAN

Army Command and Administrative Net. The high-frequency radio net which served as the principal means of overseas communications for the advisory group in Saigon until completion of the WETWASH undersea cable.

AFVN

Armed Forces Vietnam Network. Radio and TV broadcast system serving U.S. military in Vietnam.

Antenna polarization

The orientation of antenna elements in either a vertical or horizontal position, or in both positions in the case of dual-diversity propagation.

Area signal center

A group of signal teams responsible for providing communications to units within an assigned geographical area. An area signal center ties the units into the area communications system and supplements their organic communications with other headquarters in the chain of command.

ARVN

Army of the Republic of Vietnam

Audio frequency

The frequency range that can be detected as a sound by the human ear—approximately 20 to 20,000 hertz.

Authentication

A security measure designed to protect a communications system against use by unauthorized stations for fraudulent transmissions.

AUTODIN

Automatic Digital Network. A worldwide system that provided rapid, high-capacity data and teletype communications. Installed in South Vietnam in 1968.

AUTOSEVOCOM

Automatic Secure Voice Communications. A worldwide system that provided a secure-voice network with dial capability. Installed in South Vietnam in 1969.

AUTOVON

Automatic Voice Network. A worldwide system that provided long-distance dial telephone communications. Installed in South Vietnam in 1969.

BACKPORCH

Multichannel radio network using tropospheric scatter propagation installed in 1962 between five major cities in South Vietnam and Thailand.

Binh tram

Large support bases along the Ho Chi Minh Trail.

Brevity code

A code which has as its sole purpose the short-ening of messages rather than the conceal-ment of their contents.

Call sign

Any combination of characters, numbers, or pronounceable words, which identifies a com-munications facility, unit, or individual; used primarily for establishing and maintaining communications.

Carrier

A radio wave, usually sinusoidal, which is modulated to transmit signals.

CEEIA

The Communications-Electronics Engineering and Installation Agency. Established in South Vietnam in 1967.

Chain of command

The succession of commanding officers from a superior to a subordinate through which com-mand is exercised.

Channel

A means of telecommunications on a system. The capacity of a system is measured by the number of independent channels it can provide.

CINCPAC	Commander in Chief, Pacific. Located in Hawaii and responsible for the entire Pacific theater (PACOM), which included Southeast Asia.
Class IV projects	The construction of fixed facilities.
Command post (CP)	A unit's headquarters from which command and control are centrally exercised.
Common-user circuit	A circuit allocated to furnish communications paths between switching centers to provide communications service on a common basis to all connected stations or subscribers.
Communications-Electronics Operating Instructions (CEOI or SOI)	A series of orders, call signs, and frequencies issued for the technical control and coordination of the signal communication activities of a command.
Communications-Electronics Standing Instructions (CESI or SSI)	A series of technical instructions required to coordinate and control the communications-electronics operations of the command.
COMSEA	Communications Evaluation in Southeast Asia. A study conducted in 1969–1970 to assess communications operations in Southeast Asia.
Communications security (COMSEC)	Measures taken to prevent unauthorized persons from gaining information of value from communications.
COMUSMACTHAI	Commander, United States Military Assistance Command, Thailand
COMUSMACV	Commander, United States Military Assistance Command, Vietnam
CONARC	Continental Army Command. Headquarters responsible for U.S. Army activities in the United States, to include the training and doctrine development undertaken at the U.S. Army signal schools.
Continuous wave (CW)	Morse code transmissions achieved by on and off keying of a carrier wave.

CORDS — Civil Operations and Revolutionary Development Support. The agency responsible for the pacification and nonmilitary counterinsurgency programs in South Vietnam.

COSVN — Central Office for South Vietnam

CQ net — Viet Cong on-call radio net

CRITICOMM — The National Security Agency's worldwide high-speed teletype network.

CROSSBOW — A troposcatter system employing tactical equipment installed in 1963 to supplement BACKPORCH.

CTZ — Corps tactical zone. South Vietnam was divided into four military regions.

DCA — Defense Communications Agency. Formed in 1960 to coordinate worldwide interservice communications.

DCA-PAC — Defense Communications Agency, Pacific

DCA-SAM — Defense Communications Agency, Southeast Asia Mainland

DCO — Dial central office. Facility that handles the interconnection of dial telephone links.

DCS — Defense Communications System. A worldwide network of interservice communications.

DECCA — A navigational system which used receivers installed in aircraft and powerful ground-based transmitters to permit pilots to find their locations by matching signal readings with charts containing flight paths.

Electronic counter-countermeasures (ECCM) — Actions taken to ensure friendly effective use of the electromagnetic spectrum.

490

Electronic countermeasures (ECM)	Actions taken to prevent or reduce the effectiveness of enemy communications-electronics equipment and tactics employing electromagnetic radiations to exploit the enemy's use of such radiations.
ECOM	U.S. Army Electronics Command. The agency based at Fort Monmouth responsible for all signal logistics.
Electronic warfare (EW)	Military use of electronics involving actions taken to prevent or reduce an enemy's effective use of radiated electromagnetic energy, and actions taken to ensure one's own effective use of radiated electromagnetic energy.
Emergency action console	A telephone with direct access to a number of hot lines and point-to-point circuits.
FFV	Field Force, Vietnam. Designation of the two corps-size U.S. operational headquarters in South Vietnam.
Flash, Immediate, and Red Rocket	High message precedences
Frequency	The number of recurrences of a periodic phenomenon in a unit of time. In specifying electrical frequency, the unit of time is the second; the frequency is expressed in hertz (Hz) (meaning cycle(s) per second). Radio frequencies are normally expressed kilohertz (kHz) at and below 999 kilohertz, and in megahertz (MHz) above this frequency.
Frequency division multiplex (FDM)	A multiplex system in which the available transmission frequency range is divided into narrower bands, each used for a separate channel.
Ground wave	That portion of the transmitted radio wave that travels near the surface of the earth.

491

Hertz	A unit of frequency equivalent to one cycle per second.
HF	High frequency
ICS	Integrated Communications System. Name of the long-lines communications network in South Vietnam after it was transferred to the South Vietnamese in 1971.
Ionosphere	The region of the atmosphere, extending from roughly 40 to 250 miles altitude, in which there is appreciable ionization. The presence of charged particles in this region profoundly affects the propagation of electromagnetic radiations of long wavelengths.
IWCS	Integrated Wideband Communications System. Name of the long-lines communications network in South Vietnam before it was transferred to the South Vietnamese in 1971. Also called Southeast Asia Wideband Communications System.
J–1	Assistant chief of staff for personnel
J–2	Assistant chief of staff for intelligence
J–3	Assistant chief of staff for operations
J–4	Assistant chief of staff for logistics
J–6	Assistant chief of staff for communications-electronics
J–7	Assistant chief of staff for communications intelligence
Jamming	The deliberate radiation, reradiation, or reflection of electromagnetic energy with the object of impairing the use of electronic devices, equipment, or systems being used by an enemy.

Jiffy bags	Packages issued to maintenance shops with the preprinted address of the Sacramento Army Depot to enable return of modules for repair.
Killing zone	North Vietnamese name for the Central Highlands
Link	A general term used to indicate the existence of communications facilities between two points.
Local loop	A circuit connecting an end instrument to a switching facility or distribution point.
LOI	Letter of Instruction
MAAGV	Military Assistance Advisory Group, Vietnam. Designation of the advisory headquarters in South Vietnam.
MACV	Military Assistance Command, Vietnam. Designation of the unified command subordinate to the Pacific Command and responsible for operations in South Vietnam.
Manual central office	A telephone switchboard where interconnections are controlled by an operator.
MARS	Military Affiliate Radio System. A worldwide net of amateur radios.
Military occupational specialty (MOS)	A term used to identify a grouping of military duty positions possessing a close occupational or functional relationship.
Modulation	The process in which the amplitude, frequency, or phase of a carrier wave is varied in accordance with the waveform of a superimposed intelligence.
Multiplex	A process that enables the simultaneous use of a number of channels on a single circuit.

Net	An organization of stations capable of direct communications with each other using a common frequency or channel.
Net call sign	A call sign that represents all stations within a net.
Net control station (NCS)	A station designated to control traffic and enforce circuit discipline within a given net.
Nodal point (node)	A communications center where several major systems interconnect and circuits are transferred.
Operations and Intelligence (O&I) Net	Radio teletype net supporting advisers in Vietnam, 1962–1964.
OPLAN	Operations Plan
Point-of-origin systems	A location reference procedure using a predetermined point as a base.
Precedence	A designation assigned to a message by the originator to indicate to communications personnel the relative order of handling.
Procedure sign (PROSIGN)	One or more letters or characters or combinations thereof used to facilitate communications by conveying, in a condensed standard form, certain frequently used orders, instructions, requests, and information related to communications.
Pulse-code modulation	Pulsed modulation in which the signal is sampled periodically and each sample is quantized and transmitted as a digital binary code.
Radio direction finding (RDF)	Radio location in which only the direction of a station is determined by means of its emission.

Radio relay system	A radio transmission system in which the signals are received and transmitted from point to point by intermediate radio stations. This system, normally used in conjunction with carrier equipment, provides channels for both voice and teletype operations.
Radio silence	A period during which all or certain radio equipment capable of radiation is kept inoperative.
Radio teletypewriter (RATT)	Communication by teletypewriter over radio circuits.
Radio-wire integration (RWI)	The interconnection of wire circuits with radio facilities.
RCG	Regional Communications Group
Retransmission	Employment of a radio communications set for the purpose of rebroadcasting a message on a different frequency simultaneously with the original broadcast by means of an electrically operated linkage device between the receiver and transmitter of the set.
Retrofit	Modification of equipment already in use.
RVN	Republic of Vietnam
RVNAF	Republic of Vietnam Armed Forces
SEA-TELMA	Southeast Asia Telephone Management Agency
SECDEF	Secretary of Defense
Sideband	The frequency band, above or below the carrier, produced by the process of modulation. Single sideband (SSB) is a system of carrier transmission in which one sideband is transmitted and the other suppressed.

Signal intelligence (SIGINT)   The final product resulting from collection, evaluation, analysis, integration, and interpretation of information gathered from hostile electronic emitters. It includes communications intelligence (COMINT) and electronic intelligence (ELINT) and is used in determining enemy order of battle and planning future operations.

Site Octopus   The signal center at Tan Son Nhut from which the tentacles of the countrywide network extended.

Sked   A precise schedule which the Viet Cong followed in making routine communications contacts.

Sole-user circuit (point-to-point)   A circuit from one subscriber to another subscriber on a fixed path.

Spurs   Systems that extend communications from a terminal of a high-capacity network.

Standing operating procedures (SOP)   A set of instructions covering those features of operations which lend themselves to a definite or standardized procedure without loss of effectiveness.

Strapover   A circuit transferred from one system to another.

STRATCOM   U.S. Army Strategic Communications Command. Unit that operated worldwide communications after 1964.

SYNCOM   A joint venture between the military and the National Aeronautics and Space Administration to orbit a series of communications satellites over the equator.

System control (SYSCON)   An engineering center within a telecommunications system at which technical control of facilities is exercised.

Table of organization and equipment (TOE)	A table that prescribes the normal mission, organizational structure, personnel, and equipment requirements for a military unit and is the basis for an authorizations document.
Tactical operations center (TOC)	A facility from which staff members assist in the direction, coordination, and control of current combat support operations.
Tandem switch	A switch used primarily as a switching point for traffic between other switches.
Tape relay	A method of receiving and retransmitting messages in tape form.
Time division multiplex (TDM)	A multiplex system in which the total available circuit time is divided between the number of channels to be transmitted.
Toll test	A facility where the quality and performance of communications can be monitored and adjusted.
Traffic (communication)	All transmitted and received messages.
Tropospheric scatter	The propagation of radio waves by scattering as a result of irregularities or discontinuities in the physical properties of the troposphere.
UHF	Ultra high frequency
USAID	United States Agency for International Development
USARPAC	U.S. Army, Pacific
USARV	U.S. Army, Vietnam
USASCC	U.S. Army Strategic Communications Command
USASCV	U.S. Army Support Command, Vietnam

VHF	Very high frequency
Voice frequency	Any frequency within the part of the audio frequency range essential for the transmission of speech of commercial quality, i.e., 300–3000 Hz.
WETWASH	Undersea cable installed in 1964 between Nha Trang and the Philippine Islands.

Index

Equipment, communications *(by designation)*—Continued
TRC–77 radio, 460
TRC–80 radio, 36, 44
TRC–90 radio, 36, 44–45, 71, 76, 79–80, 92, 95, 125, 128, 146, 174, 177, 241, 316, 411, 438, 464, 468
TRC–90A radio, 80–81, 92, 104–05, 241
TRC–90B radio, 81*n*, 122, 124, 127, 241
TRC–97 terminal, 241, 464–65, 468
TRC–129 terminal, 241, 269
TRC–132 terminal, 128, 241
TSC–18 terminal, 171
TSC–54 terminal, 308
TSC–55 terminal, 112
TSC–82 terminal, 341
TTC–28 dial exchange, 292–93
VRC–12 series radio, 163, 199, 204, 279–80, 418, 446, 448, 453, 464
VRC–46 radio, 164, 364
VRC–49 radio, 164
VSC–2 terminal, 461
Erb, 1st Lt. Elisha W., 230

Favre, Maj. Rolland M., Jr., 103
Federal Aviation Administration, 282
Federal Electric Corporation, 355, 358–59, 361
Felt, Admiral Harry D., 23, 34, 36, 45–47, 49, 79–83, 95
Field Forces, Vietnam
I, 135, 150–51, 154, 163, 199–200, 236, 239, 241–42, 252, 261, 277, 390
II, 188, 191, 193–94, 197, 199–201, 203, 207–08, 212–14, 216, 223, 277, 390
Filipino civilian personnel, 11, 58*n*, 195, 335
Finley, Col. Joe W., 426
Finucane, Charles C., 413
Fiorelli, Col. Michael C., 360
Fire Base Bastogne, 279
Fleet, Seventh, 275–76
Florman, Edward, 82, 120
Fort Benning, 65, 142, 416
Fort Bragg, 46, 59, 130, 410
Fort Campbell, 149
Fort Devens, 194
Fort Gordon, 37–38, 45, 130
Fort Gordon signal school, 12, 51, 59, 138, 409–10, 412–18, 422–27, 430–32, 434, 466, 478
Fort Hood, 151
Fort Huachuca, 37–38, 239, 327, 470
Fort Lewis, 108, 127, 130, 144, 176
Fort Monmouth, 173, 198, 232, 318, 326–27

Fort Monmouth signal school, 12, 43–44, 51, 59, 75, 88, 91–92, 103–04, 123, 125, 227, 352, 409–10, 412–14, 416–17, 424–27, 430–32, 434, 442, 466, 478
Fort Riley, 216
Fort Ritchie, 75, 420
Fort Sam Houston, 37
Foster, Maj. Gen. Hugh F., Jr., 327, 355, 357, 466, 470–71
Four Party Joint Military Commission, 360
French Army, 3–8, 10, 12, 20, 25, 27, 388, 404
Frequency interference, 156–57, 200–202, 204, 210, 258–60, 280, 290, 461
Frequency management, 199–201, 211, 214, 280–81, 304–05, 475
Freund, Col. John F., 101–02
Frizen, Brig. Gen. John E., 275
Fulbright, J. William, 16
Fulcher, Sp4c. Ernest, 253

Gardner, Col. Frank K., 90, 98–99, 108, 121, 124, 128–29, 132
Gates, Thomas S., Jr., 29, 170
Gaylor, S. Sgt. Gerald H., 187*n*
General Accounting Office (GAO), 10, 107, 330, 341, 432, 456
General Support Group, 34th, 438, 463
Geneva Agreements, 1954, 7, 16, 20, 25, 29
Gentry, Lt. Col. Edwin B., 251
Georgia Technological Institute, 200
Gia Dinh Province, 63
Gia Ngia, 78, 148
Giap, Vo Nguyen, 4
Gibbs, Maj. Gen. David P., 90, 110, 130, 175, 178, 180, 184, 327
Gilpatric, Roswell, 35, 41
Go Cong Province, 355
Gorman, Capt. (USN) Henry, 119
Graham, Col. Elmer H., 271, 273, 362, 364
Green Hill, Thailand, 108, 144, 190, 306
Grombacher, Lt. Col. Gerd S., 273
Guam, 30, 112, 154, 282, 306–08, 310
Gulf of Tonkin, 276
Gustav Hirsch Company, 293

Haines, General Ralph E., Jr., 329
Haiphong, 28
Hamburger Hill, 285
Hanoi, 4–5, 18, 20, 28, 35, 207, 363, 368, 370–71

504